BIOLOGICAL FOUNDATIONS OF PSYCHIATRY
Volume 2

Biological Foundations of Psychiatry
Volume 2

Edited by

Robert G. Grenell

Section on Neurobiology
Institute of Psychiatry and
Human Behavior
University of Maryland Hospital
Baltimore, Maryland

Sabit Gabay

Biochemistry Research Laboratory
Veterans Administration Hospital
Brockton, Massachusetts

Raven Press ▪ New York

Raven Press, 1140 Avenue of the Americas, New York, New York 10036

Made in the United States of America

International Standard Book Number 0–89004–126–1
Library of Congress Catalog Card Number 74–15664

Sponsored by the Society of Biological Psychiatry

Contents of Volume 2

INTEGRATION

Contents of Volume 1

Contributors for Volumes 1 and 2

A. Michael Anch
Sleep Laboratories
Department of Psychiatry
Baylor College of Medicine
Houston, Texas 77025
and
Veterans Administration Hospital
Houston, Texas 77211

Ronald J. Bradley
Neurosciences Program and Department
of Psychiatry
University of Alabama
Birmingham, Alabama 35294

Remi J. Cadoret
Department of Psychiatry
University of Iowa
College of Medicine
Iowa City, Iowa 52242

J. A. Deutsch
Department of Psychology
University of California, San Diego
La Jolla, California 92037

J. C. Eccles
Department of Physiology
State University of New York Medical
School
Buffalo, New York 14220

Seymour Ehrenpreis
New York State Research Institute for
Neurochemistry and Drug Addiction
Wards Island
New York, New York 10035

Daniel L. Ely
Department of Physiology
University of Southern California
School of Medicine
Los Angeles, California 90007

John P. Flynn
Department of Psychiatry
Yale University School of Medicine
New Haven, Connecticut 06508

Charles E. Frohman
The Lafayette Clinic and Department of
Psychiatry
Wayne State University School of Medi-
cine
Detroit, Michigan 48202

David Galin
Langley Porter Neuropsychiatric Institute
University of California, San Francisco
and
Institute for the Study of Human Con-
sciousness
San Francisco, California 94143

Mark A. Geyer
Department of Psychiatry
University of California, San Diego
La Jolla, California 92037

Jacques S. Gottlieb
The Lafayette Clinic and Department of
Psychiatry
Wayne State University School of Medi-
cine
Detroit, Michigan 48202

R. G. Grenell
Section of Neurobiology
Institute of Psychiatry and Human Be-
havior
University of Maryland Hospital
Baltimore, Maryland 20014

Robert G. Heath
Department of Psychiatry and Neurology
Tulane University School of Medicine
New Orleans, Louisiana 70112

James P. Henry
Department of Physiology
University of Southern California
School of Medicine
Los Angeles, California 90007

Williamina A. Himwich
Nebraska Psychiatric Institute
University of Nebraska College of
Medicine
Omaha, Nebraska 68106

Leo E. Hollister
Veterans Administration Hospital and Stanford University School of Medicine
Palo Alto, California 94304

Ismet Karacan
Sleep Laboratories
Department of Psychiatry
Baylor College of Medicine
Houston, Texas 77025
and
Veterans Administration Hospital
Houston, Texas 77211

M. Kinsbourne
Hospital for Sick Children
555 University Avenue
Toronto, Ontario, Canada M5G 1X8

H. S. Koopmans
Department of Psychology
Columbia University
New York, New York 10027

Abel Lajtha
Neurosciences Department
Institute for Information Systems
University of California, San Diego
La Jolla, California 92093

Robert B. Livingston
Neurosciences Department
Institute for Information Systems
University of California, San Diego
La Jolla, California 92093

Paul D. Maclean
Laboratory of Brain Evolution and Behavior
National Institute of Mental Health
National Institutes of Health
Bethesda, Maryland 20014

Arnold J. Mandell
Department of Psychiatry
University of California, San Diego
La Jolla, California 92037

D. McCulloch
Section of Neurobiology
Institute of Psychiatry and Human Behavior
University of Maryland Hospital
Baltimore, Maryland 20014

James L. McGaugh
Department of Psychobiology
School of Biological Sciences
University of California
Irvine, California 92664

James Olds
Division of Biology
Beckman Laboratories 216–76
California Institute of Technology
Pasadena, California 91125

Karl H. Pribram
Department of Psychology
Stanford University
Stanford, California 94305

John D. Rainer
722 W. 168th Street
New York, New York 10032

Charles Shagass
Department of Psychiatry and Eastern Pennsylvania Psychiatric Institute
Temple University
Philadelphia, Pennsylvania 19104

Arthur K. Shapiro
Department of Psychiatry Special Studies Laboratory
Payne Whitney Clinic
New York Hospital
Cornell University Medical College
New York, New York 10021

John R. Smythies
Neurosciences Program and Department of Psychiatry
University of Alabama
Birmingham, Alabama 35294

David N. Teller
New York State Research Institute for Neurochemistry and Drug Addiction
Wards Island
New York, New York 10035

Ming T. Tsuang
Department of Psychiatry
University of Iowa College of Medicine
Iowa City, Iowa 52242

H. Weil-Malherbe
National Institute of Mental Health
William A. White Building,
St. Elizabeths Hospital
National Institutes of Health
Washington, D.C. 20032

Robert L. Williams

Sleep Laboratories
Department of Psychiatry
Baylor College of Medicine
Houston, Texas 77025
and
Veterans Administration Hospital
Houston, Texas 77211

Arthur Yuwiler

Neurobiochemistry Laboratory
Brentwood Veterans Administration
Hospital
Los Angeles, California 90023
and
Department of Psychiatry
University of California, Los Angeles
Los Angeles, California 90024

Foreword

Biological psychiatry is an interdisciplinary science concerned with studies of the basic foundations of behavior, including the abnormal behavior characteristic of the mentally ill.

All human behavior is mediated by events in the nervous system and, as I have pointed out elsewhere, a disembodied psyche is a scientifically meaningless concept—like the grin of the Cheshire cat without the cat. This, of course, should not imply that one cannot effectively study behavior without reference to its genetic, biochemical, and neurological determinants; but Freud himself emphasized that psychoanalysis was a therapy that he hoped in time would be superceded by advancements of basic biomedical knowledge.

Unfortunately we are still far from understanding the biological determinants of most of our behavior, including the problems psychiatrists are called upon to treat. But, just as basic biomedical research has shed much light on many clinical problems in medicine, it is expected that biological psychiatry will contribute increasingly to the ultimate advancement of clinical psychiatry, despite our ignorance which is not to be overcome by hypothetical verbal systems. As P. W. Medewar has said, "The case against a psychological system of treatment such as psychoanalysis does not really rest on the fact that it is inefficacious—for that must be true of a great many forms of medical treatment—but on the fact that belief in psychoanalysis is an important impediment to the discovery of true causes of mental illness."

Julian Huxley has pointed out that we are, of course, organizations with two aspects—a material aspect, when seen objectively from the outside, and a mental aspect, when experienced subjectively from the inside. We are simultaneously and indissolubly both matter and mind. Huxley considers the possible evolution of mind from simple organisms to man and the survival value of mental process by natural selection. He argues that mind cannot be a useless epiphenomenon. It would not have evolved unless it had been of biologic advantage in the struggle for survival. He holds that the mind-intensifying organization of animals' brains, based on the information received from the sense organs and operating through the machinery of interconnected neurons, is of advantage for the simple reason that it gives a fuller awareness of both outer and inner situations. It therefore provides a better guidance for behavior in the chaos and complexity of the situations with which animal organisms can be confronted. It endows the organism with better operational efficiency. Consciousness and behavior are emergent properties of complex nerve nets that have evolved as organs of survival.

To date, the contributions of physiology and biochemistry to the relief of psychiatric disorders have been modest ones. This would be expected from the complexities of the problems, the relative paucity of research support (until very recently), and the short time that such research has had to advance. There are, however, some important contributions. Thus the severe psychosis characteristic of pellagra due to vitamin B deficiency has disappeared throughout the South with the discovery of its cause and the use of vitamins. The psychosis of general paresis, sometimes indistinguishable in symptoms from schizophrenia, has virtually disappeared in many places since the discovery of its relation to earlier spirochete infection and the treatment of syphilis with antibiotics. Feeblemindedness accompanying the rare disease phenylketonuria is now understood to be genetically determined resulting in the lack of a specific enzyme; this can be successfully treated by preventing the ingestion of the amino acid phenylalanine that cannot be normally metabolized due to the enzyme deficit. Downs disease (mongolism), another of many genetically caused mental disorders, and many other forms of defective behavior are also coming to be understood in terms of enzyme or endocrine deficits. The new field of psychopharmacology has made important empirical advances—tranquilizer drugs have been responsible for a reduction in the patient populations of mental hospitals.

Most of us would agree that biology in its broad sense embraces the basic sciences of medicine and one might ask, if biology is the basic science of medicine, what is the technology of medicine? Lewis Thomas, President of Memorial Sloan-Kettering Cancer Center, has spoken of three technologies in medicine: high technology, half-way technology, and nontechnology. Representatives of high technologies are immunology, enabling us to prevent diseases such as small pox, diphtheria, and polio; prevention of dental caries by fluoridation of water; insecticides to eliminate malaria and yellow fever; and antibiotics for the treatment of the most serious bacterial infectious diseases. Other examples of high technologies are hormones to treat endocrinological diseases such as diabetes and basic knowledge of metabolism to prevent or correct nutritional problems. There have also been developed surprisingly effective drugs for the treatment of specific symptoms such as pain. The point of all this is that the high technology of medicine has primarily evolved from the free exercise of human curiosity, that is, from basic science. These valuable things are byproducts of exploring minds aiming to understand nature as a foundation for medical technologies. The social good of this kind of high technology is obvious and the more specific and advanced the technology, the less expensive it becomes. For example, care of a case of typhoid fever before typhoid vaccination or chemotherapeutic treatment might well cost, at today's prices, $10,000, and tuberculosis, before the use of isoniazid and streptomycin, was a major killer and its cost for patient care was enormous. Following the discovery of these drugs in the late 1940s, vastly expensive tuberculosis hospitals simply became obsolete.

The half-way technology of medicine is seen in the burgeoning activities of surgeons involved in the removal and replacements of living or artificial parts with elaborate manipulations of immunosuppressive drugs to prevent or slow rejection of the transplants. If we knew more of the basic science of immunology, transplantation could become a reliable, simpler, and less expensive process. And, if we knew more about the chemistry of vascular disease, we could perhaps prevent the very diseases that require transplantation.

The surgical and radiational attack on cancer is also half-way technology. We would not need these if we had more knowledge of the basic disease processes to enable us to prevent malignancies or treat them with specific chemotherapy and by immunization. Decisions as to who will and who will not be treated, because the half-way technology is so complicated and expensive, raise harrowing ethical problems. Polio is now treated by high technology by discovery of its viral agent and successful immunization by inoculation. Twenty years ago it was treated by half-way technology—iron lungs—a frightfully expensive and tortuous procedure. Fifty years ago it had no technology.

Thomas points out the existence of a vast soggy area of the nontechnology of medicine which accounts for a substantial fraction of the cost of today's medicine. These are supportive treatments that the physician uses because he cannot do anything else. These would include treatment of diseases such as arthritis and emphysema, and of a host of psychosomatic disorders. Nontechnologies consume the largest portion of the physician's time, often stated to be as much as 70 to 80%. The ultimate in nontechnology is psychoanalysis.

Biological psychiatry aims to bring to bear on psychiatric problems the armamentaria of physics, chemistry, cell biology, neurophysiology, psychopharmacology, and genetics. From such approaches much has been learned, and much more will be learned, about behavior, both normal and abnormal, from which one may hope to see emerge advances in high technology for treatment of the mentally ill. As examples of high technology in this field, we have mentioned the treatment of psychoses due to pellagra, general paresis, and the brain-damaging phenylketonurea. To these should be added mongolism, which can be detected *in utero* by amniocentesis, and the defective embryo aborted. There are some 1,500 diseases associated with genetics, and of these, 415 have been linked to a single dominant gene and 300 to recessive genes (each of which is a harmless carrier until mating links two similar recessive alleles together). Many of the 1,500 disorders are a result of polygenic factors and many are associated with major behavior disturbances.

Today there is a growing body of information obtainable from amniocentesis and from blood and urinary determinations of parents and the newborn that can inform prospective parents of the likelihood they may have highly defective offspring or, as in some cases, an embryo certain to become a mongoloid child. Many of these fortunately rare genetic disorders show serious mental defects to that negative eugenics; i.e., the genetics of disease is especially pertinent to biological psychiatry. Schizophrenia is now clearly known to involve a strong genetic component but this has not yet yielded a new therapeutic technology, although one may expect it to do so in time. At present, psychosurgery is still experimental and needs more research. Its potentialities of developing into a high technology for psychiatric medicine are great, despite the hysterical opposition of some to its use.

These two volumes ably review many aspects of the rapidly advancing field of biological psychiatry and should serve as a guide to the oncoming generations of investigators.

Hudson Hoagland
President Emeritus
The Worcester Foundation for
Experimental Biology
Shrewsbury, Massachusetts

Editorial Preface

The title of this two-volume set has been chosen with care. It serves to indicate what we feel the nature of the contents to be, as well as to indicate what it is not. It should be understood, then, that the discussions presented deal with particular aspects of the biological foundations of behavior and its disorders. These volumes are not, nor were they intended to be, a textbook of "biological psychiatry." Such a book might follow, but it would, of necessity, have to be of a markedly different character. It would be a straightforwardly clinical text, case oriented and designed to discuss the analysis and treatment of mental disorders on the basis of a medical rather than a psychoanalytic model.

It also must be pointed out that we are aware of serious omissions that interfere with both the continuity and the totality of the presentation. Such lacunae were not desired, nor were the areas of discussion they concern by any means less important. They occur only because of the realistic limitations of size. We have not been able to deal with all the phases of how genetic, environmental, and evolutionary factors influence brain structure and behavior of the individual; or with all the problems of consciousness and altered states thereof; or with myriad basic questions concerning relevant problems of synaptic activity, neurotransmitters, neuro- and other hormones, etc. The list could go on almost ad infinitum. We hope to deal with such problems, as well as with others, in more detail in future publications.

Despite these difficulties, we have attempted to present certain major conceptual areas and "foundation stones" as a continuum. Thus we have begun with Dr. Rainer's basic discussion of genetics. It is out of these fundamental, molecular, and genetic properties that the individual structural entities and functional mechanisms develop, which, in their relationship to the environment, form the core of the behavioral patterns of the organism.

The organismic-environmental continuum involves the operation of each on the other, and, at least from one point of view, brings us to questions concerning sensory processing, learning, memory, motivation, and so on. That is, we are led to inquire into cognitive mechanisms of the conscious organism, and, ultimately, into their malfunction, deficit, and disorder. Thus we have chosen to follow the genetic introduction with discussions dealing with such issues.

However, such physiological and psychophysiological considerations are not alone sufficient to clarify all the behavioral processes concerned. Both the organism and its environment undergo constant change during development.

Volume 2, primarily involving biochemistry and pharmacology, is devoted to problems either of or related to mental disorder. It is here that we begin to look at the application of the basic biological concepts and data to dysfunction and disease. Perhaps the greatest value of such attempts, at the present time, is to make clear the vast ignorance of both the basic scientist and the clinician, and to suggest the many paths of investigation that remain to be discovered and followed.

The final two chapters in Volume 2 deal with more theoretical aspects of the brain-mind system. The chapter by Grenell and McCulloch is a brief attempt to demonstrate the fundamental relationship of information processing to normal and abnormal behavior. The last chapter (Pribram) suggests what we hope ultimately will be the case; namely, that the time will come when such terms as "biological psychiatry" and "psychoanalytic" will no longer be needed; that biological and psychoanalytic concepts will not be considered as inimical and unrelenting, impossibly different views, but that one will be able to explain the other, and Freud's own predictions will be validated.

These volumes are the first in a series to be published under the aegis of the Society of Biological Psychiatry. We trust any omissions will be remedied in future volumes to appear as part of this major educational undertaking.

Many people have been invaluable in the production of this work. We must express our gratitude to the Society: to the other members of the Society's Committee on Publication of Educational Materials (Drs. David Kennard, Robert Heath, and John Paul Brady); to our contributing authors who agreed to help despite their 24-hour work days; and to numerous devoted people at Raven Press—particularly to Mrs. Virginia Martin, without whom many problems might never have been solved.

R. G. Grenell
and
S. Gabay

Pages from The History of the
Society of Biological Psychiatry

George N. Thompson

University of California, School of Medicine, Irvine, California 92664

Biological psychiatry is rooted deeply in the past. Some of its early origins may be traced to the Physiological Psychology of Wundt, Pavlovian Psychology, and even the early historical researches of Imhotep, Hippocrates, and other physicians interested in the biological foundations of psychiatry. We need not review the cultist excursions of psychiatry into the many ideologies of inventive minds. Through all of these offshoots, there has persisted through the centuries a fundamental series of truths that make up the central core of what we have named biological psychiatry.

The early part of the 20th century saw the development of great interest, coupled with the rapid expansion of socialist governments and, consequently, social sciences, in purely psychic speculations. The soma was almost abandoned. Despite the great interest of both scientists and the community in the social aspects of psychiatry, a small nucleus of "organically oriented" psychiatrists continued to stress the importance of the fundamental basic sciences in understanding and treating disorders of behavior and thinking.

One motivating purpose led to the founding of the Society of Biological Psychiatry, an innovation that occurred in Los Angeles, California. In 1944 two scientists who were both neurologists and psychiatrists, and who also were both research workers and clinicians, had intense interest in clinical cerebral localization of all psychological functions, as well as neurological aspects of human activity. They considered that all mental functioning had its origin in cerebral neuronal activity. This was, of course, not a new concept but was one that had long been neglected in psychiatric practice.

At the time of their completion of a textbook of psychiatry[1] with co-authorship, one of the authors, Thompson, proposed to the other, Nielsen, that there was no adequate forum for scientists with interests in the organic aspects of psychiatry to meet, exchange ideas, and express their points of view. There were in existence at that time (1944) a few organizations with specific localized interests but none with a broad comprehensive interest in the "neuronal basis of human behavior." Thompson's proposal was quickly adopted and a select group of nine founders were invited to form the nucleus of what was to become an international research organization and which was destined to profoundly influence the direction that psychiatry would take in the future. The original two scientists, George N. Thompson and Johannes M. Nielsen, expanded their number to nine.

It is of interest that all of the original nine were professors of psychiatry or psychiatry and neurology at their respective medical schools.

Many difficulties were encountered by this young organization, which held its first organizational meeting in the living room of Nielsen and Thompson at the Fairmont Hotel in San Francisco in June 1945. Nielsen served as its president for its first two years and Thompson served as its secretary-treasurer for 25 years and then as its President.

From its inception, the naming of the organization was a matter of particular interest to the "founding fathers." No less than 50 names were considered but always the name "Society of Biological Psychiatry" met with the greatest approval. I recall Spafford Ackerly from Louisville, Kentucky, saying, at a discussion of names, "Society of Biological Psychiatry—I like that." Numerous attempts were made by members to change the name, but it survived.

Rapidly the Society merged into itself related groups, The National Society of Medical Psychiatry, the Electroshock Research Association, the Carbon Dioxide Research Association, and others. The Society maintained a close liason with neurology and psychiatry by meeting just before the meeting of the American Psychiatric Association or the American Neurological Association on alternate years, but also met in conjunction with other groups. Research has always been stressed and its functions have encompassed both basic and clinical research.

The international nature of the Society was exemplified by its emblem with the words "International Research" and by its international membership. The schematic brain designed by James Papez, an early member, graces that emblem. Biological psychiatrists of all the world joined its ranks and attended its meetings. The founding members were neurologists, psychiatrists, and neurosurgeons. With the recognition of the contributions of other sciences to biological psychiatry, members in other fields were added rapidly, the only specific requirement (other than contributions to research), being an M.D. or a Ph.D. degree in a related field. The Society now numbers among its members neurologists, psychiatrists, neurosurgeons, psychologists, biochemists (including neuropsychopharmacologists), enzymologists, physicists, and others. It is through the interrelated efforts of these workers that the Society has achieved its greatness.

In response to a request from the American Psychiatric Association, the purposes of the Society were expressed in an article in the *American Journal of Psychiatry*, "The Society of Biological Psychiatry"[2]. It was specifically stated that membership should be limited to scientists interested in the biological basis of human behavior.

Although the Society of Biological Psychiatry itself is international in membership, it became apparent that scientists of many countries wished to have their own Societies and meetings. The first such Society was founded by one of our members, Dr. Schaude, who moved to Amsterdam and then founded the Dutch Society of Biological Psychiatry. There rapidly followed organizations of the Mexican, Argentinean, Japanese, and Scandinavian Societies which are actively sponsoring research and holding meetings.

It is a tribute to the energies and genius of the late Dr. Edmundo Fischer and his colleagues in Argentina that the Primero Congreso Mundial de Psiquiatria Biologica was organized and held in September 1974, in the beautiful city of Buenos Aires. At this congress, the World Federation of Biological Psychiatry was formed.

Significant milestones in the progress of the Society of Biological Psychiatry movement have been:

1. The establishing of committees to give impetus to research and other activities (1958).

2. The establishing of the annual A. E. Bennett Neuropsychiatric Foundation Research Awards in both basic and clinical psychiatry to encourage young workers in research in biological psychiatry (1958).

3. The Annual Foreign Guest Speaker Award sponsored by the Manfred Sakel Foundation of New York City (1959).

4. The amalgamation of other organizations, e.g., The American Society of Medical Psychiatry, into the Society, while maintaining its identity and purposes (1963–64).

5. The establishing of the Annual Gold Medal Award for the individual who has contributed most to the development of the science of Biological Psychiatry (1965).

6. The establishing of foreign and corresponding memberships (1969).

7. Joint meetings with other groups, e.g., The American Electroencephalographic Society, The Pavlovian Society, The American Medical Association, The American Psychiatric Association, The American Neurological Association, The American Neuropathological Association, The Canadian Neurological Association, International Psychosomatic Developmental Association, and others.

8. Liaison of the Society of Biological Psychiatry with newly established foreign Societies of Biological Psychiatry (1960–1975).

The founders of the Society always recognized that to survive, an organization must have a cause and a continuing developing purpose. There is a neverending cause and purpose of this Society, its continuing sponsorship of neverending and never completely achieved research—research into the biological basis of human behavior. In 1971 this writer wrote[3]: "It was with the hope of shining light on mental science and showing in true order and perspective the biological basis of human behavior, that this Society was founded. The Society was dedicated to scientists interested in the neuronal basis of human behavior." There has been no change from these objectives in the direction and goals of the Society.

At the time of organization of this Society, we said (1): "Psychiatry has developed an enormous superstructure and a tremendously complex culture without a foundation of material substance. It has been too poetic and too little factual." It is to be noted that the Society has set out and is attempting to build a foundation under that superstructure.

It has been noted that at the time of the founding of the Society, most of the interest of biologically oriented psychiatrists was in the field of cerebral localization. We searched for cerebral areas, cortical and subcortical, that mediated mental and personality function. At that time we hoped that, in time, the mapping of the entire cerebrum would solve all problems of mental illness. Here I quote from "Perspectives in Biological Psychiatry" (3):

> We were impressed by the finger-agnosia syndrome of Gerstmann; hemiachromatopsia, the loss of color recognition in one-half of the visual field; loss of the sense of motion; the simultanagnosia of Wolpert; the apperceptive blindness of the senile of Arnold Pick (atrophy of the occipital lobes causing total loss of power of identification through all senses.) The symbolic functions concerned with revisualization in the angular gyrus, Riddoch's syndrome of loss of interest and attention in homonymous half visual fields, Anton's syndrome of unawareness of blindness, Hughlings Jackson's "dreamy states" from irritation of the calcarine area 19, Henschen's postulate that all visual hallucinations are due to irritation of secondary and tertiary visual areas, Wernicke's area for recognition of sounds, astereognosis, or tactile agnosia, the dramatic anosagnosia of Babinski, the ideational apraxia of Nielsen [4] the complicated agnosias, such as the visual agnosias for symbols, the language formulation areas of the cortex, agraphia, alexia, all stimulated our belief that further mapping of the brain would solve psychiatric problems still unsolved.
>
> The importance of the frontal lobes relative to intellect and personality, Kleist's data concerning the "higher psychic functions of the orbital area," the evidence that the fundamental problems of personality are located in the hypothalamus, and Thompson's [5] discovery of the cerebral area essential to consciousness added weight to the importance of deeper brain structures in mental function. James Papez's discovery (following Karl Kleist) of the importance of the cingulate gyrus in emotion, and of the functions of the limbic system was another landmark in the cerebral localization of mental function.

We note that a marked change in the direction of research occurred, from the mapping of cortical areas, to the biochemistry of the brain. A new science of psychopharmacology was born. A rapid progression of discoveries of psychopharmacological agents occurred with dizzying speed. There rapidly appeared upon the horizon the phenothiazines, reserpine, lithium, imipramine, butyrophenone, d-lysergic acid, meprobamate, monoamine oxidase inhibitors, amphetamine, benzodiazepine, diphenylhydantoin, thioxanthene, the tricyclic antidepressants, and others. Other therapies, insulin coma, and electroconvulsive treatment rapidly diminished in frequency of use and in research.

The development of these agents in treatment brought forth a new question or resurrected an old one: How and why do these agents alter mental function? Is all mental illness the result of biochemical or faulty metabolism or due to genetic errors in biochemistry?

With the development of psychopharmacologic agents, and as a part of this development, there occurred an increased interest in the hormones and then the enzymes of the brain. Startling discoveries were the correlations of mental disease with discoveries of enzyme functions. The historical perspectives of this Society point to great advances in the future. We can now say with confidence, as did Ingham, that all psychology is physiology. The recent statement by a prominent psychoanalyist that "biological psychiatry seems to be the force of the future" (anonymous), points to the directions that history has taken us. We are the disciples of history and the truth of science is our leader.

The importance of molecular biology on the future of biological psychiatry is almost beyond any perspective. The importance of chemical shifts within individual nerve cells indicates possibilities for the future.

As Dr. Spafford Ackerly indicated when he said, "Biological Psychiatry—I like that," so have others, as evidenced by the recently organized Societies in many countries. Likewise, the titles of recent meetings show the impact of biological psychiatry on psychiatry as a whole. In October, 1969, Loyola University Medical Center's symposium was entitled, "The Brain and Human Behavior." A recent meeting in Baltimore was entitled, "Discoveries in Biological Psychiatry." The California Institute of Technology gave a conference entitled, "Biological Bases of Human Behavior." I cannot end this historical summary without expressing a moving *bienvenido* to all including scientists from another hemisphere. "The international character of our Society and its membership has been stressed by our emblem with international research underlining the neuronal connections of an early member's brain drawing, that of Dr. James Papez. The Society of Biological Psychiatry has elected to membership a group of Russian scientists. I received most interesting letters of appreciation from them, and was quite moved by a letter from Professor I. S. Beritashvili, of the Institute of Physiology, Georgian Academy of Sciences, who wrote in part, "I wish to thank you very much for the great honour you have done me in electing me a corresponding member of the Society of Biological Psychiatry . . . Please convey my sincere gratitude to the Council of the Society for the great honour they have done me . . . May the Society of Biological Psychiatry be as successful in the cognition of behavior of normal and diseased minds as your countrymen have been in the cognition of the moon."

The future of scientific psychiatry is the future of biological psychiatry.

REFERENCES

1. Nielsen, J. M., and Thompson, G. N. (1947): *The Engrammes of Psychiatry.* Thomas, Springfield, Ill.
2. Thompson, G. N. (1954): The society of biological psychiatry. *Am. J. Psychiatry,* 111:5.
3. Thompson, G. N. (1971): Perspectives in biological psychiatry. *Biol. Psychiatry,* 3:3–8.
4. Nielsen, J. M. (1941): *A Textbook of Clinical Neurology.* Hoeber, New York.
5. Thompson, G. N. (1951): Cerebral area essential to consciousness. *Bull. LA Neurol. Soc.,* 16:4.

Biological Foundations of Psychiatry,
edited by R. G. Grenell and S. Galay.
Raven Press, New York © 1976.

Developmental Neurobiology

Williamina A. Himwich

University of Nebraska College of Medicine, Nebraska Psychiatric Institute, Omaha, Nebraska 68106

I. THEORIES OF BRAIN DEVELOPMENT

The brain must be looked upon as a collection of organs each of which develops in its own pattern. The developmental picture and the functional relationship between the parts have given rise to many theories. The classic theory and the one that has added much clarification to data on developing brain is neurophylogenesis based on Hughling Jackson's clinical observations of the effects of neurological lesions. In this theory, the brain matures rostrally from the caudad portion progressively to the cortex. At any given time during development a caudad structure will be closer to maturity than will those structures rostral to it. This theory and the evidence for it from studies of brain function and metabolism have been thoroughly discussed by Himwich (1951, 1976). This theory embraces both phylogeny (the development of the species) and ontogeny (the development of the individual). For this reason they are used frequently as if interchangeable especially in the Eastern European literature. The classic illustration of changes in metabolism (as measured by oxygen consumption) of the parts of dog brain as the neonatal puppy progresses to adulthood is shown in Fig. 1.

Neurophylogenesis, however, does not take into account the differential rates of maturation in individual nuclei within a structure, e.g., the cerebellar nuclei. Anokhin has called such differential development systemogenesis

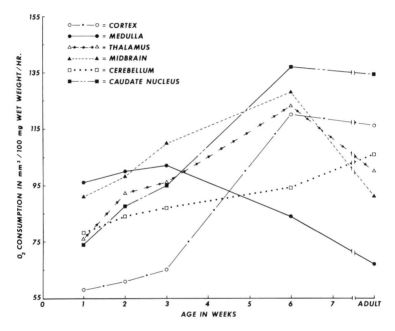

FIG. 1. Oxygen consumption of parts of the dog brain during development (Himwich, 1951a).

(Anokhin, 1974). Anokhin's theory allows for the maturation not only of nuclei but of individual cells in a nucleus to meet the functional needs of the young animal. Since these needs vary from species to species, the developmental changes would be expected to vary. This theory is so far supported by histological evidence (Anokhin, 1974, LaVelle, 1973). Biochemical techniques have not yet been able to deal with analyses of individual neurons as small as those in neonatal brain. Part of the problem lies in the difficulty of isolating individual neurons from a nucleus to say nothing of separating quantitatively the mature from the immature neuron.

The other theories of how the brain is organized functionally have so far had less relevance to problems of development because they have been applied mainly to the adult organism and have not been exploited to aid in interpretation of developmental data (for a discussion of these theories see Himwich, 1976).

It must be kept in mind that none of the theories of brain development reflect the entire picture of how the brain develops functionally, but each represents a facet that is true within its framework and that can be used to help in the explanation of biochemical and other data obtained on the developing brain. Unfortunately many studies, especially biochemical ones, are not planned in such a way as to elucidate any of these theories but rather to describe the possible biochemical reactions present in a given area of brain tissue at a given age or ages. In attempting to interpret such studies, it must be emphasized that they measure only what is possible under a given set of circumstances and the suspicion must always be entertained that other reactions would be possible if conditions were arranged in an appropriate manner to measure them.

II. ANATOMICAL DEVELOPMENT

The growth and development of the brain in all mammalian species and probably in all vertebrate species follows a very similar general pattern. The important difference between the species is not the pattern of development itself but its relation to chronological events such as birth. Both before and after birth, brain development proceeds at different paces in the various species (Fig. 2). What is true of whole brain is also true of the various sensory and motor systems within the brain such as the visual tract. Research

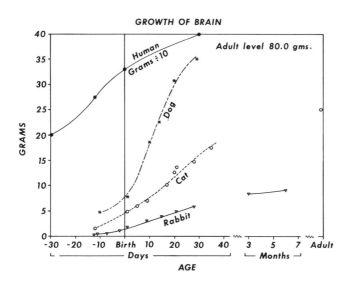

FIG. 2. Growth of the brain before and after birth in man, dog, cat, and rabbit. Birth is shown by the line perpendicular to the age axis. (Adapted from Himwich, 1964.)

data as yet are not extensive enough to allow us to draw very many intra-species comparisons on the development of individual systems.

The brain starts as a relatively small collection of cells in the neural folds. From these cells develop both the relatively simple brains of the rat and rabbit and the exceedingly complex ones of the infrahuman primates and of man. Neurons are formed, some in the area that they will occupy later in life; others migrate from sites such as the subependymal layers of the lateral ventricles and the external granular layer of the cerebellum to take up final resting places in various areas of the brain. The neurons are pushed further and further apart by the developing neuropile consisting of dendrites, axons, and glia. The rudimentary dendrites of the immature neurons develop rapidly into the complex arborization of the dendritic tree seen in the higher mammals at the same time as the axons extend and become myelinated. This development of interconnections from one neuron to another pushes the neuronal cell bodies further and further apart and results in the growth in volume so characteristic of the maturing brain.

Since the pioneering work of Altman (1962) showing postnatal genesis of neurons in rat brain, he and his colleagues have expanded their work to other species and other areas of the brain. In the rat cerebellum, there is a postnatal lag period in which stem cells (later to become neuroglia) multiply and the external granular layer increases in width. From this granular layer, cells migrate to their permanent sites and there differentiate with a concomitant decrease of cells in the external granular layer. The peak of basket cell differentiation is at 2 to 6 days of age, stellate cells at 13 days, and by 15 to 21 days the granule cells have reached 50% of their final count. Purkinje cells and basket cells have differentiated before birth (Fig. 3; Altman, 1972a,b,c).

The work of Altman's group on the rat hippocampus indicated that the primary source of neuroblasts that are to become cells of the granular layer is the internal ependymal wall of the lateral ventricles. These cells migrate via the fimbria to the dentate gyrus. There may be some multiplication en route. Approximately 10 to 15% of the granular layer appears to be formed prenatally, the other 85 to 90% after birth. The hypothetical stages of postnatal neurogenesis in the rat hippocampus have been presented by Altman (1970; see Fig. 4). Bliss, Chung, and Stirling (1974) have found well-developed synapses in the mossy fiber system at 10 days and report population spikes in all preparations by 15 days in the rat.

Other areas that have been studied intensively in the rat are the olfactory lobe (Altman, 1970). The cerebral cortex (Caley and Maxwell, 1968) and the caudate nucleus (Das and Altman, 1970). It can be assumed that, although chronologically different, the migratory paths of cells in the maturing brain are essentially the same in all mammalian species. The kitten, however, presents difficulty in the demonstration of the exact timing of events (Das and Altman, 1971) because of the failure of labeled thymidine to pass the blood-brain barrier.

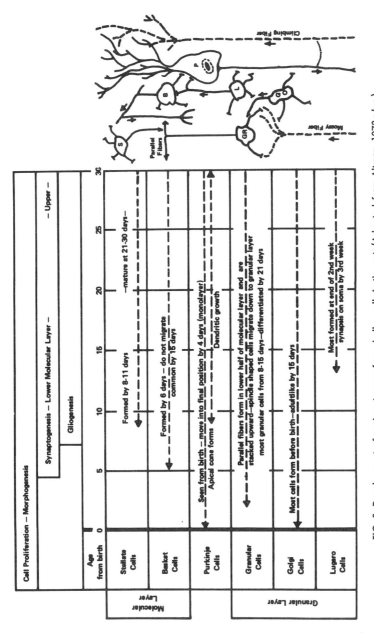

FIG. 3. Development of various types of cerebellar cells in the rat. (Adapted from Altman, 1972a,b,c.)

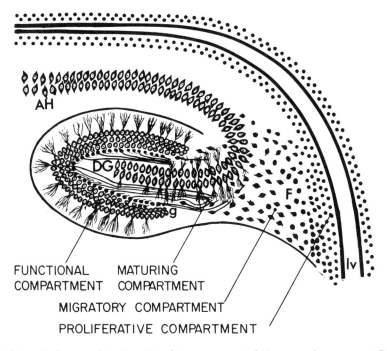

FUNCTIONAL   MATURING
COMPARTMENT COMPARTMENT

MIGRATORY COMPARTMENT

PROLIFERATIVE COMPARTMENT

FIG. 4. Schematic diagram of the hypothetical stages in postnatal hippocampal neurogenesis. This first phase in the process is the multiplication of indifferent cells in the subependymal layer of lateral ventricle (Iv)—the proliferative compartment. The second phase is the migration of indifferent cells through the fimbria (F)—the migratory compartment. The third phase is the induction of differentiation in migratory cells reaching the dendritic field of pyramidal cells of Ammon's horn (AH). The fourth phase is the migration of neuroblasts through the polymorph layer toward the granular layer (g) of the dentate gyrus (DG) with axons formed by spinning—the maturing compartment. The fifth phase is the arrival of neuroblasts in granular layer and their differentiation into functional neurons through outgrowth of dendrites—the functional compartment. (From Altman, 1970.)

The changing picture of the cells represented and their relative maturity are factors in the interpretation of the neurochemical maturation of the brain, which have not as yet been adequately considered. Purpura and Shofer (1972) have discussed in detail the development of synapses and the importance of inhibitory fibers and synapses in the developing cortex based on their elegant anatomical and electrophysiological studies. They point out the complexities involved in assessing the maturity of a neuron. The acquisition of the full complement of synapses certainly would appear to signal the end of neuronal growth and development. But synaptic inhibition is viewed by these authors as a mature process in otherwise immature cortical neurons. Excitatory activities at the synapses, however, appear to mature somewhat later.

The theory that new synapses or at least structural changes in synapses due to learning and memory is not new. Tanzi (quoted by Rutledge, Wright, and Duncan, 1974) made such a suggestion as early as 1893 (see also Cragg,

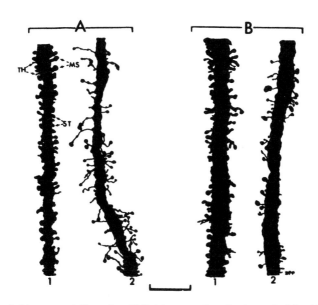

FIG. 5. Camera lucida representations of rapid Golgi preparations showing typical dendritic segments of medium-sized pyramidal neurons of motor cortex in normal subjects and profoundly retarded subjects. (A1) Nonretarded 6-month-old infant. Three basic types of spines are identified: thin (TH), stubby (ST), and mushroom-shaped (MS) spines. (A2) Dendritic segment from a 10-month-old retarded infant (biopsy). The remarkable length of the fine and sometimes entangled spines with prominent terminal heads is evident. Multiple varicosities on pedicles of these long, thin spines are occasionally seen. The MS and ST spines are rare. (B1) Normal 7-year-old child (accident case). Apical dendritic segment. (B2) Apical dendritic segment from a 12-year-old profoundly retarded child. The paucity of MS and ST spines and the presence of thin spines with abnormally expanded terminal heads are striking features of dendritic spine abnormalities in this advanced case of profound retardation. The bar is 10μm. (From Purpura, 1974.)

1974). The recent demonstration by Rutledge, Wright, and Duncan (1974) of morphological changes induced in the pyramidal cells of the cortex of adult cats undergoing long-term stimulation of the cortex is of great importance. The increases were largely in numbers of species present in apical dendrites. Similar changes were first described by Globus, Rosenzweig, Bennett, and Diamond (1973). If they can be confirmed by others, they fit well with the effects of enriched environments upon brain development and also the paper of Purpura (1974) showing dendrites dysgenesis in mentally defective children (Fig. 5).

III. BLOOD-BRAIN BARRIER

The blood-brain barrier is a general term used to describe the phenomena that restrict the passage of materials from the blood into the brain. (For discussions of the phenomena in the adult animal or man, the mechanism of action and anatomy, see Dobbing, 1961, 1968; Himwich and Himwich, 1970; and Katzman, 1972). In this chapter we are concerned only with changes in the barrier phenomena that accompany development of the brain.

It is tempting to think that in the developing brain there is no barrier to the entrance of material carried in the blood—either beneficial or toxic. Such an open-door situation has been used to explain how the brain obtains easily the substances it needs to grow and develop as well as the cerebral injury accompanying jaundice in the newborn infant. Dobbing (1961, 1968) has theorized that the permeability of the brain depends upon its metabolic needs and therefore permeability should be increased at times of greater metabolic activity such as a growth spurt. Experiments with the entrance of cholesterol into the brain tend to confirm this hypothesis (Dobbing, 1963). This theory has the beauty of a simple generalization that can explain the results of many studies, but as Dobbing (1968) himself points out the term blood-brain barrier covers a "heterogenous collection of phenomena." Substances such as cholesterol and amino acids considered to be essential for the structure of the maturing brain would fit Dobbing's hypothesis neatly, but it is hard to see how this hypothesis can cover the penetration of dyes, volatile gases, drugs, etc., as well as the blocking of the transport systems by related compounds, for example, tyrosine and/or 5-hydroxytryptophan by phenylalanine (Guroff and Udenfriend, 1962; McKean, Schanberg, and Giarman, 1962). Herlin (1956) believes the term barrier covers all phenomena that ". . . prevent, reduce, delay . . ." the entrance of materials into the brain as well as those phenomena that facilitate the process. The penetration of material could occur by any process known to be responsible for the passage of substances through a cell membrane, e.g., metabolic activity diffusion, osmosis. To be more restrictive in the definition this author feels is to imply more knowledge than we have. This wise philosophy still holds true almost 10 years after it was written.

Young mice show a relatively slow penetration of fructose into the brain as compared to the blood levels. This rate of penetration could not be influenced by hypoglycemia or ischemic anoxia, although such brains can use fructose once it has entered the brain (Thurston, Levy, Warren, and Jones, 1972).

Early studies (Schwerin, Bessman, and Waelsch, 1950) demonstrated that high levels of blood glutamate did not affect the brain level of that amino acid in the adult but did so in the young animal (see also Himwich, Petersen, and Allen, 1957). Roberts, Flexner, and Flexner (1959), however, showed that even in the adult labeled glutamate in blood exchanged with the unlabeled compound in the brain even though the level of glutamate in the brain was not raised. The elegant methods of Oldendorf (1971) for studying the penetration of substances from blood to brain have not yet been extended to young animals. Data similar to that which he (Oldendorf, 1971, 1973) has already published for adult animals would considerably advance our knowledge of the changes in the barrier phenomena as the animal matures. The only comprehensive study is that of Baños, Daniel, Moorhouse, and Pratt (1970) who compared the ratio of entry rates of radioactively labeled amino acids in rats less than 2 weeks of age and over 10 to 20 weeks old. They found that the highest ratios were for the nonessential amino acids all of which can be synthesized by mature brain. In the young animal they were taken from the blood presumably to aid in protein synthesis.

The barrier effect for inorganic ions such as phosphate (Herlin, 1956; Bakay, 1953) and potassium (Katzman and Leiderman, 1953) has been firmly established. Current interest in neurotransmitters has sparked interest in the passage of these substances through the barrier. In the adult animal (Oldendorf, 1970), the neurotransmitters—whether amino acids or amines— are not passed from the blood into the brain, although the precursor substances pass freely. In rats less than 2 weeks of age, injected mono-amines both indole and catechol—could be demonstrated by fluorescence his-tochemistry to enter the neurons after subcutaneous injection (Loizou, 1970). In 2-week-old and in adult rats norepinephrine (NE), α methyl dopa-mine, and serotonin (5-HT) did not enter the brain. Sachs (1973) found a different time of development of a protective barrier to 6-hydroxydopamine (6-OHDA) in the various brain parts. The hypothalamus showed evidence of a fully developed barrier as early as 5 days postnatally, the cerebral cortex between 7 and 9 days and the spinal cord even later.

The presence or absence of a blood-brain barrier has been used to explain how adults with jaundice avoid brain injury but the newborn may develop kernicterus under similar conditions. Although anoxia, hypoxia, hypo-glycemia, acidosis, and infections appear to play a role in newborn animals, the marked permeability of the blood-brain barrier to bilirubin is an important factor (Hirata, Matsuo, Shibata, Takatera, and Nakamura, 1968; Chen, Lin, and Lein, 1966). Albumin, on the other hand, was unable to penetrate the capillaries as early as the 15th day of gestation (Olsson, Klatzo, Sourancer, and Steinwall, 1968).

The penetration of drugs into infant and adult cat brain using labeled pentobarbital (Domek, Barlow, and Roth, 1960) showed a marked difference in distribution in the adult and the infant. The infant brain had a diffuse dis-tribution of the drug as compared to the clear anatomic pattern seen in the adult. Such age differences can materially affect the responses of children to drugs.

IV. BIOCHEMICAL MATURATION

A. Constituents

During the period of development and growth the brain loses water, falling from a moisture content of close to 98% to about 76% in the adult animal. A part of this water loss is accompanied by a corresponding deposition of lipid as the myelin sheaths are laid down. At the same time, there is a deposi-tion of protein so that both lipid and protein content rise as the brain grows in volume and as moisture decreases. The DNA content per unit of wet weight

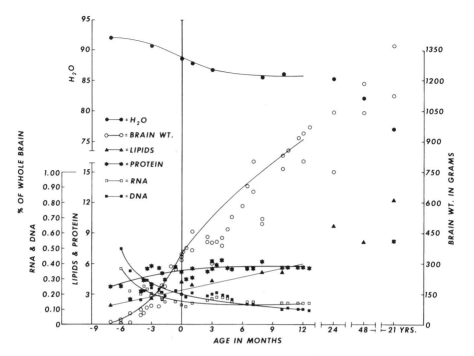

FIG. 6. Composite biochemical development of the human brain. (From W. A. Himwich, 1971.)

tends to fall during development not because of a loss of cells but because of the growing neuropile. A composite graph (Fig. 6) made up of data on developing human brain from many sources describes an overall pattern that applies to all mammalian species provided the abscissa is ignored.

Not reflected in this figure are the changes that occur in enzymes, biogenic amines, and amino acids to name a few. In the case of enzymes, the classic curve from Potter, Schneider, and Liebl (1945) correlates the rapid rise in the enzymes adenosine triphosphatase (ATPase) and succinic dehydrogenase with the period of rapid brain growth (Fig. 7). In general, in species as diverse as rat, guinea pig, and monkey (Jolley and Labby, 1960), these patterns fit most enzymes.

Although many enzymes have been studied in the different species of animals, no broad synthetic picture of substrate and product levels in relation to enzyme activity has yet been made. Such a synthesis would be an interesting contribution to our understanding of development. Space does not permit further general discussion, but the enzyme development in human brain will be discussed below and the peculiarities of various systems will be dealt with as their products and substrates are described.

Studies on human brain are limited because of the difficulties of obtaining fresh material. Himwich, Panelle, and Tucker (1963) found approximately similar activity curves for succinic dehydrogenase and oxygen consumption

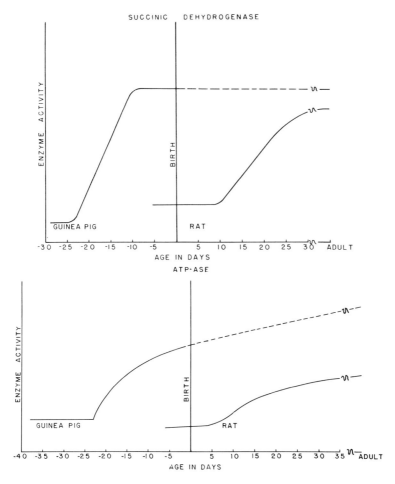

FIG. 7. Development of enzymatic activity in guinea pig and rat before and after birth. (Adapted from Potter, Schneider, and Liebl, 1945.)

in parts of human fetal brain. Youngstrom (1941) demonstrated rapid development of cholinesterase in the various parts of human fetal brain. In the basal ganglia using histochemical methods, Duckett and Pearse (1969) stained oxidative and hydrolytic enzymes as early as the 2nd month of embryonic life and cholinesterase by the 6th month. The later enzyme was present in the cytoplasm of the neurons of the lumbar segment of the spinal cord as early as movements of the hind legs could be detected (Duckett and Pearse, 1967), appearing first in the anterior horn cells of the lumbar segment and moving as development proceeded to the posterior horns and then cephalad. Chemodifferentiation as indicated by histochemical studies of cholinesterase in the hippocampus was complete by the 3rd embryonic week, although the concentration as judged by staining intensity had not reached adult levels (Mellgren, 1973).

The changes in the enzymes involved in biogenic amine metabolism are discussed below.

1. *Biogenic amines.* In rat and mouse brain, all three biogenic amines NE, 5-HT, and dopamine (DA) progressed from relatively low levels to higher ones as the brain matured. In the rat 5-HT, which was highest at birth, reached nearly adult concentrations (90%) at 25 days, NE at 40 days, whereas DA was still relatively low (75% of adult level) at 40 days of age (Agrawal, Glisson, and Himwich, 1966; Loizou and Salt, 1970; Baker and Hoff, 1972). For mouse brain the comparative figures were 15 days for 5-HT,

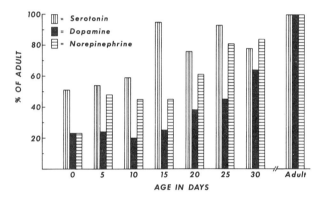

FIG. 8. Developmental changes in indole and catecholamines of mouse brain. Note the early maturity of 5-HT levels and relatively slow maturation of DA. (From Agrawal, Davis, and Himwich, 1968.)

30 days for NE, and 25 days for approximately 80% of the adult levels of DA (Fig. 8; Agrawal, Glisson, and Himwich, 1968). These species are closely related; therefore it is not surprising that the pattern of monoamine development is similar, as it is also in fetal and newborn rabbit (Pepeu and Giarman, 1962; Karki, Kuntzman, and Brodie, 1962). Important species differences, however, do exist. The neonatal monkey had 5-HT levels higher than the adult (Sladek, Tabakoff, and Garver, 1974). High neonatal values have also been reported for guinea pig (Karki et al., 1962) and fetal goat (Pepeu and Giarman, 1962). Such species differences have been interpreted as indicating the degree of maturity of the neonate of the various species. From this interpretation, it can be assumed that the monkey may be more mature at birth than usually considered to be. Sladek et al. (1974), however, suggest the neonatal values in the monkey may reflect differences in mono-amine oxidase (MAO) development and in the characteristics—binding and turnover—of intracellular 5-HT rather than maturity per se.

Seiger and Olson (1973) as well as Loizou (1972) in comprehensive studies by fluorescent histochemistry have followed the fetal development of monoamine neurons in the rat. These neurons appeared to contain transmitter substance even while they were still actively dividing, suggesting a role for these compounds other than that of neurotransmission (Olson and Seiger, 1972; Seiger and Olson, 1973). Lauder and Bloom (1974) studying the origin of monoamine neurons with similar techniques suggested in addition to their roles as neurotransmitter that they may be neurotropic especially in regulating the differentiation of receptor cells. The possibility that 5-HT may play a part in embryogenesis has been suggested by Deeb (1972), Buznikov, Sakharova, Manukhin, and Markova (1972), Buznikov, Chudakova, and Zvezkina (1964), and Burden and Lawrence (1973).

In contrast to work on the rat and to the similarity of the postnatal pattern of monoamine accumulation in rat and mouse, the fetal mouse showed no serotonergic cells before day 12 of gestation and even at birth no serotonergic axon terminals (Golden, 1973). Thus, the mouse showed 5-HT-based fluorescence at a slightly later age than the rat. The difference in visualizing 5-HT axon bundles may be the result of a technical problem or a true species difference.

Although 5-HT values are higher in the female rat, the sex-linked difference did not appear until day 12 after birth and was considered to be linked to sexual differentiation in the brain (Ladosky and Gaziri, 1970; see also Porcher and Heller, 1972). Sex differences also appeared in catecholamines (Gordon and Shellenberger, 1974) in various brain regions of the adult rat—midbrain DA, however, being the same in both sexes. No developmental analyses of such sex differences have been made.

Brain NE may be influenced in the young animal either by lesions in the diencephalon or by injection of 6-OHDA or 6-hydroxydopa (6-OHDOPA) which is decarboxylated to 6-OHDA. The primary effect of 6-OHDA is the degeneration of adrenergic neurons even in the brain if the material is injected into brain tissue, into ventricles, or systemically in the newborn (Pappas and Sobrian, 1972; Jaim-Etcheverry and Zieher, 1971; Kellogg and Lundborg, 1972a; Kostrzewa and Harper, 1974; Jonsson, Pycock, Fuxe, and Sachs, 1974). Zieher and Jaim-Etcheverry (1973) injected rats with 6-OHDOPA within 10 hr after birth and on days 2, 4, and 6 thereafter and sacrificed them at various ages for NE analyses. Brainstem NE showed a marked and persistent increase, although when whole brain was analyzed this increase was diluted by the decrease in other parts, for example, the telencephalon. It can be assumed that in the telencephalon the 6-OHDA formed from the injected 6-OHDOPA destroyed the terminals already present and/or retarded the growth of the adrenergic axons. As Sachs and Jonsson (1972) and Singh and de Champlain (1972) suggested in 6-OHDA damage in adults, there may be a backing up of NE in its passage down the axon and hence a greater concentration in the brainstem (see Dahlström and Haggendal, 1966) or in the adult the neuron may sprout anomalous axons as discussed by Moore, Björklund, and Stenevi (1971) (see also Nygran, Olson, and Seiger, 1971). Zieher and Jaim-Etcheverry (1973) found that the increase in NE in the brainstem showed a developmental response to 6-OHDA, which was partially lost in the adult brainstem response to similar treatment although even in the adult there was less depletion in the brainstem than in other areas (Iversen and Uretsky, 1971). 6-OHDA probably through its toxic effect on the neuron influences the nature of the proteins undergoing transport down the axons of the nigroneostriatal neurons (Singh, Fibiger, and McGeer, 1974).

The similar data of Pappas and Sobrian (1972) in regard to levels of NE after injection of 6-OHDOPA were accompanied by a lack of behavioral results. In part they explain the discordance between biochemical and behavioral data by assuming adrenal hypertrophy and suggesting that this increase was able to overcome any peripheral adrenergic depletion. However, they made no attempt to deal with the problem of loss of brain NE without concomitant behavioral deficit (see also Lew and Quay, 1971; Mason and Iversen, 1974).

Erinoff and Heller (1973) used diencephalic lesions in 4-day-old rat pups to reduce catecholamines. Such animals showed marked reduction of NE and DA ipsilateral to the lesion. The lesions were similar to those in the adult and resulted in an identical correlation between lesion placement and biochemistry of the telencephalon.

The ongoing increases in levels of the biogenic amines during ontogeny are accompanied by enzymatic changes. Catecholamine levels can be depleted by influencing the enzymes involved either in their formation or catabolism. Kellogg and Lundborg (1973) inhibited either tyrosine hydroxylase or dopamine β-oxidase (DA-B) enzymes necessary for the formation of catecholamines in developing animals. Their data confirm that DA-containing neurons become functionally mature at a later age than NE-containing neurons. At 4 days of age a significant decrease in NE followed inhibition of tyrosine hydroxylase in all regions containing measurable amounts of NE. As noted by Persson and Waldeck (1970), NE disappeared faster when DAB was inhibited than if tyrosine hydroxylase activity was affected. Persson and Waldeck (1970) suggested that DA neurons activated NE neurons. In that case at 1 day of age, sufficient DA was released to activate NE neurons. It is also possible that considerable storage of DA occurred in NE neurons at all ages (Thierry, Blanc, and Glowinski, 1971).

Two theories have been proposed for maturation of the indoleamine pathway (Renson, 1971), which would apply equally well to the catecholamine pathway. A biochemical hypothesis is based on the ordered assembly of the components both enzymatic and substantive as the brain matures. The neuroanatomical hypothesis suggests that all components are available within the neuron at an early age and increase as the cell makes its necessary connections for the adult responses (Loizou, 1971). Although the maturation of enzymes and their product would be expected to proceed in a harmonious way this was not the case for 5-HT, tryptophan decarboxylase (5-HTPD), MAO, or 5-hydroxyindolacetic acid (5-HIAA) in mouse brain (Baker, Hoff, and Smith, 1973, 1974). 5-HTPD matured in various brain areas considerably before 5-HT reached adult levels. In developing brain the relation between decarboxylase activity and product was strikingly different for each brain region, which also presented its own unique pattern. One member of the pair could not be used to predict the other especially in early postnatal life. The 5-HTPD pattern (Baker et al., 1973) showed some evidence of neurophylogenesis, i.e., the medulla-pons reach the adult level earlier than the telencephalon, but the cerebellar activity plateaued before the cells of that area had reached their final sites and had completely matured (Altman, 1972a).

The same investigators (Baker et al., 1974) also made parallel studies of MAO and 5-HIAA. Again an individual pattern was found for the maturation of each component in each region. As with 5-HTPD a neurophylogenetic pattern was apparent, with the cerebellum showing low but continuously increasing activity until adult life for MAO but early maturation in that region for the 5-HIAA level. In general MAO reached mature levels in all species studied before 5-HT did. In this regard it must be remembered that MAO has a multiple nature (Eiduson, 1971; Smith, Stacey, and Young, 1962; Shih and Eiduson, 1971). Part of the problem appears to rest on whether tryptophan hydroxylase (T5-H) is the limiting factor in the production of 5-HT (Bennett and Giarman, 1965; Deguchi and Barchas, 1972; Schmidt and Sanders-Bush, 1971).

Kellogg and Lundborg (1927c) demonstrated that peripheral decarboxylase played a significant role in the fate of 5-HTP in the rat after the 21st day, as did extraneuronal decarboxylase in capillaries and glia. The same timing applies to the peripheral decarboxylase for L-DOPA.

2. *DNA, RNA, and protein.* The levels of nucleic acids in the developing brain are important measures of the stage of maturation of that organ. DNA is usually considered to be the best chemical measurement of the number of cells present. This view is based on the assumption that DNA is present almost exclusively within the nucleus of the cell and is constant within the nucleus (diploid) in a given species. Each glia and neuron therefore makes an equal contribution to the quantity of DNA present. Total DNA in the brain increases as it grows, each part showing a characteristic pattern of increase (Fish and Winick, 1969) (Fig. 9). If the change in DNA is considered on the basis of a unit of wet weight, e.g., 100 mg, the level of DNA shows a slight decrease from fetal to adult life. This apparent decrease is due to the pushing apart of the cells by the developing neuropil, so that a given weight of tissue contains fewer cells and more processes in the adult than in the fetal brain and hence less DNA.

It is obvious that the period of cell division is crucial for the development of a brain with the necessary cells for the maturation and integration of function. Although many other factors may intervene before maturity, the first essential in the progress toward that maturity is the presence of an adequate number of nerve cells present either through migration, or formed by cell division or both. This principle is basic to interpretation of studies such as malnutrition in which fewer than normal cells are present in the brain. Unfortunately, at the present time there is no reliable way to distinguish between neurons and glia when DNA content of brain tissue is determined.

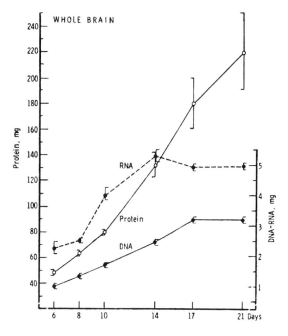

FIG. 9. Relationships between brain protein, RNA, and DNA in the developing rat brain. (From Winick, 1968.)

Winick (1968) in his studies of human brain found that DNA increased rapidly (whole brain) from 13 weeks of gestation to birth and somewhat more slowly until 5 to 6 months of postnatal life at which time the concentration reached a maximum. As Winick (1968) points out, this period when cell division is at its most rapid may be the most profitable time to attempt to affect function by interfering with cell division.

RNA in contrast to DNA is not tied to cell number but is probably the best reflection of protein synthesis. In cells that have not as yet developed a nucleolus, RNA is present in the nucleus but after the differentiation of the nucleolus RNA increases rapidly in the cytoplasm. This increase is correlated with an increase in protein synthesis (Rappoport, Fritz, and Myers, 1969). Although RNA tends to outstrip DNA in some rat brain parts, this relationship is not uniformly true for the individual parts, although it holds for whole brain both in man (Winick, 1968) and in the rat (Fish and Winick, 1969).

Many factors that affect the functioning of the brain including learning and memory appear also to influence RNA (Mahler, 1972). The difficulties in the interpretation of such data have been discussed succinctly by Agranoff (1972), who points out that the increases in RNA labeling reported were not accompanied by changes in protein labeling as would have been expected from our assumptions of the role of RNA (messenger, transfer, and ribosomal) in protein synthesis.

Protein has been included in this section rather than with amino acids because of the frequency with which DNA:protein ratios are considered. Protein:DNA ratios calculated in parts of rat brain show definite regional patterns that change with age (Fish and Winick, 1969). The relation of protein:DNA is essentially an attempt to relate the protein concentration to cell number. How much such ratios add to our knowledge of brain function as related to biochemistry is doubtful.

The total protein of whole brain increases during development with a neurophylogenetic pattern appearing in various areas of the brain (Kelley, 1956). Amino acids are incorporated most rapidly into protein during fetal and early postnatal life (Miller, 1969). There appear to be two peak times for this synthesis in the rat at 5 to 7 days and at 19 days postnatally (Miller, 1969). The determination of total protein, however, includes innumerable proteins with many roles in structure as well as function. Two brain-specific proteins appear at about the time myelination begins and are of more immediate interest (Bogoch, 1969). The S-100 protein, which is acidic, appears to be confined to glia. The changes in its concentration parallel the increase in number and size of the glia. The basic protein present in myelin also shows a developmental pattern similar to total myelin (Benjamins and McKhann, 1972). Interest in these two proteins is rapidly adding to our knowledge of their role in brain function.

3. *Amino acids.* Developmental data on the free amino acid pool are available on a number of species (Davis and Himwich, 1973; Himwich and Agrawal, 1969). The amino acids of the developing brain can be divided roughly into three groups, depending upon their changes as the brain matures. If the rat brain is used as the model, one group of amino acids diminished during maturation reaching a peak sometime early in the postnatal period and falling throughout the rest of the growth period, one group increased markedly during growth and development, and one remained approximately at the same concentration (Agrawal, Davis, and Himwich, 1966). Among the amino acids that increased, the most outstanding was glutamic acid, which dominates quantitatively the free amino acids of the brain. γ-Aminobutyric acid (GABA) the metabolic derivative of glutamic acid found only in the central nervous system (CNS) is present in a much smaller quantity. The

ratio between these two amino acids changed during maturation, as glutamic acid increased much more rapidly and to a greater final level than did GABA. In addition to their putative roles as neurotransmitters, both amino acids can be used as sources of energy.

The reasons for the changing profiles of free amino acids have not been as yet adequately unravelled. Undoubtedly they are affected by the use of amino acids in protein synthesis, the changing blood-brain barrier, as well as the total changes dependent upon the maturation of the brain including the migration and maturation of neurons. As Lajtha and Toth (1973) point out the blood values cannot be the sole determiner of the fetal or newborn brain levels since the time sequence of changes is often different in plasma and brain suggesting that the blood-brain barrier functions even at this early age.

The decrease postnatally of glutamic acid first reported by Himwich (1962) and again by Lajtha and Toth (1973) is difficult to explain. The explanation may lie in the stresses, both physiological and environmental, that surround parturition. The data reported on the mouse (Lajtha and Toth, 1973) show a prenatal fall such as was seen in the rat (Waelsch, 1951; Himwich and Petersen, 1959) and the guinea pig (Himwich, *unpublished data*). However, later work with the rat using the amino acid analyzer has failed to confirm the earlier data (Himwich and Agrawal, *unpublished data*), which remain a puzzle.

Amino acid profiles in brains from young animals can be affected by a wide variety of conditions such as isolation, malnutrition, and drugs (Himwich, 1969, Himwich and Davis, 1974), and probably by endocrine changes.

4. *Myelination.* The most obvious gross change in the brain as it matures is the deposition of myelin, the increase in myelin being considered solely responsible for brain weight increase after 100 days of age. In the rat the most rapid rate of myelination occurs at approximately 20 days, although some myelination continues well into maturity. The deposition of myelin occurs in a well-ordered sequence both anatomically (Peters, 1974) and chemically (H. E. Himwich, 1973). The composition of myelin changes as the brain matured, although the lipid–protein ratio remains the same (Norton and Poduslo, 1973). The best correlation found to date of a myelin constituent with myelin increase is for the cerebroside level.

Myelination is progressive from caudad to rostral areas although there are some tracts that myelinate early irrespective of their neurophyletic position (Fox, 1970). Chaikoff and his colleagues (Fries and Chaikoff, 1941; Fries, Changus, and Chaikoff, 1940; Fries, Entenman, Changus, and Chaikoff, 1941), who conducted the early tracer studies on myelination, showed a neurophyletic pattern for this process. The same pattern could be observed when incorporation of labeled amino acids into myelin basic protein was followed (Sammeck, Martenson, and Brady, 1971).

Myelin sheath synthesis accounted for 75% of lipid metabolism in the cord and 50% in the brain. In the young animal, myelin appeared to be metabolically more active in the caudad areas—a difference that disappeared with age. In the immature animal the protein metabolism associated with the deposition of myelin may be more than 20% of the total protein metabolism (Smith, 1973).

As myelin is formed, its composition changes. Thus it was possible for Agrawal and Davidson (1973) to discuss premyelin and mature myelin as separate chemical entities (see also Cuzner and Davison, 1968; and Smith, 1973). The knowledge of the biochemical events leading to the formation of mature myelin will add to our knowledge of why myelination is poor in diseases such as phenylketonuria and where the defect occurs in demyelinating diseases.

B. Metabolic Patterns

The most obvious result in the metabolic patterns available to the young animal in contrast to the adult is the ability of the young to withstand anoxia. Although this resistance varies from species to species, the variability rests upon the stage of maturation in which the young are born, for example, the guinea pig as compared to the rat (Fig. 10). A huge body of research has been devoted to this problem since the late 1930s. The classic explanation considers that the metabolism of the brain is the limiting factor in resistance to anoxia and that sufficient metabolism of that organ to maintain necessary functions for life can be obtained in the young animal without oxygen (see Himwich, 1951a, chap. 7). Two possibilities have been explored. First, the immature brain receives enough energy from the anerobic breakdown of

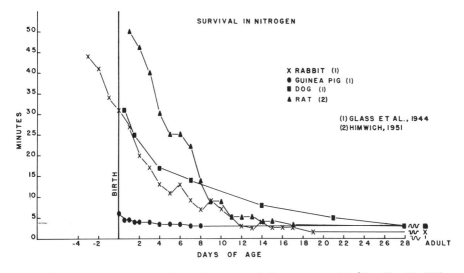

FIG. 10. Survival of various species of animals in nitrogen before and after birth. (From Himwich, 1951a; Glass et al., 1944.)

glycogen to allow survival of the young animal; second, fatty acid fragments are used to supply energy. It is quite probable that both patterns are operative. For detailed discussion of these possibilities the reader is referred to O'Neill (1974), Trevor, Shirachi, and Sutherland (1974), Himwich (1951*a*, 1976).

Some amino acids such as glutamic acid and GABA can be used by adult brain as sources of energy and presumably to an even greater extent by immature brain. The ease with which amino acids are available is influenced by the phenomenon of compartmentation. Certain amino acids notably glutamic acid and GABA are present partly in the cell body of the neuron and partly at the synapses or at least at the dendritic arborizations (Berl, 1973). The amino acid present in the cell body is readily available metabolically to yield energy. That in the dendrites appears less available and its function may be confined to neurotransmission. The development of the phenomenon of compartmentation, dependent as it is upon the growth of the dendritic tree, can be used as a measure of development of the brain. It is of course influenced by any agent that affects brain growth, such as thyroid hormone, corticosterone, and malnutrition, and is a sensitive index of normal development (Balázs and Richter, 1973).

Some indications are available that long-time administration of metabolic inhibitors may result in a metabolic escape from the inhibition in the young animal (Himwich and Davis, 1974). Cahill's (Owen, Morgan, Kemp, Sullivan, Herrera, and Cahill, 1957) work suggests that enzymes normally not active in the adult brain can be induced even in the adult. Fatty acids or their fragments are apparently not used by the mature brain unless starvation occurs. Under such emergency conditions sufficient energy to sustain the brain is supplied from the conversion of fatty acids fragments to glucose. In young animals, this conversion appears normal in the brain but disappears as the animal matures.

V. ELECTROPHYSIOLOGICAL DEVELOPMENT

A. Electroencephalogram

The development of the electrical activity of the brain as demonstrated with the EEG in various species of vertebrates has been exhaustively described by Ellingson and Rose (1970). In all species studied, the first signs of electrical activity are bursts of waves interspersed with relatively long periods of isoelectric recording. The age at which this occurs depends upon maturity of the young and has no relation to birth per se (see Esquivel de Gallardo, Fleischman, and Robert de Ramirez de Arellano, 1964; Dreyfus-Brisac, 1975). In the guinea pig, well-developed activity can be detected *in utero* (approximately 46 to 48 days after conception); in the premature human the activity described above appears after delivery. As the brain matures, the pattern traced by the EEG becomes progressively more complex. Various investigators have used different criteria to make species comparisons. Di Perri, and Himwich, Petersen (1964) used the appearance of sleep spindles. With their recording technique, they compare the age at which cat, dog, and rabbit showed definitive sleep spindles, 14, 38, and 7 days after birth, respectively (Fig. 11; Himwich, 1964). The use of other recording and implanting techniques give different results (cf. Pampiglione, 1960; Verley, 1967; Fox, 1967). The recordings from monkey (up to 24 months) and man (up to 12 years) have been compared by Caveness (1962). With the necessary adjustment for the differences in rate of development the patterns are amazingly similar. Although in monkey a sharp change with birth and the advent of spontaneous respiration has been reported (Esquivel de Gallardo et al., 1964), Dreyfus-Brisac (1975) believes that, in itself, birth of the human infant has no effect on the EEG.

Ellingson and Rose (1970) list as universal developmental trends: (1) decrease in low frequency activity, (2) increase of rhythmic alpha (or alphalike) activity during wakefulness, (3) increase in interhemispheric synchrony, (4) at first an increase in amplitude that later declines toward maturity, and (5) increase in complexity of patterns during sleep.

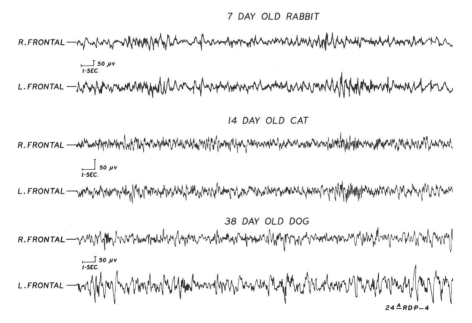

FIG. 11. Development of the cortical EEG in rabbit, cat, and dog showing the ages at which the EEG is roughly equivalent in the three species. (From DiPerri, Himwich, and Petersen, 1964.)

B. Evoked Potential

Responses can be evoked in any of the sensory areas by the use of the appropriate stimuli. In general this technique measures the ability of the tract being stimulated to transmit stimuli from point of input to the area where the response is being monitored, for example, from retina to visual cortex. The mature response appears at different ages in different species and varies with

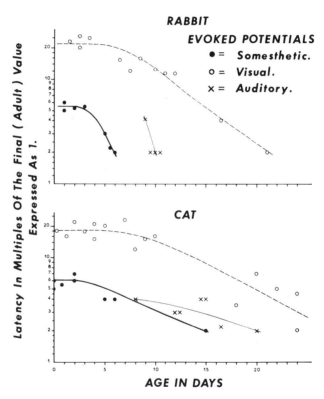

FIG. 12. Evoked responses in latency to stimuli. Relation of species and of stimuli to response. (From Scherrer et al., 1970.)

the modality being tested (Fig. 12; Scherrer, Verley, and Garma, 1970). Latency from time of stimulation and the complexity of the wave forms have been used to measure the ontogeny of the evoked potential. The visual evoked response, as an example, exhibits in the immature animal a long latency, a small amplitude response, and fatigability to repeated light flashes. As it matures the latency decreases, fatigability becomes less marked, and amplitude decreases. The wave form progresses from a simple form in which a negative wave is the first response to a sharply defined positive-negative form. The typical longitudinal sequence is similar for all mammals studied (Rose and Ellingson, 1970). In human infants Ellingson (1958*a,b,* 1960) reported a positive-negative form after birth at full term and only an electronegative response in the premature infant.

Since intensity of stimuli, time intervals between stimuli, anesthesia, and environmental factors all affect the evoked responses, correlations between laboratories or among species except in general terms are difficult. The best comparisons are probably made between species studied in the same laboratory under identical conditions as nearly as is possible and practical (Mysliveček, 1970; Scherrer, Verley, and Garma, 1970). Rose and Ellingson (1970)

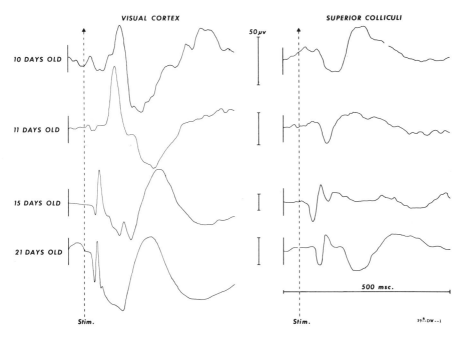

FIG. 13. Development of the visual evoked potential in the rabbit with age (control series). (From Himwich, 1967.)

attempted to use a physiologically definable event such as puberty to relate data on evoked potential from various species (Fig. 13).

C. Sleep-Wakefulness Cycles

The description of sleep-wakefulness cycles initiated a productive era in the correlation of states of consciousness and the EEG. The percentage of time spent in wakefulness (W), slow wave sleep (SWS), and paradoxical sleep (PS) or rapid eye movement (REM) sleep varies with age. In all species W remains the most constant while SWS increases at the expense of PS. This ontogenic relationship appears less true in human beings than in rat

and cat. In man (Roffwarg, Muzio, and Dement, 1966) both REM and SWS
sleep appear to decrease and W increases (Fig. 14).

In all species studied, even the guinea pig, REM sleep time decreases with
age (Jouvet-Mounier, Astic, and Lacote, 1970). The need and/or mechanisms for REM sleep at an early age are still unclear. Drugs influence sleep-
wakefulness in the developing brain just as in the adult, but the relationships
to the biogenic amine levels seem less clear in the young. Shimizu and Him-

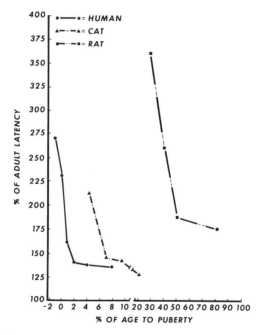

FIG. 14. Comparative latency data of visual evoked response. Percent of adult latency of the positive
wave of visual evoked response in the human, cat, and rat. Plotted as a function of percent age to puberty.
(From Rose and Ellingson, 1968.)

wich (1968a,b, 1969) studied the effect of two phenothiazines (chlorpromazine and propericiazine), haloperidol, and imipramine, as well as
amphetamine on the sleep-wakefulness cycles in developing kittens. Except
for amphetamine the effects of these drugs on wakefulness did not appear
until 16 to 18 days of age. Changes in the percentage of time spent in activated sleep and SWS were obvious as early as 1 to 3 days of age, SWS in
general being increased at the expense of PS. Amphetamine (0.3 mg/kg)
produced increases in wakefulness that were highly significant by the 16 to
18 day. SWS was also increased as the earliest effect of this drug at the expense of time spent in activated sleep.

Although the theories of biogenic control of sleep-wakefulness as advanced
principally by Jouvet (1969) appear to have a firm foundation in the adult

cat, the relation of these putative neurotransmitters in the sleep-wakefulness cycles in the developing animal, either normal or under drug treatment, is not clear. The maximum PS appears at a time when all these substances are below mature levels in the brain, and drugs known to shift levels of the neurotransmitters are not consistently reflected in changes in sleep-wakefulness ratio. However, Valatx, Jouvet, and Jouvet (1964) have suggested that PS may be older than SWS, which may depend on cortical maturation. If SWS requires a minimal anatomical component, attempts to link any change in importance in the sleep-wakefulness picture to biogenic amines may be useless in animals without the mature anatomical substrate. Such correlations can be meaningful only after the anatomical basis for SWS has been established.

VI. CONGENITAL METABOLIC DEFECTS AND THE BRAIN

Gerrod in 1909 was able to describe only four inborn errors of metabolism, but this list expanded by 1966 to over 100 conditions (Hsia, 1966) and has mushroomed since then to include several hundred pathologic states. Prominent among the inborn errors are those resulting in disturbed patterns of amino acid metabolism and/or absorption.

A. Amino Acid Imbalances

Approximately two decades ago, pediatricians and neurochemists were hopeful, even confident, that phenylketonuria (PKU) would be the first disorder of mental development to be explained and alleviated. Although a great volume of literature has been published and much is known about the effects of high phenylalanine and its metabolites in the blood upon the brain, the statement that "The cause of the mental deficiency in phenylketonuria remains obscure" made by Bickel, Boscott, and Garrard in 1955 still holds true. The best therapy appears to be dietary but the diet is usually prescribed and is probably subtlety inadequate despite every effort to prevent deficiencies. Opinion is widely divided among pediatricians as to the best time to allow the child to return to a normal diet. Although brain development appears normal on a carefully controlled diet and intelligence is above the level of mental deficiency provided the diet is instituted at an early enough age, retardation of overall body growth and problems in behavior still plague the patient and his family. With a high blood level of phenylalanine, this amino acid enters the brain freely even after the brain has matured. Phenylalanine, moreover, seems to block entrance of other amino acids such as tyrosine and tryptophan, resulting not only in low brain levels of these amino acids but also in reduced levels of biogenic amines (Yuwiler et al., 1965; McKean, 1972). The failure of amino acids to enter the brain in the normal pattern (Carver, 1965; Takada and Tada, 1970) would affect not only biogenic amines but all protein (Lindroos and Oja, 1971) deposited in the brain, including the myelin proteins. In the developing brain, RNA may also be affected (Castells, Zischka, and Addo, 1971; Chase and O'Brien, 1970). Copenhaver, Vacanti, and Carver (1973) found disaggregation of neuronal ribosomes in animals treated with *p*-chlorophenylalanine. Such ribosomal disaggregation may form the basis for the decrease in protein synthesis observed in animals with PKU.

Moreover, all of the effects of increased phenylalanine in the blood and brain and of the products of phenylalanine metabolism are not fully understood. It is possible that other metabolic problems may be present but have not as yet been uncovered. Patel, Grover, and Auerbach (1973) have followed in the human brain the effects of phenylalanine and phenylpyruvate on the metabolism of pyruvic acid, an important metabolite in the energy cycle of the brain. Their data suggest that phenylpyruvate, a product formed from phenylalanine, is more toxic to the brain of the infant than is phenylalanine itself. Güttler and Wamberg (1972) demonstrated that in children classified as hyperphenylalanemics but not mentally retarded a test load of phenylalanine could be metabolized by some unknown route.

Lipid and myelin changes in phenylketonurics during development were described first by Akert, Hable, Wang, and Waisman (1961). Menkes (1966) postulated a change in the nonhydroxy fatty acids of the glycolipids specifically the sulfatides as a possible biochemical lesion in the brain of the phenylketonuric. Although others have reported changes in lipid composition (see Crome, Tymms, and Woolf, 1962; Foote, Allen, and Agranoff, 1965; Cumings, Grundt, and Yanagihara, 1968), too few cases have been analyzed to do more than confirm a reduction of glycolipids (Shah, Peterson, and McKean, 1972). The fact that there is no increase in the level of cholesterol esters in brain differentiates phenylketonuria from the demyelinating diseases. As Davison (1973) has pointed out, the formation of cellular membranes is of great importance in the developing brain and these membranes can be affected by abnormal protein and/or lipid synthesis.

Nordyke and Roach (1974) found that high levels of phenylalanine in the rat interfered with normal development of compartmentation of amino acids in the maturing brain. The timing of the normal mature pattern of compartmentation is a more delicate method of assessing maturity than measurements of levels of constituents of the free amino acid pool.

It seems likely that there are two effects of the biochemical lesions in phenylketonuria: (1) the production of a permanent morphological (i.e., structural) defect during development, and (2) the production of behavioral and related disorders. The morphological defect would account for the mental deficiency and probably depends, in part at least, upon the influence of the high phenylalanine levels on protein and lipid synthesis. Davison (1973) sees a parallel between the reduced protein synthesis in PKU and in neonatal hypothyroidism, which also results in mental deficiency. The PKU patient whose brain has been protected by dietary control still faces, when put on a normal diet, a reduction of available amino acids for synthesis of biogenic amines in the brain as well as reduction of the synthetic processes for repair and maintenance of brain proteins and lipids. These deficits would account for the apparent improvement of mature PKU patients when dietary control is instituted (Grüttner, Maisch, and Bartelheimer, 1971) as well as some of the problems encountered in the management of PKU patients after they are freed from dietary control.

In PKU we still do not understand precisely the primary neurochemical lesion resulting from a high blood level of phenylalanine or the relative importance of various secondary lesions. The phenylalanine level in the blood and the free entry of this amino acid into brain must be of paramount importance. Why most PKU sufferers are mentally retarded but an occasional one is not is unanswered. Is there a frequently (almost always) associated genetic factor for the mental retardation? Or, conversely, is there a seldom associated factor (genetic or biochemical) that prevents brain injury in some fortunate individuals? PKU is a prime example of a disease that can be controlled without precise knowledge of the mechanisms in the brain that result in mental retardation.

It appears that most of the comments and known mechanisms of action for PKU can be applied to leucinosis or maple sugar urine disease (MSUD) and its variants (Davison, 1973). Menkes and Solcher (1967), however, point out that this disease is more acute and that early manifestations are more striking than those in PKU with more pronounced changes in white matter. As phenylalanine prevents the transport of other amino acids, leucine excess in the blood also blocks transport of amino acids into the brain and thereby effects both the amino acid pool and protein synthesis (Davison, 1973; Richter and Wainer, 1971). Other points of similarity are brain injury, which may be prevented in the young by dietary control, and the improvement of both the EEG and behavior by reduction of leucine in the diets of mature patients with the disease. Menkes and Solcher (1967) also found marked lack of myelination in an untreated child but normal myelination in a treated one. MSUD is of special interest because of the many possible variants (Dancis, Hultzer, and Rokkones, 1967).

The keto acids, especially keto-iso-caprioate, inhibit pyruvate decarboxylase as does phenylpyruvate (Auerbach and DiGeorge, 1973). Although the primary defect in MSUD has not been determined, these authors lean toward a defect in leucine metabolism as being the primary defect.

Another well-recognized aminoaciduria is homocystinuria. One patient described by Laster showed a deficiency in the brain of cystathionine synthase activity (Laster, 1965). The defect in this disease is the opposite of that in PKU in that cystathionine and cystine are lacking and it is this lack that is believed to contribute to, if not cause, the mental deficiency. Cystathioninuria, a congenitally determined error of methionine metabolism, may be only coincidentally associated with mental deficits, since patients suffering from this disease have been described with normal intelligence (Perry, Hardwick, Hansen, Love, and Israels, 1968). Pyridoxine added to the diet appears to control the convulsions that occur in some patients (Studnitz, 1969).

Abnormal metabolic patterns for two other amino acids (lysine and methionine) also produce or are concomitant with mental deficiency (Hooft, Carton, Snoeck, Timmermans, Antener, van den Hende, and Oyaert, 1968; Carson Scally, Neill, and Carré, 1968). It is of interest that high neonatal levels of tyrosine in the blood, and hence in the brain since this amino acid enters brain tissue freely, did not seem to have an adverse influence in the children reported by Martin, Fischer, Martin, and Chase (1974). They point out that conflicting reports on excessive levels of this amino acid may simply mean the concurrent appearance of tyrosinemia and some other (unknown) factor(s) that affects brain development rather than a causative effect of a high tyrosine level in blood.

Oberholzer, Levin, Burgess, and Young (1967) made the first clinical report on critically ill infants who excreted huge amounts of methylmalonate in the urine but who had no evidence of vitamin B_{12} deficiency. A deficiency of any of the enzymes involved in the metabolism of methylmalonate can lead to an excess of methylmalonate (Rosenberg and Mahoney, 1973) (Fig. 15). These children are critically ill and if they survive are apt to be mentally deficient perhaps because of the acidosis that they suffer. Rosenberg and Mahoney (1973) postulated that this acidosis is dependent upon the accumulation of other acids, fatty acids, hydroxy and/or ketoacids, in addition

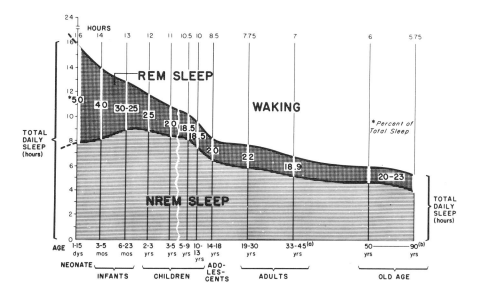

FIG. 15. Relation between waking, non-REM sleep, and REM sleep in the human being. (Adapted from Roffwarg et al., 1966.)

to methylmalonic acid. Both hyperglycemia and high ammonia content of the blood frequently accompany the methylmalonuria. Nine possible different mutations may lead to deranged metabolism of methylmalonate or vitamin B_{12}. Ketotic hyperglycemia has many similarities to methylmalonuria. Hsia, Scully, and Rosenberg (1971) found in the leucocytes from a child with ketotic hyperglycemia a defect in proprionic coenzyme A carboxylase activity. The damage to the CNS may well depend as in methylmalonuria on the acidosis present.

The imidazole peptides such as carnosine are responsible for yet another type of inborn error of metabolism, probably due to a deficiency of carnosinase. This defect in the two patients described by Perry, Hansen, Tischler, Bunting, and Berry (1967) was accompanied by severe mental deficiency and seizures. A defect in lysine metabolism resulting in the formation of sacciharopine was found in one mentally retarded patient (Carson et al., 1968).

A familial defect of methionine reabsorption has been noted in a patient with marked mental deficiency. Although the hereditary nature of the defect and the relationship to a patient with homocystinuria was established, only the girl with methionine malabsorption showed a mental defect.

Other amino acid imbalances have been described, but they appear to bear no relation to mental deficiency or to brain development.

B. Down's Syndrome

This disease, often called mongolism, was the first to be firmly linked to a chromosomal disorder (Lejeune, 1967). Although some degree of mental deficiency is the rule, the etiology, biochemically speaking, is unknown. Lassen, Christensen, Hoedt-Rasmussen, and Stewart (1966) found a normal cerebral metabolic rate in young adults with mongolism. The normal final value, however, was the result of markedly reduced cerebral blood flow compensated for by a rise in the quantity of oxygen removed from the blood. The authors point out that for their height brain weight is normal in mongoloids as is also the proportion of gray to white matter. Moreover Crome (1965) and also Greenfield (1963) concluded that there is no distinctive neuropathology in mongolism. O'Hara (1972), however, found ultrastructural changes comparable to those seen in Alzheimer's disease.

The possibility that 5-HT and NE may be deficient in the brains of mongoloids has been sparked from two directions. Platelets from such patients are low in 5-HT (Rosner, Ong, Paine, and Mahanand, 1965; Tu and Zellweger, 1965), the serum is low in dopamine-β-hydroxylase (Wetterberg, Gustavson, Bäckström, Ross and Froden, 1972; Coleman, Campbell, Freedman, Roffman, Ebstein and Goldstein, 1974). There appear to be therapeutic effects of high doses of 5-hydroxytryptophan in some children with Down's disease (Bazelon, Barnet, Lodge and Shelburne, 1968; Coleman, 1973, cf. Weise, Koch, Shaw, and Rosenfeld, 1974). Moreover Andersson, Fällström,

Lundborg, and Roos (1973) have demonstrated a low excretion of 5-HIAA in the cerebrospinal fluid of children with Down's syndrome, presumably related to an impaired formation and metabolism. The role of dopamine-β-hydroxylase is less clear. In both cases, however, since no brain tissue has been analyzed, the relationship to the mental condition is not well substantiated.

C. Lesch-Nyhan's Disease

This condition is characterized by high serum uric acid, slow development, convulsions, and increased incorporation of glycine into uric acid. The disease has only been reported in males and apparently is aided by drugs, such as probenecid, that increase the excretion of uric acid (Lesch and Nyhan, 1964; Michener, 1967; Delbarre, et al., 1972). Analyses of brain tissue have not been reported as far as we have been able to determine.

D. Sphingolipidoses

Nine distinct sphingolipidoses have been described clinically, the specific sphingolipid identified and the enzyme defect established (Table 1). In each case there is a metabolic failure to degrade a specific sphingolipid due to an absence of the required enzyme. The accumulation of the excess lipid not only in the brain, leads to the pathologies characteristic of the diseases. In addition to accumulation of lipid there is, at least in Tay-Sachs disease, an abnormal amino acid composition of the peptide associated with the ganglioside (Palo and Saifer, 1968). Whether this abnormality is due to the differences in the

TABLE 1. *Sphingolipid hydrolase activity in patients with lipid storage diseases*

Disorder	Enzyme
Gaucher's disease	Glucocerebrosidase
Infantile form	
Adult form	
Niemann-Pick disease	Sphingomyelinase
Infantile form	
Adult form	
Fabry's disease	Ceramide trihexosidase
Hemizygous males	
Heterozygous females	
Tay-Sachs disease	G_{M2} hexosaminidase
Krabbe's disease	Galactocerebrosidase
Metachromatic leukodystrophy	Sulfatidase
Ceramide lactoside lipidoses	Lactosylceramidase
Generalized gangliosidoses	G_{M1} galactosidase
Fucosidosis	

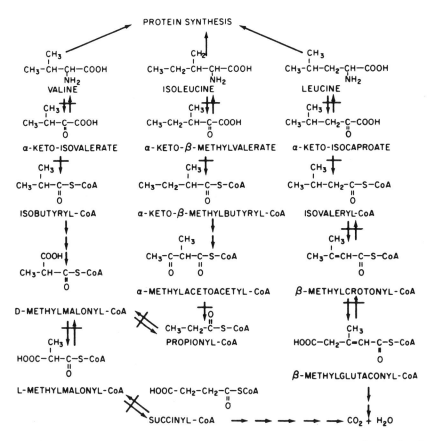

FIG. 16. Reactions involved in the genetic block that result in the inability to oxidatively decarboxylate the α-keto acid derivatives of leucine, isoleucine, and valine. The defect results in the accumulation and excretion of the three keto acids and also of the corresponding three amino acids. L-Allo-isoleucine is also formed and excreted. This acid is formed by the isomerization of α-keto-β-methylvalerate through its enol form and reversal of the transmission reaction. (From Auerbach and Di George, 1973.)

free amino acid pool or to the genetic defect is uncertain (Korey et al., 1963).

In this group of diseases antenatal diagnosis has proved most successful. Fetal cells obtained by amniocentesis and cultured show the enzymatic defect as early as the fourth month of pregnancy a time at which the pregnancy can be aborted if desired. Hopefully, we can look forward to a time when the missing enzyme can be supplied to the fetus, the catch however, is that lipid has already been accumulating abnormally in the fetus (Brady, 1972, 1973; O'Brien, 1973) as early as the abnormality can be detected.

E. Galactosemia

Of the various disorders of carbohydrate metabolism galactosemia is the most important cause of infant mortality and of mental deficiency. The block occurs at the conversion of galactose-1-phosphate to glucose-1-phosphate with the accumulation of galactose after ingestion of milk. The therapy consists of a galactose-free diet in early infancy (Hsia, 1972).

In galactokinase deficiency galactose is not phosphorylated. Brain damage does not occur in this disease but cataract formation does appear. This combination of clinical symptoms suggests that the damaging agent in brain damage may be galactose-1-phosphate and in cataract, galactitol (Hsia, 1972).

F. Glycogen Storage Diseases

Glucose-6-phosphatose deficiency is the most severe of these diseases with a profound hypoglycemia. Compensatory mechanisms, however, make it possible in some cases to have normal brain development with blood sugar levels as low as 15 mg% (Smith, Satterthwaite, and Sokoloff, 1969).

Type II glycogenosis due to deficiency of lysomal acid maltase permits the accumulation of glycogen in all tissues including the CNS and may lead to mental retardation and/or neurological symptoms (Hogan, Gutmann, Schmidt, and Gilbert, 1969).

VII. SUMMARY

The brain develops as a group of organs each with its own maturational time schedule but at the same time with interdependence among the separate parts. Both of these factors add complexities to an interpretation of any aspect of brain development, much less attempts to correlate biochemistry, anatomy, electrophysiology, and behavior. The basic patterns of development in each of these facets are now well established in all mammalian species. Their chronological relation to each other and to birth in the various species is less clear. After the neurons (or cells destined to become neurons) migrate, divide, and reach their final sites, the dendrites, axons, and synapses essential to brain function appear, multiply, and grow in volume. Axons become myelinated. These anatomical events are accompanied by the appearance and growth in amplitude and complexity of the spontaneous EEG and the decrease in latency and increase in complexity of the evoked response. Simultaneously the chemistry of the brain is changing; it is losing water and gaining weight notably because of increases in lipid and protein. Special-purpose compounds, such as neurotransmitters, become active especially at the synapses. The preferred metabolic pathways shift from those characteristic of the immature to those of the mature brain. The levels of many compounds shift during this process for reasons that are still unclear to us. As Garrigan and Chargaff pointed out in 1963 our knowledge was still so embryonic that we could not even formulate the most important questions to be asked about brain development. To our sorrow this is still true, but much progress has been made in the last 10 years and within the forseeable future we can hope to start asking those questions.

REFERENCES

Agranoff, B. W. (1972): Learning and memory: Approaches to correlating behavioral and biochemical events. In: *Basic Neurochemistry*, edited by R. W. Albers, G. J. Siegel, R. Katman, and B. W. Agranoff, pp. 645–665. Little, Brown, Boston.

Agrawal, H. C., Davis, J. M., and Himwich, W. A. (1966): Postnatal changes in free amino acid pool of rat brain. *J. Neurochem.*, 13:607–615.

Agrawal, H. C., and Davison, A. N. (1973): Myelination and amino acid imbalance in the developing brain. In: *Biochemistry of the Developing Brain, Vol. I*, edited by W. A. Himwich, pp. 143–186. Marcel Dekker, New York.

Agrawal, H. C., Glisson, S. N., and Himwich, W. A. (1966): Changes in monoamines of rat brain during postnatal ontogeny. *Biochim. Biophys. Acta*, 130:511–513.

Agrawal, H. C., Glisson, S. N., and Himwich, W. A. (1968): Developmental changes in monoamines of mouse brain. *Int. J. Neuropharmacol.*, 7:97–101.

Akert, K., Hable, K., Wang, H. L., and Waisman, H. A. (1961): Ultrastructural cerebral changes in experimental phenylketonuria. *Reports at the VII International Congress of Neurology, September, 1961*, Rome, pp. 29–32. Excerpta Medica Foundation, Amsterdam.

Altman, J. (1962): Are new neurons formed in the brains of adult mammals? *Science*, 135:1127–1128.

Altman, J. (1970): Postnatal neurogenesis and the problem of neural plasticity. In: *Developmental Neurobiology*, edited by W. A. Himwich, pp. 197–237. Charles C. Thomas, Springfield, Ill.

Altman, J. (1972a): Postnatal development of the cerebellar cortex in the rat. I. The external germinal layer and the transitional molecular layer. *J. Comp. Neurol.*, 145:353–397.

Altman, J. (1972b): Postnatal development of the cerebellar cortex in the rat. II. Phases in the maturation of Purkinje cells and of the molecular layer. *J. Comp. Neurol.*, 145:399–464.

Altman, J. (1972c): Postnatal development of the cerebellar cortex in the rat. III. Maturation of the components of the granular layer. *J. Comp. Neurol.*, 145:465–514.

Andersson, H., Fällström, S. P., Lundborg, P., and Roos, B. E. (1973): 5-Hydroxyindoleacetic acid in children with Down's syndrome. *Acta Paediatr. Scand.*, 62:158–160.

Anokhin, P. J. (1974): Systemogenesis as an evolutionary basis for the development of unconditioned reflexes. In: *Biology and Neurophysiology of the Conditioned Reflex and Its Role in Adaptive Behavior*. Pergamon Press, New York.

Auerbach, V. H., and Di George, A. M. (1973): Maple syrup urine disease. In: *Inborn Errors of Metabolism*, edited by F. A. Hommes and C. J. Van den Berg, pp. 337–354. Academic Press, New York.

Bakay, L. (1953): Studies of blood-brain barrier with radio-active phosphorus: Embryonic development of barrier. *Arch. Neurol. Psychiatry*, 70:30–39.

Baker, P. C., and Hoff, K. M. (1972): Maturation of 5-hydroxytryptamine levels in various brain regions of the mouse from 1 day postpartum to adulthood. *J. Neurochem.*, 19:2011–2015.

Baker, P. C., Hoff, K. M., and Smith, M. D. (1973): The maturation of 5-hydroxytryptophan decarboxylase in regions of the mouse brain. *Brain Res.*, 58:147–155.

Baker, P. C., Hoff, K. M., and Smith, M. D. (1974): The maturation of monoamine oxidase and 5-hydroxyindole acetic acid in regions of the mouse brain. *Brain Res.*, 65:255–264.

Balázs, R., and Richter, D. (1973): Effects of hormones on the biochemical maturation of the brain. In: *Biochemistry of the Developing Brain, Vol. I*, edited by W. A. Himwich, pp. 253–299. Marcel Dekker, New York.

Baños, G., Daniel, P. M., Moorhouse, S. R., and Pratt, O. E. (1970): The entry of amino acids into the brain of the rat during the postnatal period. *J. Physiol.*, 213:45–46P.

Bazelon, M., Barnet, A., Lodge, A., and Shelburne, S., Jr. (1968): The effect of high doses of 5-hydroxytryptophan on a patient with trisomy 21. *Brain Res.*, 11:397–411.

Benjamins, J. A., and McKhann, G. M. (1972): Neurochemistry of development. In: *Basic Neurochemistry*, edited by R. W. Albers, G. J. Siegel, R. Katzman, and B. W. Agranoff, pp. 269–298. Little, Brown, Boston.

Bennett, D. S., and Giarman, N. J. (1965): Schedule of appearance of 5-hydroxy-tryptamine (serotonin) and associate enzymes in the developing rat brain. *J. Neurochem.*, 12:911–918.

Berl, S. (1973): Metabolic compartmentation in developing brain. In: *Biochemistry of the Developing Brain, Vol. I.*, edited by W. A. Himwich, pp. 219–252. Marcel Dekker, New York.

Bickel, H., Boscott, R. J., and Gerrard, J. (1955): Observations on the biochemical error in phenylketonuria and its dietary control. In: *Biochemistry of the Developing Nervous System*, edited by H. Waelsch, pp. 417–430. Academic Press, New York.

Bliss, T. V. P., Chung, S. H., and Stirling, R. V. (1974): Structural and functional development of the mossy fibre system in the hippocampus of the post-natal rat. *J. Physiol.*, 239:92–94P.

Bogoch, S. (1969): Proteins. In: *Handbook of Neurochemistry, Vol. 1*, edited by A. Lajtha, pp. 75–92. Plenum Press, New York.

Brady, R. O. (1972): Sphingolipidoses. In: *Basic Neurochemistry*, edited by R. W. Albers, G. J. Siegel, R. Katzman, and B. W. Agranoff, pp. 485–496. Little, Brown, Boston.

Brady, R. O. (1973): The abnormal biochemistry of inherited disorders of lipid metabolism. *Fed. Proc.*, 32:1660–1667.

Burden, H. W., and Lawrence, I. E., Jr. (1973): Presence of biogenic amines in early rat development. *Am. J. Anat.*, 136:251–257.

Buznikov, G. A., Chudakova, I. V., and Zvezkina, N. D. (1964): The role of neuro-humours in early embryogenesis. I. Serotonin content of developing embryos of sea urchin and loach. *J. Embryol. Exp. Morphol.*, 12:563–573.

Buznikov, G. A., Sakharova, A. V., Manukhin, B. N., and Markova, L. N. (1972): The role of neurohumours in early embryogenesis. IV. Fluorometric and histochemical study of serotonin in cleaving eggs and larvae of sea urchins. *J. Embryol. Exp. Morphol.*, 27:339–351.

Caley, D. W., and Maxwell, D. S. (1968): An electron microscopic study of neurons during postnatal development of the rat cerebral cortex. *J. Comp. Neurol.*, 133:17–44.

Carson, N. A. J., Scally, B. G., Neill, D. W., and Carré, I. J. (1968): Saccharopinuria: A new inborn error of lysine metabolism. *Nature*, 218:679.

Carver, M. J. (1965): Influence of phenylalanine administration and liver of the rat. *J. Neurochem.*, 12:45.

Castells, S., Zischka, R., and Addo, N. (1971): Alteration in composition of deoxy-ribonucleic acid, ribonucleic acid, proteins and amino acids in brain of rats fed high and low phenylalanine diets. *Pediatr. Res.*, 5:329–334.

Caveness, W. F. (1962): *Atlas of Electroencephalography in the Developing Monkey: Macaca Mulatta*, Addison-Wesley, Reading.

Chase, H. P., and O'Brien, D. (1970): Effects of excess phenylalanine and of other amino acids on brain development in the infant rat. *Pediatr. Res.*, 4:96–102.

Chen, H. C., Lin, C. S., and Lein, I. N. (1966): Ultrastructural studies in experimental kernicterus. *Am. J. Pathol.*, 48:683–711.

Coleman, M. (1973): *Serotonin in Down's Syndrome*, American Elsevier, New York.

Coleman, M., Campbell, M., Freedman, L. S., Roffman, M., Ebstein, R. P., and Goldstein, M. (1974): Serum dopamine-β-hydroxylase levels in Down's syndrome. *Clin. Genet.*, 5:312–315.

Copenhaver, J. H., Vacanti, J. P., and Carver, M. J. (1973): Experimental maternal hyperphenylalaninemia: Disaggregation of fetal brain ribosomes. *J. Neurochem.*, 21:273–280.

Cragg, B. G. (1974): *Plasticity of synapses. Br. Med. Bull.*, 30:141–145.

Crome, K. (1965): "Down's disease." In: *Mental Deficiency,* 2nd edition, edited by L. T. Hilliard and B. H. Kirman, pp. 225–229. Churchill, London.

Crome, L., Tymms, V., and Woolf, L. I. (1962): A chemical investigation of the defects of myelination in phenylketonuria. *J. Neurol. Neurosurg. Psychiatry,* 25:143–148.

Cumings, J. N., Grundt, I. K., and Yanagihara, T. (1968): Lipid changes in the brain in phenylketonuria. *J. Neurol. Neurosurg. Psychiatry,* 31:334–337.

Cuzner, M. L., and Davison, A. N. (1968): The lipid composition of rat brain myelin and subcellular fractions during development. *Biochem. J.,* 106:29–34.

Dahlström, A., and Haggendal, J. (1966): Studies on the transport and life-span of amine storage granules in a peripheral adrenergic neuron system. *Acta Physiol. Scand.,* 67:278–288.

Dancis, J., Hutzler, J., and Rokkones, T. (1967): Intermittent branched-chain ketonuria. *N. Engl. J. Med.,* 276:84–89.

Das, G. D., and Altman, J. (1970): Postnatal neurogenesis in the caudate nucleus accumbens septi in the rat. *Brain Res.,* 21:122–127.

Das, G. D., and Altman, J. (1971): Postnatal neurogenesis in the cerebellum of the cat and tritiated thymidine autoradiography. *Brain Res.,* 30:323–330.

Davis, J. M., and Himwich, W. A. (1973): Amino acids and proteins of developing mammalian brain. In: *Biochemistry of the Developing Brain, Vol. I,* edited by W. A. Himwich, pp. 55–110. Marcel Dekker, New York.

Davison, A. N. (1973): Inborn errors of amino acid metabolism affecting myelination of the central nervous system. In: *Inborn Errors of Metabolism,* edited by F. A. Hommes and C. J. Van den Berg, pp. 55–63. Academic Press, New York.

Deeb, S. S. (1972): Inhibition of cleavage and hatching of sea urchin embryos by serotonin. *J. Exp. Zool.,* 181:79–86.

Deguichi, T., and Barchas, J. (1972): Regional distribution and developmental change of tryptophan hydroxylase activity in rat brain. *J. Neurochem.,* 19:927–929.

Delbarre, F., Auscher, C., de Gery, A., and Thang, K. V. (1972): Bases moléculaires du traitement du syndrome de Lesch-Nyhan, des syndromes apparentés et de la goutte commune. *Biochimie,* 54:709–720.

Di Perri, R., Himwich, W. A., and Petersen, J. (1964): The evolution of the EEG in the developing brain of the dog. In: *Progress in Brain Research, Vol. 9, The Developing Brain,* edited by W. A. Himwich and H. E. Himwich, pp. 89–92. Elsevier, Amsterdam.

Dobbing, J. (1961): The blood-brain barrier. *Physiol. Rev.,* 41:130–188.

Dobbing, J. (1963): The blood-brain barrier: Some recent developments. *Guy's Hosp. Rep.,* 112:267–286.

Dobbing, J. (1968): The blood-brain barrier. In: *Applied Neurochemistry,* edited by A. N. Davison and J. Dobbing, pp. 317–331. Blackwell Scientific, Oxford.

Domek, N. S., Barlow, C. F., and Roth, L. J. (1960): An ontogenetic study of phenobarbital-C^{14} in cat brain. *J. Pharmacol. Exp. Ther.,* 130:285–293.

Dreyfus-Brisac, C. (1975): Neurophysiological studies in human premature and full-term new-borns. *Biol. Psychiatry, in press.*

Duckett, S., and Pearse, A. G. E. (1967): Histoenzymology of the developing human basal ganglia. *Histochemie,* 8:334–341.

Duckett, S., and Pearse, A. G. E. (1969): Histoenzymology of the developing spinal cord. *Anat. Rec.,* 163:59–66.

Eiduson, S. (1971): Biogenic amines in the developing brain. In: *Cellular Aspects of Neural Growth and Differentiation,* edited by D. C. Pease, pp. 391–414. University of California Press, Berkeley.

Ellingson, R. J. (1958a): Electroencephalograms of normal full-term newborns immediately after birth with observations on arousal and visual evoked responses. *Electroencephalogr. Clin. Neurophysiol.,* 10:31–50.

Ellingson, R. J. (1958b): Occipital evoked potentials in human newborns. *Electroencephalogr. Clin. Neurophysiol.,* 10:189.

Ellingson, R. J. (1960): Cortical electrical responses to visual stimulation in the human infant. *Electroencephalogr. Clin. Neurophysiol.,* 12:633–677.

Ellingson, R. J., and Rose, G. H. (1970): Ontogenesis of the electroencephalogram.

In: *Developmental Neurobiology,* edited by W. A. Himwich, pp. 441–474. Charles C Thomas, Springfield, Ill.

Erinoff, L., and Heller, A. (1973): Failure of catecholamine development following unilateral diencephalic lesions in the neonatal rat. *Brain Res.,* 58:489–493.

Esquivel de Gallardo, F. O., Fleischman, R. W., and Robert de Ramirez de Arellano, M. I. (1964): Electroencephalogram of the monkey fetus in utero and changes in it at birth. *Exp. Neurol.,* 9:73–84.

Fish, I., and Winick, M. (1969): Cellular growth in various regions of the developing rat brain. *Pediatr. Res.,* 3:407–412.

Foote, J. L., Allen, R. J., and Agranoff, B. W. (1965): Fatty acids in esters and cerebrosides of human brain in phenylketonuria. *J. Lipid Res.,* 6:518–524.

Fox, M. W. (1967): Postnatal development of the EEG in the dog. II. Development of electrocortical activity. *J. Small Anim. Pract.,* 8:77–107.

Fox, M. W. (1970): Reflex development and behavioral organization. In: *Developmental Neurobiology,* edited by W. A. Himwich, pp. 553–580. Charles C Thomas, Springfield, Ill.

Fries, B. A., and Chaikoff, I. L. (1941): The phosphorus metabolism of the brain as measured with radioactive phosphorus. *J. Biol. Chem.,* 141:479–485.

Fries, B. A., Changus, G. W., and Chaikoff, I. L. (1940): Radioactive phosphorus as an indicator of phospholipid metabolism. IX. The influence of age on the phospholipid metabolism of various parts of the central nervous system of the rat. The comparative phospholipid activity of various parts of the central nervous system of the rat. *J. Biol. Chem.,* 132:23–34.

Fries, B. A., Entenman, C., Changus, G. W., and Chaikoff, I. L. (1941): The deposition of lipids in various parts of the central nervous system of the developing rat. *J. Biol. Chem.,* 137:303–310.

Garrigan, O. W., and Chargaff, E. (1963): Studies on the mucolipids and the cerebrosides of chicken brain during embryonic development. *Biochim. Biophys. Acta,* 70:452–464.

Gerrod, A. E. (1909): *Inborn Errors of Metabolism,* Frowde, Hodder and Stoughton, London.

Glass, H. G., Snyder, F. F., and Webster, E. (1943–1944): The rate of decline in resistance to anoxia of rabbits, dogs, and guinea pigs from the onset of viability to adult life. *Am. J. Physiol.,* 140:609–615.

Globus, A., Rosenzweig, M. R., Bennett, E. L., and Diamond, M. C. (1973): Effects of differential experience on dendritic spine counts in rat cerebral cortex. *J. Comp. Physiol. Psychol.,* 82:175–181.

Golden, G. S. (1973): Prenatal development of the biogenic amine systems of the mouse brain. *Dev. Biol.,* 33:300–311.

Gordon, J. H., and Shellenberger, M. K. (1974): Regional catecholamine content in the rat brain: Sex differences and correlation with motor activity. *Neuropharmacology,* 13:129–137.

Greenfield, J. C. (1963): *Neuropathology,* 2nd edition, pp. 352–354. Edward Arnold, London.

Grüttner, R., Maisch, H., and Bartelheimer, H. K. (1971): Evaluation of late initiation of therapy. In: *Phenylketonuria,* edited by H. Bickel, F. P. Hudson, and L. I. Woolf, pp. 277–279. Verlag, Stuttgart.

Guroff, G., and Udenfriend, S. (1962): Studies on aromatic amino acid uptake by rat brain *in vivo. J. Biol. Chem.,* 237:803–806.

Güttler, F., and Wamberg, E. (1972): Persistent hyperphenylalaninemia. *Acta Paediatr. Scand.,* 61:321–328.

Herlin, L. (1956): On phosphate exchange in the central nervous system with special reference to metabolic activity in barriers. *Acta Physiol. Scand.,* 37:Suppl. 127.

Himwich, H. E. (1951a): Cerebral metabolism during growth of lower mammals. A biochemical basis for neurophylogenesis. In: *Brain Metabolism and Cerebral Disorders,* edited by H. E. Himwich, chap. pp. 124–176. Williams and Wilkins, Baltimore.

Himwich, H. E. (1951b): *Brain Metabolism and Cerebral Disorders.* Williams and Wilkins, Baltimore.

Himwich, H. E. (1973): Early studies of the developing brain. In: *Biochemistry of the*

Developing Brain, Vol. 1, edited by W. A. Himwich, pp. 1–54. Marcel Dekker, New York.

Himwich, H. E. (1976): *Brain Metabolism and Cerebral Disorders,* 2nd edition. Spectrum Publications, New York.

Himwich, W. A. (1962): Biochemical and neurophysiological development of the brain in the neonatal period. In: *International Review of Neurobiology, Vol. 4,* edited by C. C. Pfeiffer and J. R. Smythies, pp. 117–158. Academic Press, New York.

Himwich, W. A. (1964): Summary. In: *Progress in Brain Research, Vol. 9, The Developing Brain,* edited by W. A. Himwich and H. E. Himwich, pp. 170–173. Elsevier, Amsterdam.

Himwich, W. A. (1968): Multi-disciplined studies of the visual system in developing rabbits. In: *Ontogenesis of the Brain,* edited by L. Jílek and S. Trojan, pp. 269–276. Charles University, Prague.

Himwich, W. A. (1969): The effect of environment on the developing brain. In: *The Future of the Brain Sciences,* edited by S. Bogoch, pp. 237–252. Plenum Press, New York.

Himwich, W. A. (1971): Biochemical processes of nervous system development. In: *The Biopsychology of Development,* edited by E. Tobach, L. R. Aronson, and E. Shaw, pp. 173–194. Academic Press, New York.

Himwich, W. A., and Agrawal, H. C. (1969): Amino acids. In: *Handbook of Neurochemistry, Vol. 1, Chemical Architecture of the Nervous System,* edited by A. Lajtha, pp. 33–52. Plenum Press, New York.

Himwich, W. A., and Davis, J. M. (1974): Free amino acids in the developing brain as affected by drugs. In: *Drugs and the Developing Brain,* edited by A. Vernadakis and N. Weiner, pp. 231–241. Plenum Press, New York.

Himwich, W. A., and Himwich, H. E. (1970): Cerebral circulation, blood-brain barrier, and cerebrospinal fluid. In: *Duke's Physiology of Domestic Animals,* edited by M. J. Swenson. Comstock Publishing Associates, Ithaca.

Himwich, W. A., Pennelle, D. K., and Tucker, B. E. (1963): Comparative biochemical development of fetal human, dog and rabbit brain. In: *Recent Advances In Biological Psychiatry, Vol. 5,* edited by Joseph Wortis, pp. 263–278. Plenum Press, New York.

Himwich, W. A., and Petersen, J. C. (1959): Correlation of chemical maturation of the brain in various species with neurologic behavior. In: *Biological Psychiatry, Vol. 1,* edited by J. H. Masserman, pp. 2–16. Grune and Stratton, New York.

Himwich, W. A., Petersen, J. C., and Allen, M. L. (1957): Hematoencephalic exchange as a function of age. *Neurology,* 7:705–710.

Hirata, Y., Matsuo, T., Shibata, M., Takatera, Y., and Nakamura, K. (1968): Experimental studies on the development of kernicterus. *Biology of the Neonate,* 12:371–377.

Hogan, G. R., Gutmann, L., Schmidt, R., and Gilbert, E. (1969): Pompe's disease. *Neurology,* 19:894.

Hooft, C., Carton, D., Snoeck, J., Timmermans, J., Antener, I., van den Hende, C., and Oyaert, W. (1968): Further investigations in the methionine malabsorption syndrome. *Helv. Paediatr. Acta,* 23:334–349.

Hsia, D. Y. Y. (1966): The screening of newborn infants for hereditary metabolic defects. In: *Progress in Clinical Pathology,* edited by M. Stefanini, pp. 493–511 Grune and Stratton, New York.

Hsia, Y. E., Scully, K. J., and Rosenberg, L. E. (1971): Inherited propionyl-CoA carboxylase deficiency in "ketotic hyperglycinemia." *J. Clin. Invest.,* 50:127.

Hsia, Y. E. (1972): Inherited disorders of amino acid, carbohydrate, and nucleic acid metabolism. In: *Basic Neurochemistry,* edited by R. W. Albers, G. J. Siegel, R. Katzman, and B. W. Agranoff, pp. 451–484. Little, Brown, Boston.

Iversen, L. L., and Uretsky, N. J. (1971): Biochemical effects of 6-hydroxydopamine on catecholamine-containing neurones in the rat central nervous system. In: *6-Hydroxydopamine and Catecholamine Neurons,* edited by T. Malfors and H. Thoenen, pp. 171–186. North-Holland Publishers, Amsterdam.

Jaim-Etcheverry, G., and Zieher, L. M. (1971): Permanent depletion of peripheral norepinephrine in rats treated at birth with 6-hydroxydopamine. *Eur. J. Pharmacol.,* 13:272–276.

Jolley, R. L., and Labby, D. H. (1960): Development of brain enzymes concerned with glutamic acid metabolism in fetal monkey and pig. *Arch. Biochem.*, 90:122–124.

Jonsson, G., Pycock, Ch., Fuxe, K., and Sachs, C. (1974): Changes in the development of central noradrenaline neurones following neonatal administration of 6-hydroxydopamine. *J. Neurochem.*, 22:419–426.

Jouvet, M. (1969): Biogenic amines and the states of sleep. *Science*, 163:32–41.

Jouvet-Mounier, D., Astic, L., and Lacote, D. (1970): Ontogenesis of the states of sleep in rat, cat, and guinea pig during the first postnatal month. *Dev. Psychobiol.*, 2:216–239.

Karki, N., Kuntzman, R., and Brodie, B. B. (1962): Storage, synthesis, and metabolism of monoamines in the developing brain. *J. Neurochem.*, 9:53–58.

Katzman, R. (1972): Blood-brain-CSF barriers. In: *Basic Neurochemistry*, edited by R. W. Albers, G. J. Siegel, R. Katzman, and B. W. Agranoff, pp. 327–339. Little, Brown, Boston.

Katzman, R., and Leiderman, P. H. (1953): Brain potassium exchange in normal adult and immature rats. *Am. J. Physiol.*, 175:263–270.

Kellogg, C., and Lundborg, P. (1972a): Ontogenic variations in responses to L-DOPA and monoamine receptor-stimulating agents. *Psychopharmacologia*, 23:187–200.

Kellogg, C., and Lundborg, P. (1972b): Production of [³H] catecholamines in the brain following peripheral administration of ³H-DOPA during pre- and postnatal development. *Brain Res.*, 36:333–342.

Kellogg, C., and Lundborg, P. (1972c): Uptake and utilization of [³H-] 5-hydroxytryptophan by brain tissue during development. *Neuropharmacology*, 11:363–372.

Kellogg, C., and Lundborg, P. (1973): Inhibition of catecholamine synthesis during ontogenic development. *Brain Res.*, 61:321–329.

Kelley, B. (1956): Age and nitrogen content of rabbit brain parts. *Am. J. Physiol.*, 13:295–304.

Korey, S. R., Gonatas, J., and Stein, A. (1963): Studies in Tay-Sachs disease. III. Biochemistry. *J. Neuropathol. Exp. Neurol.*, 22:56–66.

Kostrzewa, R. M., and Harper, J. W. (1974): Effect of 6-hydroxydopa on catecholamine-containing neurons in brains of newborn rats. *Brain Res.*, 69:174–181.

Ladosky, W., and Gaziri, L. C. J. (1970): Brain serotonin and sexual differentiation of the nervous system. *Neuroendocrinol.*, 6:168–174.

Lajtha, A., and Toth, J. (1973): Perinatal changes in the free amino acid pool of the brain in mice. *Brain Res.*, 55:238–241.

Lassen, N. A., Christensen, S., Hoedt-Rasmussen, K., and Stewart, B. M. (1966): Cerebral oxygen consumption in Down's syndrome. *Arch. Neurol.*, 15:595–602.

Laster, L. (1965): Homocystinuria due to cystathionine synthase deficiency. *Ann. Intern. Med.*, 63:1117–1142.

Lauder, J. M., and Bloom, F. E. (1974): Ontogeny of monoamine neurons in the locus coeruleus, raphe nuclei and substantia nigra of the rat. *J. Comp. Neurol.*, 155:469–481.

LaVelle, A. (1973): Levels of maturation and reactions to injury during neuronal development. In: *Progress in Brain Research, Vol. 40, Neurobiological Aspects of Maturation and Aging*, edited by D. H. Ford, pp. 161–166. American Elsevier, New York.

Lejeune, J. (1967): Chromosomal studies in psychiatry. In: *Recent Advances in Biological Psychiatry, Vol. IX*, edited by Joseph Wortis, pp. 13–20. Plenum Press, New York.

Lesch, M., and Nyhan, W. L. (1964): A familial disorder of uric acid metabolism and central nervous system function. *Am. J. Med.*, 36:561–570.

Lew, G., and Quay, W. B. (1971): Noradrenaline contents of hypothalamus and adrenal gland increased by postnatal administration of 6-hydroxydopamine. *Res. Commun. Chem. Pathol. Pharm.*, 2:807–812.

Lindroos, O. F. C., and Oja, S. S. (1971): Hyperphenylalaninemia and the exchange of tyrosine in adult rat brain. *Exp. Brain Res.*, 14:48–60.

Loizou, L. A. (1970): Uptake of monoamines into central neurones and the blood-brain barrier in the infant rat. *Br. J. Pharmacol.*, 40:800–813.

Loizou, L. A. (1971): The effect of inhibition of catecholamine synthesis on central catecholamine-containing neurones in the developing albino rat. *Br. J. Pharmacol.,* 41:41–48.

Loizou, L. A. (1972): The postnatal ontogeny of monoamine-containing neurones in the central nervous system of the albino rat. *Brain Res.,* 40:395–418.

Loizou, L. A., and Salt, P. (1970): Regional changes in monoamines of the rat brain during postnatal development. *Brain Res.,* 20:467–470.

Mahler, H. R. (1972): Nucleic acid metabolism. In: *Basic Neurochemistry,* edited by R. W. Albers, G. J. Siegel, R. Katzman, and B. W. Agranoff, pp. 245–265. Little, Brown, Boston.

Martin, H., Fischer, H. L., Martin, D. S., and Chase, H. P. (1974): The development of children with transient neonatal tyrosinemia. *J. Pediatr.,* 84:212–216.

Mason, S. T., and Iversen, S. D. (1974): Learning impairment in rats after 6-hydroxy-dopamine-induced depletion of brain catecholamines. *Nature,* 248:697–698.

McKean, C. (1972): The effects of high phenylalanine concentrations on serotonin and catecholamine metabolism in the human brain. *Brain Res.,* 47:469–476.

McKean, C., Schanberg, S. M., and Giarman, N. J. (1962): A mechanism of the indole defect in experimental phenylketonuria. *Science,* 137:604–605.

Mellgren, S. I. (1973): Distribution of acetylcholinesterase in the hippocampal region of the rat during postnatal development. *Z. Zellforsch.,* 141:375–400.

Menkes, J. H. (1966): Cerebral lipids in phenylketonuria. *Pediatrics,* 37:967–978.

Menkes, J. H., and Solcher, H. (1967): Maple syrup disease. *Arch. Neurol.,* 16:486–492.

Michener, W. M. (1967): Hyperuricemia and mental retardation. *Am. J. Dis. Child.,* 113:195–206.

Miller, S. A. (1969): Protein metabolism during growth and development. In: *Mammalian Protein Synthesis, Vol. 3,* edited by H. N. Munro. Academic Press, New York.

Moore, R. Y., Björklund, A., and Stenevi, U. (1971): Plastic changes in the adrenergic innervation of the rat septal area in response to denervation. *Brain Res.,* 33:13–35.

Mysliveček, J. (1970): Electrophysiology of the developing brain—Central and Eastern European contributions. In: *Developmental Neurobiology,* edited by W. A. Himwich, pp. 475–527. Charles C Thomas, Springfield, Ill.

Nordyke, E. L., and Roach, M. K. (1974): Effect of hyperphenylalaninemia on amino acid metabolism and compartmentation in neonatal rat brain. *Brain Res.,* 67:479–488.

Norton, W. T., and Poduslo, S. E. (1973): Myelination in rat brain: Changes in myelin composition during brain maturation. *J. Neurochem.,* 21:759–773.

Nygran, L., Olson, L., and Seiger, Å. (1971): Regeneration of monoamine-containing axons in the developing and adult spinal cord of the rat following intraspinal 6-OH-dopamine injections or transections. *Histochemie,* 25:1–15.

Oberholzer, V. G., Levin, B., Burgess, E. A., and Young, W. F. (1967): Methylmalonic aciduria. An inborn error of metabolism leading to chronic metabolic acidosis. *Arch. Dis. Child.,* 42:492.

O'Brien, J. S. (1973): Tay-Sachs disease: From enzyme to prevention. *Fed. Proc.,* 32:191–199.

Ohara, P. T. (1972): Electron microscopical study of the brain in Down's syndrome. *Brain,* 95:681–684.

Oldendorf, W. H. (1970): Measurement of brain uptake of radiolabeled substances using a tritiated water internal standard. *Brain Res.,* 24:372–376.

Oldendorf, W. H. (1971): Brain uptake of radiolabeled amino acids, amines and hexoses after arterial injection. *Am. J. Physiol.,* 221:1629–1639.

Oldendorf, W. H. (1973): Stereospecificity of blood-brain barrier permeability to amino acids. *Am. J. Physiol.,* 224:967–969.

Olson, L., and Seiger, Å. (1972): Early prenatal ontogeny of central monoamine neurons in the rat: Fluorescence histochemical observations. *Z. Anat. Entwickl. Gesch.,* 137:301–316.

Olsson, Y., Klatzo, I., Sourancer, P., and Steinwall, O. (1968): Blood-brain barrier to albumin in embryonic new born and adult rats. *Acta Neuropathol.,* 10:117–122.

O'Neill, J. (1974): Carbohydrate metabolism in the developing nervous system. In: *Biochemistry of the Developing Brain, Vol. 2,* edited by W. A. Himwich, pp. 69–122. Marcel Dekker, New York.

Owen, O. E., Morgan, A. P., Kemp, H. C., Sullivan, J. M., Herrera, M. G., and Cahill, G. F., Jr. (1957): Brain metabolism during fasting. *J. Clin. Invest.,* 46:1589–1595.

Palo, J., and Saifer, A. (1968): Free amino acids in Tay-Sachs and normal human brain gray matter. *Clin. Chim. Acta,* 22:327–334.

Pampiglione, G. (1960): The development of the EEG in the young dog. *Electroencephalogr. Clin. Neurophysiol.,* 12:760.

Pappas, B. A., and Sobrian, S. K. (1972): Neonatal sympathectomy by 6-hydroxydopamine in the rat: No effects on behavior but changes in endogenous brain norepinephrine. *Life Sci.,* 11:653–659.

Patel, M. S., Grover, W. D., and Auerbach, V. H. (1973): Pyruvate metabolism by homogenates of human brain: Effects of phenylpyruvate and implications for the etiology of the mental retardation in phenylketonuria. *J. Neurochem.,* 20:289–296.

Pepeu, G., and Giarman, N. J. (1962): Serotonin in the developing mammal. *J. Gen. Physiol.,* 45:575–583.

Perry, T. L., Hansen, S. Tischler, B., Bunting, R., and Berry, K. (1967): Carnosinemia: A new metabolic disorder associated with neurologic disease and mental defect. *N. Engl. J. Med.,* 277:1219–1227.

Perry, T. L., Hardwick, D. F., Hansen, S., Love, D., and Israels, S. (1968): Cystathioninuria in two healthy siblings. *N. Engl. J. Med.,* 278:590–592.

Persson, T., and Waldeck, B. (1970): Some problems encountered in attempting to estimate catecholamine turnover using labelled tyrosine. *J. Pharm. Pharmacol.,* 122:473–478.

Peters, A. (1974): The morphology of the developing myelin sheath. In: *Drugs and the Developing Brain,* edited by A. Vernadakis and N. Weiner, pp. 395–414. Plenum Press, New York.

Porcher, W., and Heller, A. (1972): Regional development of catecholamine biosynthesis in rat brain. *J. Neurochem.,* 19:1917–1930.

Potter, V. R., Schneider, W. C., and Liebl, G. J. (1945): Enzyme changes during growth and differentiation in the tissues of the newborn rat. *Cancer Res.,* 5:21–24.

Purpura, D. P. (1974): Dendritic spine "dysgenesis" and mental retardation. *Science,* 186:1126–1128.

Purpura, D. P., and Shofer, R. J. (1972): Principles of synaptogenesis and their application to ontogenetic studies of mammalian cerebral cortex. In: *Sleep and the Maturing Nervous System,* edited by C. D. Clemente, D. P. Purpura, and F. E. Mayer, pp. 3–32. Academic Press, New York.

Rappoport, D. A., Fritz, R. R., and Myers, J. L. (1969): Nucleic acids. In: *Handbook of Neurochemistry,* Vol. 1, edited by A. Lajtha, pp. 101–119. Plenum Press, New York.

Renson, J. (1971): Development of monoaminergic transmissions in the rat brain. In: *Chemistry and Brain Development,* edited by R. Paoletti and A. N. Davison, pp. 175–184. Plenum Press, New York.

Richter, J. J., and Wainer, A. (1971): Evidence for separate systems for the transport of neutral and basic amino acids across the blood-brain barrier. *J. Neurochem.,* 18:613–620.

Roberts, R. B., Flexner, J. B., and Flexner, L. B. (1959): Biochemical and physiological differentiation during morphogenesis. XXIII. Further observations relating to the synthesis of amino acids and proteins by the cerebral cortex and liver of the mouse. *J. Neurochem.,* 4:78–90.

Roffwarg, H. P., Muzio, J. N., and Dement, W. C. (1966): Ontogenetic development of the human sleep-dream cycle. *Science,* 152:604–619.

Rose, G., and Ellingson, R. J. (1970): Ontogenesis of evoked responses. In: *Developmental Neurobiology,* edited by W. A. Himwich, pp. 393–440. Charles C. Thomas, Springfield, Ill.

Rosenberg, L. E., and Mahoney, M. J. (1973): Inherited disorders of methylmalonate and vitamin B_{12} metabolism. A progress report. In: *Inborn Errors of Metabolism,* edited by F. A. Hommes and C. J. Van den Berg, pp. 303–320. Academic Press, New York.

Rosner, F., Ong, B. H., Paine, R. S., and Mahanand, D. (1965): Blood-serotonin activity in trisomic and translocation Down's syndrome. *Lancet,* 1:1191.

Rutledge, L. T., Wright, C., and Duncan, J. (1974): Morphological changes in pyramidal cells of mammalian neocortex associated with increased use. *Exp. Neurol.,* 44:209–228.

Sachs, C. (1973): Development of the blood-brain barrier for 6-hydroxydopamine. *J. Neurochem.,* 20:1753–1760.

Sachs, C., and Jonsson, G. (1972): Degeneration of central and peripheral noradrenaline neurons produced by 6-hydroxy-dopa. *J. Neurochem.* 19:1561–1575.

Sammeck, R., Martenson, R. E., and Brady, R. O. (1971): Studies of the metabolism of myelin basic proteins in various regions of the central nervous system of immature and adult rats. *Brain Res.,* 34:241–254.

Scherrer, J., Verley, R., and Garma, L. (1970): A review of French studies in the ontogenetical field. In: *Developmental Neurobiology,* edited by W. A. Himwich, pp. 528–549. Charles C Thomas, Springfield, Ill.

Schmidt, J. C., and Sanders-Bush, E. (1971): Tryptophan hydroxylase activity in developing rat brain. *J. Neurochem.,* 18:2549–2551.

Schwerin, P., Bessman, S. P., and Waelsch, H. (1950): The uptake of glutamic acid and glutamine by brain and other tissues of the rat and mouse. *J. Biol. Chem.,* 184:37–44.

Seiger, Å., and Olson, L. (1973): Late prenatal ontogeny of central monoamine neurons in the rat: Fluorescence histochemical observations. *Z. Anat. Entwickl. Gesch.,* 140:281–318.

Shah, S. N., Peterson, N. A., and McKean, C. M. (1972): Impaired myelin formation in experimental hyperphenylalaninaemia. *J. Neurochem.,* 19:2369–2376.

Shih, J. C., and Eiduson, S. (1971): Multiple forms of monoamine oxidase in developing brain: Tissue and substrate specificities. *J. Neurochem.,* 18:1221–1227.

Shimizu, A., and Himwich, H. E. (1968a): The effects of amphetamine on the sleep-wakefulness cycle of developing kittens. *Psychopharmacologia,* 13:161–169.

Shimizu, A., and Himwich, H. E. (1968b): The ontogeny of sleep in kittens and young rabbits. *Electroencephalogr. Clin. Neurophysiol.,* 24:307–318.

Shimizu, A., and Himwich, H. E. (1969): Effects of psychotropic drugs on the sleep-wakefulness cycle of the developing kitten. *Dev. Psychobiol.,* 2:161–167.

Singh, B., and de Champlain, J. (1972): Altered ontogenesis of central noradrenergic neurons following neonatal treatment with 6-hydroxydopamine. *Brain Res.,* 48:432–437.

Singh, V. K., Fibiger, H. C., and McGeer, P. L. M. (1974): Effects of 6-hydroxydopamine on the nature of proteins undergoing axoplasmic transport in nigroneostriatal neurons. *J. Neurochem.,* 23:601–604.

Sladek, J. R., Jr., Tabakoff, B., and Garver, D. (1974): Certain biochemical correlates of intense serotonin histofluorescence in the brain stem of the neonatal monkey. *Brain Res.,* 67:363–371.

Smith, A. L. Satterthwaite, H. S., and Sokoloff, L. (1969): Induction of brain D(-)β-hydroxybutyrate dehydrogenase activity by fasting. *Science,* 163:79.

Smith, M. E. (1973): A regional survey of myelin development: Some compositional and metabolic aspects. *J. Lipid Res.,* 14:541–551.

Smith, S. E., Stacey, R. S., and Young, I. M. (1962): 5-Hydroxytryptamine and 5-hydroxytryptophan decarboxylase activity in the developing nervous system of rats and guinea pigs. *Proc. First Int. Pharmacol. Meet.,* 8:101–105.

Studnitz, W. V. (1969): Secondary cystathioninuria. *Acta Paediatr. Scand.,* 58:173–177.

Takada, G., and Tada, K. (1970): Incorporation of ¹⁴C-leucine into brain protein in rats with hyperaminoacidemia. *Tohoku J. Exp. Med.,* 102:103–111.

Thierry, A. M., Blanc, G., and Glowinski, J. (1971): Dopamine-norepinephrine: Another regulatory step of norepinephrine synthesis in central noradrenergic neurons. *Eur. J. Pharmacol.,* 14:303–307.

Thurston, J. H., Levy, C. A., Warren, S. K., and Jones, E. M. (1972): Permeability of the blood-brain barrier to fructose and the anaerobic use of fructose in the brains of young mice. *J. Neurochem.,* 19:1685–1696.

Trevor, A. J., Shirachi, D. Y., and Sutherland, V. C. (1974): Ontogenetic aspects of cerebral metabolic relationships *in vitro.* In: *Biochemistry of the Developing Brain, Vol. 2,* edited by W. A. Himwich, pp. 123–141. Marcel Dekker, New York.

Tu, J. B., and Zellweger, H. (1965): Blood-serotonin deficiency in Down's syndrome. *Lancet,* II:715.

Valatx, J. L., Jouvet, D., and Jouvet, M. (1964): Évolution électroencéphalographique des différents états de sommeil chez le chaton. *Electroencephalogr. Clin. Neurophysiol.,* 17:218–233.

Verley, R. (1967): Les secteurs d'activites electrocorticales. Leur développement postnatal. In: *Regional Development of the Brain in Early Life,* edited by A. Minkowski, pp. 367–393. Blackwell, Oxford.

Waelsch, H. (1951): Glutamic acid in cerebral function. *Adv. Protein Chem.,* 6:299–341.

Weise, P., Koch, R., Shaw, K., and Rosenfeld, M. J. (1974): The use of 5-HTP in the treatment of Down's syndrome. *Pediatrics,* 54:165–168.

Wetterberg, L., Gustavson, K. H., Bäckström, M., Ross, S. B., and Froden, O. (1972): Low dopamine-β-hydroxylase activity in Down's syndrome. *Clin. Genet.,* 3:152–153.

Winick, M. (1968): Changes in nucleic acid and protein content of the human brain during growth. *Pediatr. Res.,* 2:352–355.

Youngstrom, K. A. (1941): Acetylcholine esterase concentration during the development of the human fetus. *J. Neurophysiol.,* 4:473–477.

Yuwiler, A., Geller, E., and Slater, G. G. (1965): On the mechanism of the brain serotonin depletion in experimental phenylketonuria. *J. Biol. Chem.,* 240:1170–1174.

Zieher, L. M., and Jaim-Etcheverry, G. (1973): Regional differences in the long-term effect of neonatal 6-hydroxydopa treatment on rat brain noradrenaline. *Brain Res.,* 60:199–207.

Biological Foundations of Psychiatry,
edited by R. G. Grenell and S. Gabay.
Raven Press, New York © 1976.

Genetic Factors in Schizophrenia

Ming T. Tsuang

Department of Psychiatry, University of Iowa, College of Medicine, Iowa City, Iowa 52242

I. INTRODUCTION

According to The Diagnostic and Statistical Manual of Mental Disorders (DSM-II, 1968), Schizophrenia "includes a group of disorders manifested by characteristic disturbances of thinking, mood and behavior." This is a very general and abstract description. The concept of schizophrenia varies from one country to another, and even from one center to another within the same country. Despite this present lack of national and international agreement on exactly what criteria constitute a diagnosis of schizophrenia, there is unanimous agreement that a psychiatric illness, from whatever causes, in fact, exists and manifests itself in disturbances of thinking, mood, and behavior, and that, for all practical purposes, can be referred to as "schizophrenia."

Various studies are underway to define this concept more clearly. Such a definition would be of immense value in psychiatric research and in international cooperation between psychiatrists; its absence, however, is more a matter of inconvenience than incapacitation to psychiatric research, and need not prevent the investigation of factors which may be associated with this illness.

After the problem of the exact nature of this illness, perhaps the most

intriguing and timely question regarding schizophrenia is whether it is pos-
sessed of a genetic component.

II. ARE THERE GENETIC FACTORS IN SCHIZOPHRENIA?

A. Twin Studies

The investigation of genetic factors in schizophrenia has frequently led to
the examination of the concordance rate for the illness between co-twins
when one twin is diagnosed as schizophrenic. Shields and Slater (1967)
summarized the then available data from twin studies (Table 1). The find-

TABLE 1. Concordance rates of schizophrenia in twins[a]

Twin pairs	No. of pairs	Concordant pairs	Concordance (%)
OS DZ[b]	430	24	5.6
SS DZ[c]	593	71	12.0
MZ[d]	437	252	57.7

[a] Pooled data based on Shields and Slater (1967).

[b] OS DZ: Opposite-sex dizygotic twins; based on six investigations from five countries.

[c] SS DZ: Same-sex dizygotic twins; based on nine investigations from seven countries.

[d] MZ: Monozygotic twins; based on 10 investigations from eight countries.

ings presented in Table 1, based as they are on a large number of investigations in several countries, provide ample indication that as the twin relationship becomes more similar from the genetic point of view—from opposite-
sex dizygotic, to same-sex dizygotic, to monozygotic—the risk will be higher
for the co-twin of a schizophrenic likewise being affected with the illness.

The investigations reported in Table 1 have not gone unchallenged. They
have been criticized as being biased with regard to sampling method,
procedure of psychiatric diagnosis, and determination of zygocity. Recent
population-based twin studies in Finland, Norway, Denmark, and the United
States have been specifically controlled for those considerations. As shown in
Table 2, these later studies agree with the general trend noted in the earlier
investigations: namely, the concordance rate for schizophrenia is higher for
monozygotic (MZ) pairs than for dizygotic pairs of twins.

The suggestion has been made in the past (Jackson, 1960) that a high
concordance rate for schizophrenia in MZ twins could be expected anyway,
because of such problems as identity confusion and weak ego formation. In
this case, MZ twins should be over-represented in samples of schizophrenics
with regard to their frequency in the general population since the very fact

of being an MZ twin would predispose to schizophrenia. However, Rosenthal (1960), among others, has shown that there is no excess of MZ twins in schizophrenic samples.

That this higher concordance rate for MZ pairs may be rightly ascribed, at least in part, to the operation of genetic factors, as opposed to totally environmental ones, may be seen from the results of studies on MZ twins reared apart. The available literature on such studies was summarized by Gottesman and Shields (1972). Eight investigations in seven countries showed that 11 of 17 MZ twin pairs reared apart were concordant for schizophrenia, a rate of 64%.

TABLE 2. Concordance rates of schizophrenia in twins[a]

		MZ pairs			DZ pairs		
		No. of pairs	Concordance		No. of pairs	Concordance	
Reference	Country		a	b		a	b
			(%)			(%)	
Tienari (1968)	Finland	16	6	36	20	5	14
Kringlen (1968)	Norway	55	25	38	90	4	10
Fischer et al. (1969)	Denmark	21	24	48	41	10	19
Pollin et al. (1969)	U.S.	80	14	35	146	4	10

[a] Based on Gottesman and Shields (1972).
a, Diagnostically certain cases only; b, also including probable schizophrenics.

B. Fostering Studies

Another method to examine the genetic component in schizophrenia which controls for environmental influences is to use fostering studies of children separated at birth from their schizophrenic mothers. Table 3 shows the findings of a study on the psychiatric disorders found in children reared in foster homes (Heston, 1966). A sample of 47 children, all of whom were separated from their schizophrenic mothers within the first 3 days of life and reared in foster homes, were followed up to a mean age of 36. They were matched for sex, type of placement, and length of time in child-care institutions, with a control group of 50 children of normal mothers. Five of the 47 foster-reared children of schizophrenic mothers were found to be schizophrenic; none in the control group was similarly affected. The differences for psychiatric disorder between the two groups were not limited to schizophrenia. As can be noted in Table 3, more cases of mental deficiency, sociopathic personality, and neurotic personality disorder were found among the children of schizophrenic mothers than among those of normal mothers.

Using a somewhat different approach, Kety et al. (1973) conducted a population-based study to determine whether schizophrenia in adoptees

TABLE 3. *Psychiatric disorders in offspring separated at birth from their mothers[a]*

Variable	Schizophrenic mother	Normal mother
Number of children	47	50
Mean age (years)	35.8	36.3
Schizophrenia	5	—
Mental deficiency, IQ < 70	4	—
Sociopathic personality	9	2
Neurotic personality disorder	13	7

[a] Based on Heston (1966).

could be accounted for by the schizophrenia in their biological relatives with whom the adoptees had no contact, or rather by schizophrenia in the biologically unrelated adoptive families. From the Danish adoption register, 33 index schizophrenics were matched with a control group of 33 normal adoptees. The results of the blind diagnostic assessment of the adoptive and biological relatives of both groups are shown in Table 4. Very significantly, the biological relatives of the schizophrenic index cases show the greatest percentage of definite schizophrenia—8.1%. The biological relatives of the controls and adoptive relatives of both controls and index cases, however, show no significant percentage of schizophrenia.

Expanding on this investigation, Wender et al. (1974) used crossfostering to see whether the environment provided by a schizophrenic parent could produce schizophrenia in an adopted child with a normal genetic composition. Three groups were studied from the Danish adoption register: (1) an adopted index group, whose biological parents had been diagnosed for schizophrenia spectrum disorder (definite, borderline, and doubtful schizophrenia); (2) an adopted control group whose biological parents were believed to be normal, matched with the index cases for sex, age, transfers to adopting parents, and socioeconomic status of adoptive home; and (3) a crossfostered group whose biological parents were believed to be normal,

TABLE 4. *Distribution of definite schizophrenia among the biological and adoptive relatives of schizophrenic index cases and controls[a]*

	No. of cases	Biological relatives	Adoptive relatives
Index	33	14/173[b] (8.1%)	1/74[b] (1.4%)
Control	33	4/174[b] (2.3%)	3/91[b] (3.3%)
p (one-sided from exact distribution)		0.013	ns

[a] Based on Kety et al. (1973).

[b] Numerators, number with definite schizophrenia; denominators, number of identified relatives (parents, sibs, half-sibs).

but whose adoptive parents had been diagnosed for schizophrenia spectrum disorder. These three groups were interviewed blindly. The group percentages of those receiving a schizophrenic diagnosis of severity equal to or greater than "probably borderline schizophrenia" ("upper pathology quartile") are shown in Table 5. The adopted index group showed the highest percentage for this diagnosis, and when this group is compared to all adoptees with normal biological parents (adopted control group + crossfostered group), the difference is statistically significant.

It can be noted from Table 5 that a higher than expected rate for this diagnosis was found among the adopted control group. Wender et al. (1974) stated that problems in drawing the control sample probably account for this difference. Their conclusion, however, is that, in this test for genetic as op-

TABLE 5. Distribution of "upper pathology quartile"[a] among adopted-index, adopted-control, and crossfostered groups[b]

Group	No. adoptees in each group	% in upper pathology quartile
Adopted index	66	19.7
Adopted control	75	10.7
Crossfostered	21	4.8

[a] "Upper pathology quartile": those with a schizophrenic diagnosis of severity equal to or greater than "probable borderline schizophrenia."

[b] Based on Wender et al. (1974).

posed to nongenetic effects in the development of schizophrenia, genetic factors exert a greater influence than does the psychopathology of the parents. Thus, the findings of both twin and fostering studies provide substantial evidence that genetic factors are operating in schizophrenia.

III. WHAT IS THE RISK FOR SCHIZOPHRENIA?

An additional way of establishing a genetic association in schizophrenia is through family studies, in which an examination is made to determine the morbidity risks to different categories of family members. A summary of the numerous and extensive family studies available for the distribution of schizophrenia is given in Table 6.

Even a casual perusal of Table 6 reveals that the closer the familial relationship, the higher the possibility of schizophrenia. A closer analysis shows several interesting relationships. The 0.86% figure for the general population is compiled from 19 investigations in six countries. This relatively low risk for the general population is in sharp contrast to the risks for schizophrenia for different classes of family members of schizophrenics, with first-degree relatives exhibiting a substantially higher risk than second-degree relatives.

These combined results for the familial distribution of risk for schizophrenia provide further evidence of a genetic component in schizophrenia. These findings, however, do not fit any classic Mendelian ratio of inheritance, creating the question of how they are to be interpreted with regard to mode of inheritance.

TABLE 6. Morbidity risk of schizophrenia[a]

Relatives of schizophrenics	Risk (%)
First-degree	
parents	4.4
siblings	8.5
neither parent schizophrenic	8.2
one parent schizophrenic	13.8
children	12.3
both parents schizophrenic	36.6
Second-degree	
uncles and aunts	2.0
nephews and nieces	2.2
grandchildren	2.8
half sibs	3.2
Third-degree	
first cousins	2.9
General population[b]	0.86

[a] Based on Slater and Cowie (1971); data mainly derived from pooled data of Zerbin-Rudin (1967), correction for age usually by shorter Weinberg method, risk 15–39; only cases of definite schizophrenia counted.

[b] Compiled from 19 investigations in six countries.

IV. HOW IS SCHIZOPHRENIA INHERITED?

Once the existence of a genetic component in schizophrenia has been established, it becomes extremely important to discover the mode of its transmission. Several theoretical models have been proposed. Although there are no definite findings available to date showing what specific kinds of genetic factors are operating in schizophrenia, these models serve a useful function in that they provide a framework within which to organize available data. They also encourage the formation of hypotheses which can then be tested against each other for credibility. Different genetic models dictate the different kinds of studies which will have to be conducted to strengthen or refute a hypothesis. Genetic models may likewise improve the possibilities of detecting premorbid cases of the illness, and provide the basis for recommendations regarding the prevention of schizophrenia by such methods as genetic counseling.

No attempt will be made here to discuss fully the extensive, and often conflicting, literature available on the mode of genetic transmission of schizophrenia. The main theories will be introduced and briefly summarized. They are, for the most part, complex, rife with exceptions to the available data, and not easily understood by those unfamiliar with the field of genetics.

Three main theories are generally recognized: the monogenic, the polygenic, and the genetic heterogeneity. Each of these has a number of variants which tend to blur the distinction between the three main categories. Generally speaking, these different models rest upon, and in some ways are dictated by, a particular assumption regarding the nature of schizophrenia— specifically, whether (1) it is a discrete illness with various manifestations (monogenic); (2) it is the manifestation of an extreme in a continuous or quasi-continuous genetic distribution (polygenic); or (3) "schizophrenia" is a generic title for several distinct illnesses, or some combination of all of these (heterogeneous).

A. Monogenic Theory

In its simplest form, the monogenic theory postulates a single, specific, schizophrenic gene, which may be homozygous (present at the same locus on both chromosomes of a specific pair) or heterozygous (present on one chromosome of the pair only). (Böök, 1953; Kallmann, 1953; Slater, 1958; Garrone, 1962; Meehl, 1962; Slater and Tsuang, 1968; Heston, 1970; Slater and Cowie, 1971; Tsuang, 1971; Karlsson, 1973). This theory actually comprises three theories: transmission by a single dominant gene of reduced penetrance; transmission by a recessive gene, in which case schizophrenia would be manifested only if the schizophrenic gene were present in both chromosomes; and transmission by both of the above modes, usually referred to as the "intermediate" theory of monogenic transmission, where schizophrenia is always manifested in homozygotes carrying the abnormal gene, but also manifested for about a quarter of heterozygotes. The intermediate theory likewise postulates "modifying genes" as precipitants in determining whether schizophrenia will be manifested in those having the specific schizophrenic gene. If true, the monogenic theory holds the most promise for identification of the specific abnormal gene responsible for schizophrenia, and the eventual effective treatment of this illness by biochemical means.

B. Polygenic Theory

In contrast to the single, specific, schizophrenic gene of the monogenic theory, the polygenic theory postulates the existence of many genes, singly insufficient to cause schizophrenia, but which in summation or combination with each other result in a genetic constitution predisposed to schizophrenia, which is then, possibly, precipitated by environmental factors (Ødegaard, 1952, 1972; Kay and Roth, 1961; Tsuang, 1965; Gottesman and Shields, 1967, 1972; Kringlen, 1967). There are two major variations of the polygenic theory. The first views the many genes as being of equal weight and normally distributed (continuous) with schizophrenia resulting from the simple additive effect of these genes at the distribution's extreme. The second view is that the many genes necessary for schizophrenia may be of unequal effect, and that once certain genes are present a threshold is passed, and that once this threshold is passed an individual may be said to have schizophrenia. This latter is usually referred to as the "threshold" or "quasi-continuous" polygenic theory (Edwards, 1960; Falconer, 1965, 1967).

C. Genetic Heterogeneity

Yet another interpretation of the genetic evidence for schizophrenia abandons the idea that a single disease is being transmitted by one or more genes in a variety of ways, and postulates, instead, that schizophrenia is not one, but a variety of diseases, each with its own causative gene or genes and mode or modes of transmission (Leonard, 1957; Inouye, 1963; ErlenmeyerKimling and Paradowski, 1966; Mitsuda, 1967; McCabe et al., 1971). The theories of genetic heterogeneity thus suggest that some forms of schizophrenia may be due to rare genes, specific for specific subtypes of schizophrenia.

V. WHAT IS INHERITED?

There is ample evidence in the literature to show that genetic factors are operating in schizophrenia. Likewise, the risks for inheriting this genetic predisposition have been calculated for various family members, and its mode of transmission speculated upon. What remains extremely unclear is the content of this genetic transmission and what, in fact, is inherited.

Those who have investigated a comprehensively inclusive group of patients have found that family members tend to exhibit several types of mental illness. Those results suggest that the genetic inheritance is of a non-specific predisposition for mental illness generally (Bleuler, 1963; Kringlen, 1967). However, when the index cases in genetic studies are more diagnostically limited and certain, the families of schizophrenics show no increased incidence of affective disorders, indicating that what is inherited is a genetic make-up favoring schizophrenic-type illness, rather than affective illness (Mitsuda, 1957; Ødegaard, 1963; Tsuang, 1967).

Workers who are able to isolate a highly homogenous clinical sample find more homogenous pairings of schizophrenic subtypes (hebephreniahebephrenia, for example) than chance would indicate (Kallmann, 1938;

Kringlen, 1967; Gottesman, 1968). However, relatives of schizophrenics of any one Kraepelinian subtype have an excessive risk for other kinds of schizophrenic illness (Fowler et al., 1974).

There is also the possibility that what is inherited is not only a type of clinical diagnosis, but also specific symptomology, such as age of onset, course, and outcome, as discussed by Tsuang (1967).

The question has also arisen as to whether schizophrenia might be caused by an inherited chromosome abnormality. The development of techniques for studying sex chromatin from buccal smears and chromosomes from peripheral blood samples have made possible the examination of populations in large series. Up to now, there is no data to indicate that a specific chromosome abnormality is associated with schizophrenia. However, studies have shown that the rate of sex chromatin abnormality is significantly higher in psychiatric population than in general population samples, indicating that sex chromosome abnormality seems to predispose to psychiatric illness generally, rather than to a specific psychiatric illness, such as schizophrenia (Tsuang, 1974).

To date there have been no conclusive findings to determine which of these theories has the most validity.

VI. HOW IMPORTANT ARE ENVIRONMENTAL FACTORS?

There is a general misunderstanding that once the presence of genetic factors has been proven, it then follows that all persons so genetically predisposed will become schizophrenic. This needs to be clarified. It is only by interaction with the environment that the genetic constitution manifests itself as schizophrenia, and all of the theories concerning the mode of transmission of schizophrenia discussed above recognize the importance of environmental precipitants. Here environmental factors include both physical and psychosocial ones.

Obviously, it would be of great value to establish which specific environmental factors precipitate the onset of schizophrenia. Such information, coupled with the knowledge of an individual's genetical constitution, would make it possible to modify or tailor an individual's environment in order to prevent the onset of schizophrenia, or, after the fact, possibly ameliorate the symptoms. Unfortunately, the diversity and complicated interaction of environmental factors which may be schizophrenia-precipitating make their discovery a difficult task. Further consideration of environmental factors is beyond the scope of the present discussion.

VII. SUMMARY

It should be apparent from the foregoing that the role of genetic factors in the causation of schizophrenia is significant, and possibly preponderant. This conclusion is based on a large body of data from twin, family, and fostering studies, which has consistently demonstrated that the rate of schizophrenia among the relatives of schizophrenics is significantly higher than for populations of unrelated individuals. The exact manner in which the genetic predisposition to schizophrenia is transmitted has not been determined although three main modes have been postulated—monogenic, polygenic, and genetic heterogeneity. Although it is apparent that the evidence for the genetic transmission of schizophrenia does not fit any classic Mendelian ratio of inheritance, it is possible to predict with a fair degree of certainty the expectation of schizophrenia in various categories of relatives. The role of physical and psychosocial environmental factors may well determine whether, and in what manner, the genetic predisposition to schizophrenia will be manifested.

ACKNOWLEDGMENTS

This work was supported in part by grants from the Iowa Mental Health Authority, and the National Institute of Mental Health Grant 1 R01 MH24189–01.

REFERENCES

American Psychiatric Association (1968): *DSM-II Diagnostic and Statistical Manual of Mental Disorders,* ed. 2. American Psychiatric Association, Washington, D.C.

Bleuler, M. (1963): Conception of schizophrenia within the last fifty years and today. *Proc. R. Soc. Med.,* 56:945–952.

Böök, J. A. (1953): A genetic and neuropsychiatric investigation of a north-Swedish population. *Acta Genet. Stat. Med. (Basel),* 4:1–100.

Edwards, J. H. (1960): The simulation of Mendelism. *Acta Genet. Stat. Med. (Basel),* 10:63–70.

Erlenmeyer-Kimling, L., and Paradowski, W. (1966): Selection and schizophrenia. *Am. Naturalist,* 100:651–665.

Falconer, D. S. (1965): The inheritance of liability to certain diseases, estimated from the incidence among relatives. *Ann. Hum. Genet.,* 29:51–76.

Falconer, D. S. (1967): The inheritance of liability to diseases with variable age of onset, with particular reference to diabetes mellitus. *Ann. Hum. Genet.,* 31:1–20.

Fischer, M., Harvald, B., and Hauge, M. (1969): A Danish twin study of schizophrenia. *Br. J. Psychiatry,* 115:981–990.

Fowler, R. C., Tsuang, M. T., Cadoret, R. J., Monnelly, E., and McCabe, M. (1974): A clinical and family comparison of paranoid and non-paranoid schizophrenics. *Br. J. Psychiatry,* April, 123.

Garrone, G. (1962): Étude statistique et génétique de la schizophrénie à Genève de 1901 à 1950. *J. Génét. Hum.,* 11:89–219.

Gottesman, I. I. (1968): Severity, concordance and diagnostic refinement in the Maudsley-Bethlem schizophrenic twin study. In: *The Transmission of Schizophrenia,* edited by D. Rosenthal and S. S. Kety. Pergamon, Oxford.

Gottesman, I. I., and Shields, J. (1967): A polygenic theory of schizophrenia. *Proc. Natl. Acad. Sci. USA,* 58:199–205.

Gottesman, I. I., and Shields, J. (1972): *Schizophrenia and Genetics: A Twin Study Vantage Point.* Academic Press, New York.

Heston, L. L. (1966): Psychiatric disorders in foster home reared children of schizophrenic mothers. *Br. J. Psychiatry,* 112:819–825.

Heston, L. L. (1970): The genetics of schizophrenic and schizoid disease. *Science,* 167: 249–256.

Inouye, E. (1963): Similarity and dissimilarity of schizophrenia in twins. *Proc. Third World Cong. Psychiatry,* 1961, 1:524–530. University of Toronto Press, Montreal.

Jackson, D. D. (1960): A critique of the literature on the genetics of schizophrenia. In: *The Etiology of Schizophrenia,* edited by D. D. Jackson. Basic Books, New York.

Kallmann, F. J. (1938): *The Genetics of Schizophrenia.* Augustin, New York.

Kallman, F. J. (1953): *Heredity in Health and Mental Disorder.* W. W. Norton & Company, Inc., New York.

Karlsson, J. L. (1973): An icelandic family study of schizophrenia. *Br. J. Psychiatry,* 123:549–554.

Kay, D. W., and Roth, M. (1961): Environmental and hereditary factors in the schizophrenias of old age ('late paraphrenia') and their bearing on the general problem of causation in schizophrenia. *J. Ment. Sci.,* 107:649–686.

Kety, S. S., Rosenthal, D., Wender, P., Schulsinger, F., and Jacobsen, B. (1973): Mental illness in the biological and adoptive families of adopted individuals who have become schizophrenic: A preliminary report based upon psychiatric interviews with the relative. Read before the annual meeting of the American Psychopathological Association. New York.

McCabe, M. S., Fowler, R. C., Cadoret, R. J., and Winokur, G. (1971): Familial differences in schizophrenia with good and poor prognosis. *Psychol. Med.,* 1:326–332.

Meehl, P. E. (1962): Schizotaxia, schizotypy, schizophrenia. *Am. Psychol.,* 17:827–838.

Mitsuda, H. (1957): Klinische-erbbiologische Untersuchung der endogenen Psychosen. *Acta Genet. (Basel),* 7:371–377.

Mitsuda, H. (1967): *Clinical Genetics in Psychiatry.* Igaku Shoin, Tokyo.

Ødegaard, Ø. (1952): La génétique dans la psychiatrie. *Proc. First World Cong. Psychiatry,* Paris, 1950. Hermann, Paris.

Ødegaard, Ø. (1963): The psychiatric disease entities in the light of a genetic investigation. *Acta Psychiat. Scand.,* 169:94–104.

Ødegaard, Ø. (1972): The multifactorial theory of inheritance in predisposition to schizophrenia. In: *Genetic Factors in "Schizophrenia,"* edited by A. R. Kaplan. Thomas, Springfield, Ill.

Pollin, W., Allen, M. G., Hoffer, A., Stabenau, J. R., and Hrubec, Z. (1969): Psychopathology in 15,909 pairs of veteran twins: Evidence for a genetic factor in the pathogenesis of schizophrenia and its relative absence in psychoneurosis. *Am. J. Psychiatry,* 126:597–610.

Rosenthal, D. (1960): Confusion of identity and the frequency of schizophrenia in twins. *Arch. Gen. Psychiatry,* 3:297–304.

Shields, J., and Slater, E. (1967): Genetic aspects of schizophrenia. *Hosp. Med.,* April, 579–584.

Slater, E. (1958): The mongenic theory of schizophrenia. *Acta Genet. Stat. Med. (Basel),* 8:50–56.

Slater, E., and Cowie, V. A. (1971): *The Genetics of Mental Disorders.* Oxford University Press, London.

Slater, E., and Tsuang, M. T. (1968): Abnormality on paternal and maternal sides: Observations in schizophrenia and manic-depression. *J. Med. Genet.,* 5:197–199.

Tienari, P. (1968): Schizophrenia in monozygotic male twins. In: The *Transmission of Schizophrenia,* edited by D. Rosenthal and S. S. Kety. Pergamon, Oxford.

Tsuang, M. T. (1965): *A study of pairs of sibs both hospitalized for mental disorder.* Ph.D. Thesis, University of London, London.

Tsuang, M. T. (1967): A study of pairs of sibs both hospitalized for mental disorder. *Br. J. Psychiatry,* 113:283–300.

Tsuang, M. T. (1971): Abnormality on paternal and maternal sides in Chinese schizophrenics. *Br. J. Psychiatry,* 118:211–214.

Tsuang, M. T. (1974): Sex chromatin anomaly in Chinese females: Psychiatric characteristics of XXX. *Br. J. Psychiatry,* 124:299–305.

Wender, P. H., Rosenthal, D., Kety, S. S., Schulsinger, F., and Welner, J. (1974): Cross-fostering: A research strategy for clarifying the role of genetic and experiential factors in the etiology of schizophrenia. *Arch. Gen. Psychiatry,* 30:121–128.

Zerbin-Rudin, E. (1967): Endogen Psychosen. In: *Humangenetik, ein kurzes handbuch,* edited by P. E. Becker. Thieme, Stuttgart.

Biological Foundations of Psychiatry,
edited by R. G. Grenell and S. Gabay.
Raven Press, New York © 1976.

Genetics of Affective Disorder

Remi J. Cadoret

Department of Psychiatry, University of Iowa, College of Medicine, Iowa City, Iowa 52242

I. INTRODUCTION

Progress in the genetics of affective disorder has been retarded by a number of practical problems. These include such factors as the difficulty in ascertainment of illness in relatives and the all-inclusive nature of affective disorder which embraces several distinct types of illness, each with different possible etiologic factors (of which a genetic element may be a component). The undoubted heterogeneity of affective disorders has rendered obsolete many early studies of inheritance in these disorders.

Because conclusions about heterogeneity of affective disorder have been a product of some of the genetic studies it is essential to consider something of the nosology of affective disorders. A useful classification, based in part on recent genetic findings, is one proposed by Robins and Guze (1972). Important elements in this classification system are: (1) affective symptoms (whether patient is or has been manic); (2) psychiatric conditions which existed prior to the onset of affective disturbance (such as alcoholism, antisocial personality, neuroses, schizophrenia, etc.); and (3) psychosocial events preceding the onset of affective symptoms (such as death of a loved one). The nosologic scheme is shown in Table 1. In discussing genetic studies it is important to consider the type of affective disorder involved and this is what we shall do here.

Genetic studies may be approached in many ways. In some experimental or observational designs, evidence of genetic etiology is direct, but in others the evidence is indirect or is confounded with other possible etiologic factors such as environment. For the most part, genetic studies in affective disorder have not been direct. There are no studies, for example, of crossfostering of adoptees as there have been for such conditions as schizophrenia (Heston, 1966), alcoholism (Goodwin et al., 1973), and antisocial personality

TABLE 1. *Nosology of affective disorders*

Type of affective disorder	Psychosocial "precipitating events"	Presence of pre-existing psychiatric condition	Characteristic affective symptoms
"Grief" reaction	Death of individual close to patient	No	Depressive syndrome
Secondary depression	Nonspecific	Yes	Depressive syndrome
Primary depression			
Bipolar affective disorder	Nonspecific	No	Depressive and/or manic syndrome
Unipolar affective disorder	Nonspecific	No	Depressive syndrome

(Schulsinger, 1972). However in the bipolar type of primary affective disorder, direct evidence of genetic etiology is available in the demonstration of genetic linkage (see below), an association which has yet to be demonstrated for any other functional psychiatric condition.

II. TWIN STUDIES

The classic approach to estimating the relative importance of genetic and environmental factors has been to compare concordance rates for monozygotic (MZ) and dizygotic (DZ) twins. A number of series of twins in which this comparison was made have been discussed in the literature. Seven series involving systematic sampling of individuals with manic-depressive psychosis (primary affective disorder) have been summarized by Price (1968). These show an overall 68% concordance for MZ pairs and 23% for DZ pairs (based upon a total of 97 MZ and 119 same-sexed DZ twin pairs). This significant difference in rates suggests that genetic factors are important in these kinds of affective disorder, but the 68% concordance falls short of the 100% expected with absolute genetic determination. Obviously other factors have a role in determining primary affective disorders. The fact that affective disorders are higher in blood relatives of individuals with affective illness (probably primary affective disorders) than in the general population has been reported for years (see review in Zerbin-Rüdin, 1967), but this kind of data is just as compatible with an environmental effect as a genetic one. The twin data provide us with some of the best evidence for the importance of genetic factors in some affective disorders.

However the conclusion that a genetic etiologic factor exists in primary affective disorder cannot be generalized to all kinds of affective disorders. In a study of twins diagnosed as neurotic, Price (1968) reported no concordance for a depressive diagnosis in 8 MZ and 16 DZ twins. These would probably represent the secondary depression type in Table 1. Similarly, genetic elements have not been demonstrated in the depressive syndrome which occurs after loss of a loved one by death (the "grief" reaction of Table 1). In a follow-up study of widows and widowers, Clayton has reported no difference in incidence of familial affective disorder between individuals who developed a "grief" reaction and those who did not (Clayton et al., 1973). A study of neurotic depression in families by Stenstedt (1966) showed a lower incidence of depressive disorders in parents and sibs (4.8%) of neurotically depressed probands compared to other relatives of probands who had manic-depressive psychosis (10.2%). The latter two studies (Clayton et al., 1973 and Stenstedt, 1966) show evidence of diminished importance of etiologic genetic factors in secondary or reactive depression which is consistent with the findings of no concordance in the twin study reported by Price (1968). Thus both twin studies and family studies indicate that the genetic factor is less important in some types of affective disorders, notably secondary depressions and the "grief" reaction. It is unfortunate that we do not have more twin data for these disorders.

III. UNIPOLAR AND BIPOLAR PRIMARY AFFECTIVE DISORDERS

Available twin data additionally contain evidence of at least two kinds of primary affective disorder: unipolar and bipolar. In North American usage, unipolar refers to an affective illness characterized solely by depression, whereas bipolar describes an affective illness characterized by one or more episodes of mania (with or without episodes of depression). In some definitions (Winokur, 1973), mania occurring in a family member would justify calling a proband with only depressive symptoms bipolar. Twin data collated by Zerbin-Rüdin (1969) showing a significant degree of "breeding true" to type of primary affective disorder is shown in Table 2. Given a bipolar twin, there is a much higher chance that the co-twin, if ill, will have a bipolar illness. This table also illustrates the characteristic higher concordance rate for MZ than for DZ twins (MZ = 60% concordant for an affective disorder; DZ = 23%), and this difference appears to be true for both unipolar and bi-

TABLE 2. Unipolar and bipolar affective disorders in twins[a]

Twin configuration	No. of pairs	
	MZ	DZ
Unipolar depressed- unipolar depressed	22	8
Bipolar-bipolar	21	1
Unipolar-bipolar	7	4
Incomplete concordance	9	7
Discordant	24	36
	83	56

[a] Data adapted from Zerbin-Rüdin (1969).

TABLE 3. *Illness of first-degree relatives by type of illness in probands*[a]

Type of illness in relatives	Bipolar probands	Unipolar probands
Bipolar	56	2
Unipolar	3	34

[a] Data from Perris (1966).

polar twin pairs. Concordance as to type does not appear to be as high for DZ twin pairs; this might suggest that other genetic factors (such as those associated with temperament variables) or environmental differences could be important.

Three studies comparing families of bipolar and unipolar probands bear out the finding that bipolar tendency runs in families (Angst, 1966; Perris, 1966; Winokur and Clayton, 1967). Of these studies, that of Perris (1966) shows the most dramatic evidence of this tendency. The data appear in Table 3 and show a high correlation between types of disorder in probands and their first-degree relatives.

In addition to this correlation of types, there are other possible genetic differences between unipolar and bipolar families. Studies of psychoses or affective illness in relatives of patients have generally shown that bipolar families have a higher incidence of these disorders and a representative group from a number of different cultures is shown in Table 4. The significance of such a genetic difference may be interpreted in a number of ways. It might mean that genetic factors are less important in unipolar depressions or that there exists a different inheritance factor. There is evidence to support both these interpretations.

With regard to the type of inheritance, the most important qualitative difference between unipolar and bipolar affective disorder is the fact that an X-linked dominant genetic factor is found in some bipolar families but not in those with unipolar illness. Evidence for this specific type of inheritance in

TABLE 4. *Incidence of psychosis in one or more relatives of unipolar and bipolar probands*

Reference	Bipolar families		Unipolar families	
	No.	Psychosis (%)	No.	Psychosis (%)
Neele (1949)	201	30	324	19
Kinkelin (1954)	51	69	89	41
Leonhard (1966)	238	40	288	26
Asano (1967)	84	62	78	53
Dorzab et al. (1971)	89	52	100	26

bipolar illness comes from two kinds of data: (1) linkage studies of families where both bipolar illness and some marker gene (a measurable trait known to be carried on the X-chromosome, such as red-green color blindness) are present in the same pedigree and thus permit correlations; and (2) study of family trees for a bipolar illness inheritance pattern that would prevail if an X-linked dominant factor were involved. Table 5 summarizes the linkage studies published to date. Significant evidence for an X-linked factor is definitely present in some families.

Using data similar to that in Table 5, some investigators have estimated linkage by statistical methods and found such evidence for X-linkage (Fieve et al., 1973). The mode of transmission is compatible with a dominant-type transmission in some of the pedigrees shown in Table 5, although some investigators argue for a modified sex-linked dominant inheritance involving a diminished penetrance of one gene or a genetic model with more than one dominant gene necessary for manifestation of the illness (Winokur and Reich, 1970). Additional evidence linking bipolar affective disorder with the X-chromosome is found in the characteristic pattern of illness that should prevail with X-linked inheritance, as observed in family-tree studies.

One outstanding consequence of X-linked inheritance is that ill fathers should not pass the condition on to their sons. Accordingly, most family studies have focused on this characteristic feature. Table 6 shows the findings in all of the studies of this type published to date. Two studies are compatible with the X-linked dominant pattern; the remainder are not compatible. In some families, illness in the sons could arise as a result of illness from the

TABLE 5. Linkage studies in bipolar affective disorder

Reference	Genetic marker	Results
Winokur and Tanna (1969)	Xg[a]	Three pedigrees informative for linkage of which ten children were compatible with X-linked transmission, one was incompatible. This difference is significant (2 of the 3 families suggest specific linkage with Xg[a] blood system which was not significant, however).
Reich and Winokur (1969)	Red-green color blindness	Two pedigrees, one with protan, one with deutan color blindness. In each pedigree, significant evidence of linkage with color blindness was found. Pedigrees suggest dominant inheritance.
Fieve et al. (1973)	Red-green color blindness	Eight* pedigrees, four with protan, four with deutan color blindness. In total protan and deutan families, significant evidence for linkage was found. Pedigrees fit a dominant inheritance.
Mendlewicz et al. (1972, 1973)	Xg[a]	Twelve* pedigrees for Xg[a]. Significant linkage reported.

* Since publication of these results two additional families with red-green color blindness (one protan, one deutan) and four families assorting for Xg[a] and affective disorder have been examined and the cumulative results are consistent with X-linkage. (J. Mendlewicz, *personal communication*.)

TABLE 6. *Father-to-son "transmission" or bipolar affective disorder*

Series compatible with X-linked transmission	Results
Winokur et al. (1970)	In 89 families *no* ill father-son pairs
Taylor and Abrams (1973)	In 55 families *no* ill father-son pairs
Series not compatible with X-linked transmission as the sole transmission possibility	
Perris (1971)	13 ill father-son pairs reported in series of 138 bipolar probands.
Dunner et al. (1970)	In 23 bipolar male patients, 4 had affectively ill fathers.
Green et al. (1973)	In 35 bipolar families 4 father-son pairs ill (no illness on maternal side).
Fieve et al. (1973)	120 bipolar probands with 13 ill father-son pairs (9 pairs no evidence of illness on maternal side).
Helzer and Winokur (1974)	30 male manics; affectively ill mothers 8(41%); affectively ill fathers, 1(5%); in another ill father-son pair, considerable affective disorder existed on the maternal side of the family.
Von Grieff et al. (1973)	In 16 male probands, 4 ill father-son pairs reported with *no* illness on maternal side; 3 ill father-son pairs did have illness on maternal side.

maternal side, however it is evident that in other families, it is unlikely that a genetic factor for the affective disorder was present on the maternal side. The most reasonable explanation of both this evidence against X-linkage and the evidence for genetic linkage is that bipolar affective disorder in *some* families is transmitted as a factor on the X-chromosome, but that in other families a different type of transmission accounts for the illness. This would be similar to the types of genetic transmission found for such diseases as retinitis pigmentosa.

While X-linkage accounts for transmission in some bipolar families this mechanism has never been described in unipolar families. Indeed, studies of affective illness inheritance pattern in unipolar families have shown that this pattern is inconsistent with a sex chromosome–linked transmission (Cadoret et al., 1970; Winokur et al., 1971; Marten et al., 1972). The most notable divergencies are in the numerous cases of father-to-son transmission and among the offspring of unipolar mothers a larger number of affected daughters than sons (in X-linked conditions, equal numbers of sons and daughters should be affected given an ill mother). The transmission as evidenced by this last pattern is also inconsistent with most types of autosomal inheritance, a circumstance which has led to the hypothesis that unipolar illness itself may be composed of several subtypes, each with its own type of transmission (if genetic), or even with little or no genetic etiology. There is considerable evidence at the present time for this hypothesis.

A number of studies have shown important familial difference by dividing unipolar probands into those whose illness had its onset before age 40, and those whose illness onset was over age 40. The main findings from this age dichotomy have been: (1) relatives of early onset probands have a higher risk for affective disorder than do relatives of late onset probands; and (2) relatives, especially males, of early onset probands exhibit more alcoholism than those of late onset. At least six independent family studies (Dorzab et al., 1971; Winokur et al., 1971; Marten et al., 1972; Winokur, 1973; Winokur et al., 1973; Woodruf et al., 1971) involving 1,255 probands have shown these differences. This heterogeneity of family history can be interpreted as evidence for at least two kinds of unipolar affective disorder, an early onset disease with high risks for alcoholism and affective disorder in relatives, and a late onset illness with low risk for alcoholism and affective disorder. The mode of transmission in each type of unipolar illness is not at all clear, and the decreased family illness in older onset depressions is an argument for possible diminished importance of a genetic factor in this condition.

REFERENCES

Angst, J. (1966): *Zur Ätiologie und Nosologie Endogener Depressive Psychosen.* Springer-Verlag, Berlin.

Asano, N. (1967): Study of manic-depressive psychosis. In: *Clinical Genetics in Psychiatry,* edited by H. Mitsuda. Igaku Shorn, Toyko.

Cadoret, R. J., Winokur, G., and Clayton, P. (1970): Family history studies VII: Manic depressive disease versus depressive disease. *Br. J. Psychiatry,* 116:625–635.

Clayton, P., Halikas, J., Maurice, W., and Robins, E. (1973): Anticipatory grief and widowhood. *Br. J. Psychiatry,* 122:47–51.

Dorzab, J., Baker, M., Cadoret, R., and Winokur, G. (1971): Depressive disease: Familial psychiatric illness. *Am. J. Psychiatry,* 127:1128–1133.

Dunner, D., Gershon, E., and Goodwin, F. K. (1970): Heritable factors in the severity of affective illness. Paper presented at 123rd annual meeting APA, San Francisco, Calif.

Fieve, R. R., Mendlewicz, J., and Fleiss, J. L. (1973): Manic depressive illness: Linkage with the Xg blood group. *Am. J. Psychiatry,* 130:1355–1359.

Fieve, R. R., Mendlewicz, J., Rainer, J. D., and Fleiss, J. (1973): A dominant X-linked factor in manic depressive illness: Studies with color blindness. Paper presented at 63rd annual meeting APA, New York City.

Goodwin, D. W., Schulsinger, R., Hermansen, L., Guze, S., and Winokur, G. (1973): Alcohol problems in adoptees raised apart from alcoholic biological parents. *Arch. Gen. Psychiatry,* 28:238–243.

Green, R., Goetzl, V., Whybrow, P., and Jackson, R. (1973): X-linked transmission of manic-depressive illness. In letters to the editor, *JAMA,* 223:1289.

Helzer, J., and Winokur, G. W. (1974): A family study of male manic depressives. *Arch. Gen. Psychiatry,* 31:73–77.

Heston, L. L. (1966): Psychiatric disorders in foster-home-reared children of schizophrenic mothers. *Br. J. Psychiatry,* 112:819–825.

Kinkelin, M. (1954): Verlauf und prognose des manisch-depressiven irreseins. *Schweiz Arch. Neurol. Psychiatrie,* 73:100–146.

Leonhard, K. (1966): *Aufteileing der endogenen psychosen,* 3rd ed. Akademie Verlag, Berlin.

Marten, S., Cadoret, R. J., Winokur, G. and Ora, E. (1972): Unipolar depression: A family history study. *Biol. Psychiatry,* 4:205–213.

Mendlewicz, J., Fleiss, J. L., and Fieve, R. R. (1972): Evidence for x-linkage in the transmission of manic-depressive illness. *JAMA,* 222:1624–1627.

Mendlewicz, J., Fleiss, J., and Fieve, R. R. (1973): X-linked dominant transmission in manic-depressive illness (linkage studies with the Xga blood group). Paper presented at 63rd annual meeting, APA, New York City.

Neele, E. (1949): *Die phasischen psychosen nach ihrem erscheinungs und erbbild.* Barth, Leipzig.

Perris, C. (1966): A study of bipolar (manic-depressive) and unipolar recurrent depressive psychosis. *Acta Psychiat. Scand. 42, Suppl.* 194. Munksgaard, Copenhagen.

Perris, C. (1971): Abnormality on paternal and maternal sides: Observations in bipolar (manic-depressive) and unipolar depressive psychosis. *Br. J. Psychiatry,* 118:207–210.

Price, J. (1968): The genetics of depressive behavior. In: *Recent Developments in Affective Disorders,* edited by A. Coppen and A. Walk, *Br. J. Psychiatry,* Special Publication No. 2.

Reich, T. and Winokur, G. (1969): Family history studies. V. The genetics of mania. *Am. J. Psychiatry,* 125:1358–1369.

Robins, E., and Guze, S. B. (1972): Classification of affective disorders: The primary-secondary, the endogenous-reactive, and the neurotic-psychotic concepts. In: *Recent Advances in the Psychobiology of the Depressive Illnesses: Proceedings of a Workshop Sponsored by NIMH,* edited by T. A. Williams, M. M. Katz, and J. Shield, Jr. U.S. Govt. Printing Office, Washington, D.C.

Schulsinger, F. (1972): Psychopathy: Heredity and environment. *Int. J. Ment. Health,* 1:190–206.

Stenstedt, A. (1966): Genetics of neurotic depression. *Acta Psychiat. Scand.,* 42:392–409.

Taylor, M., and Abrams, R. (1973): Manic states: A genetic study of early and late onset affective disorders. *Arch. Gen. Psychiatry,* 28:656–658.

Von Greiff, H., McHugh, P. R., and Stokes, P. (1973): The familial history in sixteen males with bipolar manic-depressive disorder. Paper presented at 63rd annual meeting, APA, New York City.

Winokur, G. (1973): Diagnostic and genetic aspects of affective illness. *Psychiatry Annuals,* Feb. 1973.

Winokur, G. (1973): The types of affective disorder. *J. Nerv. Ment. Dis.,* 156:82–96.

Winokur, G., Cadoret, R. J., Dorzab, J., and Baker, M. (1971): Depressive disease: A genetic study. *Arch. Gen. Psychiatry,* 24:135–144.

Winokur, G., and Clayton, P. (1967): Family history studies. I. Two types of affective disorders separated according to genetic and clinical factors. In: *Recent Advances in Biological Psychiatry,* edited by J. Wortis. Plenum, New York.

Winokur, G., Clayton, P., and Reich, T. (1970): *Manic Depressive Disease.* Mosby, St. Louis.

Winokur, G., Morrison, J., Clancy, J., and Crowe, R. (1973): The Iowa 500: Familial and clinical findings favor two kinds of depressive illness. *Comp. Psychiatry,* 14:99–107.

Winokur, G., and Reich, T. (1970): Two genetic factors in manic-depressive disease. *Comp. Psychiatry,* 11:93–99.

Winokur, G., and Tanna, V. L. (1969): Possible role of x-linked dominant factor in manic-depressive disease. *Dis. Nerv. Syst.,* 30:89–93.

Woodruf, R., Guze, S., and Clayton, P. (1971): Unipolar and bipolar primary affective disorder. *Br. J. Psychiatry,* 119:33–38.

Zerbin-Rüdin, E. (1967): Manisch-depressive psychosen; involutions psychosen. In: *Humangenetik,* edited by P. E. Becker, Bd. V/2. Thieme Verlag, Stuttgart.

Zerbin-Rüdin, E. (1969): Zur genetik der depressiven erkrankungen. In: *Das Depressive Syndrom,* edited by H. Hippius and H. Selbach. Internat. Sympos., Berlin. Urban and Schwarzenberg Publishers.

Biological Foundations of Psychiatry,
edited by R. G. Grenell and S. Gabay.
Raven Press, New York © 1976.

The Biochemistry of Schizophrenia

Ronald J. Bradley and John R. Smythies

Neurosciences Program and Department of Psychiatry, University of Alabama in Birmingham,
Birmingham, Alabama 35294

I. INTRODUCTION

The last 25 years have seen an extensive experimental effort expended in the study of psychiatric and neurologic disease. Unfortunately the hypothetico-deductive method has not allowed a brilliant sequence of theory and subsequent treatment to arise in the case of schizophrenia: although if a cure were found doubtless someone would reconstruct the past into the hypothetico-deductive model most sympathetic to that end-product and its designer.

Parkinsonism, although far from total analysis and understanding, comes closest to the ideal model, with the discovery of dopamine, its implication in the disease, and the scientifically based treatment of its deficiency with L-DOPA. The group of Parkinsonian-like conditions is now collectively named Striatal Dopamine Deficiency Syndrome, referring to their underlying biologic causality rather than the identity of the original attending physician. In schizophrenia the behavioral symptoms are still the only diagnosis and their wide and multidimensional freedom defy the application of any simplistic terminology.

However, considerable diagnostic progress has been made, since certain diseases which might have been classified as schizophrenia at one time are now known to be of biologic origin. These conditions include at least the following: syphilis, pellagra, porphyria, hypothyroidism, and amphetamine psychosis. The majority of schizophrenics remain untouched by these dramatic correlations of biology and scientific treatment, and their only amelioration has been as the result of purely adventitious advances in therapy. The most remarkable incidence of such serendipity has been the discovery of anti-psychotic drugs, such as the phenothiazines. These drugs have fortunately heralded a new era of scientific endeavor in the study of schizophrenia for their specificity implies that any understanding of their mode of action is directly relevant to the biology of schizophrenia.

In the light of the above minor erosions of the schizophrenia problem, we can view the future as a cup half-empty or half-full. If the eventual goal of neuroscience is to understand the molecular biology of behavior then we need not concern ourselves with whether or not the cure for pellagra was the first breakthrough in the biochemistry of schizophrenia. When the goal of under-standing brain function is achieved, the psychologic will become the biophysi-cal just as Fortran is reduced to a series of integrated circuits and finally the motion of electrons. Behavior will be accepted as a biochemical phenomenon, whether genetically determined or controlled by environmental stimuli.

In many ways biochemistry is probably the simplest way to tackle schizo-phrenia at this time. In psychiatry we are faced with the unparalleled com-plexity of behavior in a way analogous to the 18th century physicist at-tempting to cope with physical phenomena that could not be satisfactorily explained until the atom was cracked. Schizophrenia researchers literally poke around in the dark until they find some difference between schizophrenics and normals or some property of another biologic process that relates to schizo-phrenia in a previously unconsidered fashion. Sometimes the courageous in-vestigator will proceed immediately to a theory, which is oftentimes immedi-ately followed by a cure. Unfortunately there are so many victims of schizophrenia and their blighted families that a cure is rapidly transformed into hope and then faith. The spontaneous remission of even a few schizo-phrenics would be enough to allow the partial reinforcement effect to keep a cure alive indefinitely.

Schizophrenia has struggled free of the restricting influence of psycho-analytic etiology and is now considered to be a genetically determined disease, which might possibly someday be described in terms of altered enzymatic function. The more parsimonious version of this theory would be that a metabolite of some neurochemical significance could be overproduced and result in altered brain function. There is certainly a precedent for this in the case of congenital erythropoietic porphyria, in which a faulty regulator gene may result in the increased formation of porphyrins (Watson, Range, Tad-deini, Bossenmaier, and Cardinal, 1964).

II. GENETICS—A BIOLOGIC BASIS FOR SCHIZOPHRENIA

The proponents of both "nature" and "nurture" have laid down their arms and are content to admit to the powerful influence of environment on all aspects of mammalian genetics. Schizophrenia can best be described as the operation of biologic or psychologic aspects of the environment upon an inherent genetic susceptibility. It is altogether too early to speculate on the mode of transmission, whether it is a partially dominant gene (Slater, 1958), or whether it is a polygenic phenomenon (Rosenthal, 1963). In an authoritative review, Heston (1973) has pooled the literature to show that the concordance rate for schizophrenia in monozygotic twins is approximately 40 to 45%. This value is four times the rate for dizygotic twins and is comparable to the concordance of monozygotic twins for diabetes mellitus. However, just as blood glucose is nearly always abnormal in the nondiabetic co-twin, as many as 45% of the nonschizophrenic co-twins may be given an alternate psychiatric diagnosis bordering on the schizoid. Also Kallman (1946) had reported that in more severely schizophrenic monozygotic probands, there is a greater probability that the co-twin will also be schizophrenic. Heston (1973) also comes to the conclusion that concordance in clinical subtype is very strong but imperfect. Other fascinating evidence in favor of the genetic theory is that of 11 pairs of monozygotic twins with a schizophrenic proband described in the literature as separated prior to the first birthday, eight pairs were fully concordant, and two more were schizoid. The incidence of schizophrenia in the relatives of schizophrenics is much greater than in the general population, and as many as 50% of parents, siblings, and children of schizophrenics will have manifestations of the illness. Children of schizophrenics have a significantly elevated probability of developing schizophrenia whether they are reared with their biologic parents or in adoptive homes (Heston, 1966) and Kety, Rosenthal, Schulsinger, and Wender (1968) have found that there is a greater incidence of schizophrenia in the biologic family as compared to the adoptive family of the adopted schizophrenic.

Such evidence is very reinforcing for those of us who have searched for a biochemical difference between schizophrenics and normals over the years, but we would do better to exercise some caution over our enthusiasm. The more optimistic scientist will, however, assume that our lack of success to date is merely because we are measuring the wrong thing with the wrong instrument. Of one fact we can be certain, the coming years will herald new sensitivities and specificities of assay that will finally clear up a lot of speculation about the different levels of neurotransmitter analogues and associated enzyme activity in schizophrenia. Even if such substances are seen to be within the normal range in schizophrenics, this does not rule out their participation in the disease process, for the locus at which they act in the brain could itself be disordered. As new techniques in chemical neurobiology become available, they will be applied to the bodily fluids and brains of schizophrenics in due course. In some cases such applications will reward a half-baked theory and in other cases they will be merely a shot in the dark. In any event it is a fond hope that eventually all of schizophrenia might be unequivocally identified by biologic tests and treated on a logical basis. Truly this might involve considerable redefinition of schizophrenia per se.

III. HISTORIC DEVELOPMENTS—THEORETIC GROUNDWORK

An early landmark in the biology of schizophrenia is the work of a French physician Moreau (1845) who described the many similarities between hashish intoxication and mental illness. Thudichum (1884), often called the father of modern neurochemistry, wrote that mental illness might be caused by poisons fermented within the body. The writings of Kraepelin (1892) also propose a biochemical basis for some kinds of chronic mental disease but following the synthesis of mescaline by Spath (1919), numerous workers became interested in mescaline intoxication and its possible relationship to mental disorders. Beringer (1927) has summarized much of this early work, but it was Stockings (1940) who set the scene for contemporary thought.

> The various diseases commonly known as the psychoses are all variants of the same disease process; and that the causative agent is a toxic body, probably a toxic amine with chemical and pharmacological properties similar to those of mescaline, and having a selective action on the various higher centers of the brain. The particular centers attacked, and the nature and content of the resultant psychosis are determined by the psychophysical make-up of the individual patient and his past mental and environmental experience. Finally, that the correct method of approach to the problem of the understanding of the nature and treatment of the psychotic diseases lies in the spheres of biochemistry and pharmacology.

The first specific hypothesis was developed by Osmond and Smythies (1952). They suggested that a methylated derivative of mescaline could be formed because of a fault in the pathway from norepinephrine (NE) to epinephrine by *N*-methylation. It was proposed that *O*-methylation of NE via a methyl group from methionine or choline would lead to the production in the body of 3,4-dimethoxy phenylethanolamine, which is sufficiently like mescaline to have itself the possibility of psychotomimetic properties. Similarly they suggested 3,4-dimethoxyphenylethylamine, the ring methylated derivative of dopamine, because of its potency in producing catatonia in animals. We can evaluate this hypothesis in the light of its ability to explain the then known facts about schizophrenia. The occurrence of a biochemical abnormality within the physiologic stress mechanism would explain both the clinical relationship between schizophrenia and stress and also the chronic nature of the illness. This abnormal process might only become operative if the turnover of catecholamines reached a certain level in response to stress and then a vicious circle would result. That is to say, the abnormal metabolite would induce even greater stress, this would produce more metabolite, and so on. When Osmond and Smythies (1952) postulated the transmethylation theory of schizophrenia very little was known about the metabolism of catecholamines. Catechol-*O*-methyltransferase was first described by Axelrod and Tomchick (1958), and it is now established that norepinephrine and dopamine can be metabolized by methylation at the 3-position to form normetanephrine and 3-methoxytyramine (4-hydroxy-3-methoxy-β-phenethylamine), respectively. Benington and Morin (1968) have shown that 3-methoxytyramine is further converted to 3-methoxy-4,5-dihydroxy-β-phenethylamine in rat or rabbit liver homogenates. Daly, Axelrod, and Witkop (1962) have reported that 3,4,5-trihydroxy-β-phenethylamine can be converted to 5-hydroxy-3,4-dimethoxy-β-phenethylamine by the action of catechol-O-methyltransferase. There is therefore some evidence that enzymatic machinery is available for the production of 3,4-dimethoxy-β-phenethylamine (3,4-DMPEA), although 3,4,5-trimethoxylation to mescaline has not been measured in any preparation other than the cactus *Anhalonium lewinii*.

IV. AMINO ACID LOADING—FACILITATION OF TRANSMETHYLATION

When Himsworth and Glynn (1944) demonstrated that a methionine-deficient diet is followed by severe liver damage in rats, for a time thereafter methionine was used in the treatment of liver disease. In some patients with portal cirrhosis and chronic portal systemic encephalopathy, methionine (9 to 20 g/day) causes an intense psychotic state but the reasons for this are unclear (Phear, Ruebuer, Sherlock, and Summerskill, 1956). However, there is evidence that the effect may be blocked by chlortetracycline and is not related to blood methionine levels. It might be vaguely speculated that based on this evidence a toxic derivative of methionine is formed by the intestinal flora and due to hepatic inefficiency is able to influence the brain.

Pollin, Cardon, and Kety (1961) investigated the effects of large doses of methionine and phenylalanine in combination with a monoamine oxidase inhibitor (MAOI) on the behavior of schizophrenics. They found that methionine plus MAOI loading resulted in an increase in psychotic symptoms in four out of nine chronic schizophrenics. Phenylalanine was administered in conjunction with methionine in some instances but the indications were that it does not contribute to the exacerbation of the illness. This study also showed that methionine without MAOI had no effect on three subjects tested. After methionine treatment was terminated these behavioral changes disappeared and patients even showed some temporary improvements. Baldessarini and Kopin (1963) have shown that L-methionine loading causes marked increases in S-adenosylmethionine (SAM), a methyl donor in rat brain. It is therefore assumed that one of the possible functions of methionine loading might be to encourage the ring or side-chain methylation of some catecholamine or tryptamine derivative forming an hallucinogenic substance *in vivo,* and giving rise to the symptoms of schizophrenia. Antun, Burnett, Cooper, Daly, Smythies, and Zealley (1971a) have shown *in vivo* in the rat that methionine is a methyl donor in the formation of normetanephrine and 3-methoxy-4-hydroxyphenylglycol.

The effects of methionine and MAOI on schizophrenics have subsequently been investigated by many groups including Brune and Himwich (1962a),

Alexander, Curtis, Sprince, and Corsley (1963), Berlet, Spaide, Kohn, Bull, and Himwich (1965), Park, Baldessarini, and Kety (1965), Brune (1965), Haydu, Dhryniotis, Korenyi, and Goldschmidt (1965), Kakimoto, Sano, Kanazawa, Tsujio, and Kaneko (1967), Spaide, Tanimukai, Ginther, Bueno, and Himwich (1969) and Anath, Ban, Lehmann, and Bennet (1970). In such studies the use of an MAOI is presumed to make more biogenic amines available for methylation via methionine or to prevent the breakdown of such newly synthesized methylated psychotoxins. Notwithstanding this fact Antun, Eccleston, and Smythies (1971b) have shown that MAOI is not necessary and 250 mg/kg L-methionine by itself is sufficient to cause clinical deterioration in schizophrenia.

The majority of these studies were carried out double-blind and in some instances control administration of glycine was found to have no effect (Park, Baldessarini, and Kety, 1965; Antun et al., 1971b). There are no reports of complete failure to confirm, and thus it appears to be an established fact that L-methionine will induce an increase in symptoms in about 40% of chronic schizophrenics and has little or no effect on the other 60%. Too few detailed biochemical studies have been carried out in conjunction with methionine loading nor have such procedures been carried out on normal controls or on patients with other illnesses. Nor can one say with authority that the psychosis represents an exacerbation of the underlying schizophrenia or a superimposed toxic psychosis. Antun et al. (1971b) detected elements of both in their study but found that amounts of O-methylated metabolites of catecholamines did not increase during the course of the acute psychosis induced by L-methionine. This would not of course rule out the possibility that a derivative of tryptamine might be involved.

Brune and Himwich (1962b) have shown that betaine, which is also a methyl donor, plus MAOI has effects comparable to methionine in schizophrenia, and Spaide, Tanimukai, Ginther, Bueno, and Himwich (1967) have found that cysteine, which is not a methyl donor, has a similar effect. Lauer, Inskip, Bernsohn, and Zeeler (1958) reported that some schizophrenics became worse when given tryptophan and an MAOI. Shaw, Lucas, and Rabinovitch (1959) found that 3 g of tryptophan alone given to schizophrenic children produced bizarre behavior but was less effective in normals. Brune and Himwich (1962a) found similar effects for L-tryptophan in active schizophrenics, but found no effect on schizophrenics in remission.

It is well known that a proportion of Parkinsonian patients treated with L-DOPA will develop psychiatric side effects. Yaryura-Tobias, Diamond, and Merlis (1970) found that L-DOPA causes some deterioration of schizophrenic patients also on neuroleptic medication. Angrist, Sathananthan, and Gershon (1973) studied the effects of L-DOPA in doses of 3 to 6 g/day on schizophrenics who had been taken off neuroleptic medication for at least 1 week. Worsening of symptoms occurred in all patients tested.

Another report by Heath, Nesselhof, and Timmons (1966) claims that schizophrenics are highly resistant to the methionine antimetabolite, methionine sulfoximine (MSO). In normals MSO at over 200 mg/day produces an acute delirium with slow waves in the EEG that may be prevented by giving methionine in a ratio of 19 to 1. In a series of 10 schizophrenics Heath et al. (1966) found that MSO had no significant effect on behavior or EEG but even produced a slight alleviation of symptoms in some cases.

V. METHYLATED PRODUCTS OF BIOGENIC AMINES IN SCHIZOPHRENIA

One of the landmarks in schizophrenia research was the paper of Friedhoff and Van Winkle (1962), which showed that 3,4-DMPEA was excreted in the urine of 15 out of 19 acute schizophrenics, but was not present in 14 normal controls. A large number of studies have confirmed this important difference between schizophrenics and normals, but as Friedhoff (1967) has pointed out there are many variables at play including diet and dietary controls that are particularly difficult to interpret. Subsequently Friedhoff and Van Winkle (1963) have shown that when tritrated dopamine is infused into schizophrenics, it can be measured as 3,4-dimethoxyphenylacetic acid (DMPEAA) in the urine. They also found that the homogenate of liver biopsy material from a DMPEA positive schizophrenic produced DMPEAA from dopamine and SAM. Bourdillon, Clarke, Ridges, Sheppard, Harper, and Leslie (1965) identified a pink spot in the paper chromatograph of schizophrenic urine after solvent extraction. This colorimetric sign appeared after reaction with ninhydrin and modified Ehrlich's reagent and behaves in a manner similar to 3,4-DMPEA. Ridges (1973) has recently reviewed her own research into pink spot carried out in conjunction with Bourdillon and others and testing urine from over 800 subjects. The data show that there is a definite correlation between pink spot and schizophrenia which is not evident in normals or other mental hospital patients. The highest incidence of pink spot occurrence (over 80%) was present in Schneider-positive nonparanoid schizophrenics. Since the original work of Friedhoff and Van Winkle, many other groups in several countries have verified their claims, but smaller numbers of reports have been negative or have found no differences between the pink spots of schizophrenics and normals. It has been suggested that the pink spot is of dietary origin or is a product of the intestinal bacteria found in both schizophrenics and normals. In this respect Ridges and Bourdillon (1966) have found that neomycin, which would alter the intestinal flora, does not change the pink spot found in schizophrenia. Another objection to these studies has been that pink spot may be a metabolite of some therapeutic drug. Using gas chromatography with mass spectrometry Ridges and Harper (1970) have reported that no metabolites of phenothiazines are present in the pink spot. Stabenau, Creveling, and Daly (1970) carefully analyzed all the reported studies of urinary pink spot in the literature. They selected those 13 investigations where pure 3,4-DMPEA had been used as a control and where phenothiazine treatment had been suspended prior to the study. Out of a total of 295 schizophrenics, 141 were pink spot positive (47.8%), whereas only 36 (7.6%) of 475 nonschizophrenics were positive. In three of these studies that had been carried out blind and in four where diet had been controlled, there were no significant differences between schizophrenics and controls. In fact in the latter four studies, none of 29 schizophrenics and 10 controls had 3,4-DMPEA in the urine. Von Studnitz and Nyman (1965) showed that 3,4-DMPEA did not appear in the urine when diet was restricted to glucose, citric acid, and water but was present when an unrestricted diet was restored.

Creveling and Daly (1967) were the first to identify 3,4-DMPEA in schizophrenic urine by mass spectrometry, but also discovered that 3,4-DMPEA was present in tea (Creveling and Daly, 1969). Stabenau et al. (1970) identified large amounts of 3,4-DMPEA in the urine of normals while on unrestricted diets including tea. When these subjects were put on a glucose, citric acid, and water diet, 3,4-DMPEA disappeared from the urine and returned 2 hr after the ingestion of tea. Also Ridges (1973) using mass spectrometry has found that 3,4-DMPEA is not a component of the pink spot and Bell and Somerville (1966) were unable to find 3,4-DMPEA in this same material using a spectrofluorimetric method.

Watt, Ashcroft, Daly, and Smythies (1969) have shown that in both normals and schizophrenics the pink spot obtained by solvent extraction is equivalent to monoacetyl cadaverine and a similar pink spot obtained after ion exchange is equivalent to p-tyramine. That p-tyramine is responsible for the pink colors on chromatograms of urine has also been suggested by Boulton, Pollitt, and Majer (1967). Using fluorescent derivation and thin-layer chromatographic separation prior to mass spectrometry Seigel and Tefft (1971) identified 3,4-DMPEA in the urine of schizophrenics and in normal controls. Narasimhachari, Plaut, and Himwich (1972a) have questioned the specificity of the mass spectrometric method for such dansylated derivatives. They have reported that isothiocyanate derivatization does not betray the presence of 3,4-DMPEA in urine from schizophrenics or normals even during MAOI treatment.

As well as in normals and schizophrenics, pink spot has also been found in Parkinsonian patients, but Boulton et al. (1967) have claimed that this too is in fact p-tyramine.

Friedhoff (1973) has been unable to confirm the findings of Stabenau et al. (1970) nor has he found 3,4-DMPEA in tea itself. Nevertheless the pink spot must be taken very seriously for the literature suggests that it is present more often in schizophrenics than in normals. Its unequivocal identification is uncertain and 3,4-DMPEA may or may not be a component thereof, but some part of the story may relate to catecholamines and their methylated product in schizophrenia.

The role of serotonin (5-HT) in schizophrenia is currently commanding almost an equal billing with the catecholamines. Woolley and Shaw (1954) and Gaddum (1954) were among the first to point out that psychotropic compounds including LSD that are related to the indolic structure of 5-HT might act as antimetabolites to 5-HT in the central nervous system (CNS). Also in that year Stromberg (1954) isolated the active component from the seeds of the narcotic plant *Piptadena columbrina Benth,* and showed that it was congruent with bufotenine as synthesized by Speeter and Anthony (1954). In this paper describing a new synthetic route to tryptamine analogues Speeter and Anthony quoted the work of Dr. Nolen Connor in their laboratory who had discovered that N,N-dimethyltryptamine (DMT) alone could produce the same effects as bufotenine in dogs. Evarts (1956) described the behavioral effects of bufotenine in the monkey and also its effects on the lateral geniculate nucleus of the cat.

A study by Bumpus and Page (1955) indicated that 5-HT as well as N-methyl 5-HT and bufotenine could be found in very small quantities in the urine of normal humans. Then Fabing and Hawkins (1956) reported the hallucinogenic effects of bufotenine in humans and Szara (1956) synthesized and demonstrated the hallucinogenic nature of N,N-dimethyltryptamine also in humans. In the same year Gerard (1956) discussed the relationship between the hallucinogenic effects of drugs and schizophrenia and coined the word "psychotomimetics" to draw attention to the similarities of their effects and the clinical nature of the psychoses. Although many authors have provided evidence in validation of this simple analogy, there has always been an undercurrent of dissent. Nonetheless it is reasonable to assume that out of our vast contemporary pharmacopoeia, the hallucinogenic derivatives of tryptamine, phenethylamine, and lysergic acid offer the best model psychosis available save only amphetamine psychosis and comparable drug-induced paranoid states.

Erspamer (1959) and Fischer (1960) presented the theory that schizophrenia was due to a fault in the metabolism of 5-HT giving rise to N-methylated derivatives including bufotenine. Fischer, Vazquex, Fernandex, and Liskowski (1961) subsequently reported the presence of bufotenine in the urine of 15 schizophrenics and none in 10 normal subjects. At approximately the same time, Axelrod (1961, 1962) demonstrated the existence of an N-methyltransferase enzyme in rabbit lung that formed N,N-dimethyltrvptamine from tryptamine, bufotenine from 5-HT, and epinine from dopamine. This major discovery placed the bufotenine theory of schizophrenia on a firmer footing by showing that methylation could occur at the side-chain nitrogen as well as at phenolic hydroxy groups by way of catechol-O-methyltransferase (COMT). The Himwich group (Brune, Hohl, and Himwich, 1963) verified the exclusive presence of bufotenine in the urine of schizophrenics and have continued to carry out important research in this area. Specifically, using thin-layer and gas chromatography, they have reported the presence of bufotenine, N,N-dimethyltryptamine and 5-methoxy-N,N-dimethyltryptamine in blood from acute schizophrenics (Narasimhachari, Heller, Spaide, Haskovec, Strahilevitz, Meltzer, and Himwich, 1971) from the urine of chronic schizophrenics (Narasimhachari, Heller, Spaide, Haskovec, Fiyimori, Tabushi, and Himwich, 1970), and from drug free schizophrenics (Narasimhachari, Avalos, Fiyimori, and Himwich, 1972b). More recently Narasimhachari and Himwich (1973), using trimethylsilyl derivatization and the more specific gas chromatographic/mass spectrometric method, have again reported the presence of bufotenine in the urine of schizophrenics and autistic children but not in normal controls. Wyatt, Mandel, Ahn, Walker, and Vandel Hewel (1973a), also using a gas chromatographic/mass spectrometric method, have been unable to find N,N-dimethyltryptamine in plasma from schizophrenics, depressives, and normals, although a sensitivity below 1.8 ng/ml is claimed.

The original work of Axelrod (1961) describing N-methyltransferase activity in rabbit lung has been repeated in animal brain (Morgan and Mandell, 1969), human brain (Mandell and Morgan, 1971; Saavedra and Axelrod, 1972), human lung (Walker, Ahn, Mandel, and Vanden Hewel, 1972), human serum (Narasimhachari, Plaut, and Himwich, 1972c), and human red cells, plasma, and platelets (Wyatt, Saavedra, and Axelrod, 1973b).

Wyatt, Saavedra, Belmaker, Donnelly, Cohen, and Pollin (1973c) report that N-methyltransferase activity is elevated in schizophrenics as compared to normals, only in the case of platelets. These differences are apparently decreased by dialysis, suggesting the presence of a dialyzable unknown substance in normals that is capable of increasing the catabolism of N,N-dimethyltryptamine.

The same reservations that may be relevant to pink spot are equally serious in regard to the methylated tryptamines. Drugs, diet, bacteria, and insensitive or nonspecific chemistry may all contribute to a variety of positive claims entered in the literature. It is fair to say, however, at the present time that the indole theory is still quite appealing mainly because of the unequivocal presence of enzymes in a variety of tissues including brain that both O- and N-methylate 5-HT. As tryptamine is also found in brain, it is not unreasonable to assume that molecules similar to bufotenine and DMT may also be present. This does not of course suggest that such hallucinogenic substances are unique to the bodies of schizophrenics; they may be normal metabolites of 5-HT and tryptamine. For example using gas chromatography Greenberg (1973) has measured DMT, diethyltryptamine (DET), and 5-methoxy DMT in the urine of schizophrenics and normals. Moreover, after trimethylsilyl derivatization of the urinary indoleamines he has tentatively identified the 4-, 5-, 6-, and 7-hydroxy analogues of DMT and 5-hydroxy DET (5-OHDET) again in both schizophrenics and normals. These indoles were present in greater quantities in schizophrenics than in normals, but, although they followed the expected gas chromatographic parameters during analysis, they could not be identified by alternative test procedures including mass spectrometry. Almost all attempts to measure derivatives of phenethylamine and tryptamine in the bodily fluids of schizophrenics have simply been limited by the analytic and quantitative techniques available. It is an attainable goal to synthesize analogues of these compounds in purity and in quantity and even in radioactive forms. Unfortunately it is a formidable task to extract picogram or nanogram quantities of such substances from biologic fluids and then demonstrate their unequivocal identity. There is usually an inverse relationship between sensitivity and specificity, not to mention the fact that the extraction process itself may create a red herring.

Another interesting commentary on studies of urinary phenethylamines or indoles in schizophrenia is that out of more than 60 reports that we have perused less than 12% mention the use of blind analysis. The psychiatrist seems to appreciate the need for double blind in behavioral analysis but ignores it when using biologic or chemical indices. Perhaps he mistakenly assumes that in all cases chemical tests are less open to interpretation than is psychiatric diagnosis. It is indeed worthy that he has such a respect for chemical methods but perhaps a trifle naive on his part. Very often a blot on a piece of chromatography paper is no more informative than a Rorschach ink blot.

The study of sleep patterns in mental illness may provide valuable clues concerning underlying brain function for a variety of psychopathologic states that have been correlated with sleep disturbance. In schizophrenia one finding of considerable significance is the failure of some patients to have a normal REM rebound after experimental REM deprivation (Gillin and Wyatt, 1974). These authors relate this particular finding to a disturbance in 5-HT metabolism for the same effect is mimicked by parachlorophenylalanine (PCPA), a drug that specifically blocks the synthesis of 5-HT. Patients with carcinoid syndrome treated with PCPA develop psychotic reactions (Engelman, Lovenberg, and Sjoerdsma, 1967), thus suggesting that there could be a blockade of 5-HT receptors in schizophrenia. Wyatt, Vaughan, Galanter, Kaplan, and Green (1972) have reported that 5-HTP, the precursor of 5-HT, produces a modest improvement in some schizophrenics when administered in conjunction with a peripheral decarboxylase inhibitor. The hallucinogenic derivatives of mescaline, tryptamine, and LSD have many structural and biologic commonalities (Bradley and Smythies, 1974) and are thought to be antagonists at the 5-HT receptor; therefore this could be the mode of action of the hallucinogenic psychotoxin if it really exists.

VI. ENZYMES IN SCHIZOPHRENIA

Recently Murphy and Wyatt (1972a) reported that blood platelets from schizophrenics showed a markedly decreased MAO activity compared with normals. This is also the case in bipolar depressed patients (Murphy and Weis, 1972b). Wyatt et al. (1973d) have studied this phenomenon in a series of monozygotic twins discordant for schizophrenia. They found that the twins had significantly lower MAO activity than normals and this was highly correlated between cotwins. There was an inverse correlation between the severity of the illness and MAO activity. Since the MAO activity of the index twin and the nonschizophrenic twin is correlated they interpret those results as suggesting that the reduced platelet MAO activity is a genetic marker for increased vulnerability to the illness. The abnormal MAO level is not a secondary effect of schizophrenia, which could occur as a result of stress or drug treatment. Platelet MAO activity is similar in its substrate and inhibitor characteristics to MAO activity in brain tissue, especially hypothalamic MAO (Collins, Sandner, Williams, and Youdin, 1970). However, the platelet enzyme is electrophoretically homogenous, whereas brain MAO has more than one isoenzyme form. Nies, Robinson, Lamborn, and Lampert (1973) have provided further evidence that platelet MAO activity is influenced by genetic factors. They found that monozygous twins are closer to each other in MAO activity than dizygous or control pairs as evidenced by reduced intrapair differences and lesser variability in the monozygous group.

In view of the exacerbation of some schizophrenic illnesses by methionine and the implication of abnormal methylation, the level of methyltransferase enzymes in the brain may be important in this context since an increased number of methylated products may form if such activity is high. Hall, Hartridge, and Van Leeuwen (1969) obtained COMT from pea seedlings and injected it i.m. into schizophrenics. After 1 to 2 weeks of daily injections all four schizophrenics became worse. Matthysse and Baldessarini (1972) examined a group of schizophrenic and nonschizophrenic patients for blood COMT activity. They found that COMT levels correlated with SAM concentration in a repeatable manner when all the patients were combined in a single group. There were no differences in SAM concentration between the two groups, but there was a small mean increase in COMT activity in the schizophrenic group although not of statistical significance. The data suggested that there were individual differences in the capacity for methylation of biogenic amines. Cohn, Dunner, and Axelrod (1970) found that, although depressed women tended to have low COMT activity, schizophrenic women were not statistically different from controls. Dunner, Cohn, and Gershon (1971) repeated this work including schizophrenic patients, unipolar and bipolar affective disorders, and antisocial personalities. Women with unipolar depressions had the lowest COMT activity. This interesting finding may have some as yet obscure relationship to the finding of Prange, Wilson, Rabon, and Lipton (1969) that depressed women tend to become more responsive to antidepressant treatment after thyroid administration but men do not. Dunner et al. (1971) studied chronic schizophrenics, and a few of them appear to have high COMT activity although details were not given. Their suggestion is that COMT activity may be related to the genetic predisposition for the development of affective illness.

Another finding, which has been confirmed by various groups of investigators, is that schizophrenics are unusually resistant to injected histamine. Consistently smaller wheals in response to such injections in schizophrenic patients have been reported by various groups (Ermala and Autio, 1951; Lucy, 1954; Freedman, Redlich, and Igerscheiner, 1956; Weckowicz and Hall, 1958; Simpson and Kline, 1961). Tolerance to histamine is said to increase with increased chronicity of the illness. The smaller wheal has been reported to be significant only in chronic rather than acute schizophrenics and at least one study found no difference between schizophrenics and control groups (Jodrey and Smith, 1959). These conflicting results are possibly caused by varying techniques (e.g., intradermal, scratch, use of histamine releaser) and differing concentrations of histamine solution used. One study indicates that stronger solutions better distinguish schizophrenics from nonschizophrenics (Weckowicz and Hall, 1958). It is obvious from these studies that in contradistinction to the group averages, some schizophrenics do show strong histamine wheals and some nonschizophrenic subjects have very small wheals. In all of these studies, it must be borne in mind that schizophrenics were considered statistically as though they were a homogeneous group and no attempt was made to separate them according to other variables. Related to the finding of decreased histamine sensitivity are reports that schizophrenic patients have less incidence of allergy than normals (Simpson and Kline, 1961) and that the onset of asthmatic symptoms can be correlated with schizophrenia (Mandell and Younger, 1962). It is also reported that histamine blood levels are increased in schizophrenics as compared to normals (Ermala and Autio, 1951; Stern, Hukovic, Madjerek, and Karabaic, 1957). However, these particular studies have been challenged by Pfeiffer (1972) who has demonstrated that previous techniques do not differentiate between spermidine and histamine. Using more specific techniques he has shown that two populations of schizophrenics may be identified, having high or alternatively low blood histamine levels.

Stein and Wise (1971) have postulated that schizophrenia may be a result of deficiencies in the central noradrenergic pathways thought to be involved in pleasure or reward and thus intimately related to most of human behavior. They proposed that this deficit could be a result of the abnormal endogenous production of 6-hydroxydopamine, a substance known to cause degeneration of adrenergic nerve terminals. Adams (1972) has put forward a reasonable theory to account for the synthesis of 6-hydroxydopamine by dopamine-O-quinone under conditions that preclude intracyclization of the side chain to the aminochrome derivative. It is of considerable interest that the absence of ascorbic acid will promote this reaction (Kaufman and Friedman, 1965). Almost consistent with this hypothesis is the finding that dopamine-β-hydroxylase (DBH) activity is significantly reduced in the brains of schizophrenic patients postmortem as compared to normal controls (Wise and Stein, 1973). DBH is the enzyme converting dopamine to norepinephrine; therefore its level of activity might correlate with the functional aspects of norepinephrine mediated mechanisms in the brain. However, since DBH is required for the production of dopamine-O-quinone, the theory is confused.

Meltzer (1969) reported that the blood levels of aldolase and creatine phosphokinase are raised in certain cases of acute schizophrenia and in other psychoses, including that produced by LSD. In one patient with a cyclic illness the blood level started to rise some 1 to 2 days before the onset of the psychotic symptoms. However, Harding (1972) was unable to confirm this claim in 12 acute schizophrenics, but he did find that the levels were greatly increased in one case whose acute psychotic episode had been precipitated by d-LSD. Recently Meltzer (1972) has provided histochemic evidence of abnormalities of a myopathic or neuropathic type in skeletal muscle of 68% of psychotic patients. Furthermore 25% of the first degree relatives of these patients show an exaggerated rise in serum creatine phosphokinase (CPK) levels after activity (Meltzer and Moline, 1970). Foster and Kupfer (1973) present a good review of this whole topic. The effect is reported in a wide range of CNS disorders (encephalitis, cerebrovascular accident, cerebral trauma, sleep deprivation, and acute psychosis). They present physiologic evidence that supports their hypothesis that the raised CPK levels are a function not only of increased spontaneous motor activity but also of centrally mediated desynchronization of motor activity peaks and other circadian rhythms, such that the motor peaks occur out of phase with those metabolic cycles that may influence CPK release from muscle. Cunningham, Rich, Woodrulf, and Olney (1974) have conducted a careful study of 296 patients at Washington University. Of these only nine (3%) showed elevated CPK levels not accompanied by nonpsychiatric factors known or suspected to elevate the enzyme. Of these eight had only moderately raised levels (< 210 mU/ml: normal range 25 to 145 mU/ml). Seven of these nine patients had primary affective disorders. None were schizophrenics. They conclude that their results do not support Meltzer's suggestion that the CPK test might be useful diagnostically or prognostically in acute psychosis.

VII. BIOCHEMICAL ASPECTS OF TREATMENT

Nicotinic acid and nicotinamide (vitamin B_3) have been used as a treatment for schizophrenia and other psychiatric disorders as well as in the alleviation of pellagra, which is caused by vitamin B_3 deficiency. At one time, approximately 10% of patients in mental hospitals, at least in the southern United States, were victims of pellagra. Then in 1939 the connection was made between pellagra and the lack of nicotinic acid and it was reported that even the psychoses of pellagra were cured by small doses of nicotinic acid. The description of the various psychiatric manifestations of pellagra must surely be interpreted as similar to what is diagnosed as schizophrenia today, although pellagra is accompanied by many other physical signs not common to schizophrenia. We must rely on such descriptions of the disease as are available in the literature prior to the early forties when the cure was discovered. Nicotinic acid was added to all flour sold in the United States after that time and pellagra is now almost extinct. In 1952 Hoffer and Osmond first introduced the concept of megadoses of nicotinic acid in the treatment of schizophrenia (Hoffer, 1973). One rationale for this therapy is that nicotinic acid is a weak methyl acceptor and as such might sop up the methyl groups that could form endogenous hallucinogenic methylated derivatives of biogenic amines. However, if it is in fact useful in treating schizophrenia, then some other unknown mechanism could be involved perhaps related to the function of nicotinic adenine dinucleotide (NAD). Hoffer (1973) has postulated that pellagra and schizophrenia are NAD-deficient diseases. There are a number of studies supporting the use of vitamin B_3 in schizophrenia, and there are also many studies failing to confirm its effectiveness. These disputations are adequately reviewed by Ban (1971).

Recently two large, well-controlled, double-blind studies have presented impressive evidence that 3 g of nicotinic acid or nicotinamide daily have no advantage over placebo when given to schizophrenics in conjunction with the usual treatment. McGrath et al. (1972) studied 265 schizophrenics after 30 days and then 1 year of nicotinamide treatment and report no significant effect. Wittenborn, Weber, and Brown (1973) administered nicotinic acid to 75 schizophrenics for 2 years and also were unable to verify its treatment efficacy. The latter study showed that the only side effect observed was a pigmented hyperkeratosis in approximately ⅓ of the patients. One fact that cannot be disputed is that vitamin B_3 deficiency induces symptoms of psychoses that unquestionably implicate the essential requirement of this vitamin in normal brain function. The neurochemistry of NAD must be investigated in greater depth both in laboratory animals, normal humans, and schizophrenics. If appropriate chemical tests for normal metabolism within this pathway can be devised, then those patients whose psychoses are ameliorated by nicotinic acid (Smythies, 1974) may be carefully studied. They may in fact be subclinical pellagrans or they may suffer from enzyme abnormalities anywhere in the complex pathway from L-tryptophan or nicotinamide to NAD. L-Tryptophan has a mild tranquilizing effect in normal humans and nicotinamide has been shown to have similar effects in mice (Woolley, 1958; Beaton, Pegram, Bradley, and Smythies, 1974). Pauling, Robinson, Oxley, Bergerson, Harris, Cary, Bletheu, and Keaveny (1973) administered oral doses of nicotinamide, ascorbic acid, and pyridoxine to schizophrenics and normals and measured their excretion in the urine over a 6-hr period. They report that the schizophrenics excreted significantly less of one or more of these three vitamins than did the normals. Heyman (1963) reports that schizophrenics metabolize nicotinamide differently from normals producing less N-methylnicotinamide and more N-methyl-2-pyridone-5-carboxamide. At the present time, there is a large body of evidence to implicate the essential function of a variety of vitamins in brain function but we are woefully ignorant of their individual neurochemistry. Science should set a pressing goal to exploit this area of endeavor and to determine the real toxicity of the water soluble vitamins. At the present time, their toxicology is almost as beset with controversy as is their efficacy in the treatment of schizophrenia.

Most of the known biochemical effects of phenothiazines do not seem to relate to their therapeutic use for such effects are shared by phenothiazine derivatives with no antipsychotic potential. These nonspecific changes include interference with oxidative phosphorylation, local anesthetic activity, electron donation, and dopamine turnover (Matthysse, 1973). Kornetsky and Eliasson (1969) have suggested that chlorpromazine acts on the reticular system to block the overarousal of schizophrenia. But again the nonantipsychotic phenothiazines have the same effect on sensory EEG activation as chlorpromazine (Himwich, Rinaldi, and Willis, 1956) indicating that this is merely a tranquillizing action unconnected with antipsychotic efficacy. Van Rossum (1966) first presented the theory that the mode of action of antipsychotic drugs is via blockade of dopamine receptors. There are many different types of experimental evidence to support this.

Firstly, Kebabian, Petzold, and Greengard (1972) have shown that some antipsychotic drugs block dopamine-stimulated cyclic adenosine monophosphate (cAMP) production in homogenates of rat brain striatum. Graham and Aghajanian (1971) have found that peripherally injected amphetamine reduces spontaneous activity of NE-containing cells in the locus coeruleus and has similar effects on dopaminergic cells of the substantia nigra and midbrain ventral tegmentum (Bunney, Walters, Roth, and Aghajanian, 1973). Firing was rapidly restored by chlorpromazine or haloperidol, but promethazine, a nonantipsychotic phenothiazine, had no effect either alone or after amphetamine. It is possible to derive many theoretic explanations for these findings but Bunney et al. (1973) favor the implication of neuronal feedback inhibition as proposed by Corrodi, Fuxe, and Hokfelt (1967). When the dopaminergic cell fires in the substantia nigra, it presumably releases its neurotransmitter dopamine in the caudate nucleus. Amphetamine causes release of this dopamine and blocks its reuptake at the presynaptic membrane. The increased concentration of dopamine would cause the dopamine receptors on the caudate cell to be unnaturally stimulated; therefore it would communicate back to the dopamine releasing cell telling it to cease. Similarly, when chlorpromazine is administered it might block these dopamine receptors and in that case the cell would send a message back asking for stimulation thus increasing firing rate in the dopaminergic cell of the substantia nigra. This is a rather anthropomorphic account of neuronal interaction.

These drugs produce Parkinsonian side effects, which are thought to be due to dopamine receptor blockade in the basal ganglia. Extrapyramidal symptoms may be treated with centrally acting anticholinergics that do not interfere with the true antipsychotic effect of the drug. Peculiarly there have been a variety of studies showing that there is no meaningful relationship between Parkinsonian side effects and antipsychotic efficacy for these drugs (Crow and Gillbe, 1973), which is hard to accept if both effects are mediated by dopamine antagonism. In solution of this enigma, Miller and Hiley (1974) have elegantly demonstrated that the antipsychotics themselves have an anticholinergic propensity that is inversely correlated with incidence of Parkinsonian side effects. On the basis of this work, we may think of the antipsychotics as antagonists to both central dopamine and muscarinic acetylcholine (ACh) receptors with the ideal drug being equipotent on both systems, having the ability to exert an anticholinergic effect to balance its antidopaminergic effect on the basal ganglia. Additionally these drugs decrease the symptoms of Huntington's chorea adding support to the theory that chorea may be caused by dopamine receptor supersensitivity in the striatum (Klawans, Goetz, and Westheimer, 1972).

It is thought that amphetamine-induced stereotyped behavior is caused by the release of dopamine in the striatum (Fog, Randrup, and Pakkenberg, 1967). Van Rossum (1965) has demonstrated that phenothiazines and haloperidol antagonize this stereotyped behavior induced by amphetamine. Amphetamine causes stereotyped behavior in humans and when abused sometimes induces a paranoid psychosis, which is also counteracted by the antipsychotic drugs. Furthermore Coyle and Snyder (1969) reported that *d*-amphetamine was 10 times more potent than *l*-amphetamine in blocking reuptake of NE but only twice as potent in blocking reuptake of dopamine. As *d*-amphetamine is many times more potent than *l*-amphetamine in altering locomotor behavior but the two isomers are almost equipotent in producing stereotyped behavior, Taylor and Snyder (1971) speculated that amphetamine stimulation was mediated by NE and stereotyped behavior was related to dopaminergic mechanisms. Angrist, Shopsin, and Gershon (1971) found that *d*- and *l*-amphetamine were equipotent in causing paranoid psychoses, therefore implicating dopamine in the biochemistry of schizophrenia. This interesting theory has been challenged by a variety of conflicting studies. It now appears that in fact the reverse may be true and the *d*- and *l*-isomers may differ most in their ability to release dopamine rather than NE from the brain (Chiueh and Moore, 1974). The function of NE and dopamine in mediating locomotor stimulation or stereotyped behavior is obviously not a simple one to one relationship (Creese and Iverson, 1973). However, in support of the dopaminergic theory is the work of Phillips and Fibiger (1973), who found that *d*- and *l*-amphetamine are equipotent in facilitating self-stimulation in the dopaminergic substantia nigra while *d*- is many times more potent than *l*- when the electrode is placed in the more noradrenergic median forebrain bundle. In addition Christie and Crow (1971) have found that *d*- and *l*- amphetamine are equipotent in producing turning behavior in rats lesioned unilaterally in the substantia nigra.

The antipsychotics and reserpine cause catalepsy in animals. Reserpine depletes 5-HT as well as the catecholamines but the catalepsy is reversed by L-DOPA and not by 5-HT. It is therefore reasonable to assume that reserpine induces catalepsy by reducing the amount of dopamine in the striatum and the antipsychotics produce the same effect by blockade of dopamine receptors.

Horn and Snyder (1971) have pointed out the plausible similarities between the molecular structure of dopamine and the antipsychotic phenothiazines, but Kier (1973) has suggested that 5-HT is more closely related to these compounds than is dopamine.

Such are the main reasons to implicate dopaminergic mechanisms in schizophrenia.

VIII. ONE-CARBON METABOLISM

There is ever-increasing evidence that folic acid, the vitamin involved in the synthesis and utilization of 1-carbon units, plays a unique role in brain (Bridgers, 1970; Bridgers and McClain, 1972). Arakawa (1970) has described three groups of infants with severe brain maldevelopment and mental retardation, each associated with a different deficiency of a folate interconverting enzymes. These probable inborn errors have been detected for N^5-methyltetrahydrofolate homocysteine methyltransferase, formiminotransferase, and cyclohydrolase. Other studies in rats indicate that folate deficiency in early life may result in irreversible changes in maturation of the EEG.

In some humans there is a congenital defect in folate absorption apparently resulting in mental retardation and epilepsy. The frequency of convulsions is increased by folic acid and decreased when the patient is permitted to become folate deficient (Lanzkowsky, 1970). It is also known that patients on anticonvulsant therapy may become folate deficient. Reynolds (1968) has described schizophrenia-like symptomatology in some of these patients, which can be ameliorated by folic acid. However, the administration of folic acid caused an increase in seizure activity in some subjects and had to be discontinued. Neubauer (1970) has reported the utility of folic acid in improving the psychiatric condition of epileptic children and adolescents. Grant and Stores (1970) and Ralston, Snaith, and Hinley (1970) investigated the effects of folic acid on institutionalized epileptics but report no improvement in mental state.

Shulman (1967) has studied the incidence of psychiatric symptomatology in vitamin B_{12} deficiency. He found that mild symptoms were more prevalent in pernicious anemia than in other anemic conditions. It is known that vitamin B_{12} deficiency may cause brain degeneration (Adams and Kubik, 1944), and it should be remembered that folate deficiency alone may result in low serum B_{12}, which returns to normal after the administration of folate (Johnson, Swaninathan, and Baker, 1962). The remethylation of homocysteine to methionine by N^5-methyltetrahydrofolate is B_{12}-dependent; therefore, B_{12} has a significant role in the complex relationships between folate and methionine. Pyridoxine (B_6) is another vitamin that is necessary for many enzymatic reactions in this one-carbon pathway and has been used in the treatment of depression and schizophrenia. Another observation relating to this aspect of amino acid metabolism is the existence of unusually large numbers of schizophrenics in the families of homocystinuriacs (Carson, Cusworth, Dent, Field, Neill, and Westall, 1963; Spiro, Schinke, and Welch, 1965). Sprince, Parker, and Josephs (1969) have shown that the convulsant effects of homocysteine in the rat may be blocked by treatment with homoserine, serine, betaine, glycine, and glucose. They explain these various effects by suggesting that homoserine might compete with homocysteine for an enzyme site: serine could combine with homocysteine to form inactive metabolites, betaine could methylate homocysteine back to methionine, and glycine could be converted to serine which would combine with the homocysteine to form cystathionine. The protecting effect of glucose might indicate that homocysteine is causing hypoglycemia. Pyridoxine afforded no protection but it would be interesting to see if it augmented the effects of serine as pyridoxal phosphate is necessary for cystathionine synthetase. Beaton, Pegram, Bradley, and Smythies (1973) tested a number of amino acids other than homocysteine on the behavior and electroencephalogram of mice and rats during acute and chronic administration. L-Methionine rapidly produced significant disruption at nontoxic doses that was blocked by the simultaneous administration of equal doses of L-serine. Such results naturally suggest that the ability of methionine to exacerbate schizophrenia in some patients may not be due to the production of a psychotoxic methylated toxic alkylamine but instead may reflect some disorder in the regulation of one-carbon metabolism.

Methionine has always been considered as the source of methyl groups for N-methyltransferase in all tissues where it has been demonstrated and was the methyl donor described by Axelrod (1961) in the N-methylation of dopamine to N-methyl dopamine (epinine). Bridgers and Kaufman (1962) had already arrived at the conclusion that epinine was converted to epinephrine by dopamine-β-hydroxylase. The possibility of a pathway from dopamine to epinephrine by way of epinine was therefore established in distinction to the classic route from dopamine to epinephrine by way of NE. Bridgers and McClain (1972) in a review of their work in this area pointed to the ability of methionine to disrupt the serine biosynthetic pathway and cause a repartitioning of folate coenzyme forms. They appealed for a reexamination of the methionine effect in schizophrenia and suggested that folate might be the so-called endogenous psychotoxin in the disease. Laduron (1972a) reported that epinine was actually formed from dopamine in the bovine adrenal medulla. When he attempted to measure this phenomena in rat brain, Laduron (1972b) discovered that S-adenosylmethionine was ineffective as a methyl donor but when N^5-methyltetrahydrofolate (5-MTHF) was added to the incubation mixture in lieu of S-adenosylmethionine, epinine was formed from dopamine and N,N-dimethyldopamine was formed from epinine. Banerjee and Snyder (1973) and Hsu and Mandell (1973) have since reported that 5-MTHF rather than SAM appears to be the methyl donor of choice in a variety of tissues in which O- and N-methylation of biogenic amines can be measured. Laduron (1972b) has speculated that epinine so formed by excess 5-MTHF in the brain might play a role in schizophrenia by acting presumably as a dopamine receptor stimulator. This stimulation would then be alleviated by the antipsychotic drugs that block dopamine receptors. Levitt, Nixon, Pincus, and Bertino (1971) have found that 5-MTHF is preferentially taken up by the spinal fluid and that other folate congenors are converted to 5-MTHF prior to uptake. It is of great interest that synaptosomes contain the highest concentration of brain folate coenzymes of which approximately half is 5-MTHF. This suggests a turnover of 5-MTHF at the synapse perhaps because of its role as a methyl donor (Bridgers, McClain, and Carl, 1974).

Laduron (1974) has reported that the therapeutic dose of folic acid induces exacerbation of schizophrenia in some patients. It is naturally assumed that this effect is due to an increase in 5-MTHF and therefore in available methyl groups, resulting in the production of methylated psychotoxins. In contradistinction to this folate-induced psychosis, Freeman, Finkelstein, and Mudd (1975) have described a schizophrenic with homocystinuria who was repeatedly improved by the administration of folate. This patient had a specific deficiency in the activity of 5,10-methylenetetrahydrofolate, the enzyme which converts N-5-10-methylenetetrahydrofolate to 5-MTHF. A decrease in 5-MTHF, the source of methyl groups in the conversion of homocysteine to methionine, gives rise to increased homocysteine in blood and urine but no increase in methionine. Elevated methionine is found only in classical homocystinuria which is associated with a decrease in activity of the enzyme cystathionine synthase. However, such theories that propose a role for 5-MTHF in the methylation hypothesis of schizophrenia have recently been questioned. A number of studies have demonstrated that the product of 5-MTHF and alkylamines in enzymatic preparations from brain is not methylation of the terminal nitrogen but rather, a cyclization of the side chain (Mandel, Rosegay, Walker, Vanden Heuvel and Rokach, 1974; Meller, Rosengarten, Friedhoff, Stebbins, and Silber, 1975; Wyatt, Erdelyi, Doamaral, Elliot, Renson, and Barchas, 1975).

IX. OTHER TOXIC FACTORS ASSOCIATED WITH SCHIZOPHRENIA

It has been claimed that a protein called "taraxein" from the serum of schizophrenics will elicit schizophreniform symptoms in normal volunteers (Heath, Marteus, Leach, Cohen, and Feigley, 1958), but this effect has not been replicated (Robins, Smith, and Lowe, 1957). Winter and Flataker (1958) injected blood plasma from schizophrenics into rats and found that their rope-climbing behavior was markedly slowed. The fraction said to disrupt behavior is a plasma globulin precipitate containing α-2, β, and γ globulins, which appear to be more potent when extracted from schizophrenic serum than from normals (Bergen, 1965).

A careful study by Axelrod, Kankolenski, Small, Corvin, and Sanders (1970) using plasma from 61 schizophrenics and 61 controls does not support the contention that there are any toxic factors present exclusively in this fraction of schizophrenic plasma as measured by changes in rat rope-climbing behavior. Bergen, Mittag, Frohman, Arthur, Warner, Grinspoon, and Freeman (1968) have shown that their schizophrenic plasma factor is similar to that derived by Frohman, Luby, Tourney, Beckett, and Gottlieb (1960). It is thought that the active component is an α-2-globulin. This affects chicken erythrocytes by decreasing pyruvate production and increasing the lactate/pyruvate (L/P) ratio (Frohman et al., 1960). Gottlieb et al. (1969) have suggested that this lipoprotein is identical to a β-globulin isolated by Lozovsky, Krasnova, Factor, Polyanskaya, and Popova (1967). Frohman (1973) reviewing the work of his group describes the purification of this substance as a single α-2-globulin of molecular weight $\sim$400,000, which is 80% lipid. Optical rotary dispersion studies apparently show that the α-helical content of the protein is greater in schizophrenics than in normals but the amino acid content is the same. He provides evidence to suggest that this macromolecule promotes increased intracellular transport of tryptophan in schizophrenia by means of its unique tertiary structure. Ryan, Brown, and Durell (1966) have commented on the hemolytic activity of schizophrenic plasma on erythrocytes in relation to the L/P bioassay. They concluded that such effects were caused by complement-dependent antibodies to chicken erythrocytes and hemolysis rather than by an α-2-globulin. In order to settle this controversy, Nicol et al. (1973) have studied the effects of such hemolysins on this system measuring both lactate stimulation and typtophan uptake. Using sera from schizophrenics, control psychiatric patients, and rabbits immunized with chicken erythrocytes they found a strong correlation between hemolysis and high bioassay activity. These effects are blocked by removal of the hemolysins using antihuman immunoglobulin M (IgM) affinity chromatography or by procedures that inactivate the complement. It was also claimed that α-2-globulin was not involved in hemolysis, lactate stimulation, or typtophan uptake. No differences were ascertained between serum from schizophrenics and controls. Frohman (1968) claims that this hemolysin is a different molecule, in fact a β-2-globulin.

X. IMMUNOLOGY

Given the utility of experimental autoimmune encephalomyelitis as a model of multiple sclerosis (Carnegie, 1974) coupled with experimental evidence that myasthenia gravis may be caused by antibodies to the ACh receptor (Patrick and Lindstrom, 1973), we must seriously reconsider the immunologic state of schizophrenics. Heath and Krupp (1967) first proposed an autoimmune theory of schizophrenia, stating that schizophrenics may produce antibodies against antigens in their own limbic system. They claimed that fluorescent antiglobulin binds to the nuclei of septal neurons of postmortem schizophrenic brain (Heath and Krupp, 1967). Whittingham, Mackay, Jones, and Davies (1968) and others could not replicate this finding and found no difference between schizophrenics and normals in serum antibodies against neuronal nuclei. Solomon, Allansmith, McClellan, and Amkraut (1969) measured IgA and IgM in schizophrenic serum and reported that they are significantly elevated. Strahilevitz and Davis (1970) also found elevated IgA in schizophrenics, but no difference compared to control groups was found for IgG and IgM. Henter, Jones, and Malleson (1969) have reported abnormally high γ-globulin levels in the cerebrospinal fluid of hospitalized psychiatric patients.

Mellsop, Whittingham, and Ungar (1973) have studied some serum autoantibodies, which are thought to be indicative of autoimmune disease, but found that schizophrenics did not differ essentially from normals. Solomon and his colleagues have now determined that IgG, IgA, and IgM levels are significantly elevated in a population of schizophrenics, but those patients with the lowest IgA and IgG levels show the best prognosis (Amkraut, Solomon, Allansmith, McClellan, and Rappaport, 1973).

One of the most interesting immunologic properties of brain tissue is that it shares a unique antigenic property cross-reactive with thymocytes (Golub, 1972). These similar antigens on brain cells and thymocytes do not display species specificity and autoantibodies to them may be produced under certain circumstances (Boyse, Bressler, Tzitani, and Lardis, 1970). Luria and Domashneva (1974) have reported that sera from schizophrenics has a greatly elevated cytotoxic effect on mouse thymocytes and thymus-derived lymphocytes as compared to normal sera. This cytotoxicity was not present for bone marrow cells and could be abolished by absorption with thymocytes or brain homogenates. The sera from schizophrenics seems to contain antibodies against the antigens located on thymocytes and T-lymphocytes and therefore possibly against brain. They suggest that this immunoglobin binding to T-lymphocytes might explain the findings of Vartanyan (1969) that phytohemagglutinin has a reduced ability to transform blast cells in schizophrenics.

REFERENCES

Adams, R. N. (1972): The Stein and Wise theory of schizophrenia: A possible mechanism for 6-hydroxydopamine formation *in vivo*. *Behav. Biol.*, 7:861–866.

Adams, R. D., and Kubik, C. S. (1944): Subacute combined degeneration of the brain in pernicious anemia. *N. Engl. J. Med.*, 231:1–9.

Alexander, F., Curtis, G. C., Sprince, H., and Corsley, A. P., Jr. (1963): L-Methionine and L-tryptophane feedings in non-psychotic and schizophrenic patients with and without tranylcypromine. *J. Nerv. Ment. Dis.*, 137:135–142.

Amkraut, A., Solomon, G. F., Allansmith, M., McClellan, B., and Rappaport, M. (1973): Immunoglobulins and improvement in acute schizophrenic reactions. *Arch. Gen. Psychiatry,* 28:673–677.

Anath, J., Ban, T. A., Lehmann, H. E., and Bennet, J. (1970): Nicotinic acid in the prevention and treatment of artificially induced exacerbation of psychopathology in schizophrenics. *Can. Psychiatr. Assoc. J.,* 15:15.

Angrist, B., Sathananthan, G., and Gershon, S. (1973): Behavioral effects of L-DOPA in schizophrenic patients. *Psychopharmacologia,* 31:1–12.

Angrist, B. M., Shopsin, B., and Gershon, S. (1971): Comparative psychotomimetic effects of stereoisomers of amphetamine. *Nature,* 234:152–153.

Antun, F. T., Burnett, G. B., Cooper, A. J., Daly, R. J., Smythies, J. R., and Zealley, A. K. (1971a): The effects of L-methionine (without MAOI) in schizophrenia. *J. Psychiatr. Res.,* 8, 63–71.

Antun, F., Eccleston, D., and Smythies, J. R. (1971b): Transmethylation processes in schizophrenia. In: *Brain Chemistry and Mental Disease,* edited by B. T. Ho and W. M. McIssac. Plenum, New York.

Arakawa, T. (1970): Congenital defects in folate utilization. *Am. J. Med.,* 48:594–598.

Axelrod, J. (1961): Enzymatic formation of psychotomimetic metabolites from normally occurring compounds. *Science,* 134:343.

Axelrod, J. (1962): The enzymatic N-methylation of serotonin and other amines. *J. Pharmacol. Exp. Ther.,* 138:28–33.

Axelrod, J., and Tomichick, R. (1958): Enzymatic O-methylation of epinephrine and other catechols. *J. Biol. Chem.,* 233:702–705.

Axelrod, S., Kankolenski, P. F., Small, S. M., Corvin, A., and Sanders, B. E. (1970): Effects on rat rope-climbing of injection with blood plasma fractions from schizophrenics and normals. *J. Psychiatr. Res.,* 8:1–12.

Baldessarini, R., and Kopin, I. (1963): Assay of tissue levels of S-adenosylmethionine. *Anal. Biochem.,* 6:289–292.

Ban, T. A. (1971): *Nicotinic Acid in the Treatment of Schizophrenia.* The Canadian Mental Health Association, Toronto.

Banerjee, S. P., and Snyder, S. H. (1973): Methyltetrahydrofolic acid mediates N- and O-methylation of biogenic amines. *Science,* 182:74–75.

Beaton, J. M., Pegram, G. V., Bradley, R. J., and Smythies, J. R. (1973): Behavioral and Neurophysiological Effects of Methionine and its metabolites. *Proc. Soc. Neurosci.,* 3:193.

Beaton, J. M., Pegram, G. V., Bradley, R. J., and Smythies, J. R. (1974): The effects of nicotinamide on sleep-wake cycles in the mouse. *Experientia,* 30, 926–927.

Bell, C. E., and Somerville, A. R. (1966): Identity of the pink spot. *Nature,* 211:1405–1406.

Benington, F., and Morin, R. D. (1968): Enzymatic 5-hydroxylation of 3-methoxy-tyramine. *Experientia,* 24:33–34.

Bergen, J. R. (1965): Possible relationship of a plasma factor to schizophrenia. *Trans. N. Y. Acad. Sci.,* 28:40–46.

Bergen, J. R., Mittag, T. W., Frohman, C. E., Arthur, R. E., Warner, K. A., Grinspoon, L., and Freeman, H. (1968): Plasma factors in schizophrenia. *Archives of General Psychiatry,* 18:471–476.

Beringer, K. (1927): *Der Meskalinrausch. Seine Geschichte und Erscheinungsweise.* Springer, Berlin.

Berlet, H. H., Spaide, J., Kohn, H., Bull, C., and Himwich, H. E. (1965): Effects of reduction of tryptophan and methionine intake on urinary indole compounds and schizophrenic behavior. *J. Nerv. Ment. Dis.,* 140:297–304.

Boulton, A. A., Pollitt, R. J., and Majer, J. R. (1967): Identity of a urinary "pink spot" in schizophrenia and Parkinson's disease. *Nature,* 215:132–134.

Bourdillon, R. E., Clarke, C. A., Ridges, A. P., Sheppard, P. M., Harper, P., and Leslie, S. A. (1964): "Pink spot" in the urine of schizophrenics. *Nature,* 208:453–455.

Boyse, E. A., Bressler, E., Tzitani, C. A., and Lardis, M. (1970): Cytotoxic M auto-antibody in mouse alloantisera. *Transplantation,* 9:339–341.

Bradley, R. J., and Smythies, J. R. (1974): Interaction of LSD with biological molecules.

In: *LSD-The Total Picture,* edited by S. V. Siva-Sankar. PJD Publications, New York.

Bridgers, W. F. (1970): The relationship of the metabolic regulation of serine to phospholipid and one-carbon metabolism. *Int. J. Biochem.,* 1:495–505.

Bridgers, W. F., and Kaufman, S. (1962): The enzymatic conversion of epinine to epinephrine. *J. Biol. Chem.,* 237:526–528.

Bridgers, W. F., and McClain, L. D. (1972): Some interrelationships of pyridoxal phosphate, folic acid and serine metabolism in brain. In: *Role of Vitamin B₆ in Neurobiology,* edited by M. S. Ebadi and E. Costa. Raven Press, New York.

Brune, G. G. (1965): Metabolism of biogenic amines and psychotropic drug affects in schizophrenic patients. *Prog. Brain Res.,* 16:81–96.

Brune, G. G., and Himwich, H. E. (1962a): Effects of methionine loading on the behavior of schizophrenic patients. *J. Nerv. Ment. Dis.,* 134:447–450.

Brune, G. G., and Himwich, H. E. (1962b): Indole metabolites in schizophrenic patients: Urinary excretion. *Arch. Gen. Psychiatry,* 6:324–328.

Brune, G. G., Hohl, H. H., and Himwich, H. E. (1963): Urinary excretion of bufotenin-like substance in psychotic patients. *J. Neuropsychiatry,* 5:14–17.

Bumpus, F. M., and Page, I. H. (1955): Serotonin and its methylated derivatives in human urine. *J. Biol. Chem.,* 212:111–116.

Bunney, B. S., Walters, J. R., Roth, R. H., and Aghajanian, G. K. (1973): Dopaminergic neurons: Effect of antipsychotic drugs and amphetamine on single cell activity. *J. Pharmacol. Exp. Ther.,* 185:560–571.

Carnegie, P. R. (1974): Interaction of 5-hydroxytryptamine with the encephalitogenic protein. In: *The Neurosciences,* edited by F. O. Schmitt and F. W. Worden. MIT Press, Cambridge, Mass.

Carson, N. A., Cusworth, D. C., Dent, C. E., Field, C. M. B., Neill, D. W., and Westall, R. G. (1963): Homocystinuria: a new inborn error of metabolism associated with mental deficiency. *Arch. Dis. Child.,* 38:425–436.

Chiueh, C. C., and Moore, K. E. (1974): Relative potencies of *d*- and *l*-amphetamine on the release of dopamine from cat brain *in vivo. Res. Commun. Chem. Pathol. Pharmacol.,* 7:189–199.

Christie, J. E., and T. J. Crow (1971): Turning behavior as an index of the action of amphetamines and ephedrines on central dopamine-containing neurones. *Br. J. Pharmacol.,* 43:658–667.

Cohn, C. K., Dunner, D. L., and Axelrod, J. (1970): Reduced catechol-*O*-methyltransferase activity in red blood cells of women with primary affective disorders. *Science,* 170:1323–1324.

Collins, G. G. S., Sandner, M., Williams, E. D., and Youdim, M. B. H. (1970): Multiple forms of human brain mitochondrial monoamine oxidase. *Nature,* 225:817–820.

Corrodi, H., Fuxe, K., and Hokfelt, T. (1967): The effect of some psychoactive drugs on central monoamine neurons. *Eur. J. Pharmacol.,* 1:363–368.

Coyle, J. T., and Snyder, S. H. (1969): Catecholamine uptake by synaptosomes in homogenates of rat brains: Stereospecificity in different areas. *J. Pharmacol. Exp. Ther.,* 170:221–231.

Creese, I., and Iverson, S. D. (1973): Blockage of amphetamine-induced motor stimulation and stereotypy in the adult rat following neonatal treatment with 6-hydroxydopamine. *Brain Res.,* 55:369–382.

Creveling, C. R., and Daly, J. W. (1967): Identification of 3,4-dimethoxyphenethylamine from schizophrenic urine by mass spectrometry. *Nature,* 216:190–191.

Creveling, C. R., and Daly, J. W. (1969): Quoted in Stabenau et al. (1970).

Crow, T. J., and Gillbe, C. (1973): Dopamine antagonism and antischizophrenic potency of neuroleptic drugs. *Nature [New Biol.],* 245:27–28.

Cunningham, L. A., Rich, C. L., Woodrulf, R. A., Jr., and Olney, J. W. (1974): Creatine phosphokinase and psychiatric illness. *Br. J. Psychiatry,* 124:87–91.

Daly, J., Axelrod, J., and Witkop, B. (1962): Methylation and demethylation in relation to the in vitro metabolism of mescaline. *Ann. N.Y. Acad. Sci.,* 96:37–43.

Dunner, D. L., Cohn, C. K., and Gershon, E. S. (1971): Differential catechol-*O*-methyltransferase activity in unipolar and bipolar affective illness. *Archives of General Psychiatry,* 25:348–353.

Engleman, K., Lovenberg, W., and Sjoerdsma, A. (1967): Inhibition of serotonin synthesis by para-chlorophenylalanine in patients with the carcinoid syndrome. *N. Engl. J. Med.,* 277:1103–1108.

Ermala, P., and Autio, L. (1951): On intradermal histamine tests in schizophrenia. *Acta Psychiatr. Scand. Suppl.,* 60:136–144.

Erspamer, V. (1959): The biological significance of 5-hydroxytryptamine. Present status of the problem. *XXI International Congress of the Physiological Sciences,* Buenos Aires, pp. 216–222.

Evarts, W. V. (1956): Some effects of bufotenine and lysergic acid diethylamide on the monkey. *AMA Arch. Neurol. Psychiatry,* 75:49–53.

Fabing, H. D., and Hawkins, J. R. (1956): Intravenous bufotenine injection in the human being. *Science,* 123:886–887.

Fischer, E. (1960): Drogas alucinogenas. Su importancia en la envestigacion patogenica de la esquizofrenia. *Sem. Med. Buenos Aires,* 117:1115–1119.

Fischer, E., Vazquex, F. A., Fernandex, T. A., and Liskowski, L. (1961): Bufotenin in human urine. *Lancet,* 1:890.

Fog, R. L., Randrup, A., and Pakkenberg, H. (1967): Aminergic mechanisms in corpus striatum and amphetamine-induced stereotyped behaviour. *Psychopharmacologia,* 11:179–183.

Foster, F. G., and Kupfer, D. J. (1973): Psychomotor activity and serum creatinine phosphokinase. *Arch. Gen. Psychiatry,* 29:752–758.

Freedman, D. X., Redlich, F. D., and Igerscheiner, W. (1956): Psychosis and allergy: experimental approach. *Am. J. Psychiatry,* 112:873–877.

Freeman, J. M., Finkelstein, J. D., and Mudd, S. H. (1975): Folate-responsive homocystinuria and "schizophrenia." A defect in methylation due to deficient 5, 10-methylenetrahydrofolate reductase activity. *New Engl. J. Med.,* 292:491–496.

Friedhoff, A. J. (1967): Biochemical effects of experimental diets. *J. Psychiatr. Res.,* 5:265–271.

Friedhoff, A. J. (1973): Biogenic amines and schizophrenia. In: *Biological Psychiatry,* edited by J. Mendels. Wiley-Interscience, New York.

Friedhoff, A. J., and Van Winkle, E. (1962): Isolation and characterization of a compound from the urine of schizophrenics. *Nature,* 194:879–898.

Friedhoff, A. J., and Van Winkle, E. (1963): Conversion of dopamine to 3,4-dimethoxyphenylacetic acid in schizophrenic patients. *Nature,* 199:1271–1272.

Frohman, C. E. (1968): Studies on the plasma factors in schizophrenia. In: *Mind as a Tissue,* edited by C. Rupp. Harper and Row, New York.

Frohman, C. E. (1973): Plasma proteins and schizophrenia. In: *Biological Psychiatry,* edited by J. Mendels. Wiley-Interscience, New York.

Frohman, C. E., Luby, E. D., Tourney, G., Beckett, P. G. S., and Gottlieb, J. S. (1960): Steps toward the isolation of a serum factor in schizophrenia. *Am J. Psychiatry,* 117:401–408.

Gaddum, J. H. (1954): Drugs antagonistic to 5-hydroxy-tryptamine. In: *CIBA Conference Symposium on Hypertension,* edited by G. E. W. Wolstenholme and M. P. Cameron. Little, Brown, Boston.

Gerard, R. W. (1956): *Neuropharmacology.* Josiah Macy Jr. Foundation, New York.

Golub, E. S. (1972): The distribution of brain-associated antigen cross-reactive with mouse in the brain of other species. *J. Immunol.,* 109:168–170.

Gillin, J. C., and Wyatt, R. J. (1975): Schizophrenia. Perchance a dream? *Int. Rev. Neurobiol.,* 17, 297–338.

Gottlieb, J. S., Frohman, C. E., and Beckett, P. G. S. (1969): A theory of neuronal malfunction in schizophrenia. *Am. J. Psychiatry,* 126:149–156.

Graham, A., and Aghajanian, G. K. (1971): Effects of amphetamine on single cell activity in a catecholamine nucleus, the locus coeruleus. *Nature,* 234:100–102.

Grant, R. H. E., and Stores, O. P. R. (1970): Folic acid in folate-deficient patients with epilepsy. *Br. Med. J.,* 4:644–648.

Greenberg, R. (1973): *N,N*-dimethylated and *N,N*-diethylated indoleamines in schizophrenia. In: *Chemical Modulation of Brain Function,* edited by H. C. Sabelli. Raven Press, New York.

Hall, P., Hartridge, G., and Van Leeuwen, G. M. (1969): Effect of catechol *O*-methyltransferase in schizophrenia. *Arch. Gen. Psychiatry,* 20:573–575.

Harding, T. (1972): D. P. M. Thesis, University of Edinburgh, Edinburgh, Scotland.

Haydu, G. G., Dhryniotis, A., Korenyi, C., and Goldschmidt, L. (1965): Effects of methionine and hydroxychloroquine in schizophrenia. *Am. J. Psychiatry*, 122:560–564.

Heath, R. G., and Krupp, I. M. (1967): The biologic basis of schizophrenia: An autoimmune concept. In: *Molecular Basis of Some Aspects of Mental Activity: Proceedings Vol. 2*, edited by O. Walaas. Academic Press, New York.

Heath, R. G., Marteus, S., Leach, B. E., Cohen, M., and Feigley, C. A. (1958): Behavioral changes in nonpsychotic volunteers following administration of taraxein, substance obtained from serum of schizophrenic patients. *Am. J. Psychiatry*, 114:917–920.

Heath, R. G., Nesselhof, W., Jr., and Timmons, E. (1966): D,L-methionine-*d,l*-sulphoximine effects in schizophrenic patients. *Arch. Gen. Psychiatry*, 14:213.

Henter, R., Jones, M., and Malleson, A. (1969): Abnormal cerebrospinal fluid total protein and gamma globulin levels in 256 patients admitted to a psychiatric unit. *J. Neurol. Sci.*, 9:11–38.

Heston, L. L. (1966): Psychiatric disorders in foster home reared children of schizophrenic mothers. *Br. J. Psychiatry*, 112:819–825.

Heston, L. L. (1973): Genes and schizophrenia. In: *Biological Psychiatry*, edited by J. Mendels. Wiley-Interscience, New York.

Heyman, J. J. (1963): Nicotinamide metabolism in schizophrenics, drug addicts and normals: the effect of psychotropic drugs and hormones. *Trans. N.Y. Acad. Sci.*, 26:354–360.

Himsworth, H. P., and Glynn, L. E. (1944): Massive hepatic necrosis and diffuse hepatic fibrosis: their production by means of diet. *Clin. Sci.*, 5:93–119.

Himwich, H. E., Rinaldi, F., and Willis, D. (1956): An examination of phenothiazine derivatives with comparisons of their effects on the alerting reaction, chemical structure and therapeutic efficacy. *J. Nerv. Ment. Dis.*, 124:53–57.

Hoffer, A. (1973): Mechanism of Action of Nicotinic Acid and Nicotinamide in the treatment of schizophrenia. In: *Orthomolecular Psychiatry*, edited by D. Hawkins and L. Pauling. Freeman, San Francisco.

Horn, A. S., and Snyder, S. H. (1971): Chlorpromazine and Dopamine: Conformational similarities that correlate with the antipsychotic activity of phenothiazine drugs. *Proc. Nat. Acad. Sci. USA*, 68:2325.

Hsu, L. L. and Mandell, A. J. (1973): Multiple N-methyltransferases for aromatic alkylamines in brain. *Life Sci.*, 13:847–859.

Jodrey, L. H., and Smith, J. A. (1959): Releasable histamine levels and histamine tolerance in tissues of 291 psychotic patients. *Am. J. Psychiatry*, 115:801–807.

Johnson, S., Swaninathan, S. P., and Baker, S. J. (1962): Changes in the serum B_{12} levels in patients with megaloblastic anaemia treated with folic acid. *J. Clin. Pathol.*, 15:274–277.

Kakimoto, Y., Sano, I., Kanazawa, A., Tsujio, T., and Kaneko, S. (1967): Metabolic effects of methionine in schizophrenic patients pretreated with a monoamine oxidase inhibitor. *Nature*, 216:1110–1111.

Kallmann, F. J. (1946): The genetic theory of schizophrenia: An analysis of 691 schizophrenic twin index families. *Am. J. Psychiatry*, 103:309–322.

Kaufman, S., and Friedman, S. (1965): Dopamine β hydroxylase. *Pharmacol. Rev.*, 17:71–100.

Kebabian, J. W., Petzold, G. L., and Greengard, P. (1972): Dopamine-sensitive adenyl cyclase in caudate nucleus of rat brain, and its similarity to the dopamine receptor. *Proc. Nat. Acad. Sci. USA*, 69:2145–2149.

Kety, S., Rosenthal, D., Schulsinger, F., and Wender, P. (1968): The types and frequencies of mental illness in the biological and adoptive families of adopted schizophrenics. In: *The Transmission of Schizophrenia*, edited by S. Kety and D. Rosenthal. Pergamon Press, Oxford.

Kier, L. B. (1973): Chlorpromazine and serotonin: conformational similarities correlating with activities. *J. Theor. Biol.*, 40: 211–217.

Klawans, H. L., Jr., Goetz, C., and Westheimer, R. (1972): Pathophysiology of schizophrenia of the striatum. *Dis. Nerv. Syst.*, 33:711–719.

Kornetsky, C., and Eliasson, M. (1969): Reticular stimulation and chlorpromazine: an animal model for schizophrenia overarousal. *Science,* 165:1273–1274.

Kraepelin, E. (1892): *Uber die Beerinflussung Einfacher Psychischer Vorgaenge Durch Einige Arzneimittel,* Gustave Fischer, Jena.

Laduron, P. (1972a): N-methylation of dopamine to epinine in adrenal medulla: A new model for the biosynthesis of adrenaline. *Archives Internationales de Pharmacodynamie et de Therapie,* 195:197–208.

Laduron, P. (1972b): N-methylation of dopamine to epinine in brain tissue using N-methyltetrahydrofolic acid as the methyl donor. *Nature [New Biol.],* 238:212–213.

Laduron, P. (1974): A new hypothesis on the origin of schizophrenia. *J. Psychiat. Res.,* 11:257–258.

Lanzkowsky, P. (1970): Congenital malabsorption of folate. *Am. J. Med.,* 48:580–583.

Lauer, J. W., Inskip, W. M., Bernsohn, J., and Zeeler, E. A. (1958): Observations on schizophrenic patients after iproniazid and tryptophan. *Arch. Neurol. Psychiatry,* 80:122–130.

Levitt, M., Nixon, P. F., Pincus, J. H., and Bertino, J. R. (1971): Transport characteristics of folates in cerebrospinal fluid; a study utilizing doubly labeled 5-methyltetrahydrofolate and 5-formyltetrahydrofolate. *J. Clin. Invest.,* 50:1301–1308.

Lozovsky, D., Krasnova, A., Factor, M., Polyanskaya, N., and Popova, N. (1967): The effect of the serum of schizophrenic patients upon certain glucose transformation indices in experiments. In: *Biological Research in Schizophrenia,* edited by M. Vartanian. Ordina Lennia, Moscow.

Lucy, J. D. (1954): Histamine tolerance in schizophrenia. *Arch. Neurobiol. Psychiatry,* 71:629–639.

Luria, E. A., and Domashneva, I. V. (1974): Antibodies to thymocytes in sera of patients with schizophrenia. *Proc. Natl. Acad. Sci. USA,* 71:235–236.

Mandel, L. R., Rosegay, A., Walker, R. W., VandenHeuvel, W. J. A., and Rokach, J. (1974): 5-Methyltetrahydrofolic acid as a mediator in the formation of pyridoindoles. *Science,* 186:741–743.

Mandell, A. J., and Morgan, M. (1971): Indole (ethyl) amine N-methyltransferase in human brain. *Nature,* 230:85–87.

Mandell, A. J., and Younger, C. B. (1962): Asthma alternating with psychiatric symptomatology. *California Medicine,* 96:251–253.

Matthysse, S. (1973): Antipsychotic drug actions: A clue to the neuropathology of schizophrenia. *Fed. Proc.,* 32:200–205.

Matthysse, S., and Baldessarini, R. J. (1972): S-adenosylmethionine and catechol-O-methyl-transferase in schizophrenia. *Am. J. Psychiatry,* 128:130–132.

McClain, L. D., Carl, G. F., and Bridgers, W. F. (1974): The distribution of folate coenzymes and folate dependent enzymes in mouse brain. *J. Neurochem.,* 24:719–722.

McGrath, S. D., O'Brien, P. F., Power, P. J., and Shea, J. R. (1972): Nicotinamide treatment of schizophrenia. *Schizophrenia Bulletin,* 5:74–76.

Meller, E., Rosengarten, H., Friedhoff, A. J., Stebbins, R. D., and Silber, R. (1975): 5-Methyltetrahydrofolic acid is not a methyl donor for biogenic amines: Enzymatic formation of formaldehyde. *Science,* 187:171–173.

Mellsop, G., Whittingham, S., and Ungar, B. (1973): Schizophrenia and autoimmune serological reactions. *Arch. Gen. Psychiatry,* 28:194–196.

Meltzer, H. Y. (1969): Creatine kinase and aldolase in serum. Abnormality common to acute psychoses. *Science,* 159:1368–1370.

Meltzer, H. Y. (1972): Central core fibers in an acutely psychotic patient: Evidence for a neurogenic basis for the muscle abnormalities in the acute psychoses. *Arch. Gen. Psychiatry,* 27:125–132.

Meltzer, H. Y., and Moline, R. (1970): Plasma enzymatic activity after exercise. Study of psychiatric patients and their relatives. *Arch. Gen. Psychiatry,* 22:390–407.

Miller, R. J., and Hiley, C. R. (1974): Anti-muscarinic properties of neuroleptics and drug-induced Parkinsonism. *Nature,* 248:596–597.

Moreau, J. (1845): *Du Hachisch et de l'Alienation Mentale, Etudes psychologiques.* Librairie de Fortin, Masson et Cie, Paris.

Morgan, M., and Mandell, A. J. (1969): Indole (ethyl) amine N-methyltransferase in the brain. *Science,* 165:492–493.

Murphy, D., and Wyatt, R. J. (1972a): Reduced monoamine oxidase activity in blood platelets from schizophrenic patients. *Nature,* 238:225–226.

Murphy, D., and Weis, R. (1972b): Reduced monoamine oxidase activity in blood platelets from bipolar depressed patients. *Am. J. Psychiatry,* 128:1351–1357.

Narasimhachari, N., Heller, B., Spaide, J., Haskovec, L., Fiyimori, M., Tabushi, K., and Himwich, H. E. (1970): Comparative behavioral and biochemical effects of tranylcypromine and cysteine on normal controls and schizophrenic patients. *Life Science,* 9:Part 1, 1021–1032.

Narasimhachari, N., Plaut, J., and Himwich, H. E. (1972a): 3:4-dimethoxyphenylethyl-amine, a normal or abnormal metabolite? *J. Psychiatr. Res.,* 9:325–328.

Narasimhachari, N., Avalos, J., Fiyimori, M., and Himwich, H. E. (1972b): Studies of drug-free schizophrenics and controls. *Biological Psychiatry,* 5:311–318.

Narasimhachari, N., Plaut, J. M., and Himwich, H. E. (1972c): Indolethylamine-N-methyltransferase in serum samples of schizophrenics and normal controls. *Life Sciences,* 11:221–227.

Narasimhachari, N., Heller, B., Spaide, J., Haskovec, L., Strahilevitz, M., Meltzer, H., and Himwich, H. E. (1971): N,N-dimethylated indoleamines in blood. *Biol. Psychiatry,* 3:21–23.

Narasimhachari, N., and Himwich, H. E. (1973): GC-MS identification of bufotenin in urine samples from patients with schizophrenia or infantile autism. *Life Sci.,* 12:475–478.

Nicol, S., Seal, V. S., and Gottesman, (1973): Serum from schizophrenic patients. *Arch. Gen. Psychiatry,* 29:744–751.

Nies, A., Robinson, D. S., Lamborn, K. R., and Lampert, R. R. (1973): Genetic control of platelet and plasma monoamine oxidase activity. *Arch. Gen. Psychiatry,* 28:834–838.

Neubauer, C. (1970): Mental deterioration in epilepsy due to folate deficiency. *Br. Med. J.,* 2:759–761.

Osmond, H., and Smythies, J. R. (1952): Schizophrenia: A new approach. *J. Ment. Sci.,* 98:309–315.

Park, L. C., Baldessarini, R. J., and Kety, S. S. (1965): Methionine effects in chronic schizophrenia. *Arch. Gen. Psychiatry,* 12:346–351.

Patrick, J., and Lindstrom, J. (1973): Autoimmune response to acetylcholine receptor. *Science,* 180:871–872.

Pauling, L., Robinson, A. B., Oxley, S. S., Bergerson, M., Harris, A., Cary, P., Bletheu, J., and Keaveny, I. T. (1973): Results of a loading test of ascorbic acid, niacinamide, and pyridoxine in schizophrenic subjects and controls. In: *Orthomolecular Psychiatry,* edited by D. Hawkins and L. Pauling. Freeman, San Francisco.

Pfeiffer, C. C. (1972): Blood histamine, basophil counts and trace elements in the schizophrenias. *Rev. Can. Biol.,* 31:73–76.

Phear, E. A., Ruebuer, B., Sherlock, S., and Summerskill, W. H. J. (1956): Methionine toxicity in liver disease and its prevention by chlortetracycline. *Clin. Sci.,* 15:94–117.

Phillips, A. G. and Fibiger, H. C. (1973): Dopaminergic and noradrenergic substrates of positive reinforcement: Differential effects of *d*- and *l*-amphetamine. *Science,* 179:575–577.

Pollin, W., Cardon, P. V., Jr., and Kety, S. S. (1961): Effect of amino acid feedings in schizophrenia patients treated with iproniazid. *Science,* 133:104–105.

Prange, A. J., Wilson, I. C., Rabon, A. M., and Lipton, M. A. (1969): Enhancement of imipramine antidepressant activity by thyroid hormone. *Am. J. Psychiatry,* 126:457–469.

Ralston, A. J., Snaith, R. P., and Hinley, J. B. (1970): Effects of folic acid on fit-frequency and behavior in epileptics on anticonvulsants. *Lancet,* 1:867.

Reynolds, E. H. (1968): Mental effects of anticonvulsants and folic acid metabolism. *Brain,* 91:197–214.

Ridges, A. P. (1973): The methylation hypothesis in relation to "pink spot." In: *Orthomolecular Psychiatry,* edited by D. Hawkins and L. Pauling. Freeman, San Francisco.

Ridges, A. P., and Harper, P. (1970): Pink-spot—is it a drug artifact? *Psychiatr. Clin.,* 3:101–107.

Ridges, A. P., and Bourdillon, R. E. (1966): The pink spot. *Lancet,* 1:767.

Robins, E., Smith, K., and Lowe, I. P. (1957): Discussion of clinical studies with taraxein. In: *Neuropharmacology: Transactions of the Fourth Conference,* edited by H. A. Abramson. Josiah Macy Foundation, New York.

Rosenthal, D. (1963): *The Genain Quadruplets.* Basic Books, New York.

Ryan, J. W., Brown, J. D., and Durell, J. (1966): Antibodies affecting metabolism of chicken erythrocytes. Examination of schizophrenic and other subjects. *Science,* 151:1408–1410.

Saavedra, J. M., and Axelrod, J. (1972): Psychotomimetic N-methylated tryptamines: formation in brain *in vivo* and *in vitro*. *Science,* 172:1365–1366.

Seigel, M., and Tefft, H. (1971): "Pink spot" and its components in normal and schizophrenic urine. *J. Nerv. Ment. Dis.,* 152:412–426.

Shaw, C. R., Lucas, J., and Rabinovitch, R. D. (1959): Metabolic studies in childhood schizophrenia: Effects of tryptophan loading on indole excretion. *Arch. Neurol. Psychiatry,* 1:366–371.

Shulman, R. (1967): Vitamin B_{12} deficiency and psychiatric illness. *Br. J. Psychiatry,* 113:252–256.

Simpson, G. M., and Kline, N. S. (1961): Histamine wheal formation and mental illness. *J. Nerv. Ment. Dis.,* 133:19–24.

Slater, E. (1958): The monogenetic theory of schizophrenia. *Acta. Genet. (Basel),* 8:50.

Smythies, J. R. (1974): Nicotinamide treatment of schizophrenia. *Lancet,* 1:1450–1451.

Solomon, G. F., Allansmith, M., McClellan, B., and Amkraut, A. (1969): Immuno-globulins in psychiatric patients. *Arch. Gen. Psychiatry,* 20:272–277.

Spaide, J., Neveln, L., Tolentino, J., and Himwich, H. E. (1969): Methionine and tryptophan loading in schizophrenic patients receiving a MAO inhibitor: Correlation of behavioral and biochemical changes. *Biol. Psychiatry,* 1:227–233.

Spaide, J., Tanimukai, H., Ginther, R., Bueno, J., and Himwich, H. E. (1967): Schizophrenic behavior and urinary tryptophan metabolites associated with cysteine given with and without a monoamine oxidase inhibitor (Tranylcypromine). *Life Sci.,* 6:551–560.

Spath, E. (1919): Ueber die Anhalonium-Alkaloide. *Monatsh. Chemie (Wien),* 40: 129–154.

Speeter, M. E., and Anthony, W. C. (1954): The action of oxalyl chloride on indoles: A new approach to tryptamines. *J. Am. Chem. Soc.,* 76:6208–6210.

Spiro, H. R., Schinke, R. N., and Welch, J. P. (1965): Schizophrenia in a patient with a defect in methionine metabolism. *J. Nerv. Ment. Dis.,* 141:285–290.

Sprince, H., Parker, C. M., and Josephs, J. A., Jr. (1969): Homocysteine-Induced convulsions in the rat: Protection by homoserine, serine, betaine, glycine, and glucose. *Agents Actions,* 1:9–13.

Stabenau, J. R., Creveling, C. R., and Daly, J. W. (1970): The "pink spot" 3,4-dimethoxyphenethylamine, common tea and schizophrenia. *Am. J. Psychiatry,* 127: 611–616.

Stein, L., and Wise, C. D. (1971): Possible etiology of schizophrenia: Progressive damage to the noradrenergic reward system by 6-OHDA. *Science,* 171:1032–1036.

Stern, P., Hukovic, S., Madjerek, Z., and Karabaic, S. (1957): Histamingehalt in blute von schizophrenikern. *Arch. Int. Pharmacodyn. Ther.,* 109:294–299.

Stockings, G. T. (1940): A clinical study of the mescaline psychosis with special reference to the mechanism of the genesis of schizophrenia and other psychotic states. *J. Ment. Sci.,* 86:29–47.

Strahilevitz, M., and Davis, S. D. (1970): Increased IgA in schizophrenic patients. *Lancet,* 11:370.

Stromberg, V. L. (1954): The isolation of bufotenine from peptadena peregrina. *J. Am. Chem. Soc.,* 76:1707.

Szara, S. (1956): Dimethyltryptamine: Its metabolism in man; the relation of its psychotic effect to serotonin metabolism. *Experientia,* 12:441–442.

Taylor, K. M., and Snyder, S. H. (1971): Differential effects of *d*- and *l*-amphetamine on behavior and on catecholamine disposition in dopamine and norepinephrine containing neurons of rat brain. *Brain Res.,* 28:295–309.

Thudichum, J. L. W. (1884): *Treatise on the Chemical Constitution of the Brain.* Bailliere, Tindall and Cox, London.

Van Rossum, J. M. (1965): Different types of sympathomimetic alpha-receptors. *J. Phar. Pharmacol.,* 17:202–216.

Van Rossum, J. M. (1966): The significance of dopamine-receptor blockade for the mechanism of action of neuroleptic drugs. *Int. Pharmacodyn. Ther.,* 160:492.

Vartanyan, M. E. (1969): *Schizophrenia: Clinical Aspects and Pathogenesis.* Medgiz, Moscow.

Von Studnitz, W., and Nyman, G. E. (1965): Excretion of 3,4-dimethoxyphenethylamine in schizophrenia. *Acta Psychiatr. Scand.,* 41:117–121.

Walker, R. W., Ahn, H. S., Mandel, L. R., and Vanden Hewel, W. J. A. (1972): Identification of N,N-dimethyltryptamine as the product of an *in vitro* enzymatic methylation. *Anal. Biochem.,* 47:228–234.

Watson, C. J., Range, W., Taddeini, L., Bossenmaier, I., and Cardinal, R. (1964): A suggested control gene mechanism for the excessive production of types I and III porphyrins in congenital erythroporetic porphyria. *Proc. Nat. Acad. Sci. USA,* 52:478–485.

Watt, J. A. G., Ashcroft, G. W., Daly, R. J., and Smythies, J. R. (1969): Urine volume and pink spots in schizophrenia and health. *Nature,* 221:971–972.

Weckowicz, T. E., and Hall, R. (1958): Skin histamine reaction in schizophrenic and non-schizophrenic mental patients. *J. Nerv. Ment. Dis.,* 126:413–470.

Whittingham, S., Mackay, I. R., Jones, I. H., and Davies, B. (1968): Absence of brain antibodies in patients with schizophrenia. *Br. Med. J.,* 1:347–348.

Winter, C. A., and Flataker, L. (1958): Effect of blood plasma from psychotic patients upon performance of trained rats. *Am. Med. Assoc. Arch. Neurol. Psychiatry,* 80: 441–449.

Wise, C. D., and Stein, L. (1973): Dopamine-β-hydroxylase deficits in the brains of schizophrenic patients. *Science,* 181:344–347.

Wittenborn, J. R., Weber, E. S. P., and Brown, M. (1973): Niacin in the long-term treatment of schizophrenia. *Arch. Gen. Psychiatry,* 28:308–315.

Woolley, D. W. (1958): Tranquilizing and antiserotonin activity of nicotinamide. *Science,* 128:1277–1278.

Woolley, D. W., and Shaw, K. N. F. (1954): A biological and pharmacological suggestion about certain mental disorders. *Proc. Nat. Acad. Sci.,* 40:228–231.

Wyatt, R. J., Vaughan, T., Galanter, M., Kaplan, J., and Green, R. (1972): Behavioral changes of chronic schizophrenic patients given 1-5-hydroxytryptophan. *Science,* 177:1124–1126.

Wyatt, R. J., Mandel, L. R., Ahn, H. S., Walker, R. W., and Vanden Hewel, W. J. A. (1973a): Gas chromatographic-mass spectrometric isotope dilution determination of N,N-dimethyltryptamine concentrations in normal and psychiatric patients. *Psychopharmacologia,* 31:265–270.

Wyatt, R. J., Saavedra, J. M., and Axelrod, J. (1973b): A dimethyltryptamine-forming enzyme in human blood. *Am. J. Psychiatry,* 130:754–760.

Wyatt, R. J., Saavedra, J. M., Belmaker, R., Cohen, S., and Pollin, W. (1973c): The dimethyltryptamine forming enzyme in blood platelets: a study in monozygotic twins discordant for schizophrenia. *Am. J. Psychiatry,* 130:1359–1361.

Wyatt, R. J., Murphy, D., and Belmaker, R., Donnelly, C., Cohen, S., and Pollin, W. (1973d): Reduced monoamine oxidase activity in platelets: A possible genetic marker for vulnerability to schizophrenia. *Science,* 173:916–918.

Wyatt, R. J., Erdelyi, E., Doamaral, J. R., Elliot, G. R., Renson, J., and Barchas, J. D. (1975): Tryptoline formation by a preparation from brain with 5-methyltetrahydrofolic acid and tryptamine. *Science,* 187:853–855.

Yaryura-Tobias, J. A., Diamond, B., and Merlis, S. (1970): The action of L-DOPA on schizophrenic patients (a preliminary report). *Curr. Ther. Res.,* 12:528–531.

Biological Foundations of Psychiatry,
edited by R. G. Grenell and S. Gabay.
Raven Press, New York © 1976.

The Biochemistry of Affective Disorders

H. Weil-Malherbe

National Institute of Mental Health, William A. White Building, Saint Elizabeths Hospital, Washington, D.C. 20032

Biochemical changes in mental disorders may be of two kinds. Some are secondary effects due to stress, to increased or decreased physical activity, malnutrition, long-term institutionalization, and last but not least to therapeutic intervention. Such effects are unspecific and of limited interest.

What we usually have in mind when we speak of the biochemistry of psychosis are biochemical changes of a different kind. They are those specifically related to the pathogenesis of the morbid condition inasmuch as they contribute themselves to its development or accompany the pathologic symptoms as sequelae of a common cause. The classic examples for such a relationship are the inborn metabolic errors.

It is not always easy to keep the two types of biochemistry apart. All too often effects believed to be primary and specific have in the end turned out to be secondary and unspecific. Many psychiatrists would even deny the existence of primary biochemical factors in psychoses altogether; to them the term "biochemistry of psychosis" is a contradiction in itself, since it implies a concept of psychosis involving a somatic component, a cellular disorganization, a more or less predictable course, and a susceptibility to physical treatments; in other words it implies a medical model of psychosis.

If the medical model is today widely accepted, at least for the two large groups of functional psychoses, schizophrenia and affective disorders, it is due to a series of developments that we shall attempt to trace in this article with respect to the affective disorders. The biochemistry of affective disorders has been reviewed by many authors, the present writer among them. Those interested in earlier work and related bibliography are referred to the previous reviews (Weil-Malherbe and Szara, 1971; Weil-Malherbe, 1972). Some aspects that have been considered elsewhere were omitted, such as the relationship of affective disorders to the endocrine system which is treated in Chapter 17 (*this volume*) and the changes of carbohydrate metabolism in affective disorders, an area in which no recent developments are to be recorded. This chapter describes developments of the last 4 or 5 years.

I. THE GENETICS OF AFFECTIVE DISORDERS

Perhaps the most crucial of the developments in favor of a partly somatic etiology of affective disorders was the recognition of a genetic factor. Although its full discussion is not within the scope of this review, it must be mentioned briefly, not only because of its obvious relevance to the existence of a biochemical factor, but also because of its relevance for the classification of affective disorders.

The genetic factor has been demonstrated by the classic method of comparing concordance rates between pairs of mono- and dizygotic twins. Weil-Malherbe and Szara (1971, p. 55) compiled data from six publications and obtained the figures shown in Table 1. The morbidity in the dizygotic pairs of twins corresponds to that observed in other close relatives of patients with affective disorders and, although much higher than the incidence of the disease in the general population (0.5–1.0%, it is very much lower than the incidence in the monozygotic pairs of twins. In five of the original publications, the twin data were extracted from hospital admission records. This procedure has been criticized as being biased in favor of the more severe cases where the genetic load may have been unduly strong. Older figures indicating a high concordance rate for schizophrenia in monozygotic twins were revised downward in more recent studies based on birth registers crossmatched with registers of mental illness. Our compilation included one such study from a Danish population (Harvald and Hauge, 1956). It arrived at a concordance rate of 50% for 10 pairs of monozygotic twins and of 2.6%

for 39 pairs of male dizygotic twins and therefore confirms the strong effect of the genetic factor.

These twin studies did not systematically differentiate between unipolar and bipolar affective psychoses, but it is nevertheless clear that a significant number of cases that were concordant for affective psychosis were discordant for type of disorder (about 25%; Gershon, Dunner, and Goodwin, 1971); in the discordant pairs, one twin suffered from cycles of mania and depression, whereas the other twin presumably had only recurrent bouts of depression (cases of mania without depression are very rare). We must conclude that in these cases the gene for manic illness had incomplete penetrance.

Recent studies of family histories (Reich, Clayton, and Winokur, 1969; Mendlewicz, Fleiss, and Fieve, 1972; Fieve, Mendlewicz, and Fleiss, 1973b) have suggested that bipolar affective disorder is transmitted by an X-linked dominant gene, with color blindness or the presence of the Xg blood group

TABLE 1. *The genetic factor demonstrated by comparison of concordance rates*

Twins	Number of pairs	Concordance (%)
Monozygotic	96	76.0
Same-sexed dizygotic	226	22.0

serving as X-linked markers. In the pedigrees of these families, bipolar and unipolar cases occur with about equal frequency.

If therefore some patients with a unipolar phenotype have a bipolar genotype, the question arises if this is true for all unipolar patients. The studies of Angst (1968) and Perris (1968) made the existence of a separate, genetically distinct unipolar group, with a higher incidence in women probable. This group seems to correspond to Winokur's (1972) "depression spectrum disease" whereas his "pure depressive disease" might represent crypto-bipolar cases with a bipolar genotype and a unipolar phenotype. Although some biochemical differences between unipolar and bipolar affective disorders have been described, we are as yet unable to distinguish biochemically between "true unipolar" and "crypto-bipolar" illness.

II. BRAIN MONOAMINES AND BEHAVIOR

A. The Different Systems of Monoamines

The opening of the modern era in our concepts of affective disorders is marked by two milestones, the discovery of the effects of reserpine and the discovery of the inhibitors of monoamine oxidase (MAO). The mechanism of action of these drugs implicated the same group of cell constituents, the biogenic monoamines, whose occurrence in the brain and possible function as neurotransmitters were discovered at about the same time. Those of interest in this context are the two catecholamines, norepinephrine and dopamine, and 5-hydroxytryptamine or serotonin. These three amines are associated with three distinct groups of neurons, now designated as adrenergic, dopaminergic, and serotonergic. The cell bodies of the adrenergic neurons of the central nervous system are mainly located in the locus coeruleus and the reticular formation of pons and medulla oblongata. From there, fibers descend into the spinal cord and ascend by way of the peduncles to the cerebellum and by way of the medial forebrain bundle to the limbic system, the hypothalamic nuclei, the preoptic area, and the neocortex. The dopaminergic neurons seem to consist of several distinct groups. The main group contains cell bodies in the zona compacta of the substantia nigra; its fibers run in the crus cerebri and the internal capsule to the neostriatum. Another group originates in the nucleus interpeduncularis and terminates at the nucleus accumbens and the tuberculum olfactorium. A short dopaminergic tract connects cell bodies in the arcuate and anterior periventricular nuclei with nerve terminals surrounding the primary capillary plexus in the median eminence. The cell bodies of the serotonergic neurons, finally, are situated in the midbrain raphe nuclei. Descending fibers go to the spinal cord and ascending fibers terminate in the lateral and anterior hypothalamus, the limbic system, and other parts of the forebrain (Dahlström and Fuxe, 1964; Andén, Carlsson, Dahlström, Fuxe, Hillarp, and Larsson, 1964; Andén, Dahlström, Fuxe, and Larsson, 1965; Andén, Dahlström, Fuxe, Larsson, Olson, and Ungerstedt, 1966; Fuxe, 1965).

In addition to their occurrence in specific neuronal systems, the following facts, among many other observations, support the assumption that these monoamines function either as synaptic transmitters themselves or are very intimately connected with the process of synaptic transmission: (1) they are contained in "presynaptic vesicles," (2) they are discharged from these vesicles directly into the synaptic cleft, following a depolarization of the neuronal membrane, and (3) they are substrates of a saturable, specific, high-affinity uptake system that ensures their passage through the neuronal membrane into the nerve terminal.

In 1957 Brodie and Shore suggested, with rare acumen and intuition, that norepinephrine acted as transmitter in the ergotropic system and that serotonin acted as a transmitter in the trophotropic system. The terms ergotropic and trophotropic were introduced by Hess (1954) to describe functional autonomic systems in the central nervous system roughly corresponding to the anatomic distinction between the sympathetic and parasympathetic systems. Whereas the trophotropic system is concerned with conservation, relaxation, and restitution, the function of the ergotropic system is related to defense, aggression, energy expenditure, and adaptation to environmental change. Brodie and Shore's classification has stood the test of time remarkably well, despite some apparent contradictions and inconsistencies which, in most cases, have found a satisfactory explanation.

B. Correlation of Drug Effects on Brain Monoamines and Behavior

Whereas reserpine depletes and the group of MAO inhibitors raises the levels of brain monoamines, neither one nor the other discriminates between the catecholamines and serotonin. It is difficult therefore to be sure which behavioral effect should be assigned to a particular neurotransmitter. Fortunately we now have drugs that achieve the same result but in a more specific manner. Inhibition of tyrosine hydroxylase, the first and rate-limiting enzyme in the biosynthesis of catecholamines, leads to a depletion of dopamine and norepinephrine. The drug that is usually used for this purpose is α-methyl-p-tyrosine (αMpT). Depletion of norepinephrine alone is possible by inhibition of dopamine-β-hydroxylase with diethyldithiocarbamate or other copper-chelating agents. Intraventricular injection of 6-hydroxydopamine has been used to bring about the irreversible destruction of adrenergic nerve endings; with higher doses and after a longer interval, dopaminergic nerve endings are also affected. Similarly there are drugs, such as p-chlorophenylalanine (pCPA), that specifically inhibit tryptophan hydroxylase and thereby deplete brain serotonin. A drug with an action on serotonergic nerve endings analogous to 6-hydroxydopamine is 5,7-dihydroxytryptamine (Baumgarten, Björklund, Lachenmayer, and Nobin, 1973a; Baumgarten, Victor, and Lovenberg, 1973b).

Specific increases in the level of a particular neurotransmitter can be obtained by the administration of the respective amino acid precursor, L-3,4-dihydroxyphenylalanine (DOPA) and L-5-hydroxytryptophan (5-HTP). The effect can be enhanced by the simultaneous administration of an inhibitor of MAO (although this will also cause accumulation of other endogenous amines) or by a combination with a peripherally acting inhibitor of aromatic amino acid decarboxylase (DOPA decarboxylase). Such a drug, e.g., α-methyl-DOPA-hydrazine or one of its congeners, has the effect of preventing the decarboxylation of the amino acid in peripheral tissues, thus making a larger proportion available for penetration into the brain where the drug cannot follow (Bartholini, Burkard, Pletscher, and Bates, 1967).

The functions of the ergotropic and trophotropic systems are partly antagonistic. Hence depression of one should have effects similar to those produced by stimulation of the other or, expressed in terms of transmitter economy, depletion of the adrenergic transmitter should have approximately the same effect as accumulation of the serotonergic transmitter and vice versa. This is in fact what has been observed, although in many cases the absolute levels of one or the other transmitter seem to be of less significance than their ratio. Thus there is a similarity between the behavioral effects of αMpT (the inhibitor of catecholamine synthesis) and 5-HTP (the prescursor of serotonin) on the one hand and between pCPA (the inhibitor of serotonin synthesis) and of DOPA (the precursor of catecholamines) on the other.

The administration of αMpT produces motor inactivity, sedation, and a deterioration in the performance of trained animals, effects that are reversible by treatment with DOPA, a MAO inhibitor or both. A gradual adaptation to the effects of αMpT takes place during chronic treatment (for a comprehensive bibliography see Weil-Malherbe and Szara, 1971, p. 22). In monkeys, αMpT produced social withdrawal, akinesia, and a huddled posture identical with that observed after separation of adolescent monkeys from their mothers (Redmond, Maas, Kling, and Dekirmenjian, 1971). The behavioral effects of 6-hydroxydopamine are similar to those of αMpT (Laverty and Taylor, 1970).

In low doses, 5-HTP produces sedation, drowsiness, lethargy, and a sleep pattern in the electroencephalogram (EEG). In reserpinized animals 5-HTP induced tremors and convulsions but did not restore alertness; on the contrary it inhibited the arousal response to adrenergic stimulation. In cats made sleepless by the administration of pCPA, 5-HTP restored sleep (for references see Weil-Malherbe and Szara, 1971, p. 22–23).

The administration of pCPA, on the other hand, leads to increased motor activity, sexual arousal in males of various species, insomnia in cats and rats, and an increase of aggressive muricidal behavior in rats. By reducing emotionality and fear, pCPA facilitates learning in maze tests and conditioned avoidance response tests (Fibiger and Campbell, 1971; Weil-Malherbe and Szara, 1971, p. 23; Aprison and Hingtgen, 1972). Treatment of rats with 5,6- or 5,7-dihydroxytryptamine similarly led to irritability, hypersensitivity, motor hyperactivity, sexual arousal, and fighting (Baumgarten, Evetts, Holman, Iversen, Vogt, and Wilson, 1972; Baumgarten and Schlossberger, 1973; Baumgarten et al., 1973a,b).

The effects of DOPA administration also resemble those of pCPA. It improves the performance of trained animals in conditioned response tests, increases aggression and biting responses in mice, and restores alertness in reserpinized animals. In man and animals, it produces insomnia and an arousal pattern in the EEG (Weil-Malherbe and Szara, 1971, p. 22–23). In combination with an inhibitor of MAO, DOPA produces extreme, often lethal arousal (Jones, 1972).

The behavioral functions of adrenergic and dopaminergic neurons are not identical. From the work of Randrup and Snyder and their colleagues (Fog, Randrup, and Pakkenberg, 1967; Randrup and Jonas, 1967; Taylor and Snyder, 1971), it may be concluded that norepinephrine is specifically involved in mediating locomotor stimulation, whereas dopamine takes part in inducing a stereotyped motor behavior characterized by bizarre posturing and compulsive gnawing.

Substantial support for the concepts of Hess and Brodie has come from sleep studies, suggesting an essential role of serotonergic neurons in the induction of sleep. Jouvet (Jouvet, 1965, 1973) showed that insomnia could be elicited in cats by inhibiting serotonin synthesis with pCPA or by destroying the serotonergic neurons in the raphe nuclei. The effects of pCPA, although not those of surgery, were reversible by the administration of 5-HTP. Destruction of the adrenergic neurons in the locus coeruleus, on the other hand, prolonged sleep and prevented the appearance of bursts of paradoxical or rapid-eye-movement (REM) sleep, phases of sleep apparently associated with increased cortical activity. This observation suggests a positive effect of adrenergic neurons on REM sleep. Other observations, however, seem to suggest the opposite effect, a contradiction which has not yet been satisfactorily explained; thus αMpT increased REM sleep in rat and man, an effect antagonized by DOPA (King and Jewett, 1971; Wyatt, Portnoy, Kupfer, Snyder, and Engelman, 1971). 6-Hydroxydopamine likewise increased REM sleep (Hartmann, Chung, Draskoczy, and Schildkraut, 1971b).

In man, tryptophan, the precursor-once-removed of serotonin, has a soporific effect (Wyatt, Engelman, Kupfer, Fram, Sjoerdsma and Snyder, 1970b; Hartmann, Chung, and Chien, 1971a; Wyatt, 1972). The effect of 5-HTP on sleep in man is more complex, for reasons to be discussed. DOPA administration in man increases sleep latency and REM latency; it reduces REM sleep and in higher doses also slow-wave sleep (Wyatt, Chase, Scott, Snyder and Engleman, 1970a, 1971).

C. The Effects of Stress

If the adrenergic neurons of the central nervous system are activated in states of emergency, one would expect increased utilization of the adrenergic transmitter as a result of stress. Severe stresses were indeed shown by numerous investigators to decrease the norepinephrine levels in the brains of various animals, whereas the levels of dopamine and serotonin remained unchanged or even increased (for data and references see Weil-Malherbe and Szara, 1971, p. 18–19).

Owing to the ambiguity inherent in the interpretation of concentration changes, the turnover rate of a neurotransmitter is a better index of neuronal activity. An increased turnover not only of norepinephrine but also of dopamine (Bliss and Ailion, 1971) has indeed been demonstrated in many kinds of stress and a decreased turnover in sedation. Stress also increases the turnover of brain serotonin despite the absence of a decrease in level (Weil-Malherbe and Szara, 1971, p. 20; Bliss, Thatcher, and Ailion, 1972). This is really not surprising since both the ergotropic and the trophotropic system will be called upon in emergencies. Stress-induced acceleration of norepinephrine turnover may be related to defensive-aggressive functions, whereas the increased turnover of brain serotonin may be related to fear, pain, and emotional arousal. The fact that the concentration of brain norepinephrine is often reduced by stress, whereas that of serotonin remains unchanged or is even increased despite a similar increase of turnover, can be explained by the slower rate of synthesis of norepinephrine than of serotonin.

According to Thierry, Blanc, and Glowinski (1971), norepinephrine is distributed between a small functional compartment and a large storage pool. During a short stress only the functional compartment was depleted, but during a longer stress the contents of both compartments were utilized at an increased rate. A short stress affected dopamine in the same way as norepinephrine, but had no effect on the utilization of serotonin. Longer stress, however, also increased serotonin release. Newly synthesized as well as freshly retrieved transmitter first passes into the functional pool and is therefore utilized in preference to the storage pool; however, even newly synthesized and newly retrieved transmitters are utilized at different rates, the newly synthesized norepinephrine having a shorter half-life than the newly retrieved norepinephrine. The accelerated turnover of norepinephrine may persist for several hours after the termination of the acute stress (Stone, 1971).

Tyrosine hydroxylase, the rate-limiting enzyme of catecholamine biosynthesis, is subject to competitive end-product inhibition by norepinephrine (Nagatsu, Levitt, and Udenfriend, 1964). An increased utilization of norepinephrine, by relieving the inhibition, would be expected to accelerate the rate of norepinephrine synthesis, a form of direct positive feedback representing an immediate response to acute stress. Another form of immediate adaptation recently described (Welch, Hendley, and Turek, 1974) results in a decreased affinity of the neuronal membrane for norepinephrine, decreasing its rate of reuptake into the neuron and thereby increasing its availability at the receptor site. In effect this form of adaptation to stress represents a decrease in the metabolism of the transmitter previously postulated by Welch and Welch (1968).

In addition to these short-term adaptation mechanisms, there are long-term adaptations involving the synthesis of new enzyme at an accelerated rate. This type of adaptation is mediated by the postsynaptic neuron in response to an increased impulse flow, a feedback mechanism whose exact mode of action still awaits elucidation. Chronic stresses in the form of exposure to cold, periods of immobilization or repeated electroconvulsive shocks led to increased activity of tyrosine hydroxylase in the adrenal medulla, the superior cervical ganglia, and the brain of rats, particularly in those parts of the brain containing adrenergic cell bodies, such as the medulla oblongata (Musacchio, Julou, Kety, and Glowinski, 1969; Thoenen, 1970; Lamprecht, Eichelman, Thoa, Williams, and Kopin, 1972). The activity of dopamine-β-hydroxylase was also found to be increased in the adrenal medulla and the serum of rats exposed to stress (Kvetňanský, Gewirtz, Weise, and Kopin, 1971; Lamprecht et al., 1972; Weinshilboum, Kvetňanský, Axelrod, and Kopin, 1971). These long-term effects were found to be prevented by inhibitors of protein synthesis and are therefore presumably due to increased synthesis of enzyme. The stresses sufficient to stimulate adrenal tyrosine hydroxylase activity may be of a very mild nature, consisting essentially of the psychosocial stimulation of life in a community. This was demonstrated by Axelrod, Mueller, Henry, and Stephens (1970) by comparing mice living in isolation with mice living in groups. For the psychiatrist it may be of interest that the activity of tyrosine hydroxylase and dopamine-β-hydroxylase in the adrenal medulla and the superior cervical ganglia could be stimulated by the largely emotional stress of separating young monkeys from their mothers (Breese, Smith, Mueller, Howard, Prange, Jun, Lipton, Young, McKinney, and Lewis, 1973).

D. Genetic Correlations

A genetically determined correlation between levels of brain transmitter amines and temperament has been established in a series of pure-bred strains of rats and mice. Strains which are aggressive, adventurous and exploratory often have a higher level of norepinephrine and/or a lower level of serotonin in some areas of the brain than strains which are fearful and timid, have low spontaneous motor activity and a high score of defecation (bibliography: Weil-Malherbe and Szara, 1971, p. 21). Despite their lower norepinephrine levels animals from timid strains have increased tyrosine hydroxylase activity in midbrain and striatum, indicating that they are under increased stress (Segal, Kuczenski, and Mandell, 1972).

E. False Transmitter Effects

Not all observations are in accordance with the concepts of Hess and Brodie. Those which at first sight seem discordant usually relate to experiments that resulted in a flooding of autonomic centers with high doses of transmitter amines. Such conditions are obtained when the amines are injected peripherally in an animal without a fully functional blood-brain barrier, such as the immature chick, when relatively high doses of DOPA or 5-HTP are administered peripherally, or when the amines are injected directly into the brain or the rachidial spaces. In these cases DOPA or the catecholamines may elicit sedative and soporific effects, whereas 5-HTP or serotonin may produce excitation.

That these paradoxic effects often are dose-related is shown by a series of observations. Thus intraventricular or intrathecal injection of small doses of norepinephrine increased motor activity or avoidance responses, whereas larger amounts produced sedation, immobility, somnolence, flaccidity, and stupor (Maas and Landis, 1965; Herman, 1970; Segal and Mandell, 1970; Malec and Kleinrok, 1972). 5-HTP, which in small doses produced sedation and drowsiness, produced agitation and rage in large doses (Bogdanski, Weissbach, and Udenfriend, 1958).

When stereotactically aimed microinjections of neurotransmitters are made into discrete areas of the brain, the behavioral results often depend critically on the site of injection. In some areas norepinephrine elicits hyperactivity and arousal, in others sedation and sleep. Destruction of some adrenergic neurons may lead to anorexia, of others to hyperphagia (Smith, Strohmayer, and Reis, 1972; Ahlskog and Hoebel, 1973; for a fuller discussion and references see Weil-Malherbe and Szara, 1971, p. 29–33).

The peripheral effects of catecholamines are assumed to be mediated by two different types of receptors, designated α and β, whose effects are often antagonistic. If similar classes of receptors exist centrally, some disparities might be explained. Norepinephrine, which preferentially reacts with α-receptors, at much higher levels also activates β-receptors. Thus some of the paradoxic effects may be accounted for by the fact that receptors are activated at sites not normally reached by the endogenous transmitter or only reached in subthreshold concentrations.

The principal reason for the paradoxic effects of neurotransmitters, however, is the existence of a relatively unspecific uptake mechanism in the tissues. Iversen (1963, 1965), working with the isolated perfused rat heart, showed that the uptake of norepinephrine consists of two components, uptake$_1$ and uptake$_2$. Uptake$_1$ operates at low catecholamine concentrations, has high affinity, and is highly specific and stereospecific. The amines accumulated are firmly bound. At high concentrations uptake$_2$ becomes prominent; it has a relatively low affinity and specificity. The amines taken up are partly in extraneuronal sites and are loosely bound. Both uptake$_1$ and uptake$_2$ are saturable processes obeying Michaelis-Menten kinetics. The distinction between uptake$_1$ and uptake$_2$ also holds for the brain (Snyder and Coyle, 1969).

Whether or not it is caused by the operation of uptake$_2$, it has been amply demonstrated that the administration of high doses of 5-HTP, *in vitro* or *in vivo,* may lead to the appearance of serotonin in dopaminergic and adrenergic neurons and to the depletion of dopamine and norepinephrine (Lichtensteiger, Mutzner, and Langemann, 1967; Moir and Eccleston, 1968; Feer and Wirz-Justice, 1971; Fuxe, Butcher, and Engel, 1971; Butcher, Engel, and Fuxe, 1972; Ng, Chase, Colburn, and Kopin, 1972), whereas administration of DOPA may result in the appearance of dopamine in serotonergic neurons and to displacement of serotonin (Constantinidis, Bartholini, Geissbühler, and Tissot, 1970; Butcher et al., 1972). Much of the fluorescent material produced in the formaldehyde condensation technique was located extraneuronally. Moreover, there is evidence that dopamine may be taken up by adrenergic neurons (Musacchio, Fischer, and Kopin, 1966) and norepinephrine by dopaminergic neurons (Fuxe, Hamberger, and Malmfors, 1967).

The process by which an endogenous transmitter is displaced by an exogenous amine has become known as the false transmitter effect. Initially displacement of the endogenous transmitter results in the intensification of the normal effects produced by the transmitter owing to its massive discharge. This phase is probably responsible for the paradoxic results of the transmitter amines and their precursors. It may be followed by a second phase in which the false transmitter assumes the role of the endogenous transmitter, albeit less successfully. It is feasible that dopamine may act as a false transmitter for norepinephrine and vice versa, but there is no reason to assume that an adrenergic or dopaminergic receptor would respond to the release of serotonin.

III. BRAIN MONOAMINES AND AFFECTIVE DISORDERS

The mounting evidence pointing to a connection between the function of brain neurotransmitter amines and affective disorders has led to the formulation of the monoamine hypothesis of affective disorders. It postulates a deficiency in the activity of biogenic amines in states of depression and a hyperactivity in states of mania. Such changes may be absolute or relative. In a state of absolute deficiency or absolute excess, the amount of transmitter available at the receptor site would be decreased or increased; in a state of relative deficiency or excess, the amount of transmitter available at the receptor site would be normal but the number or accessibility of receptor sites, the sensitivity of the receptor itself or the activity of synergistic or antagonistic systems would be altered. Changes in the availability of the transmitter could have many reasons. It might be because of changes in the activity or quantity of synthesizing or metabolizing enzymes or changes in the function of the storage, release, and uptake mechanisms. Changes in receptor sensitivity could involve changes in molecular configuration or changes in the function or availability of electrolytes and other cofactors. There is no doubt that such changes do occur as shown by the phenomenon of denervation supersensitivity, but little is known about the underlying mechanisms.

The question is still debated whether the principal agent postulated by the monoamine hypothesis is a catecholamine, an indoleamine, or a combination of both. All these points of view have had their protagonists.

A. Psychologic and Behavioral Evidence

Evidence in support of the monoamine hypothesis of affective disorders is of a psychologic, behavioral, pharmacologic, and clinical nature. From the psychologic and behavioral point of view, the correlation of adrenergic activity with vigilance, motor activity, and arousal, and of adrenergic deficiency with sedation, apathy, and inertia would fit into the symptomatology of mania on the one hand and of depression on the other. Also some features associated with a hyperactivity of the serotonergic system, i.e., emotional arousal, confusion, disoriented excitement, and inappropriate agitated behavior, could account for aspects of the manic syndrome, whereas a deficiency of serotonergic activity could be responsible for the restlessness, irritability, aimless agitation and insomnia frequently encountered in depression. The concept of an association of depression with hypoactivity and of mania with hyperactivity of one or the other or both monoaminergic systems presupposes an antithetic model of affective disease in which the mood is swinging from one opposite to the other, passing through a phase of normothymia with each change of phase. This concept, which is also implicit in the terminology of unipolar and bipolar illness, has been challenged by Court (1968, 1972) in whose view normothymia, depression, and mania lie on a continuum, with mania being an aggravation of depression. Most clinicians would agree that the antithetic model accounts in a more satisfactory manner for most clinical observations than the continuum model, at any rate as far as mood is concerned. There may be dimensions of sickness other than mood to which the continuum model can be applied. Bunney, Goodwin, and Murphy, (1972b) have suggested a two-layer model of bipolar affective disorder in which a dysfunction common to both phases underlies an antithetic layer of mood swings. The underlying dysfunction may be responsible for the persistence of depressive symptoms in some cases of mania. Reasoning along similar lines, Kety (1971) has suggested that the mood swings in affective disease are related to changes in brain catecholamines, depression being associated with a deficiency and mania with an excess, whereas mood lability is related to changes in brain serotonin: an increased activity of brain serotonergic neurons would stabilize the tendency to mood swings or damp their amplitude.

B. Pharmacologic Evidence

It was a series of clinical and pharmacologic observations that set into motion the revolution in our concepts of affective disorders. The impact of three groups of drugs, reserpine, the inhibitors of MAO, and the tricyclic antidepressants, were of particular consequence in this process. It gradually became apparent that drugs that depleted the brain monoamines or antagonized their effects were prone to precipitate a depressive reaction, whereas drugs that increased the concentration or the efficacy of brain monoamines had antidepressant effects.

1. Depleting Drugs

Reserpine, which depletes the stores of biogenic amines and was at one time widely used as a tranquilizing and hypotensive drug, was found to lead to depression in about 20% of cases. In 6% of cases the depression was severe enough to require hospitalization. The lag period between the start of treatment and the onset of the depressive reaction varied from 2 weeks to 1 year or more, with an average of about 5 months (Goodwin and Bunney, 1971). Another widely used antihypertensive drug, α-methyldopa, owes its antiadrenergic activity to its conversion into false transmitters; it too can lead to a depressive reaction in a significant number of cases (Bunney and Davis, 1965).

Propranolol, a drug producing blockade of the β-adrenergic receptors, has been reported to cause depression and suicide (Waal, 1967). In large doses it has been used for the apparently successful treatment of mania (Atsmon, Blum, Wijsenbeek, Maoz, Steiner, and Ziegelman, 1970).

αMpT, an inhibitor of tyrosine hydroxylase, produced sedation and sometimes a state of anxiety to the point of agitated depression when used for the treatment of patients with pheochromocytoma (Engelman, Horwitz, Jéquier, and Sjoerdsma, 1968). The drug produced an improvement in the manic state of five out of seven patients and in some cases precipitated a switch from mania to depression. Two manic patients showed an aggravation of symptoms after taking αMpT. When administered to depressed patients αMpT produced aggravation of symptoms in four out of six cases (Bunney, Gershon, Murphy, and Goodwin, 1972a; Bunney, Goodwin, Murphy, House, and Gordon, 1972c).

2. Antidepressants

The first to be used among the antidepressant drugs were the inhibitors of MAO, which raise the levels of both serotonin and catecholamines. They are now largely superseded by the tricyclic antidepressants, which act by inhibiting the neuronal membrane pump responsible for the high-affinity uptake of extraneuronal biogenic amines. Physiologically this uptake process is the foremost mechanism for terminating the activity of the neurotransmitter discharged into the synaptic gap. If the reuptake is delayed, receptor stimulation will be prolonged. The end result, therefore, is the same as that of the inhibition of intraneural MAO, which presumably leads to an overspill of free cytoplasmic transmitter.

That the action of the tricyclics is indirect rather than direct is shown by the fact that it is prevented by a preliminary depletion of monoamines, by the inhibition of their synthesis, or by receptor blockade (Weil-Malherbe and Szara, 1971, p. 59). Interesting differences have emerged in the activity of tricyclic antidepressants toward norepinephrine, dopamine, and serotonin. Secondary amines having the formula,

$$R_1-N\begin{array}{c} R_2 \\ \diagdown \\ H \end{array}$$

such as desipramine, nortriptyline, or protriptyline, have little or no effect on serotonergic or dopaminergic nerve endings, but strongly inhibit the uptake of norepinephrine in adrenergic neurons. Tertiary amines, on the other hand, which carry the group,

notably imipramine and chlorimipramine, act on both adrenergic and serotonergic terminals but are more efficient in blocking the uptake of serotonin (Carlsson, Fuxe, and Ungerstedt, 1968; Fuxe and Ungerstedt, 1968). The increased stimulation of serotonin receptors elicited by tertiary tricyclics leads by negative feedback to a reduced firing rate of the serotonergic raphe neurons (Sheard, Zolovick, and Aghajanian, 1972), a reduced impulse flow (Modigh, 1973), and a reduced turnover of serotonin in the brain (Corrodi and Fuxe, 1969; Meek and Werdinius, 1970; Schubert, Nybäck, and Sedvall, 1970). The turnover of norepinephrine in the brain of rats treated with imipramine or protriptyline was depressed by acute treatment but became accelerated during chronic treatment (Schildkraut, Winokur, Draskóczy, and Hensle, 1971).

Since MAO is a purely intracellular mitochrondrial enzyme, the tricyclic antidepressants, by inhibiting the uptake of norepinephrine also prevent its deamination and at the same time stimulate the activity of catechol-*O*-methyltransferase (COMT), an enzyme acting on extracellular catechol compounds. These agents therefore cause an increase in the formation and excretion of normetanephrine and a decrease in the formation and excretion of deaminated norepinephrine metabolites, *in vitro* and *in vivo* (Schildkraut, Klerman, Hammond, and Friend, 1964; Schildkraut, Gordon, and Durell, 1965; Schildkraut, Dodge, and Logue, 1969*a;* Schildkraut, Schanberg, Breese, and Kopin, 1969*c;* Schildkraut, Draskóczy, Gershon, Reich, and Grab, 1972). Similarly the metabolism of dopamine in rabbit brain slices was changed in the presence of protriptyline in such a way that more methoxytyramine was formed, at the expense of 3,4-dihydroxyphenylacetic acid (DOPAC) and homovanillic acid (HVA) (Jonason and Rutledge, 1968).

According to their pharmacologic action, Carlsson, Corrodi, Fuxe, and Hökfelt (1969) suggested specific indications for different groups of tricyclic antidepressants. The secondary amines, being essentially adrenergic stimulators, should be useful in increasing psychomotor activity and drive; the tertiary amines are more efficient in blocking serotonin uptake and should elicit a brightening of the mood; a third component present for instance in amitriptyline has effects similar to those of phenothiazines and should be useful for the relief of anxiety. However, attempts to verify these predictions clinically were inconclusive (Shaw, Johnson, and MacSweeney, 1972).

In labile bipolar patients, treatment with tricyclic antidepressants may precipitate a manic reaction. Especially potent in this respect are combinations of tricyclics with DOPA or with reserpine (Pöldinger, 1963; Haškoveć and Ryšánek, 1967). Prange, Wilson, Rabon, and Lipton (1969) and Prange, Wilson, Knox, McClane, and Lipton (1970) reported that the therapeutic effect of imipramine was potentiated by the simultaneous administration of thyroid hormones or thyrotropic hormone; they suggested that thyroxine enhances the sensitivity of adrenergic receptors.

Actions on the membrane pump very similar to those of the tricyclics are shown by other drugs, e.g., cocaine and amphetamine, both of which have a well-known euphoriant effect. However, their mechanism of action is more complex and their therapeutic application in depression is limited for obvious reasons.

3. The Treatment of Depression with Precursor Amino Acids

a. *DOPA*. For a number of reasons, DOPA is not the sovereign antidote to depression as one might have expected on the basis of the norepinephrine hypothesis. This is partly due to its unstable nature, rapid metabolism and relatively slow passage into the brain. Experience with the DOPA therapy of Parkinson's disease has taught us that dosages can be much higher than those formerly used, namely up to 5 or even 10 g/day, and that these high dosages have to be built up gradually. Doses can be greatly reduced and, at the same time, undesirable peripheral side effects eliminated, if DOPA is combined with a decarboxylase inhibitor whose action is confined to the periphery.

Upon the administration of L-DOPA to experimental animals the brain is flooded with dopamine whose concentration may rise by a factor of five to 10 (Weil-Malherbe and Bone, 1959; Everett and Borcherding, 1970). On the other hand, there is no increase in the level of brain norepinephrine; the level of brain serotonin is greatly reduced, no doubt owing to the false transmitter effect of dopamine on both adrenergic and serotonergic neurons (Corrodi and Fuxe, 1967; Bartholini, Da Prada, and Pletscher, 1968). The urinary excretion pattern of patients under DOPA treatment also indicates that little if any DOPA is converted to norepinephrine, since there is no increase in the excretion of norepinephrine metabolites (Calne, Karoum, Ruthven, and Sandler, 1969; O'Gorman, Borud, Khan, and Gjessing, 1970).

The complexity of the central effects of DOPA is reflected in the bewildering variety of its mental effects observed in parkinsonian patients undergoing DOPA treatment. According to Goodwin (1971) confusion and delirium was encountered in 4.4% of cases, depression in 4.2%, overactivity, restlessness, and agitation in 3.6%, paranoid psychosis and delusional ideas in 3.6%, hypomania in 1.5%, and hypersexuality in 0.9%. Severe insomnia is also a frequent complaint. In about 70% of schizophrenics receiving relatively small doses of L-DOPA a marked deterioration was observed (Sathananthan, Angrist, and Gershon, 1973). On the positive side, several authors (Jenkins and Groh, 1970; Meier and Martin, 1970; Loranger, Goodell, McDowell, Lee, and Sweet, 1973) noticed a sometimes transient intellectual improvement in Parkinsonian patients.

In the light of these observations it will be appreciated that the results of DOPA treatment in depression are contradictory and unpredictable. Although there are undoubtedly patients who respond to DOPA with dramatic improvement (Ingvarsson, 1965; Bunney, Janowsky, Goodwin, Davis, Brodie, Murphy, and Case, 1969; Persson and Wålinder, 1971), such cases are the exception. Bunny et al. (1972a) reported that only five out of 13 unipolar depressive patients improved under DOPA treatment; all of them were severely retarded. Eight out of 10 bipolar depressed patients treated with L-DOPA became hypomanic for brief periods, but some of their depressive symptoms were not reversed and coexisted with hypomanic symptoms. Discontinuation of the treatment was followed by a disappearance of hypomanic and a reappearance of depressive symptoms. Pohlmeier (1969) concluded, probably with reference to unipolar depressed patients, that L-DOPA treatment was useful for stimulating motor activity and drive, but had no direct effect on depressive mood.

b. *5-HTP.* Good results in the treatment of depression have also been claimed for 5-HTP, the immediate precursor of serotonin. Kline and Sacks (1963) injected a single small dose (25 to 50 mg) of DL-5-HTP in combination with a MAO inhibitor in a series of 20 depressed patients and reported definite or marked improvement in 18. When the experiment was repeated under double-blind conditions, only 25 to 30% of the patients showed some improvement (Kline, Sacks, and Simpson, 1964). Persson and Roos (1967) reported the successful treatment of a case, refractory to other therapies, with five injections (one per day) of 30 mg of 5-HTP. van Praag, Korf, Dols, and Schut (1972) treated five patients suffering from severe endogenous (presumably unipolar) depression with up to 3 g of DL-5-HTP by mouth, daily for 3 weeks; three patients improved and two of them relapsed when 5-HTP was replaced by a placebo. More recently Sano (1972) treated a series of bipolar depressed patients with daily doses of 50 to 300 mg of the natural isomer, L-5-HTP, by mouth. He claims to have obtained dramatic improvements in about 90% of over 100 cases, sometimes within 1 week. However, Brodie, Sack, and Siever (1973), who also used the L-form of 5-HTP but gave much larger doses (up to 3 g/day, or, when combined with a decarboxylase inhibitor, 500 mg/day) found no improvement in seven depressed (presumably unipolar) patients, all of whom were refractory to conventional treatments. Their study therefore does not replicate Sano's and does not refute his results. Combinations of L-5-HTP with inhibitors of peripheral decarboxylase, an inhibitor of MAO, or both have also been used in therapy of depression with favorable results in some cases (Matussek, Angst, Benkert, Gmür, Papousek, Rüther, and Woggon, 1974; van Praag, van den Burg, Bos, and Dols, 1974).

c. *Tryptophan.* The usefulness of L-tryptophan, the precursor of 5-HTP and therefore also of serotonin, in the treatment of depression is controversial. Coppen, Shaw, Herzberg, and Maggs (1967) found that L-tryptophan in large doses (about 9 g/day) was as effective as electroshock therapy and that its effect was only slightly increased by the addition of a MAO inhibitor. The efficacy of tryptophan was confirmed in double-blind studies (Glassman and Platman, 1969; Coppen, Noguera, and Shaw, 1970). On the other hand, Carroll, Mowbray, and Davies (1970) and Murphy, Baker, Kotin, and Bunney (1973) failed to convince themselves of any antidepressant activity of tryptophan. It may be significant that these trials were conducted mainly on unipolar depressed patients, although this is not always made explicit. Prange, Sisk, Wilson, Morris, Hall, and Carman (1973) reported the unexpected observation that L-tryptophan had a tranquilizing effect in manic patients, superior to that of chlorpromazine. The antimanic effect of L-tryptophan was confirmed by Murphy, Baker, Goodwin, Miller, Kotin, and Bunney (1974); they further reported the interesting observation that tryptophan had an antidepressant effect in bipolar patients but was without action in cases of unipolar depression.

A significant therapeutic effect of tryptophan in affective disorders or in a defined subgroup would not only be of practical but even more of theoretical interest. It is well known that the level of brain serotonin is reduced when the diet is deficient in tryptophan (Zbinden, Pletscher, and Studer, 1958; Fernstrom and Wurtman, 1971) and raised when the dietary intake of tryptophan is increased (Wang, Harwalker, and Waisman, 1962; Quay, 1963). This is due to the fact that the affinity of tryptophan hydroxylase (K_m in the presence of the natural cofactor is about 50 μM, Renson, 1973) is of the same order of magnitude as the concentration of tryptophan in the brain (23 μM in the raphe nuclei of rat brain, Deguchi, Sinha, and Barchas, 1973). Since saturation of the enzyme requires a tryptophan concentration of about 90 μM (Renson, 1973), raising the brain tryptophan level results in an increased activity of brain tryptophan hydroxylase. Moreover, since tryptophan hydroxylase only occurs in serotonergic neurons, serotonin newly formed from administered tryptophan only appears in serotonergic neurons (Aghajanian and Asher, 1971). In marked contrast to 5-HTP, tryptophan feeding does not lead to a false transmitter effect because of the unspecific accumulation of serotonin. Tryptophan might therefore provide a more specific repair of a serotonin deficiency than 5-HTP.

4. The Mechanism of Action of Lithium Treatment

The antidepressant activities of the tricyclic drugs were not predicted by the monoamine hypothesis and at first seemed to have no bearing on it. Subsequently, however, the hypothesis proved essential for the formulation of the mechanism of action of these drugs. The same development is now occurring with regard to the therapeutic effects of lithium. The mechanism of action, which is now emerging, suggests an effect of lithium on the neuronal membrane that is the direct opposite of the effect of the tricyclics, namely an apparent stimulation of transmitter uptake or an inhibition of transmitter release. This conclusion is based on the following pieces of evidence:

Colburn, Goodwin, Bunney, and Davis (1967) found that synaptosomes isolated from the brains of lithium-treated rats accumulated norepinephrine *in vitro* at a 30% faster rate than control rats; the addition of lithium *in vitro* was without effect. Similar although smaller effects were observed by Baldessarini and Yorke (1970). Working with synaptosomes isolated from mouse brain, Kuriyama and Speken (1970) obtained results comparable to those of Colburn et al. The uptake of serotonin was not accelerated. Using blood platelets *in vitro* as a model of the neuronal uptake pump, Murphy, Colburn, Davis, and Bunney (1970) studied the uptake of serotonin or metaraminol by platelets from patients with affective disorders who were being treated either with imipramine or with lithium carbonate. Treatment with imipramine led to a decrease in the initial rate of uptake of both amines whereas treatment with lithium increased it. Again the addition of lithium *in vitro* had no effect.

Katz, Chase, and Kopin (1968) exposed slices from the corpus striatum of the rat to electrical pulses, thereby increasing the efflux of norepinephrine and serotonin. When the slices were prepared from rats previously treated with lithium chloride or when lithium was added *in vitro,* the stimulation-induced release of both amines, although not their rate of spontaneous efflux, was markedly inhibited. The apparent inhibition of release may have been due to an increased speed of retrieval.

Addition of lithium salt to the perfusion fluid reduced the output of norepinephrine from the isolated, perfused cat spleen upon stimulation of the splenic nerve (Bindler, Wallach, and Gershon, 1971).

If treatment with tricyclics decreased transmitter turnover (at least in acute experiments) and decreased the formation of deaminated metabolites, treatment with lithium had precisely the opposite effects. A lithium-induced increase of transmitter turnover (Corrodi, Fuxe, Hökfelt, and Schou, 1967; Schildkraut, Logue, and Dodge, 1969b; Stern, Fieve, Neff, and Costa, 1969; Greenspan, Aronoff, and Bogdanski, 1970a; Sheard and Aghajanian, 1970; Perez-Cruet, Tagliamonte, Tagliamonte, and Gessa, 1971) and a lithium-induced increase of deamination (Schildkraut, Schanberg, and Kopin, 1966; Schildkraut et al., 1969b; Schanberg, Schildkraut, and Kopin, 1967; Haškoveć and Ryšánek, 1969; Greenspan, Schildkraut, Gordon, Baer, Aronoff, and Durrell, 1970b) are effects to be expected from the decreased availability of discharged transmitter and the correspondingly enhanced intracellular accumulation.

Along with its stimulating effect on serotonin uptake, lithium also accelerates the uptake of tryptophan by synaptosomes (Knapp and Mandell, 1973) and consequently increases the levels of brain tryptophan (Perez-Cruet et al., 1971; Schubert, 1973).

Studies on the effects of chronic lithium treatment in man and animals revealed antiadrenergic as well as antiserotonergic features. Greenspan et al. (1970a) noted that rats became sedated, somnolent, and hypoactive. In mice and rats aggressivity diminished (Weischer, 1969; Sheard, 1970). In man lithium decreased the pressor effect of infused norepinephrine, but did not affect the response to infused tyramine. This was interpreted to indicate an accelerated uptake of norepinephrine without effect on tyramine uptake (Fann, Davis, Janowsky, Cavanaugh, Kaufmann, Griffith, and Oates, 1972). According to Schildkraut (1974), prolonged lithium treatment led to a gradual decrease in the excretion of norepinephrine and its metabolites in one manic patient. Dopamine excretion, which Messiha, Savage, Turek, and Hanlon (1974) found to be increased in eight out of 10 manic patients, was reduced to normal levels with lithium treatment. Whereas these effects are referable to antiadrenergic activity, an effect described by Harrison-Read and Steinberg (1971) suggests an antiserotonergic action; rats developed a hypersensitivity to foot shock after 2 weeks of treatment with lithium chloride, an effect which was prevented by injection of 5-HTP.

Further aspects of the effects of lithium will be discussed in the sections on cyclic AMP and electrolyte metabolism.

5. The Effect of Rubidium Salts in Depression

The effects of another alkali metal ion, rubidium, seem to be the reverse of those of lithium and akin to those of antidepressants. Rubidium salts facilitate the release of brain norepinephrine (Stolk, Nowack, Barchas, and Platman, 1970) and increase motor activity, aggressivity, and EEG activation in monkeys (Meltzer, Taylor, Platman, and Fieve, 1969). Mice injected with morphine showed intense stereotyped hyperactivity; lithium treatment inhibited this effect, whereas rubidium, DOPA, and 5-HTP administration enhanced it (Carroll and Sharp, 1971).

A preliminary clinical study of rubidium salts was conducted by Fieve et al. (1973a). A favorable response was noted in two out of five depressed patients.

C. Clinical Evidence: Amines and Their Metabolites in Tissues and Body Fluids

1. Changes in Brain Tissue

The most direct approach to the study of brain neurotransmitter amines is their determination in the affected brain itself. It has been chosen by several groups who compared brains from depressed patients dying by suicide with the brains of victims of sudden death from other causes. Such a comparison is beset by a large number of uncontrollable variables liable to influence the levels of brain transmitter amines. Besides age and sex there are such factors as the nutritional state of the subject, not only at the time of death but also during the days and weeks preceding it, the possible use of drugs immediately before death or during periods preceding death, the duration of premortal stress (even suicides may linger on for days) and postmortal changes during the time elapsed between death and analysis which in one study (Bourne, Bunney, Colburn, Davis, Davis, Shaw, and Coppen, 1968) averaged 6 months. Even the time of day at which death occurred may be of importance in view of the marked diurnal variation in the concentration of brain transmitter amines. The finding of a first group of investigators (Shaw, Camps, and Eccleston, 1967) of a lower serotonin content in the brainstem of depressed suicides than in the controls was not confirmed in a subsequent study by Bourne et al. (1968), who instead found a lower level of 5-hydroxyindoleacetic acid (5-HIAA) in the brains of suicides than in those of controls. A third group (Pare, Yeung, Price, and Stacey, 1969) found no differences in 5-HIAA levels between suicide and control brains, but confirmed the difference in serotonin levels. This, however, disappeared when cases were matched for age and was therefore probably an effect of age. More recently, Lloyd, Farley, Deck, and Hornykiewicz (1974) compared the brains of five suicides (three of them due to drug overdose) with five cases of sudden death from cardiovascular causes. Whether caused by drugs or not, there was a significant decrease of serotonin in the brains of suicides in two out of six raphe nuclei. Grote, Moses, Robins, Hudgens, and Croninger (1974) studied enzymes involved in catecholamine metabolism in the brains of suicides but found no differences from the controls.

2. Changes in Cerebrospinal Fluid

For insight into the metabolism of the central nervous system, the next best thing to the brain itself is the cerebrospinal fluid (CSF). Largely for methodologic reasons the studies on CSF have focused on three substances: HVA, a metabolite of dopamine; 3-methoxy-4-hydroxyphenylglycol (MHPG), a metabolite of norepinephrine; and 5-HIAA, a metabolite of serotonin (Fig. 1).

It is generally assumed that the concentrations of these metabolites in the CSF reflect the metabolism of their amine precursors in the brain and this is to some extent borne out by the fact that procedures that increase or decrease the synthesis of the transmitters in the brain have similar effects on the metabolites in CSF. Thus, αMpT, the inhibitor of tyrosine hydroxylase, reduced the concentration of HVA in CSF by over 40% (Brodie, Murphy, Goodwin, and Bunney, 1971; Bunney, Brodie, Murphy, and Goodwin, 1971). The level of MHPG in CSF was reduced by inhibitors of tyrosine hydroxylase as well as by those of dopamine-β-hydroxylase (Chase, Gordon, and Ng, 1973). The administration of L-DOPA or of a combination of L-DOPA with a peripheral decarboxylase inhibitor led to an increase of the

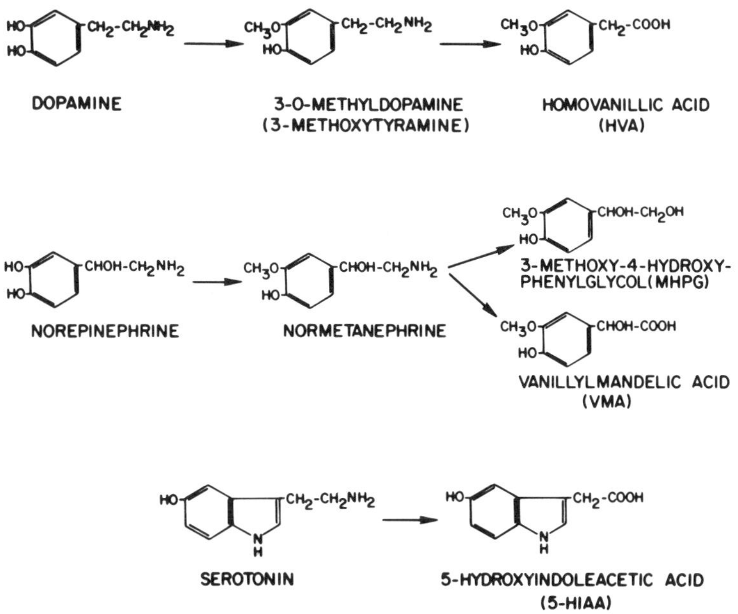

FIG. 1. The three neurotransmitters, dopamine, norepinephrine, and serotonin, and their principal metabolites (abbreviated).

level of HVA in CSF (Bunney et al., 1972a). The level of 5-HIAA was reduced in the cisternal CSF of rats 10 to 14 days after lesioning of the raphe nuclei (Cohen and Bowers, 1972). The oral administration of tryptophan in man was followed by an increase of the 5-HIAA level in lumbar CSF (Dunner and Goodwin, 1972; Ashcroft et al., 1973; Murphy et al., 1973a and b) whereas injection of 5-HTP had the same effect in experiments on dogs (Andersson and Roos, 1968; Ashcroft, Blackburn, Eccleston, Glen, Hartley, Kinloch, Lonergan, Murray, and Pullar, 1973a; Ashcroft, Crawford, Cundall, Davidson, Dobson, Dow, Eccleston, Loose, and Pullar, 1973b).

The passage of HVA and 5-HIAA from CSF into the blood is mediated by an active transport system that is inhibited by probenecid. Probenecid has frequently been used, alone or in combination with a precursor such as tryptophan, to measure the rate of formation of the acid metabolites of dopamine and serotonin. The elimination of MHPG does not seem to be affected by probenecid.

The concentration of metabolites in the CSF is highest in ventricular fluid, lowest in lumbar fluid, and intermediate in cisternal fluid (Moir, Ashcroft, Crawford, Eccleston, and Guldberg, 1970). The concentration of 5-HIAA in lumbar fluid is increased by mild exercise, presumably due to increased mixing of lumbar fluid with fluid from more rostral portions of the rachidial space (Fotherby, Ashcroft, Affleck, and Forrest, 1963). Post, Gordon, Goodwin, and Bunney (1973a) persuaded moderately depressed patients to simulate manic hyperactivity for 4 hr before lumbar puncture and found CSF levels of 5-HIAA and HVA to be correlated with the degree of motor activity.

Another factor to be considered is age. According to Bowers and Gerbode (1968) the age group over 55 had higher CSF levels of both 5-HIAA and HVA than younger people. The middle-aged group between 35 and 55 had lower levels of 5-HIAA than either younger or older age groups.

In order to obtain valid results, therefore, subjects have to be matched with regard to diet, motor activity, and age. A fourth desideratum, that of a truly normal control group, is usually not realizable; neurologic or schizophrenic patients are often used as controls.

Not surprisingly in view of the factors discussed the observations on record are by no means unanimous.

a. *MHPG*. MHPG levels in depressed patients were found to be decreased (Gordon and Oliver, 1971; Post, Kotin, Goodwin, and Gordon, 1973b) or unchanged (Wilk, Shopsin, Gershon, and Suhl, 1972; Shaw, O'Keefe, MacSweeney, Brooksbank, Noguera, and Coppen, 1973). In mania levels were increased and returned to normal after lithium treatment according to Wilk et al. (1972).

b. *HVA*. In mania HVA levels may be increased (Sjöström and Roos, 1972) or unchanged (Mendels, Frazer, Fitzgerald, Ramsey, and Stokes, 1972; Ashcroft et al., 1973a). Ashcroft et al. (1973a) noted a drop below normal levels upon recovery from mania. Most authors agree that HVA levels tend to be decreased in cases of depression (Roos and Sjöström, 1969; Nordin, Ottosson, and Roos, 1971; Papeschi and McClure, 1971; Mendels et al., 1972; Ashcroft et al., 1973a). Ashcroft et al. (1973a) found decreases mainly in cases of unipolar depression; depressed bipolar patients had normal values. The reduced levels found in unipolar depression did not return to the norm upon recovery. Depressed patients responded to the administration of probenecid with a smaller rise of the HVA level than controls (Roos and Sjöström, 1969; van Praag and Korf, 1971b; Goodwin, Post, Dunner, and Gordon, 1973; Sjöström, 1973). By and large therefore the changes in the concentrations of the catecholamine metabolites MHPG and HVA if significant conform to those expected from the monoamine hypothesis of affective disorders, i.e., a decrease in depression and an increase in mania.

c. *5-HIAA*. Investigators are about evenly divided between those who found no change of 5-HIAA levels in the CSF in either mania or depression (Papeschi and McClure, 1971; Sjöström and Roos, 1972; Wilk et al., 1972) and those who found decreases in either mania or depression or both (Ashcroft, Crawford, Eccleston, Sharman, MacDougall, Stanton, and Binns, 1966; Dencker, Molm, Roos, and Werdinius, 1966; van Praag and Korf, 1971a; Mendels et al., 1972; Coppen, Prange, Whybrow, and Noguera,

1972c). Ashcroft et al. (1973a) found no change in bipolar depression but a decrease in unipolar depression, similar to what they found for HVA. Whenever values were decreased in mania or depression, they failed to return to the normal range after recovery, except in some cases of mania that had been treated with lithium (Mendels, 1971; Wilk et al., 1972). The response of 5-HIAA levels to probenecid was usually found to be reduced in depression as well as in mania (van Praag and Korf, 1971a; Sjöström and Roos, 1972), and this effect was more marked in bipolar than in unipolar depression (van Praag, Korf, and Schut, 1973).

According to Coppen, Brooksbank, and Peet (1972a), the concentration of tryptophan is also significantly diminished in the CSF of both manic and depressed patients although, in contrast to the findings with regard to 5-HIAA, the tryptophan level was restored to normal upon recovery. The question arises whether the lowering of the 5-HIAA levels is due to a deficiency in the supply or metabolism of tryptophan. As already mentioned administration of tryptophan raises the content of 5-HIAA in CSF (Dunner and Goodwin, 1972). Bowers (1970) noticed that this reaction was inadequate in some depressed patients and suggested an inhibition of serotonin synthesis in these cases. However, Ashcroft et al. (1973b) found no differences between unipolar depressed patients, bipolar depressed patients, and neurologic patients in their capacity to convert orally administered tryptophan to 5-HIAA in CSF and concluded that the low level of 5-HIAA in the CSF of depressed patients was not caused by a reduced tryptophan hydroxylase activity but rather by a low level of activity in the serotonergic neurons. In keeping with this suggestion, Dunner and Goodwin (1972) observed no clinical improvement in depressed patients when their CSF concentration of 5-HIAA was raised by tryptophan administration.

Van Praag et al. (1972) reported that depressed patients who subsequently proved responsive to treatment with 5-HTP reacted to probenecid with a smaller increment of 5-HIAA in CSF than patients who did not improve under 5-HTP treatment. In their opinion the probenecid test is useful for screening out suitable candidates for 5-HTP treatment.

It should be mentioned that a decrease in the CSF level of 5-HIAA is not specific for affective disorders but also occurs for instance in Parkinsonism (Guldberg, Turner, Hanieh, Ashcroft, Crawford, Perry, and Gillingham, 1967; Johansson and Roos, 1967), LSD-psychosis (Bowers, 1972), and schizophrenia (Fotherby et al., 1963; Bowers, Heninger, and Gerbode, 1969).

3. Changes in Blood

a. *Catecholamine levels in plasma.* Using a highly specific and sensitive double-label isotope dilution method, Wyatt et al. (1971) estimated the resting concentration of epinephrine and norepinephrine in the plasma of depressed patients and found it to be elevated. However, 10 of their 13 patients were diagnosed as neurotic depressions; two patients with endogenous depression had approximately normal values and one bipolar depressed patient with an elevated value was very agitated. The elevation of the catecholamine levels in this study might therefore have been the result of anxiety or motor activity.

b. *Estimation of enzyme activities.* Several enzymes involved in mono-amine metabolism occur in the blood and are measured on the assumption that changes of their activities reflect more generalized changes. No difference from the normal range and no correlation to diagnosis or mood was found in the activity of serum dopamine-β-hydroxylase (Shopsin, Freedman, Goldstein, and Gershon, 1972). When, however, the activity of this enzyme was gauged by infusing [^{3}H]dopamine and measuring the appearance of labeled norepinephrine metabolites in the saliva, norepinephrine synthesis was found to be increased in bipolar patients during their manic, but not during their depressed phase (Rosenblatt, Leighton, and Chanley, 1973).

Murphy and Weiss (1972) determined the activity of MAO in blood platelets and found it to be reduced in bipolar depressed patients but normal in unipolar depressed patients. The bipolar patients also excreted more tryptamine than the unipolar patients, which meant that the inhibition of MAO was not confined to blood platelets only. The mean age was about the same in the groups of patients and controls, an important point since MAO activity levels are known to increase with age (Novick, 1961; Robinson, Davis, Nies, Ravaris, and Sylwester, 1971). In fact it has been suggested that the increase of MAO activity with age might be a predisposing factor for involutional depression (Robinson et al., 1971). In contrast to the results of Murphy and Weiss (1972) Nies, Robinson, Ravaris, and Davis (1971) found the mean platelet MAO activity to be significantly higher in depressed patients than in control subjects of comparable age.

The enzyme COMT occurs in red blood cells. Its activity was found to be reduced in the red blood cells of women suffering from depression and more so in unipolar- than in bipolar-depressed women. No change was found in the erythrocytes of depressed men (Dunner, Cohn, Gershon, and Goodwin, 1971).

In a series of papers, Meltzer (1973; see also Weil-Malherbe and Szara, 1971, pp. 125–127) showed that serum creatine phosphokinase activity may be increased in acute psychotics, whether suffering from schizophrenia or affective disorders. The effect is probably due to stress and motor activity (Foster and Kupfer, 1973).

4. Changes in Urinary Excretion

a. *Excretion of catecholamines and catecholamine metabolites.* An increased excretion of total (free + conjugated) catecholamines during the manic phase and a reduced excretion during the depressed phase of bipolar illness was first noted by Ström-Olsen and Weil-Malherbe (1958) and has since been confirmed repeatedly. The excretion changes are seen with each of the three catecholamines, epinephrine, norepinephrine, and dopamine. According to Bunney et al. (1972b) the increase of norepinephrine excretion precedes the mood swing from depression to mania by about 24 hr, and similar phase shifts have since been observed for the excretion of MHPG (Jones, Maas, Dekirmenjian, and Fawcett, 1973) and cyclic AMP (Paul, Cramer, and Bunney, 1971a). Occasionally very high rates of norepinephrine excretion are found in cases of psychotic depression (Bunney, Davis, Weil-Malherbe, and Smith, 1967).

Studies of this kind have been criticized on the grounds that they reflect peripheral rather than cerebral events and that they are subject to interference from physical activity, incidental stress, dietary effects, and the rate of diuresis. Maas and Landis (1968) have advocated the estimation of urinary MHPG as more faithfully reflecting the central metabolism of norepinephrine than other metabolites. However, as shown by Ebert, Post, and Goodwin (1972), even the excretion of MHPG is not immune against peripheral effects, as it is substantially elevated by physical activity in depressed patients in the absence of any psychologic improvement. It is arguable whether the preoccupation with peripheral effects is justified. It may be assumed that the activity of the peripheral sympathetic system usually reflects the activity of the central sympathetic system. A low degree of motor activity is no accident, and, although it can be stimulated artificially, it can if spontaneous serve as an indicator of central sympathetic activity. Be this as it may, the fact is that the results of MHPG estimations in urine are substantially the same as those revealed by the estimations of the urinary catecholamines themselves or of some of their other metabolites, such as normetanephrine and VMA, namely a decreased rate of excretion at the height of depression, an increase during improvement, and a further increase during a manic phase (Greenspan, Schildkraut, Gordon, Levy, and Durell, 1969; Greenspan et al., 1970b; Rubin and Overall, 1970; Bojanovsky, 1971; Bond, Jenner, and Sampson, 1972; Maas, Fawcett, and Dekirmenjian, 1972; Jones et al., 1973). According to Schildkraut, Keeler, Papousek, and Hartmann (1973), MHPG excretion is significantly lower in patients with bipolar depression than in those with unipolar or "characterologic" depression.

b. *Indole excretion.* Studies of the urinary excretion of 5-HIAA in affective disorders yielded contradictory and inconclusive results (for references see Weil-Malherbe and Szara, 1971, pp. 69–70).

Coppen, Shaw, Malleson, Eccleston, and Gundy (1965) measured the tryptamine output of depressed patients and found that it was significantly lower during the depressed phase than after recovery. The patients were reported to have been on a constant regimen of food and fluid intake, although only during the 24 hr of actual urine collection, and no details are supplied of the diet offered or of the control of its consumption, a rather crucial point in view of the anorexia of many depressed patients and of the variation of tryptamine excretion with protein ingestion (Berlet, Spaide, Kohl, Bull, and Himwich, 1965). According to Perry, Hestrin, MacDougall, and Hansen (1966), urinary tryptamine is largely if not entirely a product of intestinal bacteria and varies with the degree of intestinal stasis. Although this has been disputed by DeQuattro and Sjoerdsma (1967), it is a factor that should not be neglected. It is not too surprising therefore that the results of Coppen et al. (1965) were not confirmed by Prange, Wilson, Knox, McClane, Breese, Martin, Alltop, and Lipton (1972) or by Frazer, Pandey, and Mendels (1973). Murphy and Weiss (1972) even observed an increased excretion of tryptamine in bipolar patients during the depressed phase.

Coppen et al. (1965) further reported that depressed patients, when given a test dose of L-tryptophan by mouth, responded with a significantly smaller increment of tryptamine excretion before than after recovery. It has been suggested that this effect is due to an increase in the activity of liver tryptophan pyrrolase in depression. Tryptophan pyrrolase converts tryptophan to formylkynurenine by an oxidative splitting of the pyrrole ring, a reaction that unfolds the chief pathway of tryptophan metabolism. Tryptophan pyrrolase is an inducible enzyme, and its activity is known to be increased by corticosteroids (Altman and Greengard, 1966), which are frequently elevated in the plasma of depressed patients. Green and Curzon (1968) showed that an injection of hydrocortisone produced a sharp rise of tryptophan pyrrolase in rat liver followed a few hours later by a marked decrease of the levels of serotonin and 5-HIAA in the brain, presumably because more tryptophan was metabolized in the liver and less was entering the brain. In support of the hypothesis that liver tryptophan pyrrolase activity is increased in depression, Curzon and Bridges (1970) reported that the excretion of kynurenine and 3-hydroxykynurenine was increased in a group of female depressed patients in response to an oral dose of L-tryptophan, compared to a control group. However, Frazer et al. (1973) found no significant differences between groups of depressed and nondepressed psychiatric patients in the excretion of nine tryptophan metabolites, either with regard to basal levels or to increments elicited by a tryptophan load. Yuwiler, Wetterberg, and Geller (1971), although confirming the fact that the level of rat brain serotonin was reduced by a corticosteroid injection, were able to achieve increases in the activity of liver tryptophan pyrrolase with a different drug and found under these conditions the concentration of rat brain serotonin to be increased rather than reduced. They doubt therefore that the changes in the tryptophan metabolism of depressed patients can be attributed to an increased activity of liver tryptophan pyrrolase. Hillier, Hillier, and Redfern (1974) also came to the conclusion that there is no correlation between liver tryptophan pyrrolase activity and levels or turnover of brain serotonin in the rat.

Tryptophan is the only amino acid that occurs in plasma largely in bound form, combined with albumin (McMenamy and Oncley, 1958). The ratio of free to bound tryptophan in plasma is affected by many factors, e.g., by competition with higher fatty acids, which are also bound to albumin. It seems that the level of tryptophan in the brain depends only on the concentration of free, not of total, tryptophan in plasma (Tagliamonte, Biggio, Vargiu, and Gessa, 1973). According to Coppen, Eccleston, and Peet (1972b,1973) the concentration of free tryptophan was found to be significantly lower in a group of female depressed patients than in female controls, although there was no difference in the concentration of total plasma tryptophan. The levels of free tryptophan increased after recovery. This factor could account for the decreased levels of tryptophan and 5-HIAA in CSF. It should be recalled, on the other hand, that Ashcroft et al. (1973b) concluded that there was no impediment to the entry of tryptophan into the brain or to its subsequent metabolism in cases of depression.

c. *The excretion of cyclic adenosine 3′,5′-monophosphate.* A decreased excretion of cyclic adenosine 3′,5′-monophosphate (cyclic AMP) in depression, an increased excretion in hypomania, and a return toward the normal range from either direction upon recovery has been reported (Abdulla and Hamadah, 1970; Paul, Ditzion, Pauk, and Janowsky, 1970). The severity of symptoms was correlated with the extent of excretion changes (Paul, Cramer, and Goodwin, 1971b). A marked and sometimes transient increase of cyclic AMP excretion, usually occurring 1 to 2 days before the clinical change, was associated with the transition from depression to mania in bipolar patients (Paul et al., 1971a).

These results are compatible with the catecholamine hypothesis of affective disorders, since the activity of adenyl cyclase, the enzyme responsible for the formation of cyclic AMP, is regulated by the activity of adrenergic neurons. Cyclic AMP in fact is regarded as a second messenger mediating between adrenergic nerve endings and some effector cells. The evaluation of the cyclic AMP excretion data is therefore open to the same kind of criticism that has been leveled at the catecholamine excretion data, namely that they reflect degrees of peripheral, mainly muscular, activity rather than neuronal activity (Berg and Glinsmann, 1970; Eccleston, Loose, Pullar, and Sugden, 1970; Robison, Coppen, Whybrow, and Prange, 1970).

It should also be mentioned that some authors failed to find any correlation between levels of cyclic AMP excretion and levels of mood in manic-depressive patients with regular periods of mood swings (Brown, Salway, Albano, Hullin, and Ekins, 1972; Hullin, Salway, Allsopp, Barnes, Albano, and Brown, 1974); others did find a reduced excretion in cases of depression and a return to normal during improvement, but this applied equally to cases of endogenous and neurotic depression (Sinanan, Keatinge, Beckett, and Love, 1975).

Tricyclic antidepressants were found to increase the content of cyclic AMP in brain slices (Kodama, Matsukado, Suzuki, Tanaka, and Shimizu, 1971), possibly through an inhibition of phosphodiesterase (Abdulla and Hamadah, 1970; Ramsden, 1970; Somerville, Rabouhans, and Smith, 1970). Lithium, on the other hand, inhibited adenyl cyclase in brain extracts at low concentrations (Douša and Hechter, 1970); at higher concentrations, lithium inhibited adenyl cyclase and its activation by norepinephrine in brain slices (Palmer, Robison, Manian, and Sulser, 1972). Lithium also inhibited the activation of adenyl cyclase by thyrotropic hormone in sheep thyroid homogenate (Burke, 1970); moreover chronic lithium treatment of rats for 3 to 4 weeks was found to lead to a severe inhibition of adenyl cyclase activity in kidney slices (Geisler, Wraae, and Oleson, 1972). These effects are consistent with the proadrenergic activity of tricyclic antidepressants and the antiadrenergic activity of the lithium ion.

Cramer, Goodwin, Post, and Bunney (1972) measured the concentration of cyclic AMP in CSF. They found that baseline levels were increased in depressed but not in manic patients, in comparison with a group of neurologic patients. In response to probenecid, cyclic AMP levels increased to about the same extent in depressed and in neurologic patients, but the increase was strongest in two manic patients.

IV. ELECTROLYTE METABOLISM IN AFFECTIVE DISORDERS

A. Sodium Distribution

A disturbance of water and salt metabolism in affective disorders has been suspected, since early investigators described changes in the output of water and electrolytes, particularly sodium, fluctuating with mood changes. The introduction of isotope methods and the interest engendered by the therapeutic effects of the lithium ion gave fresh impetus to research in this area. For a fuller discussion of earlier work, the reader is referred to previous reviews (Coppen, 1965; Durell, Baer, and Green, 1970; Weil-Malherbe and Szara, 1971; Baer, 1973).

Evidence from isotope dilution experiments suggested that the sodium pool available for rapid exchange with isotopic sodium in depressed patients shrank when they improved under electroconvulsive therapy (ECT) treatment indicating that depression was associated with a retention of sodium (Gibbons, 1960). From the studies of Coppen and Shaw (1963), it appeared that the retention of sodium is at least partly intracellular. Coppen, Shaw, Malleson, and Costain (1966) found this phenomenon not only in depression but also, and in even more extreme form, in mania. Normal values were reestablished after recovery. Since Coppen's results were obtained by an indirect and somewhat involved method, it is important that the retention of sodium was confirmed in three out of four depressed patients by the method of whole-body counting; the retention decreased during recovery and counts remained in the normal range when one of the patients became hypomanic (Baer, Durell, Bunney, Levy, and Cardon, 1969). In a few other hypomanic patients, Baer, Durell, Bunney, Levy, Murphy, Greenspan, and Cardon (1970a) using an isotope dilution method found only a slight tendency toward sodium retention. A more extensive reinvestigation of Coppen's claims regarding sodium retention in mania would be desirable, especially in view of the fact that the continuum hypothesis of affective disorders rests largely on these data.

Aldosterone excretion (Murphy, Goodwin, and Bunney, 1969) and aldosterone production rates (Allsopp, Levell, Stitch, and Hullin, 1972) were found to be higher during the manic than during the depressive phases of bipolar illness. Since aldosterone secretion induces sodium retention, these observations would be consistent with an increased sodium retention in mania, although there are many other factors affecting sodium balance and aldosterone activity.

A retention of sodium, particularly of intracellular sodium, in patients with affective disorders suggests a deficiency of the sodium pump or of the enzyme Na^+, K^+-dependent adenosine triphosphatase (ATPase), which is located in the cell membrane and is intimately involved in the function of the sodium pump. On the basis of an analysis of salivary secretion, Glen, Ongley, and Robinson (1968) concluded that the reabsorption of sodium ions by the collecting ducts of the parotid gland was diminished during manic as well as depressive episodes of affective disorders, an observation in accordance with the assumption of a sodium pump deficiency in both phases of bipolar illness.

Recently sodium transport has been studied in red blood cells. Naylor, McNamee, and Moody (1971) determined the sodium content of erythrocytes from female patients with psychotic depression and found that it fell during recovery. The sodium content of red blood cells from patients with neurotic depression was low to start with and did not change during recovery. In manic patients Glen and Rollo (quoted by Glen and Reading, 1973) found a significantly reduced sodium content of erythrocytes. These observations therefore suggest a sodium retention only in depressed patients and the opposite change, an overexpulsion of sodium, in manic patients. Changes in opposite directions are also suggested by the report of Dick, Dick, LePoidevin, and Naylor (1972) who measured the activity of the Na^+, K^+-dependent ATPase in red blood cells in groups of depressed female patients. In those suffering from psychotic depression but not in those with neurotic depression, mood ratings and enzyme activity were significantly correlated throughout the course of the illness from admission to discharge. In a single case of a bipolar patient, four cycles of mania and depression were correlated with four cycles of enzyme activity. A reduced activity of the sodium pump in the erythrocytes of 25 manic-depressive patients during the manic phase as well as during remission has been reported by Hokin-Neaverson, Spiegel, and Lewis (1974).

B. The Effect of Lithium Treatment on Electrolyte Metabolism

Lithium is now recommended not only for the treatment and prophylaxis of mania but also for the prophylaxis and even for the treatment of recurrent depression, especially bipolar depression (Baastrup and Schou, 1967; Goodwin, Murphy, and Bunney, 1969; Goodwin, Murphy, Dunner, and Bunney, 1972). Lithium administration leads to characteristic changes in electrolyte output. On the first day of treatment, it increases the output of sodium, potassium, and water; this phase is followed by several days of decreased excretion and eventually by a return to a balanced output (Baer, Platman, Kassir, and Fieve, 1971). The phase of water and electrolyte retention is associated with a transient increase of aldosterone excretion, amounting to about 50%, on the average (Murphy et al., 1969).

Several authors (Trautner, Morris, Noack, and Gershon, 1955; Gershon and Yuwiler, 1960; Hullin, Swinscoe, McDonald, and Dransfield, 1968; Greenspan, Goodwin, Bunney, and Durell, 1968a; Greenspan, Green, and Durell, 1968b) have noticed an unusual retention of lithium by manic patients, coupled with an increased tolerance for marginally toxic doses. This tendency can be combated by increased intake of sodium (Platman and Fieve, 1969) but only at the expense of a decreased therapeutic effect of lithium (Demers and Heninger, 1971). Almy and Taylor (1973) measured the half-life of a single standard dose of lithium and found it to be about 18 hr in control patients with character disorders and about 36 hr in acutely manic patients. The mean serum levels did not differ in the two groups, nor was there a difference in urine volume. One is tempted to speculate that this retention of lithium by the manic patient is the result of an increased aldosterone secretion previously referred to.

In rats chronic lithium administration led to an increase of cumulative sodium excretion and to a decrease of tissue sodium, more so in the brain (9.6%) than in the rest of the body (6.2%) (Baer, Kassir, and Fieve, 1970b). Lithium also accumulated in bone where it displaced sodium and calcium (Birch and Jenner, 1973).

The effects of lithium on the sodium spaces in man have also been investigated. Lithium treatment increased the sodium space in all patients, and it increased the amount of exchangeable sodium particularly in those patients who showed marked improvement as a result of the treatment (Baer et al., 1970a; Aronoff, Evens, and Durell, 1971). These changes might indicate increased sodium retention, but are more likely caused by increased mobilization of tissue sodium, including parts of the sodium of bone. The total body counts of endogenous potassium (^{40}K) decreased after two weeks of lithium treatment in depressed patients but increased in manic patients (Murphy and Bunney, 1971). Whereas the effect in the depressed patients is as expected, the effect in the manic patients is difficult to explain. It might be related to the high retention of lithium in these patients.

Lithium displaces not only sodium and potassium from tissues but also calcium and magnesium. According to a series of authors (Trautner et al., 1955; Nielsen, 1964; Tupin, Schlagenhauf, and Creson, 1968; Aronoff et al., 1971; Birch and Jenner, 1973) lithium treatment increases the urinary excretion and the serum levels of magnesium; there is no consensus concerning its effects on calcium.

In vitro experiments have shown that lithium, at concentrations of 3 to 6 mM (the therapeutic serum level is 1 mM or less), stimulated sodium efflux from red blood cells (Glen, Bradbury, and Wilson, 1972). Glen and Reading (1973) quoted unpublished work of Dewar, Kinloch, and Reading who studied the properties of synaptosomes prepared from the brain of rats treated with lithium for increasing periods. After a small initial inhibition of the ouabain-sensitive Na^+, K^+-dependent ATPase located in the heavy membrane fraction, the main effect was a pronounced increase of the ouabain-insensitive Mg^{2+}-activated ATPase associated with the light membrane and vesicle fraction. This calls to mind the recent work of Berl, Puszkin, and Nicklas (1973), who described an actomyosin-like brain protein having the properties of a Mg^{2+}-activated ATPase. They called it neurostenin and suggested that it promotes the exocytosis of the vesicular contents through contractile membrane pores. Through an effect on this protein lithium might conceivably affect the processes of transmitter storage and release.

Glen and Reading (1973) speculate that in depression, where intracellular sodium is increased, lithium would remain largely extracellular and would stimulate the sodium pump, whereas in manic patients where, as they assume, intracellular sodium is low, lithium would be retained inside the cell where it would compete with and inhibit the efflux of sodium, thus in effect inhibiting the sodium pump. Lithium would thus correct overswings in sodium distribution in both directions.

The effects of sodium and potassium gradients on the excitability of nervous membranes and the effects of calcium and magnesium on membrane permeability and enzyme reactions invite speculations on the mechanism of the therapeutic effects of lithium. Although sufficient evidence is at hand to make the existence of such a connection seem highly probable, a detailed interpretation is as yet beyond our grasp.

V. CONCLUSION

It remains for us to discuss some questions that have emerged from this survey.

1. Are the biochemical changes observed of a primary or a secondary nature? Some of the effects described may be the result of stress. There is no doubt that patients with affective disorders are under continuous, severe,

and prolonged stress. Stress may be responsible for an overactivity of adrenal cortical hormones, and they in turn may induce a variety of effects. Since there is stress in depression as well as in mania, those changes that are in the same direction under both conditions have to be carefully examined as to whether they are stress-induced. This applies particularly to the changes in electrolyte distribution, known to be regulated by adrenocortical and pituitary hormones.

2. Is there any evidence in support of the monoamine hypothesis of affective disorders? The foundation of the hypothesis was and remains the observation that monoamine depletors or antagonists are antimanic and prone to induce depression and that replenishers of amine stores or drugs prolonging the active life of a discharged transmitter are antidepressants and may precipitate mania in those with the requisite genetic disposition. In accordance with the antithetic concept of high amine activity in mania and low amine activity in depression are a series of observations concerning the urinary excretion rates of catecholamines, various catecholamine metabolites, and of cyclic AMP, the second messenger of the adrenergic (and dopaminergic?) systems, all showing decreased excretion during the depressed phase and increased excretion during the manic phase. Also in agreement are the observations on the levels of MHPG and HVA in the CSF, which, although not invariably significant, tend to show increases in mania and decreases in depression. There is finally the observation of Rosenblatt et al. (1973) indicating that the rate of norepinephrine synthesis in salivary glands is accelerated during the manic phase of bipolar illness.

Detre, Himmelhoch, Swartzburg, Anderson, Byck, and Kupfer (1972) recently reported that hypersomnia is not unusual during the depressed phase of bipolar illness. Because in mania of course sleep is greatly curtailed, these changes fit the concept of adrenergic underactivity in depression and adrenergic overactivity in mania.

On the other hand, some changes observed in the manic phase are in the same direction as those observed in the depressed phase. There seems to be a tendency (again not uniformly acknowledged) for CSF levels of tryptophan and 5-HIAA to be reduced in both phases. A favorable response to tryptophan administration has been described not only in depression but also in mania (Prange et al., 1973).

It will be noted that changes in opposite directions relate to catechols and changes in the same direction to indoles. This is in keeping with Kety's suggestion (1971) that the direction of mood swings is controlled by the rate of activity of the adrenergic system, whereas the stability of mood is associated with the rate of activity of the serotonergic system.

Coppen's observation of sodium retention in both depression and mania has not yet been definitively confirmed, at least as far as mania is concerned. Recent observations on red blood cells suggest an increased activity of Na^+, K^+-dependent ATPase and a decreased sodium content during mania and the reverse in depression. An attempt has also been made to explain the therapeutic effects of lithium in both mania and depression as a correction of overswings in opposite directions. It therefore seems premature to marshal the results of the electrolyte studies in support of either the concept of an antithetic or that of a continuum model.

3. Is it possible to differentiate between unipolar and bipolar depression by laboratory techniques? Several biochemical differences between unipolar and bipolar depressed patients have been mentioned in this review. Thus the level of HVA and 5-HIAA in the CSF has been found to be lower in unipolar than in bipolar depression (Ashcroft et al., 1973a), whereas the increment of 5-HIAA in response to probenecid was lower in CSF of bipolar than of unipolar depression (van Praag et al., 1973). The enzyme COMT was found to be lower in red blood cells of unipolar depressed females than in those of bipolar depressed females, a difference absent in men (Dunner et al., 1971). On the other hand, it has been reported that the enzyme MAO was low in platelets from bipolar depressed patients and normal in unipolar depressed patients (Murphy and Weiss, 1972). Bipolar depressed patients seem to sleep more than unipolar depressed patients (Detre et al., 1972).

The excretion of 17-hydroxycorticosteroids is reduced more strongly in bipolar than in unipolar depression (Dunner, Goodwin, Gershon, Murphy, and Bunney, 1972), whereas the plasma levels of growth hormone indicate a reduced secretion in response to insulin or L-DOPA administration in unipolar depression (Sachar, Frantz, Altman, and Sassin, 1973). According to Buchsbaum, Goodwin, Murphy, and Borge (1971) bipolar depressed patients showed a relatively greater increment of average evoked responses to light stimuli of increasing intensity than unipolar patients.

None of these tests could be used to discriminate by itself between unipolar and bipolar depression. Collectively they represent a strong case for the biologic distinctness of the two forms. As previously pointed out, there is reason to believe that more than one form of unipolar depression exists but their biologic differentiation is a task for the future.

REFERENCES

Abdulla, Y. H., and Hamadah, K. (1970): 3'5'-Cyclic adenosine monophosphate in depression and mania. *Lancet,* 1:378–381.

Aghajanian, G. K., and Asher, I. M. (1971): Histochemical fluorescence of raphe neurons: selective enhancement by tryptophan. *Science,* 172:1159–1161.

Ahlskog, J. E., and Hoebel, B. G. (1973): Overeating and obesity from damage to a noradrenergic system in the brain. *Science,* 182:166–169.

Allsopp, M. N. E., Levell, M. J., Stitch, S. R., and Hullin, R. P. (1972): Aldosterone production rates in manic-depressive psychosis. *Br. J. Psychiatry,* 120:399–404.

Almy, G. L., and Taylor, M. A. (1973): Lithium retention in mania. *Arch. Gen. Psychiatry,* 29:232–234.

Altman, K., and Greengard, O. (1966): Tryptophan pyrrolase induced in human liver by hydrocortisone: effect on excretion of kynurenine. *Science,* 151:332–333.

Andén, N. E., Carlsson, A., Dahlström, A., Fuxe, K., Hillarp, N. A., and Larsson, K.

(1964): Demonstration and mapping out of nigroneostriatal dopamine neurons. *Life Sci.,* 3:523–530.

Andén, N. E., Dahlström, A., Fuxe, K., and Larsson, K. (1965): Mapping out of catecholamine and 5-hydroxytryptamine neurons innervating the telencephelon and diencephalon. *Life Sci.,* 4:1275–1279.

Andén, N. E., Dahlström, A., Fuxe, K., Larsson, K., Olson, L., and Ungerstedt, U. (1966): Ascending monoamine neurons to the telencephalon and diencephalon. *Acta Physiol. Scand.,* 67:313–326.

Andersson, H., and Roos, B. E. (1968): 5-Hydroxyindoleacetic acid in cerebrospinal fluid after administration of 5-hydroxytryptophan I. *Acta Pharmacol. Toxicol.,* 26:293–297.

Angst, J. (1968): Zur Atiologie and Nosologie endogener depressiver Psychosen. *Dtsch. Med. Wochenschr.,* 93:1451–1454.

Aprison, M. H., and Hingtgen, J. N. (1972): Serotonin and behavior: a brief summary. *Fed. Proc.,* 31:121–129.

Aronoff, M. S., Evens, R. G., and Durell, J. (1971): Effect of lithium salts on electrolyte metabolism. *J. Psychiatr. Res.,* 8:139–159.

Ashcroft, G. W., Blackburn, I. M., Eccleston, D., Glen, A. I. M., Hartley, W., Kinloch, N. E., Lonergan, M., Murray, L. G., and Pullar I. A. (1973a): Changes on recovery in the concentration of tryptophan and the biogenic amine metabolites in the cerebrospinal fluid of patients with affective illness. *Psychol. Med.,* 3:319–325

Ashcroft, G. W., Crawford, T. B. B., Cundall, R. L., Davidson, D. L., Dobson, J., Dow, R. C., Eccleston, D., Loose, R. W., and Pullar I. A. (1973b): 5-Hydroxytryptamine metabolism in affective illness: the effect of tryptophan administration. *Psychol. Med.,* 3:326–332.

Ashcroft, G. W., Crawford, T. B. B., Eccleston, D., Sharman, D. F., MacDougall, E. J., Stanton, J. B., and Binns, J. K. (1966): 5-Hydroxyindole compounds in the cerebrospinal fluid of patients with psychiatric or neurological diseases. *Lancet,* 2:1049–1052.

Atsmon, A., Blum, I., Wijsenbeek, H., Maoz, B., Steiner, M., and Ziegelman, G. (1970): The short-term effects of adrenergic blocking agents in a small group of psychotic patients. Preliminary clinical observations. *Psychiatr. Neurol. Neurochir.,* 74:251–258.

Axelrod, J., Mueller, R. A., Henry, J. P., and Stephens, P. M. (1970): Changes in enzymes involved in the biosynthesis and metabolism of noradrenaline and adrenaline after psychosocial stimulation. *Nature,* 225:1059–1060.

Baastrup, P. C., and Schou, M. (1967): Lithium as a prophylactic agent. Its effect against recurrent depressions and manic-depressive psychosis. *Arch. Gen. Psychiatry,* 16:162–172.

Baer, L. (1973): Electrolyte metabolism in psychiatric disorders. In: *Biological Psychiatry,* edited by J. Mendels, pp. 199–234. Wiley, New York.

Baer, L., Durell, J., Bunney, W. E., Jr., Levy, B. S., and Cardon, P. V. (1969): Sodium -22 retention and 17-hydroxycorticosteroid excretion in affective disorders: a preliminary report. *J. Psychiatr. Res.,* 6:289–297.

Baer, L., Durell, J., Bunney, W. E., Jr., Levy, B. S., Murphy, D. L., Greenspan, K., and Cardon, P. V. (1970a): Sodium balance and distribution in lithium carbonate therapy. *Arch. Gen. Psychiatry,* 22:40–44.

Baer, L., Kassir, S., and Fieve, R. (1970b): Lithium induced changes in electrolyte balance and tissue electrolyte concentration. *Psychopharmacologia,* 17:216–224.

Baer, L., Platman, S. R., Kassir, S., and Fieve, R. R. (1971): Mechanisms of renal lithium handling and their relationship to mineralocorticoids: a dissociation between sodium and lithium ions. *J. Psychiatr. Res.,* 8:91–105.

Baldessarini, R. J., and Yorke, C. (1970): Effects of lithium and of pH on synaptosomal metabolism of noradrenaline. *Nature,* 228:1301–1303.

Bartholini, G., Burkard, W. P., Pletscher, A., and Bates, H. M. (1967): Increase of cerebral catecholamines caused by 3,4-dihydroxyphenylalanine after inhibition of peripheral decarboxylase. *Nature,* 215:852–853.

Bartholini, G., DaPrada, M., and Pletscher, A. (1968): Decrease of cerebral 5-hydroxytryptamine by 3,4-dihydroxyphenylalanine after inhibition of extracerebral decarboxylase. *J. Pharm. Pharmacol.,* 20:228–229.

Baumgarten, H. G., Björklund, A., Lachenmayer, L., and Nobin, A. (1973a): Evaluation of the effects of 5,7-dihydroxytryptamine on serotonin and catecholamine neurons in the rat CNS. *Acta Physiol. Scand.* [Suppl.] 391.

Baumgarten, H. G., Evetts, K. D., Holman, R. B., Iversen, L. L., Vogt, M., and Wilson, G. (1972): Effects of 5,6-dihydroxytryptamine on monoaminergic neurons in the central nervous system of the rat. *J. Neurochem.*, 19:1587–1597.

Baumgarten, H. G., and Schlossberger, H. G. (1973): Effects of 5,6-dihydroxytryptamine on brain monoamine neurons in the rat. In: *Serotonin and Behavior*, edited by J. Barchas and and E. Usdin, pp. 209–224. Academic Press, New York.

Baumgarten, H. G., Victor, S. J., and Lovenberg, W. (1973b): Effect of intraventricular injection of 5,7-dihydroxytryptamine on regional tryptophan hydroxylase of rat brain. *J. Neurochem,* 21:251–253.

Berg, G. R., and Glinsmann, W. H. (1970): Cyclic AMP in depression and mania. *Lancet,* 1:834.

Berl, S., Puszkin, S., and Nicklas, W. J. (1973): Actomyosin-like protein in brain. *Science,* 179:441–446.

Berlet, H. H., Spaide, J., Kohl, H., Bull, C., and Himwich, H. E. (1965): Effects of reduction of tryptophan and methionine intake on urinary indole compounds and schizophrenic behavior. *J. Nerv. Ment. Dis.,* 140:297–304.

Bindler, E. H., Wallach, M. B., and Gershon, S. (1971): Effect of lithium on the release of ^{14}C-norepinephrine by nerve stimulation from the perfused cat spleen. *Arch. Int. Pharmacodyn.,* 190:150–154.

Birch, N. J., and Jenner, F. A. (1973): The distribution of lithium and its effects on the distribution and excretion of other ions in the rat. *Br. J. Pharmacol.,* 47:586–594.

Bliss, E. L., and Ailion, J. (1971): Relationship of stress and activity to brain dopamine and homovanillic acid. *Life Sci.,* 10:1161–1169.

Bliss, E. L., Thatcher, W., and Ailion, J. (1972): Relationship of stress to brain serotonin and 5-hydroxyindoleacetic acid. *J. Psychiatr. Res.,* 9:71–80.

Bogdanski, D. F., Weissbach, H., and Udenfriend, S. (1958): Pharmacological studies with the serotonin precursor, 5-hydroxytryptophan. *J. Pharmacol. Exp. Ther.,* 122:182–194.

Bojanovsky, J. (1971): Einige biochemische Korrelate einer 48 stündigen periodischen Psychose. *Psychiatr. Clin.,* 4:336–346.

Bond, P. A., Jenner, F. A., and Sampson, G. A. (1972): Daily variations of the urine content of 3-methoxy-4-hydroxyphenylglycol in two manic-depressive patients. *Psychol. Med.,* 2:81–85.

Bourne, H. R., Bunney, W. E., Jr., Colburn, R. W., Davis, J. M., Davis, J. N., Shaw, D. M., and Coppen, A. J (1968): Noradrenaline, 5-hydroxytryptamine and 5-hydroxyindoleacetic acid in hindbrains of suicidal patients. *Lancet,* 2:805–808.

Bowers, M. B., Jr. (1970): 5-HT metabolism in psychiatric syndromes. *Lancet,* 2:1029.

Bowers, M. B., Jr. (1972): Acute psychosis induced by psychotomimetic drug abuse. II. Neurochemical findngs. *Arch. Gen. Psychiatry,* 27:440–442.

Bowers, M. B., Jr., and Gerbode, F. A. (1968): Relationship of monoamine metabolites in human cerebrospinal fluid to age. *Nature,* 219:1256–1257.

Bowers, M. B., Jr., Heninger, G. R., and Gerbode, F. (1969): Cerebrospinal fluid 5-hydroxyindoleacetic acid and homovanillic acid in psychiatric patients. *Int. J. Neuropharmacol.,* 8:255–262.

Breese, G. R., Smith, R. D., Mueller, R. A., Howard, J. L., Prange, A. J., Jr., Lipton, M. A., Young, L. D., McKinney, W. T., and Lewis, J. K. (1973): Induction of adrenal catecholamine synthesising enzymes following mother-infant separation. *Nature* [New Biol.], 246:94–96.

Brodie, B. B., and Shore, P. A. (1957): A concept for a role of serotonin and norepinephrine as chemical mediators in the brain. *Ann. N. Y. Acad. Sci.,* 66:631–642.

Brodie, H. K. H., Murphy, D. L., Goodwin, F. K., and Bunney, W. E., Jr. (1971): Catecholamines and mania: The effect of alpha-methyl-para-tyrosine on manic behavior and catecholamine metabolism. *Clin. Pharmacol. Ther.,* 12:218–224.

Brodie, H. K. H., Sack, R., and Siever, L. (1973): Clinical studies of L-5-hydroxytryptophan in depression. In: *Serotonin and Behavior*, edited by J. Barchas and E. Usdin. pp. 549–559. Academic Press, New York.

Brown, B. L., Salway, J. G., Albano, J. D. M., Hullin, R. P., and Ekins, R. P. (1972): Urinary excretion of cyclic AMP and manic-depressive psychosis. *Br. J. Psychiatry,* 120:405–408.

Buchsbaum, M., Goodwin, F., Murphy, D., and Borge, G. (1971): AER in affective disorders. *Am. J. Psychiatry,* 128:19–25.

Bunney, W. E., Jr., Brodie, H. K. H., Murphy, D. L., and Goodwin, F. K. (1971): Studies of alpha-methyl-para-tyrosine, L-DOPA and L-tryptophan in depression and mania. *Am. J. Psychiatry,* 127:872–881.

Bunney, W. E., Jr., and Davis, J. M. (1965): Norepinephrine in depressive reactions. A review. *Arch. Gen. Psychiatry,* 13:483–494.

Bunney, W. E., Jr., Davis, J. M., Weil-Malherbe, H., and Smith, E. R. B. (1967): Biochemical changes in psychotic depression. *Arch. Gen. Psychiatry,* 16:448–460.

Bunney, W. E., Jr., Gershon, E. S., Murphy, D. L., and Goodwin, F. K. (1972a): Psychobiological and pharmacological studies of manic-depressive illness. *J. Psychiatr. Res.,* 9:207–226.

Bunney, W. E., Jr., Goodwin, F. K., and Murphy, D. L. (1972b): The "switch-process" in manic-depressive illness. III. Theoretical implications. *Arch. Gen. Psychiatry,* 27:312–317.

Bunney, W. E., Jr., Goodwin, F. K., Murphy, D. L., House, K. M., and Gordon, E. K. (1972c): The "switch-process" in manic-depressive illness. II. Relationship to catecholamines, REM sleep and drugs. *Arch. Gen. Psychiatry,* 27:304–309.

Bunney, W. E., Jr., Janowsky, D. S., Goodwin, F. K., Davis, J. M., Brodie, H. K. H., Murphy, D. L., and Chase, T. N. (1969): Effect of L-DOPA on depression. *Lancet,* 1:885–886.

Burke, G. (1970): Effects of cations and ouabain on thyroid adenyl cyclase. *Biochim. Biophys. Acta,* 220:30–41.

Butcher, L. L., Engel, J., and Fuxe, K. (1972): Behavioral, biochemical and histochemical analyses for the central effects of monamine precursors after peripheral decarboxylase inhibition. *Brain Res.,* 41:387–411.

Calne, D. B., Karoum, F., Ruthven, C. R. J., and Sandler, M. (1969): The metabolism of orally administered L-DOPA in Parkinsonism. *Br. J. Pharmacol.,* 37:57–68.

Carlsson, A., Corrodi, H., Fuxe, K., and Hökfelt, T. (1969): Effect of antidepressant drugs on the depletion of intraneuronal brain 5-hydroxytryptamine stores caused by 4-methyl-α-ethyl-meta-tyramine. *Eur. J. Pharmacol.,* 5:357–366.

Carlsson, A., Fuxe, K., and Ungerstedt, U. (1968): The effect of imipramine on central 5-hydroxytryptamine neurons. *J. Pharm. Pharmacol.,* 20:150–151.

Carroll, B. J., Mowbray, R. M., and Davies, B. (1970): Sequential comparison of L-tryptophan with E.C.T. in severe depression. *Lancet,* 1:967–969.

Carroll, B. J., and Sharp, P. T. (1971): Rubidium and lithium: Opposite effects on amine-mediated excitement. *Science,* 172:1355–1357.

Chase, T. N., Gordon, E. K., and Ng, L. K. Y. (1973): Norepinephrine metabolism in the central nervous system of man: studies using 3-methoxy-4-hydroxyphenylethylene glycol levels in cerebrospinal fluid. *J. Neurochem.,* 21:581–587.

Cohen, A. H., and Bowers, M. B., Jr. (1972): 5-Hydroxyindoleacetic acid in rat forebrain and cerebrospinal fluid following dorsal and median midbrain raphe lesions. *Brain Res.,* 39:519–522.

Colburn, R. W., Goodwin, F. K., Bunney, W. E., Jr., and Davis, J. M. (1967): Effect of lithium on the uptake of noradrenaline by synaptosomes. *Nature,* 215:1395–1397.

Constantinidis, J., Bartholini, G., Geissbühler, F., and Tissot, R. (1970): La barrière capillaire enzymatique pour la dopa au niveau de quelques noyaux du tronc cérébral. *Experientia,* 26:381–383.

Coppen, A. (1965): Mineral metabolism in affective disorders. *Br. J. Psychiatry,* 111: 1133–1142.

Coppen, A., Brooksbank, B. W. L., and Peet, M. (1972a): Tryptophan concentration in the cerebrospinal fluid of depressive patients. *Lancet,* 1:1393.

Coppen, A., Eccleston, E. G., and Peet, M. (1972b): Total and free tryptophan concentration in the plasma of depressive patients. *Lancet,* 2:1415–1416.

Coppen, A., Eccleston, E. G., and Peet, M. (1973): Total and free tryptophan concentration in the plasma of depressive patients. *Lancet*, 2:60–63.

Coppen, A., Noguera, R., and Shaw, D. M. (1970): L-tryptophan in depression. *Lancet*, 1:1111.

Coppen, A., Prange, A. J., Jr., Whybrow, P. C., and Noguera, R. (1972c): Abnormalities of indolamines in affective disorders. *Arch. Gen. Psychiatry*, 26:474–478.

Coppen, A., and Shaw, D. M. (1963): Mineral metabolism in melancholia. *Br. Med. J.*, 2:1439–1444.

Coppen, A., Shaw, D. M., Herzberg, B., and Maggs, R. (1967): Tryptophan in the treatment of depression. *Lancet*, 2:1178–1180.

Coppen, A., Shaw, D. M., Malleson, A., and Costain, R. (1966): Mineral metabolism in mania. *Br. Med. J.*, 1:71–75.

Coppen, A., Shaw, D. M., Malleson, A., Eccleston, E., and Gundy, G. (1965): Tryptamine metabolism in depression. *Br. J. Psychiatry*, 111:993–997.

Corrodi, H., and Fuxe, K. (1967): The effect of catecholamine precursors and monoamine oxidase inhibition on the amine levels of central catecholamine neurons after reserpine treatment or tyrosine hydroxylase inhibition. *Life Sci.*, 6:1345–1350.

Corrodi, H., and Fuxe, K. (1969): Decreased turnover in central 5-HT nerve terminals induced by antidepressant drugs of the imipramine type. *Eur. J. Pharmacol.*, 7:56–59.

Corrodi, H., Fuxe, K., Hökfelt, T., and Schou, M. (1967): The effect of lithium on cerebral monoamine neurons. *Psychopharmacologia*, 11:345–353.

Court, J. H. (1968): Manic-depressive psychosis: an alternative conceptual model. *Br. J. Psychiatry*, 114:1523–1530.

Court, J. H. (1972): The continuum model as a resolution of paradoxes in manic-depressive psychosis. *Br. J. Psychiatry*, 120:133–141.

Cramer, H., Goodwin, F. K., Post, R. M., and Bunney, W. E., Jr. (1972): Effects of probenecid and exercise on cerebrospinal-fluid cyclic AMP in affective illness. *Lancet*, 1:1346–1347.

Curzon, G., and Bridges, P. K. (1970): Tryptophan metabolism in depression. *J. Neurol. Neurosurg. Psychiatry*, 33:698–704.

Dahlström, A., and Fuxe, K. (1964): Localization of monoamines in the lower brain stem. *Experientia*, 20:398.

Deguchi, T., Sinha, A. K., and Barchas, J. D. (1973): Biosynthesis of serotonin in raphé nuclei of rat brain: effect of p-chlorophenylalanine. *J. Neurochem.*, 20:1329–1336.

Demers, R. G., and Heninger, G. R. (1971): Sodium intake and lithium treatment in mania. *Am. J. Psychiatry*, 128:100–104.

Dencker, S. J., Malm, U., Roos, B. E., and Werdinius, B. (1966): Acid monoamine metabolites of cerebrospinal fluid in mental depression and mania. *J. Neurochem.*, 13:1545–1548.

DeQuattro, V. L., and Sjoerdsma, A. (1967): Origin of urinary tyramine and tryptamine. *Clin. Chim. Acta*, 16:227–233.

Detre, T., Himmelhoch, J., Swartzburg, M., Anderson, C. M., Byck, R., and Kupfer, D. J. (1972): Hypersomnia and manic-depressive disease. *Am. J. Psychiatry*, 128:1303–1305.

Dick, D. A. T., Dick, E. G., LePoidevin, D., and Naylor, G. J. (1972): Sodium and potassium transport in depressive illness. *J. Physiol.*, 227:30–31P.

Dousa, T., and Hechter, O. (1970): Lithium and brain adenyl cyclase. *Lancet*, 1:834–835.

Dunner, D. L., Cohn, C. K., Gershon, E. S., and Goodwin, F. K. (1971): Differential catechol-O-methyl transferase activity in unipolar and bipolar affective illness. *Arch. Gen. Psychiatry*, 25:348–353.

Dunner, D. L., and Goodwin, F. K. (1972): Effect of L-tryptophan on brain serotonin metabolism in depressed patients. *Arch. Gen. Psychiatry*, 26:364–366.

Dunner, D. L., Goodwin, F. K., Gershon, E. S., Murphy, D. L., and Bunney, W. E., Jr. (1972): Excretion of 17-OHCS in unipolar and bipolar depressed patients. *Arch. Gen. Psychiatry*, 26:360–363.

Durell, J., Baer, L., and Green, R. (1970): Electrolytes and psychoses. In: *Biochemistry*,

Schizophrenias and Affective Illness, edited by H. E. Himwich, pp. 283–307. Williams and Wilkins, Baltimore.

Ebert, M. H., Post, R. M., and Goodwin, F. K. (1972): Effect of physical activity on urinary MHPG excretion in depressed patients. *Lancet,* 2:766.

Eccleston, D., Loose, R., Pullar, I. A., and Sugden, R. F. (1970): Exercise and urinary excretion of cyclic AMP. *Lancet,* 2:612.

Engelman, K., Horwitz, D., Jéquier, E., and Sjoerdsma, A. (1968): Biochemical and pharmacological effects of α-methyltyrosine in man. *J. Clin. Invest.,* 47:577–594.

Everett, G. M., and Borcherding, J. W. (1970): L-DOPA: Effect on concentrations of dopamine norepinephrine and serotonin in brains of mice. *Science,* 168:849–850.

Fann, W. E., Davis, J. M., Janowsky, D. S., Cavanaugh, J. H., Kaufmann, J. S., Griffith, J. D., and Oates, J. A. (1972): Effects of lithium on adrenergic function in man. *Clin. Pharmacol. Ther.,* 13:71–77.

Feer, H., and Wirz-Justice, A. (1971): The effect of 5-hydroxytryphophan on the efflux of noradrenaline from brain slices. *Experientia,* 27:885–886.

Fernstrom, J. D., and Wurtman, R. J. (1971): Effect of chronic corn consumption on serotonin content of rat brain. *Nature [New Biol.],* 234:62–64.

Fibiger, H. C., and Campbell, B. A. (1971): The effect of para-chlorophenylalanine on spontaneous locomotor activity in the rat. *Neuropharmacology,* 10:25–32.

Fieve, R. R., Meltzer, H., Dunner, D. L., Levitt, M., Mendlewicz, J., and Thomas, A. (1973*a*): Rubidium: biochemical, behavioral and metabolic studies in humans. *Am. J. Psychiatry,* 130:55–61.

Fieve, R. R., Mendlewicz, J., and Fleiss, J. L. (1973*b*): Manic-depressive illness: linkage with the Xg blood group. *Am. J. Psychiatry,* 130:1355–1359.

Fog, R. L., Randrup, A., and Pakkenberg, H. (1967): Aminergic mechanisms in corpus striatum and amphetamine-induced stereotyped behavior. *Psychopharmacologia,* 11:179–183.

Foster, F. G., and Kupfer, D. J. (1973): Psychomotor activity and serum creatine phosphokinase activity. *Arch. Gen. Psychiatry,* 29:752–758.

Fotherby, K., Ashcroft, G. W., Affleck, G. W., and Forrest, A. D. (1963): Studies on sodium transfer and 5-hydroxyindoles in depressive illness. *J. Neurol. Neurosurg. Psychiatry,* 26:71–73.

Frazer, A., Pandey, G. N., and Mendels, J. (1973): Metabolism of tryptophan in depressive disease. *Arch. Gen. Psychiatry,* 29:528–535.

Fuxe, K. (1965): Evidence for the existence of monoamine neurons in the central nervous system. Thesis, Stockholm.

Fuxe, K., Butcher, L. L., and Engel, J. (1971): DL-5-Hydroxytryptophan-induced changes in central monoamine neurons after peripheral decarboxylase inhibition. *J. Pharm. Pharmacol.,* 23:420–424.

Fuxe, K., Hamberger, B., and Malmfors, T. (1967): The effect of drugs on accumulation of monoamines in tubero-infundibular dopamine neurons. *Eur. J. Pharmacol.,* 1:334–341.

Fuxe, K., and Ungerstedt, U. (1968): Histochemical studies on the effect of (+)-amphetamine, drugs of the imipramine group and tryptamine on central catecholamine and 5-hydroxytryptamine neurons after intraventricular injection of catecholamines and 5-hydroxytryptamine. *Eur. J. Pharmacol.,* 4:135–144.

Geisler, A., Wraae, O., and Oleson, O. V. (1972): Adenyl cyclase activity in kidneys of rats with lithium-induced polyuria. *Acta Pharmacol. Toxicol.,* 31:203–208.

Gershon, E. S., Dunner, D. L., and Goodwin, F. K. (1971): Toward a biology of affective disorders. Genetic contributions. *Arch. Gen. Psychiatry,* 25:1–15.

Gershon, S., and Yuwiler, A. (1960): Lithium ion: a specific psychopharmacological approach to the treatment of mania. *J. Neuropsychiatry,* 1:229–241.

Gibbons, J. L. (1960): Total body sodium and potassium in depressive illness. *Clin. Sci.,* 19:133–138.

Glassman, A. H., and Platman, S. R. (1969): Potentiation of a monoamine oxidase inhibitor by tryptophan. *J. Psychiatr. Res.,* 7:83–88.

Glen, A. I. M., Bradbury, M. W. B., and Wilson, J. (1972): Stimulation of the sodium pump in the red blood cell by lithium and potassium. *Nature,* 239:399–401.

Glen, A. I. M., Ongley, G. C., and Robinson, K. (1968): Diminished membrane transport in manic-depressive psychosis and recurrent depression. *Lancet,* 2:241–243.

Glen, A. I. M., and Reading, H. W. (1973): Regulatory action of lithium in manic-depressive illness. *Lancet,* 2:1239–1241.

Goodwin, F. K. (1971): Behavioral effects of L-DOPA in man. *Semin. Psychiatry,* 3:477–492.

Goodwin, F. K., and Bunney, W. E., Jr. (1971): Depressions following reserpine: a reevaluation. *Semin. Psychiatry,* 3:435–448.

Goodwin, F. K., Murphy, D. L., and Bunney, W. E., Jr. (1969): Lithium-carbonate treatment in depression and mania. A longitudinal double-blind study. *Arch. Gen. Psychiatry,* 21:486–496.

Goodwin, F. K., Murphy, D. L., Dunner, D. L., and Bunney, W. E., Jr. (1972): Lithium response in unipolar versus bipolar depression. *Am. J. Psychiatry,* 129:44–47.

Goodwin, F. K., Post, R. M., Dunner, D. L., and Gordon, E. K. (1973): Cerebrospinal fluid amine metabolites in affective illness: the probenecid technique. *Am. J. Psychiatry,* 130:73–79.

Gordon, E. K., and Oliver, J. (1971): 3-Methoxy-4-hydroxyphenylethylene glycol in human cerebrospinal fluid. *Clin. Chim. Acta,* 35:145–150.

Green, A. R., and Curzon, G. (1968): Decrease of 5-hydroxytryptamine in the brain provoked by hydrocortisone and its prevention by allopurinol. *Nature,* 220:1095–1097.

Greenspan, K., Aronoff, M. S., and Bogdanski, D. F. (1970a): Effects of lithium carbonate on turnover and metabolism of norepinephrine in the rat brain-correlation to gross behavioral effects. *Pharmacology,* 3:129–136.

Greenspan, K., Goodwin, F. K., Bunney, W. E., and Durell, J. (1968a): Lithium ion retention and distribution. Patterns during acute mania and normothymia. *Arch. Gen. Psychiatry,* 19:664–673.

Greenspan, K., Green, R., and Durell, J. (1968b): Retention and distribution patterns of lithium, a pharmacological tool in studying the pathophysiology of manic-depressive psychosis. *Am. J. Psychiatry,* 125:512–519.

Greenspan, K., Schildkraut, J. J., Gordon, E. K., Baer, L., Aronoff, M. S., and Durell, J. (1970b): Catecholamine metabolism in affective disorders-III. MHPG and other catecholamine metabolites in patients treated with lithium carbonate. *J. Psychiatr. Res.,* 7:171–183.

Greenspan, K., Schildkraut, J. J., Gordon, E. K., Levy, B., and Durell, J. (1969): Catecholamine metabolism in affective disorders. II. Norepinephrine, normetanephrine, epinephrine, metanephrine and VMA excretion in hypomanic patients. *Arch. Gen. Psychiatry,* 21:710–716.

Grote, S. S., Moses, S. G., Robins, E., Hudgens, R. W., and Croninger, A. B. (1974): A study of selected catecholamine metabolizing enzymes. A comparison of depressive suicides and alcoholic suicides with controls. *J. Neurochem.,* 23:791–802.

Guldberg, H. C., Turner, J. W., Hanieh, A., Ashcroft, G. W., Crawford, T. B. B., Perry, W. L. M., and Gillingham, F. J. (1967): On the occurrence of homovanillic acid and 5-hydroxyindol-3-ylacetic acid in the ventricular C.S.F. of patients suffering from Parkinsonism. *Confin. Neurol.,* 29:73–77.

Harrison-Read, P. E., and Steinberg, H. (1971): Lithium-induced hypersensitivity to foot shock in rats and the role of 5-hydroxytryptophan. *Nature [New Biol.],* 232:120–121.

Hartmann, E., Chung, R., and Chien, C. P. (1971a): L-Tryptophane and sleep. *Psychopharmacologia,* 19:114–127.

Hartmann, E., Chung, R., Draskoczy, P. R., and Schildkraut, J. J. (1971b): Effects of 6-hydroxydopamine on sleep in the rat. *Nature,* 233:425–427.

Harvald, B., and Hauge, M. (1956): Catamnestic investigation of Danish twins. *Dan. Med. Bull.,* 3:150–158.

Haškoveć, L., and Ryšánek, K. (1967): The action of reserpine in imipramine resistant patients. Clinical and biochemical study. *Psychopharmacologia,* 11:18–30.

Haškoveć, L., and Ryšánek, K. (1969): Die Wirkung von Lithium auf den Metabolismus der Katecholamine und Indolalkylamine beim Menschen. *Arzneimittelforschung,* 19:426–427.

Herman, Z. S. (1970): The effects of noradrenaline on rat's behavior. *Psychopharmacologia,* 16:369–374.

Hess, W. R. (1954): *Diencephalon. Autonomic and Extrapyramidal Functions.* Grune and Stratton, New York.

Hillier, J., Hillier, J. G., and Redfern, P. H. (1974): The effect of hydrocortisone on tryptophan metabolism in the rat. *J. Pharm. Pharmacol.* 26:suppl., 119 p.

Hokin-Neaverson, M., Spiegel, D. A., and Lewis, W. C. (1974): Deficiency of erythrocyte sodium pump activity in bipolar manic-depressive psychosis. *Life Sci.,* 15:1739–1748.

Hullin, R. P., Salway, J. G., Allsopp, M. N. E., Barnes, G. D., Albano, J. D. M., and Brown, B. L. (1974): Urinary cyclic AMP in the switch process from depression to mania. *Br. J. Psychiatry,* 125:457–458.

Hullin, R. P., Swinscoe, J. C., McDonald, R., and Dransfield, G. A. (1968): Metabolic balance studies on the effect of lithium salts in manic-depressive psychosis. *Br. J. Psychiatry,* 114:1561–1574.

Ingvarsson, C. G. (1965): Orientierende klinische Versuche zur Wirkung des Dioxy-phenylalanins (L-DOPA) bei endogener Depression. *Arzneimittelforschung,* 15:849–852.

Iversen, L. L. (1963): The uptake of noradrenaline by the isolated perfused rat heart. *Br. J. Pharmacol.,* 21:523–537.

Iversen, L. L. (1965): The uptake of catecholamines at high perfusion concentrations in the rat isolated heart: a novel catecholamine uptake process. *Br. J. Pharmacol.,* 25:18–33.

Jenkins, R. B., and Groh, R. H. (1970): Psychic effects in patients treated with levodopa. *JAMA,* 212:2265.

Johansson, B., and Roos, B. E. (1967): 5-Hydroxyindoleacetic and homovanillic acid levels in the cerebrospinal fluid of healthy volunteers and patients with Parkinson's syndrome. *Life Sci.,* 6:1449–1454.

Jonason, J., and Rutledge, C. O. (1968): The effect of protriptyline on the metabolism of dopamine and noradrenaline in rabbit brain *in vitro. Acta Physiol. Scand.,* 73:161–174.

Jones, B. E. (1972): The respective involvement of noradrenaline and its deaminated metabolites in waking and paradoxical sleep: a neuropharmacological model. *Brain Res.,* 39:121–136.

Jones, F. D., Maas, J. W., Dekirmenjian, H., and Fawcett, J. A. (1973): Urinary catecholamine metabolites during behavioral changes in a patient with manic-depressive cycles. *Science,* 179:300–302.

Jouvet, M. (1965): Paradoxical sleep—a study of its nature and mechanisms. In: *Sleep Mechanisms, Vol. 18, Progress in Brain Research,* edited by K. Akert, C. Bally, and J. P. Schadé, pp. 20–62. Amsterdam, Elsevier.

Jouvet, M. (1973): Serotonin and sleep in the cat. In: *Serotonin and Behavior,* edited by J. Barchas and E. Usdin, pp. 385–400. Academic Press, New York.

Katz, R. I., Chase, T. N., and Kopin, I. J. (1968): Evoked release of norepinephrine and serotonin from brain slices: Inhibition by lithium. *Science,* 162:466–467.

Kety, S. (1971): Brain amines and affective disorders. In: *Brain Chemistry and Mental Disease,* edited by B. T. Ho and W. M. McIsaac, pp. 237–244. Plenum Press, New York.

King, C. D., and Jewett, R. E. (1971): The effects of α-methyltyrosine on sleep and brain norepinephrine in cats. *J. Pharmacol. Exp. Ther.,* 177:188–195

Kline, N. S., and Sacks, W. (1963): Relief of depression within one day using an M.A.O. inhibitor and intravenous 5-HTP. *Am. J. Psychiatry,* 120:274–275.

Kline, N. S., Sacks, W., and Simpson, G. M. (1964): Further studies on one day treatment of depression with 5-HTP. *Am. J. Psychiatry,* 121:379–381.

Knapp, S., and Mandell, A. J. (1973): Short- and long-term lithium administration: effects on the brain's serotonergic biosynthetic systems. *Science,* 180:645–647.

Kodama, T., Matsukado, Y., Suzuki, T., Tanaka, S., and Shimizu, H. (1971): Stimu-lated formation of adenosine 3′,5′-monophosphate by desipramine in brain slices. *Biochim. Biophys. Acta,* 252:165–170.

Kuriyama, K., and Speken, R. (1970): Effect of lithium on content and uptake of norepinephrine and 5-hydroxytryptamine in mouse brain synaptosomes and mito-chondria. *Life Sci (I),* 9:1213–1220.

Kvetnaňský, R., Gewirtz, G. P., Weise, V. K., and Kopin, I. J. (1971): Enhanced synthesis of adrenal dopamine-β-hydroxylase induced by repeated immobilization in rats. *Mol. Pharmacol.,* 7:81–86.

Lamprecht, F., Eichelman, B., Thoa, N. B., Williams, R. B., and Kopin, I. J. (1972): Rat fighting behavior: serum dopamine-β-hydroxylase and hypothalamic tyrosine hydroxylase. *Science,* 177:1214–1215.

Laverty, R., and Taylor, K. M. (1970): Effects of intraventricular 2,4,5-trihydroxyphenylethylamine (6-hydroxydopamine) on rat behavior and brain catecholamine metabolism. *Br. J. Pharmacol.,* 40:836–846.

Lichtensteiger, W., Mutzner, U., and Langemann, H. (1967): Uptake of 5-hydroxytryptamine and 5-hydroxytryptophan by neurons of the central nervous system normally containing catecholamines. *J. Neurochem.,* 14:489–497.

Lloyd, K. G., Farley, I. J., Deck, J. H. N., and Hornykiewicz, O. (1974): Serotonin and 5-hydroxyindoleacetic acid in discrete areas of the brainstem of suicide victims and control patients. *Adv. Biochem. Psychopharmacol.,* 11:387–397.

Loranger, A. W., Goodell, H., McDowell, F. H., Lee, J. E., and Sweet, R. D. (1973): Parkinsonism, L-dopa and intelligence. *Am. J. Psychiatry,* 130:1386–1389.

Maas, J. W., Fawcett, J. A., and Dekirmenjian, H. (1972): Catecholamine metabolism, depressive illness and drug response. *Arch. Gen. Psychiatry,* 26:252–262.

Maas, J. W., and Landis, D. H. (1965): Brain norepinephrine and behavior. *Psychosom. Med.,* 27:399–407.

Maas, J. W., and Landis, D. H. (1968): *In vivo* studies of the metabolism of norepinephrine in the central nervous system. *J. Pharmacol. Exp. Ther.,* 163:147–162.

Malec, D., and Kleinrok, Z. (1972): The spontaneous motility of rats after intraventricular injection of dopamine. *Neuropharmacology,* 11:331–336.

Matussek, N., Angst, J., Benkert, O., Gmür, M., Papousek, M., Rüther, E., and Woggon, B. (1974): The effect of L-5-hydroxytryptophan alone and in combination with a decarboxylase inhibitor (Ro 4–4602) in depressive patients. *Adv. Biochem. Psychopharmacol.,* 11:399–404.

McMenamy, R. H., and Oncley, J. L. (1958): The specific binding of L-tryptophan to serum albumin. *J. Biol. Chem.,* 233:1436–1447.

Meek, J., and Werdinius, B. (1970): Hydroxytryptamine turnover decreases by the antidepressant drug chlorimipramine. *J. Pharm. Pharmacol.,* 22:141–143.

Meier, M. J., and Martin, W. E. (1970): Intellectual changes associated with levodopa therapy. *JAMA,* 213:465–466.

Meltzer, H. Y. (1973): Skeletal muscle abnormalities in patients with affective disorders. *J. Psychiatr. Res.,* 10:43–57.

Meltzer, H. L., Taylor, R. M., Platman, S. R., and Fieve, R. R. (1969): Rubidium: a potential modifier of affect and behavior. *Nature,* 223:321–322.

Mendels, J. (1971): Relationship between depression and mania. *Lancet,* 1:342.

Mendels, J., Frazer, A., Fitzgerald, R. G., Ramsey, T. A., and Stokes, J. W. (1972): Biogenic amine metabolites in cerebrospinal fluid of depressed and manic patients. *Science,* 175:1380–1382.

Mendlewicz, J., Fleiss, J. L., and Fieve, R. R. (1972): Evidence for X linkage in the transmission of manic-depressive illness. *JAMA,* 222:1624–1627.

Messiha, F. S., Savage, C., Turek, I., and Hanlon, T. E. (1974): A psychopharmacological study of catecholamines in affective disorders. *J. Nerv. Ment. Dis.,* 158:338–347.

Modigh, K. (1973): Effect of chlorimipramine on the rate of tryptophan hydroxylation in the intact and transected spinal cord. *J. Pharm. Pharmacol.,* 25:926–928.

Moir, A. T. B., Ashcroft, G. W., Crawford, T. B. B., Eccleston, D., and Guldberg, H. C. (1970): Cerebral metabolites in cerebrospinal fluid as a biochemical approach to the brain. *Brain,* 93:357–368.

Moir, A. T. B., and Eccleston, D. (1968): The effects of precursor loading in the cerebral metabolism of 5-hydroxyindoles. *J. Neurochem.,* 15:1093–1108.

Murphy, D. L., Baker, M., Goodwin, F. K., Miller, H., Kotin, J., and Bunney, W. E., Jr. (1974): L-Tryptophan in affective disorders: indoleamine changes and differential clinical effects. *Psychopharmacologia,* 34:11–20.

Murphy, D. L., Baker, M., Kotin, J., and Bunney, W. E., Jr. (1973): Behavioral and metabolic effects of L-tryptophan in unipolar depressed patients. In: *Serotonin and*

Behavior, edited by J. Barchas and E. Usdin, pp. 529–537. Academic Press, New York.

Murphy, D. L., and Bunney, W. E., Jr. (1971): Total body potassium changes during lithium administration. *J. Nerv. Ment. Dis.,* 152:381–389.

Murphy, D. L., Colburn, R. W., Davis, J. M., and Bunney, W. E., Jr. (1970): Imipramine and lithium effects on biogenic amine transport in depressed and manic-depressed patients. *Am. J. Psychiatry,* 127:339–345.

Murphy, D. L., Goodwin, F. K., and Bunney, W. E., Jr. (1969): Aldosterone and sodium response to lithium administration in man. *Lancet,* 2:458–460.

Murphy, D. L., and Weiss, R. (1972): Reduced monoamine oxidase activity in blood platelets from bipolar depressed patients. *Am. J. Psychiatry,* 128:1351–1357.

Musacchio, J. M., Fischer, J. E., and Kopin, I. J. (1966): Subcellular distribution and release by sympathetic nerve stimulation of dopamine and α-methyl dopamine. *J. Pharmacol.,* 152:51–55.

Musacchio, J. M., Julou, L., Kety, S. S., and Glowinski, J. (1969): Increase in rat brain tyrosine hydroxylase activity produced by electro-convulsive shock. *Proc. Nat. Acad. Sci. USA,* 63:1117–1119.

Nagatsu, T., Levitt, M., and Udenfriend, S. (1964): Tyrosine hydroxylase: the initial step in norepinephrine biosynthesis. *J. Biol. Chem.,* 239:2910–2917.

Naylor, G. J., McNamee, H. B., and Moody, J. P. (1971): Changes in erythrocyte sodium and potassium on recovery from a depressive illness. *Br. J. Psychiatry,* 118: 219–223.

Ng, L. K. Y., Chase, T. N., Colburn, R. W., and Kopin, I. J. (1972): Release of [^{3}H]dopamine by L-5-hydroxytryptophan. *Brain Res.,* 45:499–505.

Nielsen, J. (1964): Magnesium-lithium studies. 1. Serum and erythrocyte magnesium in patients with manic states during lithium treatment. *Acta Psychiatr. Scand.,* 40: 190–195.

Nies, A., Robinson, D. S., Ravaris, C. L., and Davis, J. M. (1971): Amines and monoamine oxidase in relation to aging and depression in man. *Psychosom. Med.,* 33:470.

Nordin, G., Ottosson, J. O., and Roos, B. E. (1971): Influence of convulsive therapy on 5-hydroxyindole acetic acid and homovanillic acid in cerebrospinal fluid in endogenous depression. *Psychopharmacologia,* 20:315–320.

Novick, W. J., Jr. (1961): Effect of age and thyroid hormones on the monoamine oxidase of rat heart. *Endocrinology,* 69:55–59.

O'Gorman, L. P., Borud, P., Khan, I. A., and Gjessing, L. R. (1970): The metabolism of L-3,4-dihydroxyphenylalanine in man. *Clin. Chim. Acta,* 29:111–119.

Palmer, G. C., Robinson, G. A., Manian, A. A., and Sulser, F. (1972): Modification by psychotropic drugs of the cyclic AMP response to norepinephrine in the rat brain *in vitro. Psychopharmacologia,* 23:201–211.

Papeschi, R., and McClure, D. J. (1971): Homovanillic and 5-hydroxyindoleacetic acid in cerebrospinal fluid of depressed patients. *Arch. Gen. Psychiatry,* 25:354–358.

Pare, C. M. B., Yeung, D. P. H., Price, K., and Stacey, R. S. (1969): 5-Hydroxytryptamine, noradrenaline and dopamine in brainstem, hypothalamus and caudate nucleus of controls and of patients committing suicide by coal-gas poisoning. *Lancet,* 2:133–135.

Paul, M. I., Cramer, H., and Bunney, W. E., Jr. (1971a): Urinary adenosine 3',5'-monophosphate in the switch process from depression to mania. *Science,* 171:300–302.

Paul, M. I., Cramer, H., and Goodwin, F. K. (1971b): Urinary cyclic AMP excretion in depression and mania. Effects of levodopa and lithium carbonate. *Arch. Gen. Psychiatry,* 24:327–333.

Paul, M. I., Ditzion, B. R., Pauk, G. L., and Janowsky, D. S. (1970): Urinary adenosine 3',5'-monophosphate excretion in affective disorders. *Am. J. Psychiatry,* 126:1493–1497.

Perez-Cruet, J., Tagliamonte, A., Tagliamonte, P., and Gessa, G. L. (1971): Stimulation of serotonin synthesis by lithium. *J. Pharmacol. Exp. Ther.,* 178:325–330.

Perris, C. (1968): Genetic transmission of depressive psychoses. *Acta Psychiatr. Scand. Suppl.,* 203:45–52.

Perry, T. L., Hestrin, M., MacDougall, L., and Hansen, S. (1966): Urinary amines of intestinal bacterial origin. *Clin. Chim. Acta,* 14:116–123.

Persson, T., Roos, B. E. (1967): 5-Hydroxytryptophan for depression. *Lancet,* 2:987.

Persson, T., and Wålinder, J. (1971): L-Dopa in the treatment of depressive symptoms. *Br. J. Psychiatry,* 119:277–278.

Platman, S. R., and Fieve, R. R. (1969): Lithium retention and excretion. *Arch. Gen. Psychiatry,* 20:285–289.

Pohlmeier, H. (1969): Anwendungsmöglichkeiten psychologischer Methoden für die Beurteilung des L-Dopa-Effekts bei gehemmten Depressionen. *Arzneimittelforschung,* 19:470–472.

Pöldinger, W. (1963): Combined administration of desipramine and reserpine in depressed patients. *Psychopharmacologia,* 4:308–310.

Post, R. M., Gordon, E. K., Goodwin, F. K., and Bunney, W. E., Jr. (1973a): Central norepinephrine metabolism in affective illness: MHPG in the cerebrospinal fluid. *Science,* 179:1002–1003.

Post, R. M., Kotin, J., Goodwin, F. K., and Gordon, E. K. (1973b): Psychomotor activity and cerebrospinal fluid amine metabolites in affective illness. *Am. J. Psychiatry,* 130:67–72.

van Praag, H. M., and Korf, J. (1971a): Endogenous depressions with and without disturbances in the 5-hydroxytryptamine metabolism: a biochemical classification? *Psychopharmacologia,* 19:148–152.

van Praag, H. M., and Korf, J. (1971b): Retarded depression and the dopamine metabolism. *Psychopharmacologia,* 19:199–203.

van Praag, H. M., Korf, J., Dols, L. C. W., and Schut, T. (1972): A pilot study of the predictive value of the probenecid test in application of 5-hydroxytryptophan as antidepressant. *Psychopharmacologia,* 25:14–21.

van Praag, H. M., Korf, J., and Schut, D. (1973): Cerebral monoamines and depression. An investigation with the probenecid technique. *Arch. Gen. Psychiatry,* 28:827–831.

van Praag, H. M., van den Burg, W., Bos, E. R. H., and Dols, L. C. W. (1974): 5-Hydroxytryptophan in combination with clomipramine in "therapy-resistant" depressions. *Psychopharmacologia,* 38:267–269.

Prange, A. J., Jr., Sisk, J. L., Wilson, I. C., Morris, C. E., Hall, C. D., and Carman, J. S. (1973): Balance, permission and discrimination among amines: A theoretical consideration of the actions of L-tryptophan in disorders of movements and affect. In: *Serotonin and Behavior,* edited by J. Barchas and E. Usdin, pp. 539–548. Academic Press, New York.

Prange, A. J., Jr., Wilson, I. C., Knox, A. E., McClane, T. K., Breese, G. R., Martin, B. R., Alltop, L. B., and Lipton, M. A. (1972): Thyroid + imipramine clinical and chemical interaction: evidence for a receptor deficit in depression. *J. Psychiatr. Res.,* 9:187–205.

Prange, A. J., Jr., Wilson, I. C., Knox, A., McClane, T. K., and Lipton, M. A. (1970): Enhancement of imipramine by thyroid stimulating hormone: clinical and theoretical implications. *Am. J. Psychiatry,* 127:191–199.

Prange, A. J., Jr., Wilson, I. C., Rabon, A. M., and Lipton, M. A. (1969): Enhancement of imipramine antidepressant activity by thyroid hormone. *Am. J. Psychiatry,* 126:457–469.

Quay, W. B. (1963): Effect of dietary phenylalanine and tryptophan on pineal and hypothalamic serotonin levels. *Proc. Soc. Exp. Biol. Med.,* 114:718–727.

Ramsden, E. N. (1970): Cyclic AMP in depression and mania. *Lancet,* 2:108.

Randrup, A., and Jonas, W. (1967): Brain dopamine and the amphetamine-reserpine interaction. *J. Pharm. Pharmacol.,* 19:483–484.

Redmond, D. E., Maas, J. W., Kling, A., and Dekirmenjian, H. (1971): Changes in primate social behavior after treatment with alpha-methyl-para-tyrosine. *Psychosom. Med.,* 33:97–113.

Reich, T., Clayton, P. J., and Winokur, G. (1969): Family history studies. V: The genetics of mania. *Am. J. Psychiatry,* 125:1358–1369.

Renson, J. (1973): Assays and properties of tryptophan 5-hydroxylase. In: *Serotonin and Behavior,* edited by J. Barchas and E. Usdin, pp. 19–32. Academic Press, New York.

Robinson, D. S., Davis, J. M., Nies, A., Ravaris, C. L., and Sylwester, D. (1971): Relation of sex and aging to monoamine oxidase activity of human brain, plasma and platelets. *Arch. Gen. Psychiatry,* 24:536–539.

Robison, G. A., Coppen, A. J., Whybrow, P. C., and Prange, A. J. (1970): Cyclic AMP in affective disorders. *Lancet,* 2:1028–1029.

Roos, B. E., and Sjöström, R. (1969): 5-Hydroxyindoleacetic acid (and homovanillic acid) levels in the cerebrospinal fluid after probenecid application in patients with manic-depressive psychosis. *Pharmacol. Clin.,* 1:153–155.

Rosenblatt, S., Leighton, W. P., and Chanley, J. D. (1973): Dopamine-β-hydroxylase: evidence for increased activity in sympathetic neurons during psychotic states. *Science,* 182:923–924.

Rubin, R. T., and Overall, J. E. (1970): Manifest psychopathology and urine biochemical measures. *Arch. Gen. Psychiatry,* 22:45–57.

Sachar, E. J., Frantz, A. G., Altman, N., and Sassin, J. (1973): Growth hormone and prolactin in unipolar and bipolar depressed patients: Responses to hypoglycemia and L-dopa. *Am. J. Psychiatry,* 130:1362–1367.

Sano, I. (1972): L-5-Hydroxytryptophan (L-5-HTP) Therapie. *Fol. Psychiatr. Neurol. Japon.,* 26:7–17.

Sathananthan, G., Angrist, B. M., and Gershon, S. (1973): Response threshold to l-dopa in psychiatric patients. *Biol. Psychiatry.* 7:139–146.

Schanberg, S. M., Schildkraut, J. J., and Kopin, I. J. (1967): The effects of psychoactive drugs on norepinephrine-³H metabolism in brain. *Biochem. Pharmacol.,* 16:393–399.

Schildkraut, J. J. (1974): The effects of lithium on norepinephrine turnover and metabolism: basis and clinical studies. *J. Nerv. Ment. Dis.,* 158:348–360.

Schildkraut, J. J., Dodge, G. A., and Logue, M. A. (1969a): Effects of tricyclic antidepressants on the uptake and metabolism of intracisternally administered norepinephrine-H³ in rat brain. *J. Psychiatr. Res.,* 7:29–34.

Schildkraut, J. J., Draskóczy, P. R., Gershon, E. S., Reich, P., and Grab, E. L. (1972): Catecholamine metabolism in affective disorders. IV. Preliminary studies of norepinephrine metabolism in depressed patients treated with amitriptyline. *J. Psychiatr. Res.,* 9:173–185.

Schildkraut, J. J., Gordon, E. K., and Durell, J. (1965): Catecholamine metabolism in affective disorders: I. Normetanephrine and VMA excretion in depressed patients treated with imipramine. *J. Psychiatr. Res.,* 3:213–228.

Schildkraut, J. J., Keeler, B. A., Papousek, M., and Hartmann, E. (1973): MHPG excretion in depressive disorders: relation to clinical subtypes and desynchronized sleep. *Science,* 181:762–764.

Schildkraut, J. J., Klerman, G. L., Hammond, R., and Friend, D. G. (1964): Excretion of 3-methoxy-4-hydroxymandelic acid (VMA) in depressed patients treated with antidepressant drugs. *J. Psychiatr. Res.,* 2:257–265.

Schildkraut, J. J., Logue, M. A., and Dodge, G. A. (1969b): The effects of lithium salts on the turnover and metabolism of norepinephrine in rat brain. *Psychopharmacologia,* 14:135–141.

Schildkraut, J. J., Schanberg, S. M., Breese, G. R., and Kopin, I. J. (1969c): Effects of psychoactive drugs on the metabolism of intracisternally administered serotonin in rat brain. *Biochem. Pharmacol.,* 18:1971–1978.

Schildkraut, J. J., Schanberg, S. M., and Kopin, I. J. (1966): The effects of lithium ion on H³-norepinephrine metabolism in brain. *Life Sci.,* 5:1479–1483.

Schildkraut, J. J., Winokur, A., Draskóczy, P. R., and Hensle, J. H. (1971): Changes in norepinephrine turnover in rat brain during chronic administration of imipramine and protriptyline: A possible explanation for the delay in onset of clinical antidepressant effects. *Am. J. Psychiatry,* 127:1032–1039.

Schubert, J. (1973): Effect of chronic lithium treatment on monoamine metabolism in rat brain. *Psychopharmacologia,* 32:301–311.

Schubert, J., Nybäck, H., and Sedvall, G. (1970): Effect of antidepressant drugs on accumulation and disappearance of monoamines formed *in vivo* from labelled precursors in mouse brain. *J. Pharm. Pharmacol.,* 22:136–138.

Segal, D. C., Kuczenski, R. T., and Mandell, A. J. (1972): Strain differences in behavior and brain tyrosine hydroxylase activity. *Behav. Biol.,* 7:75–81.

Segal, D. S., and Mandell, A. J. (1970): Behavioral activation of rats during intraventricular infusion of norepinephrine. *Proc. Natl. Acad. Sci.,* 66:289–293.

Shaw, D. M., Camps, F. E., and Eccleston, E. G. (1967): 5-Hydroxytryptamine in the hind brain of depressive suicides. *Br. J. Psychiatry,* 113:1407–1411.

Shaw, D. M., Johnson, A. L., and MacSweeney, D. A. (1972): Tricyclic antidepressants and tryptophan in unipolar affective disorder. *Lancet,* 2:1245.

Shaw, D. M., O'Keefe, R., MacSweeney, D. A., Brooksbank, B. W. L., Noguera, R., and Coppen, A. (1973): 3-Methoxy-4-hydroxyphenylglycol in depression. *Psychol. Med.,* 3:333–336.

Sheard, M. H. (1970): Effect of lithium on foot shock aggression in rats. *Nature,* 228:284–285.

Sheard, M. H., and Aghajanian, G. K. (1970): Neuronally activated metabolism of brain serotonin: effect of lithium. *Life Sci. (I),* 9:285–290.

Sheard, M. H., Zolovick, A., and Aghajanian, G. K. (1972): Raphé neurons: Effect of tricyclic antidepressant drugs. *Brain Res.,* 43:690–694.

Shopsin, B., Freedman, L. S., Goldstein, M., and Gershon, S. (1972): Serum dopamine-β-hydroxylase (DβH) activity and affective states. *Psychopharmacologia,* 27:11–16.

Sinanan, K., Keatinge, A. M. B., Beckett, P. G. S., and Love, W. C. (1975): Urinary cyclic AMP in "endogenous" and neurotic depression. *Br. J. Psychiat.,* 126:49–55.

Sjöström, R. (1973): 5-Hydroxyindoleacetic acid and homovanillic acid in cerebrospinal fluid in manic-depressive psychosis and the effect of probenecid treatment. *Eur. J. Clin. Pharmacol.,* 6:75–80.

Sjöström, R., and Roos, B. E. (1972): 5-Hydroxyindolacetic acid and homovanillic acid in cerebrospinal fluid in manic-depressive psychosis. *Eur. J. Clin. Pharmacol.,* 4:170–176.

Smith, G. P., Strohmayer, A. J., and Reis, D. J. (1972): Effect of lateral hypothalamic injections of 6-hydroxydopamine on food and water intake in rats. *Nature [New Biol.],* 235:27–28.

Snyder, S. H. and Coyle, J. T. (1969): Regional differences in H^3-norepinephrine and H^3-dopamine uptake into rat brain homogenates. *J. Pharmacol. Exp. Ther.,* 165:78–86.

Somerville, A. R., Rabouhans, M. L., and Smith, A. A. (1970): Adenosine 3':5'-cyclic monophosphate phosphodiesterase: Kinetic and inhibitor studies. *Biochem. J.,* 120: 11P–12P.

Stern, D. N., Fieve, R. R., Neff, N. H., and Costa, E. (1969): The effect of lithium chloride administration on brain and heart norepinephrine turnover rates. *Psychopharmacologia,* 14:315–322.

Stolk, J. M., Nowack, W. J., Barchas, J. D., and Platman, S. R. (1970): Brain norepinephrine: enhanced turnover after rubidium treatment. *Science,* 168:501–503.

Stone, E. A. (1971): Hypothalamic norepinephrine after acute stress. *Brain Res.,* 35:260–263.

Ström-Olsen, R., and Weil-Malherbe, H. (1958): Humoral changes in manic-depressive psychosis with particular reference to the excretion of catecholamines in urine. *J. Ment. Sci.,* 104:696–704.

Tagliamonte, A., Biggio, G., Vargiu, L., and Gessa, G. L. (1973): Free tryptophan in serum controls brain tryptophan level and serotonin synthesis. *Life Sci.,* 12:277–287.

Taylor, K. M., and Snyder, S. H. (1971): Differential effects of D- and L-amphetamine on behavior and on catecholamine disposition in dopamine and norepinephrine containing neurons of rat brain. *Brain Res.,* 28:295–309.

Thierry, A. M., Blanc, G., and Glowinski, J. (1971): Effect of stress on the disposition of catecholamines localized in various intraneuronal storage forms in the brain stem of the rat. *J. Neurochem.,* 18:449–461.

Thoenen, H. (1970): Induction of tyrosine hydroxylase in peripheral and central adrenergic neurones by cold exposure of rats. *Nature,* 228:861–862.

Trautner, E. M., Morris, R., Noack, C. H., and Gershon, S. (1955): The excretion and retention of ingested lithium and its effect on the ionic balance of man. *Med. J. Austr.,* 2:280–291.

Tupin, J. P., Schlagenhauf, C. K., and Creson, D. L. (1968): Lithium effects on electrolyte excretion. *Am. J. Psychiatry,* 125:536–543.

Waal, H. J. (1967): Propranolol-induced depression. *Br. Med. J.,* 2:50.

Wang, H. L., Harwalkar, V. R., and Waisman, H. A. (1962): Effect of dietary phenylalanine and tryptophan on brain serotonin. *Arch. Biochem. Biophys.,* 97:181–184.

Weil-Malherbe, H. (1972): The biochemistry of affective disorders. In: *Handbook of Neurochemistry, Vol. 7,* edited by A. Lajtha, pp. 371–416. Plenum Press, New York.

Weil-Malherbe, H., and Bone, A. D. (1959): The effect of reserpine on the intracellular distribution of catecholamines in the brain stem of the rabbit. *J. Neurochem.,* 4:251–263.

Weil-Malherbe, H., and Szara, S. I. (1971): *The Biochemistry of Functional and Experimental Psychoses.* Thomas, Springfield, Ill.

Weinshilbaum, R. M., Kvetňanský, R., Axelrod, J., and Kopin, I. J. (1971): Elevation of serum dopamine-β-hydroxylase activity with forced immobilization. *Nature [New Biol.],* 230:287–288.

Weischer, M. L. (1969): Über die anti-aggressive Wirkung von Lithium. *Psychopharmacologia,* 15:245–254.

Welch, B. L., Hendley, E. D., and Turek, I. (1974): Norepinephrine uptake into cerebral cortical synaptosomes after one fight or electroconvulsive shock. *Science,* 183:220–221.

Welch, B. L., and Welch, A. S. (1968): Differential activation by restraint stress of a mechanism to conserve brain catecholamines and serotonin in mice differing in excitability. *Nature,* 218:575–577.

Wilk, S., Shopsin, B., Gershon, S., and Suhl, M. (1972): Cerebrospinal fluid levels of MHPG in affective disorders. *Nature,* 235:440–441.

Winokur, G. (1972): Types of depressive illness. *Br. J. Psychiatry,* 120:265–266.

Wyatt, R. J. (1972): The serotonin-catecholamine-dream bicycle: a clinical study. *Biol. Psychiatry,* 5:33–64.

Wyatt, R. J., Chase, T. N., Scott, J., Snyder, F., and Engelman, K. (1970a): Effect of L-dopa on the sleep of man. *Nature,* 228:999–1001.

Wyatt, R. J., Engelman, K., Kupfer, D. J., Fram, D. H., Sjoerdsma, A., and Snyder, F. (1970b): Effects of L-tryptophan (a natural sedative) on human sleep. *Lancet,* 2:842–846.

Wyatt, R. J., Portnoy, B., Kupfer, D. J., Snyder, F., and Engelman, K. (1971): Resting plasma catecholamine concentrations in patients with depression and anxiety. *Arch. Gen. Psychiatry,* 24:65–70.

Yuwiler, A., Wetterberg, L., and Geller, E. (1971): Relationship between alternate routes of tryptophan metabolism following administration of tryptophan peroxidase inducers or stressors. *J. Neurochem.,* 18:593–599.

Zbinden, G., Pletscher, A., and Studer, A. (1958): Alimentary influence on the enterochromaffin cells and the 5-hydroxytryptamine content of brain and intestine. *Z. Gesam. Exp. Med.,* 129:615–620.

Biological Foundations of Psychiatry,
edited by R. G. Grenell and S. Gabay.
Raven Press, New York © 1976.

Hallucinations: Chemical and Physiological

Arnold J. Mandell and Mark A. Geyer

Department of Psychiatry, University of California at San Diego, La Jolla, California 92037

I. INTRODUCTION

The effects of hallucinogens as a class epitomize the complexity faced by biological psychiatrists today as they try to relate chemistry, neurochemistry, and neurophysiology to clinical phenomena. Hallucinogenic drug-induced behaviors often fall outside our classical diagnostic compendium; cosmic consciousness, ecstatic "insights," and unorthodox life styles in company with well regulated ego function challenge many of the assumptions and operations of psychopathological theory, and demand a humble view of man's capacity to "control" his brain. It is difficult to characterize the subjective states produced by these agents in terms of the expression or neutralization of pure sexuality or aggression.

Psychiatric philosophers fall into one of two camps: those who feel that the music of life comes before the words, and those who feel that the words precede the music. Learning theory, psychoanalytical insights, the science of decision making, mathematical models for cognitive processes—views of the word merchants—are significantly challenged by some of the effects of hallucinogenic drugs. On the other hand, instinctive theories are frequently devastated by the happenstances provoked in people's lives by these same drugs.

When scientific positions become politicized, change almost inevitably requires a massive phenomenon, which in and of itself destroys preconception or political maneuver. No longer are there six ways to come to a predictive position about the sun rising. Nor could we remain unaware of the incredible energy available in atomic and subatomic particles after the detonation of the first atomic bomb. Likewise, hallucinogenic drugs produce massively awesome phenomena in man that can and do become prepotent over any of our trivial theories of how drugs may work and caution us not to become too grandiose in our feelings that we understand how man's brain functions. The following discussion, albeit limited by the state of the art, surveys some aspects of hallucinogenic drug action, which will doubtless be increasingly in the scientific focus in the future.

II. HALLUCINOGEN STRUCTURE AND FUNCTION

A. Phenylethylamines

Structurally, the simplest hallucinogens are substituted phenylethylamines, of which the prototype is mescaline (3,4,5-trimethoxyphenylethylamine; Fig. 1). Because mescaline is one of the least active drugs in this category (with an

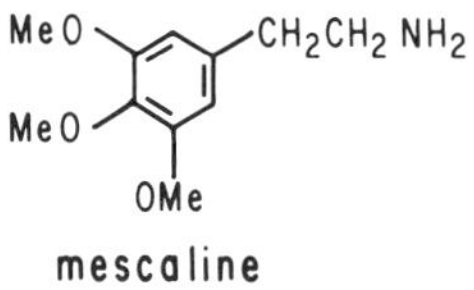

FIG. 1. The major phenylethylamine hallucinogen.

active dose range of about 200 to 500 mg), behavioral pharmacologists usually designate the potency of related compounds in *mescaline units*. Mescaline's chemical structure is remarkably like that of the catecholamines and 3,4-dimethoxyphenylethylamine, one candidate for the role of endogenous hallucinogen. By shifting methyl and methoxy groups to different positions about the carbon ring, Shulgin (1973) and others (Smythies, 1970) have created a number of exotic compounds, most notably the methoxy-amphetamine series. Several of these compounds are natural constituents of the peyote cactus (*Lophophora williamsii*) although few of the naturally occurring derivatives are as potent as mescaline. Peyote has been widely used among

American Indians in the Southwest, and legally so under the auspices of the Native American Church.

B. Indolealkylamines

A second, more complex category of hallucinogens is made up of indolealkylamines, the simplest being N,N-dimethyltryptamine (DMT) (Fig. 2). Most of these compounds are active when given parenterally. Other derivatives include 5-methoxy-N,N-dimethyltryptamine, which is relatively potent in humans in the microgram dose range, the 4-hydroxy compound psilocybin, which is active in humans, and the N,N-dimethyl derivative of serotonin, bufotenin, which is not active in humans. Psilocybin is the active principal in the sacred mushroom of Mexico. Both bufotenin and DMT have been found in the hallucinogenic snuffs of South America. Other snuffs and

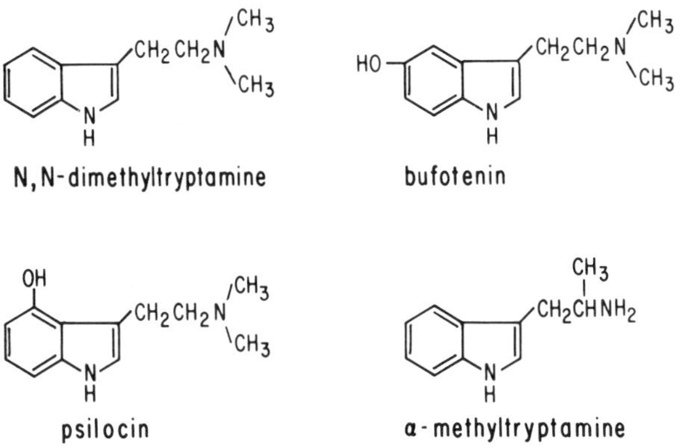

FIG. 2. Some hallucinogenic indoleamines.

drinks such as parica contain harmine or harmaline, β-carboline derivatives, which are reported to be euphorigens of indoleamine origin. The latter compounds have three-ring aromatic systems which are similar to that of lysergic acid diethylamide (LSD).

C. Ergot Alkaloids

Other hallucinogenic compounds are ergot alkaloids, and of these LSD, which is active in man in doses of 25 to 200 μg, is the most potent (Fig. 3). Most experimental changes in the structure of LSD apparently weaken its euphorigenic activity, and there seems to be little potential for productive structural alteration in the ergot alkaloids in general. An indole alkaloid with a larger ring structure, ibogaine, although not very potent, is used by some

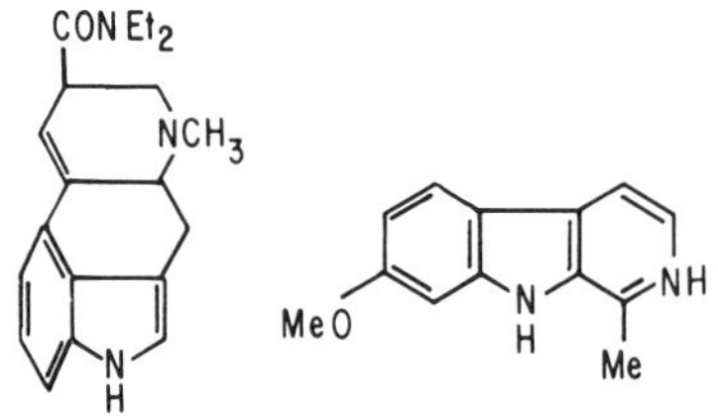

FIG. 3. More complex hallucinogenic indole alkaloids.

L S D - 25   **harmine**

African natives to remain motionless for periods of time while stalking game; it produces confusion, drunkenness, and hallucinations if taken in large doses.

D. Cannabinols

The active components of the cannabinols are characterized either by a three-ring system or by one easily convertible to three rings, a structure which differs significantly from the aromatic amine constellation of the other euphoro-hallucinogens. Delta-3-tetrahydrocannabinol (THC) and delta-9-tetrahydrocannabinol have been studied most extensively, but substitutions in the parent position of the right-hand ring (Fig. 4) increase the potency over

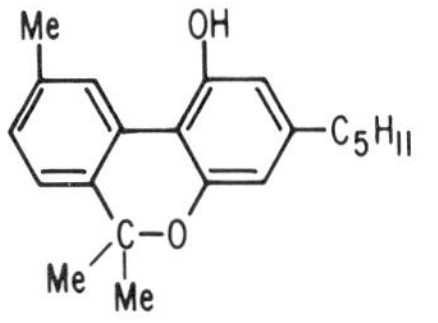

FIG. 4. Cannabinol.

a thousand fold. The dose-response characteristics of THC differ from those of LSD in one significant way: with increasing doses and over longer periods of time, instead of being stimulated, subjects get sleepy and experience frequent bursts of dreaming during several hours of drug-induced sleep. The euphoric giggling and uncontrollable laughter associated with THC are much more predictable than similar phenomena produced on occasion by other hallucinogens.

E. Glycolate Esters

A number of hallucinogenic compounds in which the substituted glycolic acid side chains are *meta* instead of *para* to the nitrogen of the piperidine ring have been synthesized and tested (Abood, 1970; Fig. 5). Of these, 1-methyl-3-piperidylcyclopentylphenylglycolate is the most powerful, and Ditran® the best known. They can cause delusional thinking, disorientation, and hallucinations. Another piperidine derivative is phencylclidine (PCP),

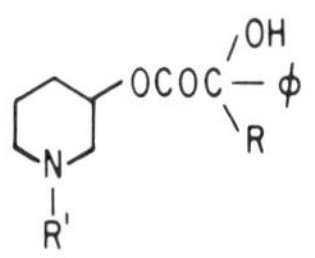

FIG. 5. A model of the piperidine-derived glycolate series.

which was originally thought to prevent sensory impulses from reaching nerve centers. Low doses of PCP produce the primary (Bleulerian) signs of schizophrenia (flattened affect, thought disorder, and emotional withdrawal) without the secondary signs (delusions or hallucinations). Psychotic reactions are frequent with larger doses and have resulted in many emergency hospitalizations because PCP is a common adulterant in street samples of hallucinogens.

F. Anticholinergics

Anticholinergic compounds should also be mentioned in the context of hallucinogenic activity. However, some authorities exclude this group, of which atropine is representative, because at low doses atropine does not produce significant euphoria (unlike other hallucinogens), and at high doses the hallucinations and delusions it produces are not later recalled (again, unlike other hallucinogens). Disruption of short-term memory is known with the cannabinols, but not permanent memory loss as is associated with the use of the belladonna alkaloids. Psychiatrists are prone to label as organic psychosis the confusion, delirium, and hallucinations associated with anticholinergic administration. Anticholinergics such as the belladonna alkaloids have been used for ages, most prominently by medieval witches and by the oracles of Delphi. These compounds are common in the *Solanaceae* family, which includes mandrake, nightshade, and *Datura* such as jimson weed.

III. STRUCTURE-FUNCTION STUDIES

Attempts to understand the conformation of brain receptors relevant to hallucinogenic action are frustrated by the fact that the molecular structure of a drug also determines its distribution in the body, uptake in the brain, and vulnerability to detoxification mechanisms. Potency can be increased by impairing a site of detoxification, as with substitution of a methyl group in the alpha position in the mescaline series to produce the methoxy-amphetamines, precluding oxidative deamination. Shulgin (1973) has placed a bromine atom in the *para* position and obtained a considerable increase in the potency of the methoxy-amphetamine derivatives. Methoxy substitution in various positions probably alters the basicity or electron configuration of the benzene ring and interferes with metabolic hydroxylation of the ring. Amphetamine is a case in point: without halogens or methoxy groups on the ring, *para* hydroxylation and further substitutions to form sulfates or glucuronides are possible detoxification mechanisms. Theoretically, blocking of that common site for hydroxylation would change the configuration and detour the substance from the usual pathway for detoxification and excretion. In fact, *para*-methoxy-amphetamine has now appeared in the street drug traffic as a potent hallucinogen with effects not unlike those of 3,4-methylenedioxyphenyliso-propylamine (MDA). Only further investigation of the *para* hydroxylation pathway in man will show if these speculations are valid. At any rate, in addition to enhancing potency, certain substitutions on the mescaline ring may enhance the benignity or reduce the maleficence of the compound. The newest compounds derived from systematic variation of methyl, ethyl, or methoxy substitutions are potent in doses smaller than 1 mg, and their perceptual and sensory effects are spread over a wide dose range.

Alternatively, distribution and uptake of a drug may be delimiting, as in the case of bufotenin, where the exposed polar group prevents its uptake into the brain. On the other hand, bufotenin's 5-methoxy derivative (which does not have the exposed 5-hydroxy group) is a potent hallucinogen in man at 3 to 5 μg/kg. All told, dose-response curves, uptake, distribution, and detoxification mechanisms must be considered before relationships between structure and function can be attributed to the conformation of brain receptors.

Theorists have approached hallucinogenic structure and function in four ways: (1) the indole hypothesis, (2) the phenylethylamine hypothesis, (3) molecular orbital models, and (4) discrimination of stereoisomers.

Viewed in planar representations, the indole nucleus is a common structural feature of hallucinogens. LSD has an indole nucleus, as do DMT, 5-methoxy DMT, psilocin, psilocybin, and the serotonin derivatives. Although phenylethylamine derivatives (mescaline and the methoxy-amphetamines) can be represented as indole-like if the alkylamine side chain is bent around in juxtaposition to the substituted benzene ring, pseudo indole conformations are improbable. Such speculations lack analysis of the tertiary structures and accurate calculation of the forms requiring the least energy for stabilization. For instance, when bent around the side chain would not be in the same plane as the single aromatic system, and in the methoxy-amphetamine compounds the side chain is obviously less stable than the pyrole component of the true indole nucleus. Although indole-like models may be made from phenylethylamines, there has been no evidence that such conformations occur at the tonicity, pH, or liquid biologic environment of the brain.

In the phenylethylamine hypothesis mescaline is the reference compound. Systematically altering the position and kind of ring substitution and the length of the side chain in these series, Shulgin (1973) has found maximum potency with 2,4,5-ring substitution and a side chain of three carbons leading to the amine nitrogen. Moreover, N-methylation of the substituted phenyl-ethylamines *reduces* activity, whereas it does the opposite in substituted indoleamines.

The potency of these compounds may be a function of either the charge-transfer potential or the energy of the highest occupied molecular orbit of the ring; both are indices of the electron donating capacity of the aromatic system. Some theorists associate hallucinogens that contain indole nuclei with the phenylethylamines on the basis of molecular orbital calculations demonstrating that the pyrole component of the indole ring donates electrons to the pi system of the benzene ring the same way that methoxy groups do in mescaline and the methoxy-amphetamines. They suggest that the N-methyl substituent in the D ring of LSD could function as a terminal amine. Thus, the indole theorists claim to explain mescaline and the methoxy-amphetamines, and the phenylethylamine theorists claim to explain LSD and the DMT derivatives.

Molecular orbital and other quantum mechanical calculations have their limitations as predictors of central activity, however. It is too easy to be impressed by efforts to predict drug activity by such means, which leave much to chance with compounds larger than three or four carbon rings; repeated passes through a computer program would be necessary to obtain consistent data, and this has not been done. Quantum mechanical calculations presently are not specific enough to define tertiary structure except on an *ad hoc* basis, and no current mathematical models serve well here. The conceptual and qualitative contributions of the mathematical approach far exceed any hard data.

Newer analyses of hallucinogenic structure and function involve the resolution of optically asymmetrical stereoisomers. It is known, for example, that *l*-LSD and iso-LSD are inactive, whereas *d*-LSD is active. More recently, working with the methoxy-amphetamine series, Shulgin has shown that the levorotatory form of 2,5-dimethoxy-4-methylamphetamine (DOM), with the alpha carbon as the asymmetric center, affects perceptual experience without sympathomimetic stimulation, whereas the latter does occur with the dextrorotatory form. The resolution of optical isomers and their clinical trials promise the possible fractionation of hallucinogenic compounds into agents that either expand perception and cognition or produce disruptive excitement, respectively, and more useful drugs may be the result.

As attempts to gain understanding of the relationships between the structure and the function of hallucinogens, the reports of small numbers of sensitive, experienced drug users have not gained much scientific credibility. A number of psychopharmacologists have found, however, that people who have had experience with many drugs can predict accurately the addictive, euphorigenic, and other effects of a new drug after an appropriate dose, and that later parametric experiments confirm their impressions. Although similar dependent variables (Sidman avoidance, etc.) appear in animal models for screening drugs in the research of Smythies (1970) and others, the relationships between drug effects in animals and in humans have not been clearly established, and major difficulties confront pharmacologic researchers. For example, of the methoxy-amphetamines, 2,5-dimethoxy-4-ethylamphetamine (DOET) is reputedly more benign than DOM. Actually, their potencies differ slightly, but a full hallucinatory psychosis is possible with either agent if the doses are equalized properly. So full dose-response curves are the *sine qua non* of clinical drug research, just as they are of studies in animal pharmacology.

IV. NEUROPHYSIOLOGY

With the possible exception of the anticholinergics, hallucinogens have a number of physiological and neurophysiological effects in common, usually including mydriasis, elevated heart rate and blood pressure, hyper-reflexia, tachypnea, increased muscle tension, occasional ataxia, nausea and vomiting, salivation, lacrimation, leukocytosis, and increased sensitivity to internal and external stimuli. Most of these phenomena are concomitants of general physiological arousal, and stimulation of the autonomic nervous system is noted for almost all the mescaline and methoxy-amphetamine derivatives at one dose or another, as well as for the ergot alkaloids and indolealkylamines.

After moderate doses of LSD, mescaline, or similar compounds human and animal EEGs are altered, although not dramatically, typically showing low amplitude, high frequency. Efforts to locate the primary sites of this general neurophysiological arousal have been reviewed by Brawley and Duffield (1972). In animals the effect is maintained after cervical transection of the spinal cord, but can be precluded by a post-collicular transection. As yet the role of peripheral sensory input in CNS arousal produced by hallucinogenic drugs is not known. As originally suggested by Bradley and Key (1958), hallucinogens may increase the response of the reticular formation to collateral sensory input, with little direct influence on reticulocortical transmission. LSD lowers the threshold for electrocortical activation and retards habituation of responsive units to repeated stimuli, but has little direct effect on the brainstem polysensory neurons. Possibly the serotonergic cells of the raphe nuclei, which extend from the midbrain to the medulla, are significantly involved in these phenomena. At low doses LSD lowers the threshold for cortical arousal produced by noises or reticular stimulation, and the raphe neurons are inhibited. With larger doses high voltage slow rhythms often result, and the arousal threshold may be raised. LSD has also been reported to increase the duration of Rapid Eye Movement (REM) sleep periods in humans; slow wave sleep is often reduced and interrupted more frequently by REM periods.

Hallucinogens have been studied also in relation to average evoked response. In cats anesthetized with barbiturates LSD was found to suppress the late responses of sensory evoked potentials. However, small doses of LSD have also been found to increase the later portion of sensory evoked responses in unanesthetized, curarized animals. In humans somatosensory and visual evoked responses are suppressed by LSD, but long-latency discharges are often increased. Winters and Wallach (1970) have suggested one of the more integrated descriptions of the cortical evoked response to hallucinogens: a continuum that begins with high-frequency low-voltage activity concomitant with heightened reticular unit activity and progresses to an eventual decrease in evoked responses.

In general, the studies of evoked responses in specific sensory systems have been inconclusive, which supports the view that hallucinogens act primarily on the nonspecific reticular systems. Alterations in the electrical activity of limbic structures are more easily interpreted and have been related to the attentional, arousal, and affective functions currently attributed to those structures in the forebrain. Perhaps the most dramatic responses are the limbic cortex and hippocampal beta seizures observed in the cat after 25 to 100 μg/kg of LSD (Adey, Dennis, and Bell, 1962). Most studies report a suppression of hippocampal theta rhythms after LSD. Temporal lobe limbic cortex activity also appears to be altered in complex ways.

Working with microelectrodes, investigators have found that very low doses of hallucinogens (particularly LSD) suppress the firing rates of the dorsal and median raphe neurons (Aghajanian, Sheard, and Foote, 1970), which include most of the serotonergic cells in mammalian brain and may include other indoleamine transmitters as well. In peripheral systems, low doses of LSD have been shown to facilitate the actions of serotonin, although conflicting evidence has been reported. Excitation of reticular formation cells or cortical neurons by iontophoretic application of serotonin can be blocked by LSD, whereas electrophoretic depression of neural cells by serotonin is not antagonized by LSD. Generally, LSD has been reported to suppress the spontaneous firing of some neurons in most areas of the brain including the lateral geniculate (Tebecis and DiMaria, 1972) and the ventral hippocampus (Haigler and Aghajanian, 1974). One notable exception is the spontaneous activity of the retinal ganglion cells, which increases after administration of LSD or certain other hallucinogenic drugs. Recently Haigler and Aghajanian (1973, 1974) systematically compared the effects of mescaline, LSD, and serotonin on cells of the raphe nuclei, and cells receiving serotonergic input by iontophoresis and systemic administration. LSD and serotonin inhibited raphe neurons and cells normally innervated by serotonergic terminals, while serotonin excited neurons in other regions (in unanesthetized rats). When given intravenously in low doses, LSD still depressed raphe cell activity and caused a subtle increase in the tonic firing rates of cells normally receiving serotonergic input. These results may indicate that LSD acts primarily by inhibition of the raphe nuclei cell bodies, thus releasing the postsynaptic neurons from serotonergic inhibition.

Many efforts to explain hallucinogenic drug action are derived from the similarities between these compounds and endogenous neurotransmitters in the brain. The indolealkylamines and the indole moiety of LSD may act by blocking receptor sites or interfering with normal transmission in the serotonergic pathways. Methoxy-amphetamines and phenylethylamines are related to dopamine, while the anticholinergic compounds resemble acetylcholine. However, attempts to relate specific transmission in these systems to neurophysiological responses have been far from satisfactory. For example, many of the phenylethylamine euphorigens appear to be as active as the indole alkaloids or the indoleamines in depressing the activity of serotonergic cells in the dorsal raphe if the doses are related to the differences in potency these agents manifest in man.

V. NEUROCHEMICAL MECHANISMS

The serotonergic cell bodies of the midbrain, pons, and medulla (the raphe nuclei) project into the forebrain (striatum and limbic forebrain structures) as well as to the lumbosacral cord. Serotonin, because its indole nucleus is identical to that of LSD, has been extensively studied in relation to hallucinogens. Gaddum (1953) and Woolley and Shaw (1954) demonstrated that LSD could block the agonistic actions of serotonin in gastrointestinal and clam heart neuromuscular junctions. Giarman and Freedman (1965) applied that model in the examination of the effect of LSD on serotonin and its major metabolite 5-hydroxyindoleacetic acid (5-HIAA) in forebrain. Subcellular fractionation showed that LSD, DMT, and psilocyin increase serotonin and decrease 5-HIAA in nerve endings, whereas non-psychoactive analogues of LSD do not. Subsequently, with Aghajanian's (Aghajanian et al., 1970) discovery that very small doses of LSD inhibit the spontaneous firing of the cells of the dorsal and median raphe nuclei, the serotonergic system of the brain was established as one of the most sensitive to hallucinogens.

Major adaptive changes occur in the serotonergic system after the administration of narcotic drugs, and the responses of the system to psychoactive drugs are dampened by lithium (cf., the "highs" of marijuana or LSD, which are reduced or prevented by lithium). In general, most if not all hallucinogens reduce the rate of turnover of brain serotonin.

A variety of treatments which alter the activity of brain serotonergic pathways influence the behavioral effects of hallucinogens. For example, pretreatment with reserpine or tetrabenazine (which release much of the vesicular store of serotonin and lead to depletion of the transmitter) enhances the effects of a threshold dose of LSD in rats. Similarly, a specific inhibitor of serotonin biosynthesis, parachlorophenylalanine (PCPA) potentiates the behavioral effects of LSD, where alpha methyltyrosine (an inhibitor of catecholamine biosynthesis) does not (Appel, Lovell, and Freedman, 1970). The potentiation may be related to the insomnia produced by PCPA (and by raphe nuclei lesions). The serotonergic system has been implicated in the induction of normal sleep (Jouvet, 1969), and it is known that sleep-deprivation by itself potentiates the effect of LSD (Safer, 1970).

The serotonin pathways in brain relate to still other behavioral effects which may be relevant to the effects of hallucinogens. Electrical stimulation of the raphe nuclei impairs the habituation of startle responses in rats. This effect has been attributed to either an increase in the activity of serotonergic processes (Sheard and Aghajanian, 1968) or, alternatively, to tetanic stimulation resulting in functional impairment of serotonergic synapses (Brawley and Duffield, 1972). The latter interpretation is more consistent with the observation that PCPA attenuates habituation to auditory stimuli in rats (Connor, Stolk, Barchas, and Levine, 1970; Carlton and Advokat, 1973). Swonger and Rech (1972) have also reported that in situations involving sufficient arousal serotonin increases habituation or inhibition of response. Most recently Davis and Sheard (1974) have suggested that sensitization to sensory input may be more relevant to the effects of serotonergic manipulation than is habituation *per se*. They lesioned the raphe nuclei in rats and observed no change in the rate of habituation to the acoustic startle response while the degree of sensitization to the startle stimuli was significantly increased by destruction of the serotonergic cell bodies.

Infusions of serotonin into the ventricles of the brain decrease the responsiveness of rats to repetitive stimuli. Conversely, the hallucinogenic congener of serotonin, bufotenin, increases the startle response of rats when infused intraventricularly to circumvent the blood-brain barrier (Geyer, Warbritton, Menkes, Zook, and Mandell, 1975). Mescaline appears to have effects similar to those of bufotenin.

The serotonergic system has also been implicated in the central control of arousal, as first suggested by Brodie and Shore (1957). Presumably acting reciprocally with the noradrenergic pathways in brain, serotonin is believed to exert an inhibitory influence on behavioral arousal. Some of the apparently sympathomimetic effects of hallucinogens may reflect disinhibition of serotonergic inhibitory tone. Alternatively, direct activation of catecholaminergic systems, especially with related drugs such as mescaline, may be responsible for much of the arousal and the phases of excitement produced by hallucinogens. Although some evidence indicates that phenylethylamine hallucinogens may in fact block noradrenergic transmission, the most compelling data suggest that an increase in the rate of turnover of brain norepinephrine is a specific action of these drugs (Leonard, 1973).

The effects on brain dopamine are apparently more complex; increases and decreases have been noted at different times. LSD has less dramatic effects on catecholaminergic activity than do phenylethylamines like mescaline or even other indoleamines like psilocybin (Stolk, Kaufman, Hanlon, Barchas, and Nisula, 1975). It is conceivable that the differential in potency between the effects of LSD and psilocybin on serotonergic processes (and on hallucinogenesis in man) is not maintained in studies of catecholamine systems. The multiplicity of effects obtained with some hallucinogens may relate to larger doses having greater potential to influence a variety of systems rather than to a structurally-determined difference in potency. It will be of continuing interest to learn which alterations in brain neurotransmitters best parallel the effects in humans when adequate, systematic dose-response studies begin to appear.

A controversy has evolved over whether LSD acts primarily as a blocker of postsynaptic serotonergic receptors or as an agonist. The commonly reported decrease in serotonin turnover in several brain regions has been thought by some to be a metabolic correlate of an apparent feedback inhibition of raphe unit firing. Recently Aghajanian has shown that section of the tract upstream from the raphe cell bodies does not eliminate the electrical silence induced by LSD, which may suggest the involvement of short-axoned recurrent collaterals or a direct effect on raphe cell bodies. Whether an antagonism or stimulation of serotonin function is the primary effect has not been established, although most of the current data suggest that increases in brain serotonin decrease responses to LSD, and that reductions in brain serotonin augment the effects of the drug.

Studies of the neurochemistry of chronic or repeated drug administration have become essential, with respect to both the clinical phenomena and the neurobiological adaptive mechanisms which may be involved in progressive and long lasting changes in human beings. The hallucinogens are perhaps the fastest inducers of tachyphylaxis of all centrally active agents, and this tolerance constitutes a formidable barrier to biochemical theories of psychosis that involve the notion of an aberrant metabolite. How could such a substance produce psychosis for days, weeks, or months on end when tolerance to analogous compounds develops so quickly? Bridger (1975) and Wyatt and Gillin (1975) have demonstrated in animals that the excitatory component of the action of hallucinogens such as mescaline and DMT becomes more marked after repeated drug administration, i.e., there is a reverse tolerance (increased sensitivity) to some of the features of the syndrome. Work remaining to be done on the development and failure of tolerance may have important implications for the pathophysiology of psychosis as well as the peculiar intolerance of interpersonal disturbance manifested by heavy and chronic users of hallucinogens.

VI. ANIMAL MODELS FOR BEHAVIORAL EFFECTS

In a literal sense most of the systematic research on hallucinogens is irrelevant, or at best inferential, if *hallucinations* are the subject of study. Most of this work has been done in animals, in which hallucinations can neither be observed nor reported. Likewise, euphoric states are not readily amenable to study in animals. Nevertheless, animal behavioral models have been extensively explored and have yielded some interesting data about perceptual variables.

Since human research with euphorigens and hallucinogens is limited, the development of animal models for the assessment of behavioral effects has been prerequisite to investigations of relationships between structure and function, the effects of dose upon response, and pharmacological interactions. To screen new drugs and study the biochemical, physiological, and psychological effects of hallucinogens, especially LSD, investigators have used many species: insects, spiders, fish, birds, amphibians, carnivores, rabbits, rodents, primates, even elephants. Depending on dose and species, the drugs can produce hypo- or hyperactivity, aggression or docility, catatonia, peculiar postures, marked autonomic stimulation, incoordination, and hypersensitivity to sensory stimuli. In contrast to their exquisite potency in man, they usually must be administered in large, toxic doses to produce readily observable effects in animals.

A few useful behavioral tests have evolved from systematic research with various forms of instrumental learning. LSD in sufficiently large doses impairs most psychomotor tasks that involve sustained, goal-directed responses. LSD reduces operant behavior maintained by positive reinforcement such as food or electrical stimulation of the lateral hypothalamus. In rats trained to bar-press for food on a fixed ratio schedule, a paradigm apparently more sensitive with respect to LSD than either variable or fixed interval schedules, the relative potencies of various psychoactive drugs were roughly comparable to those reported for humans, and the alterations were often dependent upon dose (Appel, 1968). Appel suggests that the depression of response rate may be due to a reduction in the value of the food as a reinforcer. Perhaps distractability and physiological arousal, as well as the usual increase in reaction time, contributed to the decrement in performance. Motor inhibition was apparently not involved because similar behavior was maintained by different contingencies even after high doses of LSD. This model, like most, is complicated by the fact that the time course of qualitatively different effects is influenced by both the dose and the route of administration of the drug.

The particular effect of hallucinogens on a fixed-ratio responding which has received the most attention is the so-called *hallucinogenic pause*. A wide variety of such drugs produce characteristic intermittent pauses in responding, and rapid tolerance to this effect has been shown to occur with several hallucinogens (Rech, Tilson, and Marquis, 1975).

Generally, operant behavior maintained by aversive contingencies is relatively resistant to the actions of hallucinogens; results vary quantitatively and qualitatively with species and paradigms. Some dose-related effects have been measured in the Lashley III underwater maze, which is spatially complex, but tests in simpler mazes are less sensitive (Uyeno and Mitoma, 1969). Frustrated by the variability of shuttlebox measures, Smythies (1970) developed a fairly sensitive avoidance response paradigm with rats based on the basic Sidman avoidance procedure and sophisticated analysis of data. He differentiated the effects of hallucinogens from the distinctive response patterns produced by other psychoactive agents like chlorpromazine, reserpine, amphetamine, and imipramine. This model has been employed successfully in some limited structure-function and drug interaction studies. Bridger (1975) has reported both excitatory and inhibitory effects of mescaline on shuttlebox avoidance behavior in rats. Both acute and chronic administration of mescaline improved acquisition, while acute administration inhibited previously acquired shuttle avoidance. Tolerance occurred only to the latter effect.

Since humans commonly report a variety of perceptual changes from hallucinogens, animal experiments have been designed to assess alterations in the visual and auditory modalities. Spatial disorientation and impaired visual discrimination of size have been noted in monkeys. Either increases or decreases in the accuracy of visual discrimination can be demonstrated, depending upon the animal and the dose range. Visual thresholds are often raised, although responses to visual stimuli are typically exaggerated. Alterations in time perception, tactile discrimination, and auditory generalization, especially in the face of difficult tasks or complex stimuli, have been reported for several species. A pervasive effect of low doses of hallucinogens in animals is an increased responsiveness to sensory stimuli. It is still not clear whether these compounds result in augmented sensitization to stimuli, impairment of the process of habituation, or both. Increased responsiveness has been demonstrated for most sense modalities either by testing the rate of habituation to a given stimulus or by showing increased responses after previous habituation. For example, DMT has been shown to impair long-term habituation of startle responses in rats (Davis and Bear, 1972). Similar findings have been obtained with a variety of psychophysical tests in humans. This heteromodal phenomenon may account for the distractability and disorganized attentional mechanisms commonly reported after hallucinogens are administered.

VII. DRUG EFFECTS AND HUMAN PHENOMENOLOGY

Research with hallucinogens has been curiously successful, for more often than not the hypotheses tested tend to be supported by the results obtained, although they may contradict other apparently reliable evidence. Experimental set uniquely complicates these studies because hallucinogens alter perceptual and experiential matrixes. Bereft of the usual means of synthesis, subjects are extremely influenced by their own expectations and those of the researchers as they seek to integrate what they are experiencing.

Despite the variability of particular effects, some general characteristics of hallucinogenic experiences can be described. After extensive observations of the effects of LSD and mescaline, Masters and Houston (1966, p. 5) list the following recurrent elements:

> . . . Changes in visual, auditory, tactile, olfactory, gustatory, and kinesthetic perception; changes in experiencing time and space; changes in the rate and

content of thought; body image changes; hallucinations; vivid images—eidetic images—seen with the eyes closed; greatly heightened awareness of color; abrupt and frequent mood and affect changes; heightened suggestibility; enhanced recall or memory; depersonalization and ego dissolution; dual, multiple, and fragmentized consciousness; seeming awareness of internal organs and processes of the body; upsurge of unconscious materials; enhanced awareness of linguistic nuances; increased sensitivity to nonverbal clues; sense of capacity to communicate much better by nonverbal means; . . . and, in general, apprehension of a world that has slipped the chains of normal categorical ordering.

Parallels between these drugs effects and functions now ascribed to the right hemisphere of the brain provoke speculation: might the common effects of hallucinogens be comprehensible in terms of a shift in the relative activities of the cerebral hemispheres? The concept of cerebral dominance, which once emphasized the verbal, mathematical, and analytical thought of the left or "major" hemisphere has been revised to accommodate functions now attributed to the right cerebral hemisphere. Studies of unilaterally hemispherectomized patients and persons who have undergone cerebral commissurotomies (split-brain preparation) reveal specific nonverbal functions controlled by the right hemisphere. For example, careful testing of commissurotomized patients (Nebes, 1971) indicates that the right brain is superior in the perception of part-whole relationships. The neurosurgical stimulation experiments of Penfield and Roberts (1959) also indicate the preeminence of the right lobes in visual imagery and sensations involving the passage of time. Semmes (1968) studied ipsilateral and contralateral sensorimotor capacities and found sensory and motor functions represented focally in the left hemisphere and more diffusely in the right. She suggests that left hemispheric specialization might reflect convergence of similar functional units and that in the more diffusely organized right hemisphere the convergence of dissimilar functional elements might better serve multimodal integration. Gazzaniga's experiments with monkeys (1970) demonstrate that the two hemispheres reflect independent and sometimes conflicting reinforcement histories, and Bogen (1969) has pointed out that some cultures tend to foster preferential development of one or the other hemisphere. By virtue of its explicit verbal capacities and characteristic rational processing, the functions of the left hemisphere have been consistently reinforced in Western culture (Bogen, 1969; Galin, 1974). As reinforcement, acculturation, and information processing have been related to shifts in the relative activities of the cortical hemispheres, so may hallucinogens effect the emergence of right hemispheric modes of consciousness. Indeed, Osmond's term *psychedelic* or *mind-manifesting* could be applied to an increased awareness of right hemispheric functions during hallucinogenic experiences, as might the term *mysticomimetic*.

It seems clear that the lateral specialization of human cerebral cortex provides two distinct and complementary modes of consciousness and that they function more or less in concert with one another. By virtue of its focal organization and sequential processing, the left side is best suited for verbal, mathematical, and analytical thought, whereas spatial orientation, artistic talent, visuoconstructive ability, and abstraction of part-whole relationships may well depend on the more diffuse organization which characterizes the right hemisphere. The startling perceptual experiences produced by hallucinogenic drugs might be more comprehensible in light of the capacity of the right hemisphere for simultaneous integration of information. The heteromodal influx of perceptions produced by increased attentiveness and sensitization to sensory stimuli may overwhelm the systematic sequential processing of the language hemisphere and invoke the analogical, integrative mode of the right hemisphere to consolidate the perceptual flood.

The most typical effects of both hallucinogens and right hemispheric disturbances are heteromodal changes in perception, preeminently visual functions and spatial orientations (Bogen, 1969). Klüver (1966), detailing the perceptual changes brought about by mescaline, noted increased visual imagery, contrast, depth perception, localization of sounds, expressiveness of faces, visual after-images, topographic perception, and eidetic imagery. He also reported alterations in subjective time estimates, body images, perceptions of the size of objects, and a variety of synesthesias in which one sensory stimulus results in perception in another sense modality. The eminent neurologist Teuber also noted the similarities between the effects of mescaline and right temporal lobe epilepsy (Efron, 1970). Serafetinides (1965) studied the perceptual effects of LSD in patients with epileptic foci in either the right or the left temporal lobes. Those with abnormal activity in the right hemisphere reported twice as many perceptual effects as the others, although the two groups experienced identical somatic and autonomic effects. Studies of information processing have confirmed the differential capacities of the two cortices on a variety of tasks (Ornstein, 1972). For example, spatial tasks produce a marked shift toward right hemispheric activity (lower EEG amplitude), while verbal tasks do the opposite. Some experimental evidence suggests that drugs other than those usually considered hallucinogens may shift the relative balance between the functions of the two hemispheres in specific directions. Sugerman, Goldstein, Marjerrison, and Stoltzfuss (1973), by integrating the electrical (EEG) activity over homologous areas of the right and left hemispheres in normal subjects, have measured the ratio of the activities of the two hemispheres. They report that amphetamine produced a relative increase in left hemispheric functioning, while D-675, a hallucinogen, resulted in the reverse effect at a low dose, and an even more dramatic shift to the right at a high dose.

The appreciation of music and art is dramatically emphasized in most subjective accounts of hallucinogenic experience, and increases in artistic creativity and understanding are claimed by some to be common with LSD. The influence which hallucinogenic experiences have had on artists and musicians is significant in several cultures, and conversely, the reported significance of music in shaping the hallucinogenic experience itself is undeniable. The right hemisphere has been implicated in a variety of artistic endeavors. In music, the discrimination of tonal patterns, appreciation of melody, and perception of rhythm have been demonstrated to emanate from the right cerebrum (Milner, 1962). Galin (1974) has reviewed some of the evidence for right hemispheric dominance in artistic, visuospatial, and some emotional functions, suggesting that much of right hemispheric functioning is similar to primary process thinking.

Some accounts of the long-term psychological effects of chronic use of hallucinogens also suggest the dichotomous modes of consciousness represented by the two cerebral hemispheres. Goode (1970) aptly summarized some characteristics of chronic marijuana smokers, characteristics often deemed unacceptable in Western culture, which fall under the rubric of an *amotivational syndrome:*

> . . . Some of the results seem to be an increasing irrelevance of realism; the loss of interest in plot in films and novels; a glorification of the irrational and seemingly nonsensical; an increased faith in the logic of the viscera, rather than in the intellect; a heightened sense for the absurd; an abandonment of traditional and 'linear' reasoning sequences, and the substitution of 'mosaic' and fragmentary lines of attack; bursts of insight rather than chains of thought; connectives relying on internal relevance, rather than a commonly understood and widely accepted succession of events and thoughts. (p. 172).

VIII. COMPARABILITY OF DRUG-INDUCED AND NATURALLY OCCURRING PSYCHOTIC STATES

Since the introduction of hallucinogens into the armamentarium of experimental psychopathology, a great deal of ink has been spilled concerning whether the phenomenology of experience induced by hallucinogenic drugs resembles in any way that of naturally occurring psychotic episodes. The initial, more lyrical descriptions of the drug-induced phenomena were taken at face value as similar to distortions of perception and/or psychological processes associated with such syndromes as schizophrenia (Masters and Houston, 1966). However, by the criteria of the classical primary signs of schizophrenia (Kraepelin, 1919; Vigotsky, 1934; Bleuler, 1952; Schneider, 1959), many psychodiagnosticians feel that primary thought disorder is absent in drug-induced hallucinosis in spite of the superficial similarity of hallucinations or, with large doses of drug, auditory hallucinations or delusional thinking. Some others have argued that the episodes resembling psychotic states are probably dependent upon some predilection in the experimental subject or patient allowing unique or idiosyncratic responses to this kind of drug. That is, hallucinogenic drug experiences that resemble schizophrenic episodes occur because the patients themselves have such a tendency or such an adaptive or defensive structure latent within them (Monroe, Heath, Mickle, and Llewellyn,

1957; Grof, 1967). European and American studies in the late 1950s and 1960s were based on the premise that borderline schizophrenics or patients with schizophrenic episodes in their history are more vulnerable to a standard dose or dose-response test of hallucinogenic drug vis-à-vis personality disintegration than normal controls. They failed to demonstrate the validity of that hypothesis (Cohen, 1964). Even among schizophrenic patient populations so-called "bad trips" were idiosyncratic and unpredictable in occurrence. Clinicians who have participated in such research acknowledge that the people whose ego functions they expected to be the most disrupted by the hallucinogenic drug experience were often the least affected. Thus the most simple of the potential relationships between the actions of hallucinogenic drugs and the syndromes of severe psychopathology appear in considerable doubt. That the acute effect of the drug mimics a type of schizophrenic episode (by means of a common biochemical mechanism?) or that hallucinogenic drugs can precipitate psychotic reactions in genetically prone individuals is not documented in the literature.

Some clinicians attempt to refine the discrimination between hallucinogenic drug experience and naturally occurring psychosis by examining the drug experience from the standpoint of signs of *organic* psychosis. In a general way, they emphasize distortions that can occur in perceptions of color, shape, and patterns rather than the drug-induced changes involving highly personal imaginings of voices or persons intimately involved in the psychodynamic focus of the individual.

In fact, such discriminations are far from easily made (Cohen, 1967; Ungerleider and Fisher, 1967). For example, the expectation, the circumstances under which the drug is taken, the set reported by the patient or his companions has become a prominent part of the clinician's matrix of comprehension. Once he ascertains that a drug has or has not been taken in an acute psychiatric emergency, it is difficult, if not impossible, to delineate *post hoc* what might or might not have been drug-induced in the circumstances. Paranoid breaks have been diagnosed, for instance, in patients who felt they had been given hallucinogenic drugs, and who came to the doctor reporting such a circumstance, when in fact later investigation revealed that no drug was involved. The reverse kind of situation has also occurred—the blind administration of hallucinogens and associated diagnosis of functional psychiatric disease. From the literature and the authors' experience, it becomes clear that the two phenomena have not been well differentiated. Such distinctions as more versus less organic, more perceptual versus more psychodynamic, or other commonly accepted clinical criteria are probably not as helpful as we had hoped. That is not to say that the primary pathology or the moving force of the personality disintegration is the same in both cases, but that the similarities may be the expression of man's limited armamentarium for coping with various degrees of ego disruption. In other words, the similarities in phenomenology may be due to similarities not in the primary etiological agent or its neurobiological mechanisms, but in the psychological, psychosocial, or psychobiological defenses used to handle this kind of CNS disruption.

Malcolm Bowers (1973), using an assortment of objective descriptive scales (with and without drugs, as they may or may not have been suspected), reported that the premorbid adjustment scales he used were just as efficacious in predicting the outcome for drug-induced psychosis as they had been for naturally occurring schizophrenia. His examination focused on the phase after the acute episode, in which the drug use was associated with disruption of function with or without later psychosocial regression in coping style following the severe psychotic episodes involving drugs. The poor premorbid patient often settled into a chronic pattern not discriminable from that seen in schizophrenic patients.

Thus it might be informative to look for similarities between hallucinogenic drug experience and psychosis *after* severe acute episodes or following chronic use. The lethargy, flatness, tendency to interpersonal withdrawal, inertia, a kind of failure to thrive, a disintegration of psychosocial coping mechanisms, the condition, in short, of the "acid freak" may constitute a syndrome similar to that of chronic schizophrenia or process schizophrenia. Bowers's results are consistent with the range of pathology seen in the emergency room of the UCLA Neuropsychiatric Institute during the years when hallucinogen overdoses provided many patients for observation (Ungerleider and Fisher, 1967).

In addition to the post-acute phase, similarities between functional and drug-induced hallucinogenic phenomena may occur very early in a drug's course of action. The onset of action for most hallucinogens ranges from a half hour or so to two hours after administration. Early in this period there are subtle and progressive changes in thought style and processes, withdrawal of focus to the self, highly personalized meanings, a gradual disintegration of psychological boundaries, a fusion with what one perceives to be the world, experiences of ecstasy, and a number of other phenomena that resemble descriptions of early or "primary" signs of schizophrenia or the schizo-affective disorders (Rumke, 1923). These disturbances of thought and feeling early in the drug's onset of action may more resemble the real phenomenology of schizophrenia than those that occur under the maximal direct influence of the drug. There is little relevant research available in this promising area as yet.

Perhaps hallucinogenic drug-induced psychopathology and naturally occurring schizophreniform, schizophrenic, or schizo-affective disorders ought to be more systematically examined at these two times, i.e., *before* the full-blown drug-induced distortions in affect, thought, and apperception, and *after,* during the state of anergy following single or repeated administrations. The present supposition is that at those two times vulnerability might be more easily assessed. Furthermore, the criteria for describing the early drug effects could be derived from studies of the so-called fundamental thought disorders of the schizophrenic process and might even be useful in further refining them.

IX. ENDOGENOUS HALLUCINOGENS: MECHANISM OR MYTH?

For a number of years, workers in neurochemistry, neurobiology, psychiatry, and biological psychiatry, well represented in this book, have looked for single or complicated etiological agents that might produce one or another of the major mental disorders. During the early days of the infectious disease revolution, with the discoveries of agents causing illnesses and the development of treatments to kill the agents and prevent or cure the illnesses, some of the efforts to examine such parameters led to bizarre experiments in psychiatric research. For example, because unusual indolic compounds in the urine of hospitalized mental patients were found to have come from coliform bacilli, some experimenters in America and Europe tried removing colons from psychotics to see what the psychiatric effects would be. As might be expected, this dominant theme in American medical research, the quest for specific infectious causes of disease, continued to influence psychiatric research. Since the 1930s, documented genetic neurometabolic disorders with behavioral and mental symptoms have ranged from phenylketonuria (Knox, 1966) to the cerebellar ataxia and psychosis of Hartnup Disease (Jepson, 1966). The Harley-Mason methylation hypothesis (Osmond and Smythies, 1952), which suggested that normally peripherally active amines became centrally active and disruptive when a polar group, either the hydroxy or the terminal nitrogen, was methylated, generated a great deal of research leading to the discovery of enzymes in the brain that catalyzed the formation of dimethoxyphenylethylamine or dimethyltryptamine or N,N-dimethyl-serotonin (Friedhoff and Van Winkle, 1962; Mandell, 1973a). The chemical details may yet lead down a long road before the processes are elucidated definitively (Hsu and Mandell, 1975). Only now are investigations prompted by the chemical resemblance between hallucinogenic drugs and neurotransmitters in the brain becoming well focused. The most conspicuous theory currently is the dopamine hypothesis, which takes into account the resemblance of amphetamine psychosis to paranoid psychosis, the effects of antipsychotic drugs on dopamine receptors, and stereochemical data (Snyder, 1974).

Thus, the neurometabolic matrix of research has pointed to two possible metabolic aberrances: the presence of an abnormal substance such as dimethoxyphenylethylamine, DMT or bufotenin, or too much of a normal metabolite such as dopamine. However, simple bidimensional models of central modulatory synaptic transmission (substances going *up* or *down*) are appearing more and more inadequate. For example, simple reuptake or release of transmitters as models of drug actions seem as though they would not maintain expression over long periods of time, from the standpoints of either metabolic activity or its behavioral reflections. An increasing number of mechanisms are being elucidated (Mandell, 1973a,b, 1975; Mandell, Segal, Kuczenski, and Knapp, 1972), which have as their apparent purpose or organization the dampening of alterations in the homeostatic balances of excitability in synaptic systems. Changes in receptor sensitivity, uptake of substrate into nerve endings for transformation into transmitters, acute changes in conformation or physical state of neurotransmitter biosynthetic enzymes, changes in the synthesis or degradation rate of those enzymes, and perhaps their variable axoplasmic flow rates, all appear to be directed toward dampening excitability. In addition, convergence of excitatory and inhibitory systems, such as the interaction speculated to occur between dopamine and acetylcholine in the striatum (Kuczenski, Segal, and Mandell, 1975) or between the catecholamines and serotonin (Brodie, Comer, Coste, and Dlabac, 1966) have as their underlying theme a balance between excitation and inhibition, implicit in the statement that the excitation of one system leads toward compensation in the other. The current arguments are about whether such compensatory changes occur in parallel or in sequence, whether their effects are presynaptic or postsynaptic, and whether their effects come about via ion exchange mechanisms, small molecule regulators, alterations in vesicular impingement (exocytosis), or other neuromolecular mechanisms.

From a neurobiological point of view it is difficult to imagine a psychosis based on a disorder that produced an aberrant amine or too much of a normal amine remaining active over hours, days, weeks, or months, disrupting CNS function to produce a consistent syndrome. Why doesn't the brain dampen out such aberrant excitation or inhibition, through parallel, sequential, or modulatory systems? If such mechanisms are available, why aren't they invoked?

It is well known that hallucinogenic drugs, particularly the indole alkaloid group, but certainly the phenylethylamines as well, quickly produce tolerance or tachyphylaxis. The "street people" know that LSD taken on consecutive days begins to fail to work; with increasing doses it just doesn't do the same things. Recent studies by Bridger (1975) have suggested that tolerance can develop to one set of behavioral responses to hallucinogenic drugs and not to another. Whether this represents differential rates of accrual for such phenomena or actual failure to affect one versus another remains to be seen. In some cases, *sensitization* to psychoactive agents appears to occur. For example, Segal and Mandell (1974) have reported that the stereotypy response of rats to amphetamine, when measured in an activity chamber over a long period of time, appears to be, if anything, more easily elicited as a result of previous experience with the drug. Such easy elicitation has been seen as long as a week or two after the last exposure to the drug. So, although the matter is far from settled, there may be factors of progressive sensitization as well as factors of loss of sensitivity with repeated exposure to psychoactive drugs. Nonetheless, in man, the hallucinogenic drugs bring out, as well as any other drug family, the problem presented by a chemical model of psychosis: how could an aberrant molecule, such as a methylated indoleamine or a methoxylated phenylethylamine, continue to have psychotogenic properties over time?

That question suggests another which we do not yet have the tools to explore adequately, and that involves the concept of the neurobiological defense apparatus of the human brain. Might it be possible that psychopathologically affected individuals differ from normal humans in their capacities to dampen or balance inhibitory or excitatory disruptions of the brain? The defect may be, not necessarily in the perturbating agent, but in the dampening response to the perturbating agent. In the psychological literature some authors seem to be coming to grips with such underlying possibilities, e.g., the failure to habituate quickly to the galvanic skin response and the theory of hyperdrive states leading to broad plateaux of stimulus generalization and lack of discrimination in cognitive processes and selections in schizophrenic thought (Chapman, 1958; Mednick, 1955; Broen and Storms, 1961; Silverman, 1967).

Unfortunately, the neurometabolic literature is conspicuously lacking in genetic diseases that have as their expression such a defect in a regulatory mechanism. Although losses or diminution in enzymatic pathways have been documented and their ramifications explored, defects in the *regulation* of these systems, e.g., insensitivity to feedback or failure to respond to a metabolic load with new enzyme synthesis, have not been systematically studied, nor has a good example been found. From the standpoint of psychological theories, neurobiological adaptive mechanisms may be the next frontier of drug research in relation to psychopathological conditions, and it will no doubt involve examination of rates of habituation, the development of tolerance, and the development of coping or dampening mechanisms as they relate to hallucinogenic drugs. Until that time the query "Endogenous hallucinogens, mechanism or myth?" for the explanation of the so-called functional psychoses remains unanswered.

REFERENCES

Abood, L. G. (1970): Stereochemical and membrane studies with the psychotomimetic glycolate esters. In: *Psychotomimetic Drugs,* edited by D. H. Efron. Raven Press, New York.

Adey, W. R., Dennis, F. R., and Bell, B. J. (1962): Effects of LSD-25, psilocybin and psilocin on temporal lobe EEG patterns and learned behavior in the cat. *Neurology* 12:591–602.

Aghajanian, G. K., Sheard, M. H., and Foote, W. E. (1970): LSD and mescaline: Comparison of effects on single units in the midbrain raphe. In: *Psychotomimetic Drugs,* edited by D. H. Efron. Raven Press, New York.

Appel, J. B. (1968): The effect of psychotomimetic drugs on animal behavior. In: *Psychopharmacology—A Review of Progress 1957–1967,* edited by D. H. Efron. USPHS, Washington, D. C.

Appel, J. B., Lovell, R. A., and Freedman, D. X. (1970): Alterations in the behavioral effects of LSD by pretreatment with p-chlorophenylalanine and α-methyl-p-tyrosine. Psychopharmacologia (Berl.) 18:387–406.

Bleuler, M. (1952): Dementia Praecox, or the Group of Schizophrenias, translated by J. Zinkin. International Universities Press, New York.

Bogen, J. E. (1969): The other side of the brain II: An appositional mind. Bull. Los Angeles Neurol. Soc. 34:135–162.

Bowers, M. B., Jr. (1973): LSD-related states as models of psychosis. In: Psychopathology and Psychopharmacology, edited by J. O. Cole, A. M. Freedman, and A. J. Friedhoff. Johns Hopkins Univ. Press, Baltimore.

Bradley, P. B., and Key, B. J. (1958): The effects of drugs on arousal responses produced by electrical stimulation of the reticular formation of the brain stem. Electroencephalogr. Clin. Neurophysiol. 10:97–110.

Brawley, P., and Duffield, J. C. (1972): The pharmacology of hallucinogens. Pharmacol. Rev. 24:31–66.

Bridger, W. H. (1975): Good trip or bad trip: the roles of tolerance and stress in hallucinogenic drug action. In: Advances in Biochemical Psychopharmacology, Vol. 13: Neurobiological Mechanisms of Adaptation and Behavior, edited by A. J. Mandell. Raven Press, New York.

Brodie, B. B., Comer, M. S., Coste, E., and Dlabac, A. (1966): Role of brain serotonin in the mechanism of the central action of reserpine. J. Pharmacol. Exp. Ther. 152:340–349.

Brodie, B. B., and Shore, P. A. (1957): A concept for a role of serotonin and norepinephrine as chemical mediators in the brain. Ann. N.Y. Acad. Sci. 66:631–638.

Broen, W. E. Jr., and Storms, L. H. (1961): A reaction potential ceiling and response decrements in complex situations. Psychol. Rev. 68:405–415.

Carlton, P. L., and Advokat, C. (1973): Attenuated habituation due to parachlorophenylalanine. Pharmacol. Biochem. Behav. 1:657–663.

Chapman, L. J. (1958): Intrusion of associative responses into schizophrenic conceptual performance. J. Abnormal Soc. Psychol. 56:374–379.

Cohen, S. (1964): Drugs of Hallucination. Secker and Warburg, London.

Cohen, S. (1967): Beyond Within: The LSD Story. Atheneum, New York.

Connor, R. L., Stolk, J. M., Barchas, J. D., and Levine, S. (1970): PCPA and habituation to repetitive auditory startle stimuli in rats. Physiol. Behav. 5:1215–1219.

Davis, M., and Bear, H. D. (1972): Effects of N,N-dimethyltryptamine on retention of startle response habituation in the rat. Psychopharmacologia 27:29–44.

Davis, M., and Sheard, M. H. (1974): Habituation and sensitization of the rat startle response: effects of raphe lesions. Physiol. Behav. 12:425–431.

Efron, D. H., editor (1970): Psychotomimetic Drugs. Raven Press, New York.

Friedhoff, A. J., and Van Winkle, E. (1962): Isolation and characterization of a compound from the urine of schizophrenics. Nature 194:897–989.

Gaddum, J. H. (1953): Antagonism between lysergic acid diethylamide and 5-hydroxytryptamine. J. Physiol. (Lond.) 121:15–19.

Galin, D. (1974): Implications for psychiatry of left and right cerebral specialization. Arch. Gen. Psychiatry 31:572–583.

Gazzaniga, M. S. (1970): The Bisected Brain. Appleton-Century-Crofts, New York.

Geyer, M. A., Warbritton, J. D., Menkes, D. B., Zook, J. A., and Mandell, A. J. (1975): Opposite effects of intraventricular serotonin and bufotenin on rat startle responses. Pharmacol. Biochem. Behav., vol. 3, no. 4.

Giarman, N. J., and Freedman, D. X. (1965): Biochemical aspects of the action of psychotomimetic drugs. Pharmacol. Rev. 17:1–25.

Goode, E. (1970): Marijuana and the politics of reality. In: The New Social Drug: Cultural, Medical, and Legal Perspectives on Marijuana, edited by D. E. Smith. Prentice-Hall, Englewood Cliffs, New Jersey.

Grof, S. (1967): Use of LSD-25 in personality diagnostics and therapy of psychogenic disorders. In: The Use of LSD in Psychotherapy and Alcoholism. Vol. III. Bobbs-Merrill, Indianapolis.

Haigler, H. J., and Aghajanian, G. K. (1973): Mescaline and LSD: Direct and indirect effects on serotonin-containing neurons in brain. Eur. J. Pharmacol. 21:153–160.

Haigler, H. J., and Aghajanian, G. K. (1974): Lysergic acid diethylamide and serotonin: A comparison of effects on serotonergic neurons and neurons receiving a serotonergic input. *J. Pharmacol. Exp. Ther.* 188:688–699.

Hsu, L. L., and Mandell, A. J. (1975): Enzymatic formation of tetrahydro-β-carboline and 5-methyltetrahydrofolic acid in rat brain fractions: Regional and subcellular distribution. *J. Neurochem.* 24:631–636.

Jepson, J. B. (1966): Hartnup disease. In: *The Metabolic Basis of Inherited Disease*, edited by J. B. Stanbury, J. B. Wyngaarden, and D. S. Frederickson. McGraw-Hill, New York.

Jouvet, M. (1969): Biogenic amines and the states of sleep. *Science* 163:32–41.

Klüver, H. (1966): *Mescal and Mechanisms of Hallucinations*. University of Chicago Press, Chicago.

Knox, W. E. (1966): Phenylketonuria. In: *The Metabolic Basis of Inherited Disease*, edited by J. B. Stanbury, J. B. Wyngaarden, and D. S. Frederickson. McGraw-Hill, New York.

Kraepelin, E. (1919): *Dementia Praecox and Paraphrenia*. 8th German edition translated by R. M. Barclay and G. M. Robertson. Livingstone, Edinburgh.

Kuczenski, R., Segal, D. S., and Mandell, A. J. (1975): Regional and subcellular distribution and the kinetic properties of rat brain choline acetyltransferase—Some functional considerations. *J. Neurochem.* 24:39–47.

Leonard, B. E. (1973): Some effects of the hallucinogenic drug 2,5-dimethoxy-4-methylamphetamine on the metabolism of biogenic amines in the rat brain. *Psychopharmacologica (Berl.)* 32:33–49.

Mandell, A. J. (1973a): Neurobiological barriers to euphoria. *Am. Scientist* 61:565–573.

Mandell, A. J. (1973b): Redundant macromolecular mechanisms in central synaptic regulation. In: *New Concepts in Neurotransmitter Regulation*, edited by A. J. Mandell. Plenum Press, New York.

Mandell, A. J. (1975): Neurobiological mechanisms of presynaptic metabolic adaptation and their organization: implications for a pathophysiology of the affective disorders. In: *Advances in Biochemical Pharmacology, Vol. 13: Neurobiological Mechanisms of Adaptation and Behavior*, edited by A. J. Mandell. Raven Press, New York.

Mandell, A. J., Segal, D. S., Kuczenski, R., and Knapp. S. (1972): Some macromolecular mechanisms in CNS neurotransmitter pharmacology and their psychobiological organization. In: *Chemistry of Mood, Motivation, and Memory*, edited by J. McGaugh. Plenum Press, New York.

Masters, R. E. L., and Houston, J. (1966): *The Varieties of Psychedelic Experience*. Holt, Rinehart, and Winston, New York.

Mednick, S. A. (1955): Distortions of the gradient of stimulus generalization related to cortical brain damage and schizophrenia. *J. Abnormal Soc. Psychol.* 51:536–542.

Milner, B. (1962): Laterality effects in audition. In: *Interhemispheric Relations and Cerebral Dominance*, edited by V. B. Mountcastle. Johns Hopkins University Press, Baltimore.

Monroe, R. R., Heath, R. C., Mickle, W. A., and Llewellyn, R. C. (1957): Correlation of rhinencephalic electrograms with behavior: a study on humans under the influence of LSD and mescaline. *Electroencephalogr. Clin. Neurophysiol.* 9:623–642.

Nebes, R. (1971): Superiority of the minor hemisphere in commissurotomized man for perception of part-whole relations. *Cortex* 7:333–349.

Ornstein, R. D. (1972): *The Psychology of Consciousness*. Freeman, San Francisco.

Osmond, H., and Smythies, J. (1952): Schizophrenia: A new approach. *J. Ment. Sci.* 98:305–315.

Penfield, W., and Roberts, L. (1959): *Speech and Brain Mechanisms*. Princeton University Press, Princeton.

Rech, R. H., Tilson, H. A., and Marquis, W. J. (1975): Adaptive changes in behavior after repeated administration of various psychoactive drugs. In: *Advances in Biochemical Pharmacology, Vol. 13: Neurobiological Mechanisms of Adaptation and Behavior*, edited by A. J. Mandell. Raven Press, New York.

Rumke, D. H. (1923): *Phaenomen en klinisch—psychiatriche studie oven gelucksgevaal*. Proefschrift E. Idjo, Leiden.

Safer, D. J. (1970): The effect of LSD on sleep-deprived men. *Psychopharmacologia* (Berl.) 17:414–424.

Schneider, K. (1959): *Clinical Psychopathology,* translated by M. W. Hamilton. Grune and Stratton, New York.

Segal, D. S., and Mandell, A. J. (1974): Long-term administration of d-amphetamine: progressive augmentation of motor activity and stereotypy. *Pharmacol. Biochem. Behav.* 2:249–255.

Semmes, J. (1968): Hemispheric specialization: a possible clue to mechanism. *Neuropsychologia* 6:11–26.

Serafetinides, E. A. (1965): The significance of temporal lobes and of hemispheric dominance in the production of the LSD-25 symptomatology in man: a study of epileptic patients before and after temporal lobectomy. *Neuropsychologia* 3:69–76.

Sheard, M. H., and Aghajjanian, G. K. (1968): Stimulation of midbrain raphe neurons: behavioural effects of serotonin release. *Life Sci.* 7:19–25.

Shulgin, A. T. (1973): Mescaline: The chemistry and pharmacology of its analogs. *Lloydia* 36:46–58.

Silverman, J. (1967): Variations in cognitive control and psychophysiological defense in the schizophrenias. *Psychosomat. Med.* 29:225–245.

Smythies, J. R., editor (1970): *The Mode of Action of Psychotomimetic Drugs.* NRP Bulletin, Vol. 8, MIT Press, Boston.

Snyder, S. H. (1974): *Madness and the Brain.* McGraw-Hill, New York.

Stolk, J. M., Kaufman, M. E., Hanlon, D. P., Barchas, J. D., and Nisula, B. C. (1975): Brain dopamine-β-hydroxylase activity *in vivo:* Pharmacological, endocrinological and psychological implications for adaptation. In: *Advances in Biochemical Psychopharmacology, Vol. 13: Neurobiological Mechanisms of Adaptation and Behavior,* edited by A. J. Mandell. Raven Press, New York.

Sugerman, A. A., Goldstein, L., Marjerrison, G., and Stoltzfuss, N. (1973): Recent research in EEG amplitude analysis. *Dis. Nerv. Syst.* 34:162–171.

Swonger, A. K., and Rech, R. H. (1972): Serotonergic and cholinergic involvement in habituation of activity and spontaneous alternation of rats in a Y maze. *J. Comp. Physiol. Psychol.* 81:509–522.

Tebecis, A. K., and DiMaria, A. (1972): A re-evaluation of the mode of action of 5-hydroxytryptamine on lateral geniculate neurones: comparisons with catecholamines and LSD. *Exp. Brain Res.* 14:480–493.

Ungerleider, J. T., and Fisher, D. (1967): The problems of LSD-25 and emotional disorder. *Calif. Med.* 106:49–55.

Uyeno, E. T., and Mitoma, C. (1969): The relative effectiveness of several hallucinogens in disrupting maze performance by rats. *Psychopharmacologia* 16:73–79.

Vigotsky, L. S. (1934): Thought in schizophrenia. *Arch. Neurol. Psychiat.* 31:1063–1077.

Winters, S. D., and Wallach, M. B. (1970): Drug-induced states of CNS excitation: A theory of hallucinosis. In: *Psychotomimetic Drugs,* edited by D. H. Efron. Raven Press, New York.

Woolley, D. W., and Shaw, E. (1954): A biochemical and pharmacological suggestion about certain mental disorders. *Proc. Nat. Acad. Sci. USA* 40:228–231.

Wyatt, R. J., and Gillin, J. C. (1975): The development of tolerance to and dependence on endogenous neurotransmitters. In: *Advances in Biochemical Psychopharmacology, Vol. 13: Neurobiological Mechanisms of Adaptation and Behavior,* edited by A. J. Mandell. Raven Press, New York.

Biological Foundations of Psychiatry,
edited by R. G. Grenell and S. Gabay.
Raven Press, New York © 1976.

Model Psychoses

Charles E. Frohman and Jacques S. Gottlieb

The Lafayette Clinic and Department of Psychiatry, Wayne State University School of Medicine, Detroit, Michigan 48202

I. INTRODUCTION

For many years the production of model psychoses has interested research workers studying mental diseases. Production of a model of any organic disease in animals can be a very useful tool for research. In the case of diabetes mellitus, the use of alloxan permitted the production of diabetic animals so that the disease could be studied without having to obtain live human tissue. In cancer research carcinogens have been used to produce cancers in animals whose tissues could subsequently be studied. On the other hand, it is very difficult, if not impossible, to obtain living tissue from the central nervous system of human beings. Therefore it would be a great help to research workers to be able to produce model psychoses in both humans and in animals. It would be extremely useful if we could first learn how to produce the symptoms of a mental disease in humans, then repeat the same procedure in animals so we could study samples of their brains.

There are several methods of producing conditions that at least resemble known psychoses (Luby and Gottlieb, 1971). A number of deprivational states are known to lead to psychotic reactions, some of which may imitate many of the symptoms of some mental diseases. Sensory deprivation has been known to cause a number of symptoms that resemble those in schizophrenia (Brawley and Pos, 1967). Sleep deprivation also appears to produce a number of symptoms that mimic psychoses (West et al., 1962). Both deprivational states have been studied at some length. Reports of psychotic symptoms resulting from rapid-eye-movement (REM) sleep deprivation have been published but not confirmed in all cases by workers who have tried to repeat them (Dement, 1960; Jouvet and Mounier, 1960). Finally stimulus deprivation in animals has been shown to produce psychotomimetic symptoms (Beach and Janes, 1954). The first section of this chapter will deal with the symptoms elicited by deprivational states and the possible mechanisms of symptom production. It will examine the relationship of the symptoms to known psychotic disorders and attempt to assess the value of deprivation techniques in the study of mental illness.

Model psychoses, which partly resemble some mental diseases, can also be produced biochemically rather than by controlling stimulus input (Farnsworth, 1968). Very early in history, it was known that eating certain plants caused psychotomimetic effects. The second portion of this chapter will concern itself with model psychoses produced by drugs first isolated from these plants. Ancient man felt that he was deriving a mystic, magical, or religious experience from them. In more recent times, they have been used by individuals who feel that they stimulate personality development, promote spiritual growth, and expand reality. Some psychiatrists have attempted to

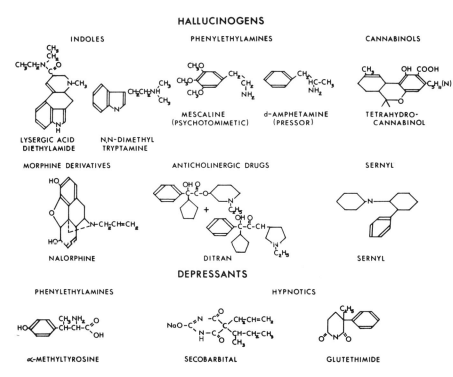

FIG. 1. Structures of some psychotomimetic drugs.

treat mentally ill patients with psychotomimetic drugs. The ingestion of toxic plant materials, such as mushrooms of the Amanita and Psilocybe genera or extracts of the peyote cactus, may mimic a number of symptoms of schizophrenia. The South American cohoba and the sacred Mexican mushroom teonanacatyl also produce psychotomimetic symptoms. Ergot, which is derived from wheat rust, is a highly active psychotomimetic material containing, among other compounds, lysergic acid diethylamide (LSD). In the 17th century, whole villages in southern France went temporarily insane from eating rust-infected wheat. Many other plants, such as *Cannabis sativa* (hemp), *Myristica fragrans* (nutmeg), and *Ipomoea violacea* (morning glory) contain psychotomimetic compounds. The presence of psychotomimetic compounds occurs in 10 different plant families; the chemical substances responsible for their effects are different in eight of the 10 families. The list of chemical compounds with psychotomimetic properties includes methylated indoles, methylated catecholamines, morphine derivatives, isoquinucleides, ergolines, tropanes, and isoxazoles (Farnsworth, 1968). Structures of some of the psychotomimetic compounds are shown in Fig. 1. Many of these drugs have been widely studied and used in attempts to produce model psychoses for research purposes.

II. DEPRIVATIONAL STATES

A. Sensory Deprivation

It has been recognized that isolation causes many changes in the psyche. In every culture the hermit, the isolate, and the recluse have been considered to be peculiar. Small (1900) has reviewed the biographies and discussed the various peculiarities of 100 famous people who lived isolated or semi-isolated lives. Nine of these 100 people had hallucinations, eight of them actually being famous for the visions they had received; eight regressed to the negative state. Even before organized experiments were conducted on the effects of sensory isolation, it was known that these conditions produced peculiarities. In many religions isolation is used to evoke religious experiences. The basis of organization of many monastic orders is isolation from the world. Other religions also incorporate sensory isolation as part of their rituals. Buddhism, yoga, and many primitive religions use isolation as a stimulant for mystic experiences.

During the Korean War, brainwashing (sensory underload followed by sensory overload) caused extensive psychologic changes in American prisoners of war (Bexton, Heron, and Scott, 1954). Following the Korean War, many experimenters began working on sensory deprivation in order to determine exactly what was represented by this phenomenon. The results were confusing; they appeared to be affected by three factors, two uncontrollable and one controllable, the experimenter himself being one of the uncontrollable factors. Even with various experimenters using the same technique, varied results were obtained. More important than the experimenter is the subject. Some subjects are much less responsive to sensory deprivation than others. This ability to resist the effect of sensory deprivation may be called by many different names (introversion, ego strength), but whatever it is called it most certainly exists. Under such circumstances, results from subject to subject are not consistent. In addition the type of sensory input modifications used to produce the conditions is very important in determining the type of results obtained.

The types of sensory modification can be divided into four general types. The first is maximum deprivation of sensory input, an example of which can be found in the work of Lilly (1956). It is of course impossible to stop all sensory input, but Lilly's work came as close to this as possible. He placed the subject nude in a tank of water carefully kept at body temperature with a facial mask that shut out light and sound but permitted the subject to breathe. It must be realized that sensory input is still received by the individual but that the sensory input received would certainly be monotonous. The technique of Lilly is probably the best for producing hallucinations and psychotic reactions, or at least it does so more rapidly than many of the others. Again monotony of sensory input has been the historic cause of many psychotic symptoms in people placed in situations of extreme monotony (Lilly, 1956). Hallucinations have often been reported among long-distance night truck drivers (Heron, 1957).

A second type of modification of sensory input is reduced patterning of sensory input, which could be described as perceptual isolation (Heron, 1961). In this type of isolation, extreme monotony is also the rule, and normal sensory input becomes quite distorted. The individual wears translucent goggles so that he receives light stimulations all the time, but these stimulations are merely of a monotonous color. They contain no recognizable forms or figures. His limbs are placed in cardboard sleeves and cuffs so that the tactile sensations are again monotonous and not those normally encountered.

The third type consists of stimulations imposed on monotony (Kubie, 1961). The individual is put in a tank-type respirator with restrictive vision. The auditory latitude and intensity then can be manipulated so that actual overload may occur.

The fourth type of modification involves gross distortion of perceptual images such as in delayed auditory feedback. This type produces quite different symptoms than the others, and will be considered only briefly here. Instead of hallucinations and thinking disturbances caused by the other three types of sensory manipulation, this type usually results in stuttering, anger, and utter confusion (Freedman, Grunebaum, and Greenblatt, 1961).

The other types of deprivation often result first in a reduction in work performance followed later by an increment in work performance and a decrease in discriminatory ability. In early stages of deprivation, the subject feels sleepy but later becomes exhilarated, and his performance on many tests may be facilitated (Myers, 1965). Deficiency in visual motor coordination, changes in size and color perception, loss of accuracy in tactile, spatial, and apparent movement are experienced. Hallucinations frequently occur, and thinking disturbances are often present. Finally a panic state and paranoia develop. The resultant symptoms resemble those of schizophrenia rather closely. At the same time, they resemble even more closely the effects of administering the drug phencyclidine (Sernyl®).

Many theories have been advanced as to how sensory deprivation causes its effects. The mechanisms suggested offer explanations at different levels of physiologic and psychologic functioning. Whereas many arguments have been advanced for the importance of one theory or mechanism over another, on studying the theories it becomes quite clear that they are not mutually exclusive and that they primarily represent the attempts of workers in different fields of endeavor to explain the phenomena in terms of their own bias.

Attempts have been made to explain the problem on the basis of psychoanalytic theory (Kubie, 1961). Sensory deprivation can, under certain circumstances, be likened to sleep. The hallucinations developed by sensory isolation are more like dreams than they are like hallucinations. Kubie (1961) points out that, even though sleep is usually considered a beneficial situation, under certain circumstances it can be psychonoxious. Many times people wake up from sleep disturbed and with a great deal of anxiety. Effects of sensory deprivation would entail a shift in psychophysiologic balance toward enteroceptive dominance. The crucial interference with reality contact experienced by the subject decreases the efficiency of the secondary processes of mentation, causing a decrease in repressive mechanism until ego boundaries are either altered or exceeded, therefore producing the symptoms that occur in sensory deprivation. This model is not particularly useful to the biologist attempting to find either a cause or an explanation of the model psychosis.

Freedman, Grunebaum, and Greenblatt (1961), presenting a cognitive theory of stimulus deprivation, point out that perception requires a great deal of support from previously acquired spatial schemata. When the subject is presented with either too little or disordered perceptive input, his previously acquired spatial schemata becomes useless. He cannot modify the old schemata or develop a new one because he cannot extract the necessary amount of information from the paucity of incoming perceptual stimuli to do this. Therefore either real, external stimuli are misinterpreted, or nonstimulated, internally generated signals arise. Thus, shapes change, walls bulge, floors move, nonexistent tactile sensations are observed, etc. When new experiences are presented to the individual, all of the misinterpretations may disappear.

Lindsley (1961), among others, presented a theory that suggested that the ascending reticular activating system is affected. The reticular activating system, along with the diffuse thalamocortical projection system, provides the mechanism of general arousal alerting, and of a special attentional mechanism. Interaction between the cortex and the reticular system is accomplished through the corticofugal system. The reticular formation may serve as a homeostat adjusting input-output relations. With sensory deprivation a void is created, and the central nervous system attempts to keep the reticular system and the cortex functioning on an activating basis. Without external stimulation or internal generation, the result is boredom, inactivity, and sleep. With an excess of a certain type of stimulation, behavioral immobilization and confusion may result. All of the conditions for providing sensory modification upset the balance of the regulating system (the ascending reticular activating system). When this happens persistently, perception is disrupted; attention gives way to distractability, and interest to boredom.

In addition to the theory of the ascending reticular activating system involvement, Inglis (1956) developed a theory involving feedback, which emphasized the early work of Hebb (1949). Still another somewhat related theory has been proposed by Brawley and Pos (1967). Brawley suggests that the sensory input regulating system of the central nervous system is a critical factor in the production of hallucinosis and psychotic experience. Wisely, he does not attempt to pinpoint the area where this occurs, but does suggest that information underload can be the result of many diverse phenomena, sensory deprivation being only one of them. In accomplishing a solution to the deprivation, chains of cell assemblies and phase sequences are set off. These solutions are checked back against the elements of the problem to evaluate quality of fit. This is done by a feedback control loop. All of this requires storage capacity in the brain. Sensory deprivation thus has a deleterious effect on cognitive functioning by depriving the problem-solving organism of the retrieval of the stored information upon which decisions must be made. As older stimuli decay, the oscillation of the solution search becomes wider and wider and picks up inappropriate internal data with which to solve a problem (Brawley and Pos, 1967). Genetic factors, conditioning processes, anxiety, and other causes may be involved. Certainly the cause can be toxic as in the cases of the drug-induced psychoses described later in this chapter. It has been shown that drugs like LSD block nerve transmission in certain areas. Examples are the block of ganglionic transmission in the lateral geniculate, in the visual pathway (Evarts, Landau, Freygang, and Marshall, 1955), and an effect on transcallosally evoked potentials (Marrazzi, 1962). Phencyclidine, whose effects very closely resemble sensory deprivation, depresses energy production in neural cells and, therefore, by depleting the energy of the cells could very easily cause sensory deprivation using the above-described mechanism. Any of the drugs that supposedly antagonize neurotransmitters could also lead to this type of stimulus deficit.

Certainly much more important to the physiologist or biochemist is the cause of the stimulus deficit.

B. Sleep Deprivation

Long periods of sleep deprivation can result in the production of a model psychosis. Periods of wakefulness for as long as 10 days result in the subject becoming irritable, argumentative, and disoriented in time and space (Katz and Landis, 1935). A group of medical students who were sleep deprived for 72 hr showed hallucinations, irritability, and intellectual deterioration (Bliss, Clark, and West, 1959). As soon as a regular sleep pattern was restored all of the effects vanished. Probably very important is the amount of Stage IV sleep lost during the sleep-deprived period (Berger and Oswald, 1962). The early stages of sleep deprivation produce cerebral irritability (Rodin, Luby, and Gottlieb, 1962), but beyond 48 hr the irritability decreases. Alpha activity decreases in the EEG record, and stimuli that normally block alpha rhythm now elicit it. Psychologic performance becomes poor because of periods of drowsiness or lapsing. These lapses are preceded by a shift in EEG rhythm from alpha to theta. Decrements in perceptual motor efficiency occur only during the lapses (Williams, Lubin, and Goodnow, 1959). It may be that central changes that occur in sleep deprivation accelerate the accumulation of reactive inhibition (Cohen, Grisell, and Ax, 1962).

Sleep deprivation has only minor effects on catecholamine output, and these could be related more to changes in physical activity than to a direct effect of the deprivation (Tyler, Goodman, and Rothman, 1947). Sleep deprivation has a profound effect on energy production systems (Luby, Frohman, Grisell, Lenzo, and Gottlieb, 1960). Turnover and levels of adenosine triphosphate (ATP) have been measured in blood cells of the sleep-deprived individual. With sleep deprivation, levels of ATP began to drop. This drop in ATP level stimulated an increased turnover of ATP as measured by the incorporation of labeled phosphorus into the molecule. The increase in ATP turnover continued until the 2nd or 3rd day, at which time it dropped precipitously. Performance on many of the psychologic tests correlated with energy production (Cohen and Grisell, 1963). Certainly a drop in energy metabolism could inhibit the transmission of energy impulses and the storage of information in the brain so that a situation resembling stimulus deprivation could exist.

Dement (1960) reported that depriving subjects of REM sleep (dream deprivation) resulted in anxiety, irritability, difficulty in concentrating, and some psychotomimetic effects. However, after studying a great number of cases, he concluded that the effects were not dramatic or severe enough to permit unequivocal conclusions (Dement and Fisher, 1963). It was impossible to determine if the few effects observed were the result of REM deprivation or sleep deprivation. REM sleep can be destroyed in animals by the surgical destruction of the nucleus pontis caudalis and the nucleus pontis oralis (Dement, 1965). In cats striking behavioral changes appear after 2 or 3 weeks of suppression of REM sleep in this manner. They exhibit bizarre behavior and some of their actions suggested that they were hallucinating. However, it is probable that the hallucinations and bizarre behavior were caused by something other than absence of REM sleep (Jouvet, 1967). All in all, REM deprivation does not appear to produce a severe model psychosis.

III. CHEMICALLY INDUCED PSYCHOSES

The easiest means of producing model psychoses is by drug administration. However, the psychoses produced in this manner are often not as simple as they appear at first glance. Many drugs related to indoles produce psychotomimetic symptoms. Since these drugs are serotonin analogues, one would assume that the symptoms would result from some effect of the drugs on serotonin; however, this may not be the case. If serotonin is involved, we must consider the problem of whether the drug is an agonist or an antagonist to serotonin or whether the drug just affects serotonin turnover (Brown, 1957; Curtis and Davis, 1962; Aghajanian and Weiss, 1968). The second group of psychotomimetic compounds, the phenylethylamines, theoretically should owe their action to the effects on catecholamines. However, it cannot be clearly demonstrated that the psychotomimetic symptoms result from catecholamine disturbance. Again the agonist-antagonist problem presents itself. Reasonably these first two classes of compounds should produce entirely different symptoms, since they should be acting on two different and opposing neurotransmitter systems. Instead the symptoms produced by the two types of drugs are indistinguishable from each other. It is often difficult to differentiate between the symptoms produced by mescaline (a phenylethylamine derivative) and dimethyl tryptamine (an indoleamine derivative). Smythies has shown that distances between functional groups in mescaline and even in tetrahydrocannabinol resemble those in the 5-hydroxyindoleamines and that they could all be acting on the same centers (Smythies and Antun, 1969). To complicate matters even more, considerable cross-tolerance exists between the indoleamines and the phenylethylamines (Appel and Freedman, 1968), again strongly indicating that both groups of compounds are acting on the same centers. The next group of compounds, the cannabis derivatives, usually produce milder symptoms than either of the other two groups, but the symptoms closely resemble those of the indoleamine derivatives and phenylethylamine derivatives (Paton and Pertinee, 1973). Some morphine derivatives produce symptoms identical with the other groups, also with cross-tolerance. It is true that barbiturates and amphetamines produce symptoms that are somewhat different from the others, but phencyclidine-related compounds and the acetylcholine analogues produce symptoms similar to those produced by the other hallucinogens.

The picture of symptoms produced by psychotomimetic compounds is complicated by the fact that the symptoms themselves can be drastically altered by the environment (Hollister, 1964). Administering marijuana in a bleak laboratory setting can often produce a lesser psychotomimetic effect than can be produced by administering a placebo in a psychedelic setting (Caldwell, Meyers, Domino, and Merriam, 1969). One of the most striking differences between the naturally occurring psychoses and the drug-induced psychoses is the ability of outside forces to influence the outcome of the drug-induced symptoms. With LSD and many compounds of this type, the investigator is actually able to control the symptoms by his power of suggestion. The degree of stress the subject is under at the time of administration of the drug is also instrumental in determining the nature and severity of symptoms produced by the drug (Lowe and Williams, 1972).

In general, the qualities of hallucinations from drugs reported by non-schizophrenics differ greatly from those reported by schizophrenic patients. Many more visual hallucinations are present (Hollister, 1964). Reality has a much more evanescent quality in these model psychoses. It must be kept in mind when considering the symptoms of a particular drug that they are quite variable from individual to individual and from situation to situation in the same individual, and that when studying the metabolic effects of psychotomimetic drugs many of the effects noted may be the result of behavioral changes in the individual rather than the cause, so that these effects may be only indirectly related to the drug administered.

A. Drugs that Mimic Schizophrenia

1. Psychotomimetic Indole Derivatives

An indole derivative (LSD) is probably the most thoroughly studied of the psychotomimetic compounds. It was originally thought to be a serotonin antagonist and indeed it does antagonize many of the functions of serotonin in the body. It prevents the effect of serotonin on the contraction of uterine muscle and has been shown to antagonize many other serotonin functions (Gaddum, 1953). It produces a number of symptoms, both physical and mental. It causes hyperthermia (axillary temperatures often rise to 106°F) and hypertension (pulse rate increases and the blood pressure rises) (Freedman and Hirsch, 1971). It often causes irrelevant hysteria that cuts across periods of stupor (Hollister, 1964). The subject often experiences distress in the midst of delight. Coherence of the subject's ideas then becomes vague. Despite the hyperthermia, he feels chilliness of the extremities. He becomes intoxicated and may believe his eyes are beholding the infinite. In many people ingestion of the drug becomes almost a religious experience. The subject experiences hallucinations and makes errors in identifying objects. Sounds take on color and colors contain music. This description not only holds for LSD and the other indole derivatives but for many of the other psychotomimetic drugs.

The symptoms differ from schizophrenia in a number of ways. In schizophrenia most hallucinations are aural, whereas in most drug psychoses they are visual. With drug-induced psychoses, the thought disturbance is much less severe than in schizophrenia. Perceptual disorders predominate in the model psychoses. With a high dosage of drugs, the consciousness of the subject is quite often altered, and the drug psychoses can easily be affected by the environment.

LSD depresses reward learning but has very little effect on avoidance learning, possibly an indication that LSD affects the enjoyment of pleasure (Lowe and Williams, 1972). It must be remembered, however, that the administration of LSD to many subjects is quite pleasurable, so that this alteration is certainly not the same as the anhedonia experienced by so many schizophrenics (Bridger, 1968). In a stress situation LSD is more likely to incite the subject, whereas in a nonstress situation it is more likely to inhibit the subject. LSD has been used in treating many psychotic conditions; the claims of success, although not completely substantiated, are numerous (Whitaker, 1964). It is also claimed that LSD will relieve the symptoms of asthma (Abramson, 1968). It is interesting to note that by using a number of LSD derivatives with varied antiserotonin action (as measured by uterine contraction), the relief of asthma correlates almost perfectly with the antiserotonin activity of the compound. This is not remarkable since asthma is also concerned with the contraction of smooth muscle. On the other hand, the psychotomimetic effects of the drug do not correlate at all with antiserotonin activity measured in this manner (Dixon, 1968). Some analogues of LSD that have high antiserotonin activity as measured by the effect on uterine contraction have no psychedelic effects at all, whereas others with little or no antiserotonergic action are strong psychotomimetic agents.

Labeled LSD administered to animals is found bound in the cerebral cortex, the caudate nucleus, the midbrain, the medulla, and the epithelium of the choroid plexus. Unbound LSD is localized in the pituitary gland, pineal body, cerebellum, hippocampus, and choroid plexus (Diab, Freedman, and Roth, 1971; Diab and Roth, 1972). LSD is not found in the nucleus or the cytoplasm of the cell. It is bound weakly to synaptosomes and with medium strength to the synaptic membranes in the cortex (Farrow and Van Vunakis, 1973). This binding to the synaptic membranes suggests that the compound could interfere with the transmission of nerve impulses across the synapse.

The picture of the effect of LSD on metabolism is confusing. Conflicting reports have been presented for practically every function. Much effort has been expended to elucidate the effect of LSD on serotonin. In reviewing this work, it must be kept firmly in mind that the psychotomimetic effects of LSD-like compounds do not correlate with the antiserotonin action of these compounds. Therefore it is risky to attempt to propose a direct relationship between serotonin systems and LSD action. It is also important to note that an individual serotonin analogue may antagonize serotonin in one system and be agonistic in another. Therefore the results of testing the effect of a psychotomimetic compound on a single system involving serotonin, such as uterine contraction, may not be meaningful when applied to other serotonergic systems.

LSD counteracts the inactivity and immobilization in animals is caused by the administration of serotonin, but this could be a physical effect involving the muscle (Brown, 1957). Large doses of LSD have been reported by some workers to cause an increase in serotonin and a decrease in 5-hydroxyindoleacetic acid (Diaz, Njai, and Costa, 1968; Kabes, Fink, Somtev, Urba, and Madlo, 1972). This has by no means been confirmed by all workers (Randic and Padjen, 1971). In fact the most consistent thing about the reports of changes in the serotonin level after LSD administration is their inconsistency. The level of serotonin is not markedly and consistently affected by LSD. More likely is the possibility that the drug affects serotonin turnover. It has been shown that LSD blocks the usual increase in serotonin turnover caused by elevated temperature (Aghajanian and Weiss, 1968). If serotonin levels did increase with LSD administration, it would be hard to reconcile this data with the fact that reserpine, which lowers serotonin levels, potentiates the effect of LSD on behavior. Tonge (1969) claims that LSD decreases the rate of depletion of serotonin after administration of p-chlorophenylalanine (PCPA). The synthesis of serotonin is inhibited by PCPA. Therefore, the effect of LSD must be either to block the effect of PCPA or to slow the release of bound serotonin. LSD also inhibits the loss of serotonin after administration of reserpine, so it must be assumed that the compound slows down the release of bound serotonin. It has already been stated that reserpine potentiates the action of LSD. We then have two compounds (LSD and reserpine) that have opposite effects on serotonin storage but the same effect on certain aspects of behavior. It must be inferred that the behavioral effect of LSD cannot be mediated through its effect on serotonin storage in a simple fashion. This is confirmed by the observations reported above that serotonin antagonism with respect to the contraction of uterine muscle does not correlate with behavioral effects. This does not rule out the possibility that serotonin may be indirectly involved.

Pretreatment of an animal with PCPA intensifies the behavioral effects of LSD (Appel, Lovell, and Freedman, 1970). Since PCPA inhibits the synthesis of serotonin, one would be tempted to assume that the effect of LSD must be to antagonize serotonin. However, this effect does not occur until 12 days after pretreatment, probably too late to be attributed to a direct effect on serotonin (Diaz et al., 1968). The evidence presented above does not rule out the possibility that LSD prevents the release of bound serotonin. In fact this possibility fits with almost all data reported; however, it may be a secondary effect. Serotonin is released from the synaptosomes as a result of activity arriving at the presynaptic terminal. Since LSD is concentrated in the postsynaptic membrane (Farrow et al., 1973), its presence may interfere with the passage of activity across the synapse.

The effect of LSD on the firing of neurons also gives rise to controversial data, probably because its effect is not the same on all neurons. In studies using a single cell of the buccal ganglion of a snake, reserpine decreased transmission, whereas LSD actually increased the size of excitatory postsynaptic potentials (Cottrell, 1970). In these neurons at least, the hypothesis is not upheld. In single neurons of the cat, LSD antagonizes serotonin excitation (Boakes, Bradley, Briggs, and Dray, 1970). It also antagonizes glutamate excitation of neurons excited by serotonin. Surprisingly it has no effect on neurons normally inhibited by serotonin.

Chlorpromazine dampens the effects of LSD (Hollister, 1964). This would suggest that dopamine may be involved in LSD action. In general LSD causes desynchronization of the EEG, demonstrating that it has some effect on spontaneous electrical activity of neurons (Rodin and Luby, 1966). It also causes an increase in the percentage of fast waves (Shagass and Schwartz, 1964) and increases the signal-to-noise ratio (Elevenon and Boissier, 1972).

Structural similarities exist between the indoleamines and the catecholamines, and one class can be converted to the other through compounds like adrenochrome (Hoffer and Osmond, 1967). Indoleamines and catecholamines bear close relationships in the neurons, because the means of formation of both are almost identical and because the presence of one class inhibits the production of the other. It is only logical to assume that the indoleamines could be acting through their effect on the catecholamines. Much evidence has accumulated that the adrenergic system also may be involved in the effect of LSD. All alpha- and beta-adrenergic blocking drugs inhibit LSD-induced aberrant behavior, whereas D-2 brom-LSD, a strong serotonin analogue, has no behavioral effects (Dixon, 1968). In other words some catecholamine antagonists seem to affect the LSD action more than some indoleamine antagonists. It should be mentioned, however, that this lack of behavioral effect of the brom-LSD could be a consequence of its inability to enter into the membrane. However, alpha-methyl-p-tyrosine, an inhibitor of norepinephrine synthesis, does not have the same effect on LSD activity as PCPA, an inhibitor of serotonin synthesis. Pretreatment with alpha-methyl-p-tyrosine in the hands of one group did not affect behavior, whereas another group claimed that it prevented the behavioral effects but not the hyperthermia (Horita and Hamilton, 1969; Appel, Lovell, and Freedman, 1970). Little change is noticed in either norepinephrine or dopamine levels in LSD-treated animals. LSD had no effect on the decreased levels of norepinephrine caused by alpha-methyl-p-tyrosine (Leonard and Tonge, 1969). This compound inhibits norepinephrine synthesis. However, LSD did increase the depletion of norepinephrine and dopamine produced by alpha-methyl-m-tyrosine, a compound that produces depletion by the replacement of norepinephrine and dopamine in the storage granules. Under such circumstances it could be assumed that, unlike the effect on bound serotonin, LSD causes the release of bound norepinephrine and bound dopamine. However, this release probably occurs intracellularly rather than in the synaptic cleft (Siva Sankar and Domjan, 1973). This free norepinephrine will then be rapidly disposed of by monoamine oxidase. The result is a drop in available norepinephrine and dopamine and of course an increase in the turnover of norepinephrine and dopamine. LSD apparently causes a binding of serotonin in nerve endings and a release of norepinephrine. In fact both LSD and reserpine cause a release of norepinephrine by neurons. This fits better with the potentiation of LSD action by reserpine than does the effect on serotonin. Reserpine, which potentiates the behavioral effects of LSD, actually affects serotonin binding in a manner opposite to that of LSD but affects norepinephrine binding the same way as LSD. The effect of reserpine is too complicated to be described as merely lowering the levels of serotonin and norepinephrine. It first temporarily raises the levels. Immediately after administration of reserpine, both serotonin and norepinephrine are released from the bound state so that the immediate effect is an increase in the levels of free serotonin and norepinephrine. The long-range effect, however, is depletion of both of these compounds since the freed amines are rapidly disposed of by enzymes.

One group claimed that LSD did not affect acetylcholine levels in rat brain (Graiman and Pepeu, 1962), whereas another claimed that after administration of LSD, acetylcholine level increased (Kabes, Fink, Somtev, Urbo, and Madlo, 1972). At the same time, activity of cholinergic nerves decreased so that the cholinergic system might also be involved in the action of LSD.

LSD causes a drop in eosinophils, that would indicate that the adrenal cortex might also be involved, but the compound causes no change in the level of circulating corticoids (Sackler, Williams, and Sparber, 1963; Hollister, 1969).

After reviewing the multiple effects of LSD on metabolism, one must return to the fact that LSD causes tremendous changes in the rate of activity in the subject and in the behavior of the subject. Many of the changes noted in metabolism may be more the result of these changes in the behavior than the cause. As stated earlier, an LSD-induced psychosis can be affected markedly by the environment. In fact, nearly opposite symptoms can be made to appear by changing the environmental conditions. This may explain, to some extent, the conflicting results from metabolic studies.

It has been reported that LSD causes chromosome damage. However, results here are no more consistent than are those concerning its metabolism. Cohen reports that definite *in vitro* damage results from the administration of LSD (Cohen, Marinello, and Baek, 1967). Sparkes reports that there was no *in vivo* chromosome damage noted in a number of normal drug users studied, although this number was quite small (Sparkes, Melnyk, and Bozzett, 1968).

However, Jacobson, in studying 148 pregnancies of LSD users, found that 83 of the fetuses were born live, and 65 were aborted (Jacobson and Berlin, 1972). Four out of 14 therapeutic abortions gave abnormal fetuses. Of the 83 born alive, eight had major birth defects—a strong indication of the damaging nature of LSD.

In a certain percentage of LSD users, spontaneous "flashbacks" occur without the administration of LSD, and many of these users become so psychotic that it is necessary to hospitalize them (Moskowitz, 1971). This phase of LSD action will be covered in another section, but it should be emphasized that the danger of producing LSD psychoses must be of constant concern.

Many other indoleamines cause psychotomimetic symptoms resembling those of LSD, although most of them require larger doses than LSD. Tryptamine, a normally occurring metabolite, is one of the compounds that can cause psychotomimetic symptoms (Martin and Eades, 1970; Martin and Sloan, 1970). Its effects are much milder than those of LSD, and the duration is much shorter. Tryptamine and many of its derivatives cross the blood-brain barrier very easily in man (Green and Sawyer, 1960). Dimethyltryptamine (DMT) is a far more active psychotomimetic agent than tryptamine (Szara, Rockland, Rosenthal, and Handlon, 1966). Administration of DMT causes an increase in systolic blood pressure, increase in pupil diameter, tremors, gross athetoid movements, hallucinations, disorientation of body image, perceptual disturbances, and paranoid ideation. Duration of symptoms is usually very short, probably because the compound is rapidly metabolized. The quality of the drug experience varies greatly with the environment (Szara and Faillace, 1968). Two groups of workers using exactly the same dosage of DMT produced almost opposite kinds of symptoms in groups of subjects. Boszormenyi, Der, and Nazg (1962), administering the drug in a pleasant reinforced situation, produced primarily elation and an increase in creativity, whereas Szara et al. (1966), in a bare laboratory situation, produced depression and paranoid ideation with practically no creative drive. This exemplifies quite markedly how the symptoms of this group of psychotomimetics can be influenced by the experimenter.

The amount of DMT necessary to produce symptoms is much larger than the amount of LSD (Rosenberg, Isbel, Miner, and Logan, 1964). Ordinarily, 1.5 μg of LSD per kilogram of body weight will produce psychotomimetic symptoms, whereas it requires 500 μg of DMT to produce the same type of symptoms.

DMT is slowly demethylated and the resulting tryptamine is oxidized to 3-indoleacetic acid, but demethylation appears to be too slow to account for the short duration of DMT effects (Szara et al., 1966). Both DMT and diethyltryptamine (DET) are hydroxylated in the 6-position to produce, respectively, 6-hydroxy-DMT and 6-hydroxy-DET. These are then conjugated with glucuronic acid and excreted. The severity of symptoms produced by DET correlates with the amount of 6-hydroxy-DET excreted; therefore it is a possibility that the actual psychotomimetic agents are the 6-hydroxy derivatives of the methylated tryptamines rather than the DMT or DET. A whole group of indoleamines produce the symptoms: DMT, DET, psilocin, psilocybin, 5-hydroxy-DMT, 5-methoxy-DMT (one of the more active derivatives), and alpha-methyltryptamine and its mono and dimethyl derivatives. 6-Fluoro-DET produces all the physical symptoms of the psychotomimetic indoleamines, i.e., dizziness, increased blood pressure, numbness, tingling, chills, nausea, blurred vision, dry mouth, weakness, and distorted images (Faillace, Vourlekis, and Szara, 1967). However, it produces none of the thought disturbances of hallucinations produced by the other compounds. This is another indication that the active psychotomimetic compound may be the 6-hydroxy derivative since 6-fluoro-DET cannot be hydroxylated in the 6-position. 6-Fluoro-DET produced many of the symptoms associated with interference with serotonin metabolism and did not produce the mental symptoms, which is another strong indication that the reason this class of compounds produces its psychotomimetic effects is not because it consists of analogues of serotonin but, possibly, because of hydroxylation in the 6-position. However, other studies involving hydroxy, methoxy, and benzyl substitutions in the 5-, 6-, and 7-positions of tryptamine show that the 6-substituted derivatives cause hyperthermia and the other physical symptoms of psychotomimetics, but only the 5-substituted compounds have high behavioral activity (Hunt and Brimblecombe, 1967). In one experiment 6-hydroxy DMT showed little or no behavioral effects (Rosenberg, Isbel, and Miner, 1963). Were this the active compound, one would expect it to produce strong behavioral effects. However, the crucial experiment would be to test 5-methoxy, 6-hydroxytryptamine since the 5-substituted position also appears to be important in producing psychotomimetic effects.

It seems reasonable that whatever the mechanism of action, it is the same for all of the indole derivatives. DMT increases the brain levels of serotonin and causes a fall in 5-hydroxyindoleacetic acid (Freedman, Gottlieb, and Lovell, 1970). On the other hand in some neurons it may have a direct stimulating action on serotonin (Szara, Morton, and Aikens, 1967). Like LSD it apparently antagonizes serotonin in some neurons and acts as an agonist in others.

As in the case of LSD, norepinephrine appears to be related to the behavioral effects. Norepinephrine antagonizes the excitement caused by 5-hydroxy-DMT in chick embryos (Rauzzino and Siefter, 1967). 2, 3,-delta-H-tryptamine produces catatonia in rats (Daly, Mauger, Yonemitsu, Antonov, Lapase, and Witkop, 1967). The only reported difference between the metabolic effects of any members of this group of psychotomimetic indoles is that LSD decreases the level of serotonin in the forebrain, whereas DMT increases it (Randic and Padjen, 1971). The workers interpreted this as indicating that LSD blocks serotonin synthesis, and DMT inhibits serotonin uptake, but other work has already indicated that this is not the case.

The most consistent effect of the indoleamines seems to be that of blocking receptor sites in the neuron. It still remains to be determined which receptor sites are blocked: those that are sensitive to serotonin, those sensitive to norepinephrine, or a specific group of receptors that may be affected by either.

2. Phenylethylamine Derivatives

A second class of compounds possessing psychotomimetic activity are those related to phenylethylamine, the basic structure from which epinephrine, norepinephrine, and dopamine are derived. It would be very comfortable to assume that the action of the phenylethylamine derivatives is connected with agonism or antagonism of the catecholamines. The phenylethylamine derivatives can be divided into two different classes, those with primarily psychotomimetic effects such as mescaline and those with primarily pressor effects such as amphetamine. Indeed in the case of the amphetamines, many of their actions arise directly from their effect on catecholamines; however, in the case of those with primarily psychotomimetic effects, as was the case with the indoleamines, the mode of action is not at all clear. The amphetamines, although they produce some symptoms resembling schizophrenia, also tend to mimic mania. It is usually only after long administration of the drugs that the schizophrenia-like symptoms occur.

In the phenylethylamine series substitutions in the 3-, 4-, and 5-positions increase hallucinogenic activity (Smythies, Johnston, and Bradley, 1969). These substitutions can be made with hydroxy, methoxy, or even benzoxy groups. Most important is the para or 4-position substitution. 4-Methoxy substitution produces a very long-lasting hallucinogen (Smythies, Johnston, Bradley, Bennington, Morin, and Clark, 1967). If methyl groups are substituted instead of methoxy groups, amphetamine-like activity increases greatly but not hallucinogenic activity. An exception can be found in metanephrine and normetanephrine, which possess very little hallucinogenic activity and yet are substituted in the 3- and 4-positions with methoxy groups (Innes and Nickerson, 1970).

3,4-Dimethoxyphenylethylamine (DMPEA), found by Friedhoff and Hollister (1966) in urine from schizophrenic patients, surprisingly has no hallucinogenic properties in man (Brown, McGeer, and Moser, 1968), yet it differs from mescaline only in the lack of a methoxy group in the 5-position on the ring. It has been shown to have the same effect as mescaline in lower animals and affects rat climbing delay time in the same way as plasma from schizophrenic patients (Ernst, 1962; Bergen, 1965). The difference in effects on humans and lower mammals may be related to differences in metabolic handling. In human beings approximately 80% of administered DMPEA is excreted either as unchanged DMPEA or as dimethoxyphenyl acetic acid (DMPAA) within 24 hr after administration (Friedhoff and Hollister, 1966). In contrast, only about 25% of 3,4,5-trimethoxyphenylethylamine (TMPEA, mescaline) is found as the unchanged compound or the acid in the urine within 24 hr. The rest of the TMPEA is unaccounted for.

The most well known of the phenylethylamine psychotomimetic drugs is mescaline. It is the major constituent of peyote, which is so important in many American Indian religious ceremonies (Farnsworth, 1968). Mescaline does have pressor effects (Denber, 1964), but they are minor compared with the psychotomimetic effects. Its administration causes hypertension, anxiety, muscle tension, sensations of hot and cold, dilated pupils, and cold skin. All of these symptoms can be attributed to potentiated effect on the catecholamines. In addition the subject becomes apprehensive and fearful. He has delusions, illusions, hallucinations, and ideas of depersonalization. He quite often goes into a panic state. Chlorpromazine blocks the effect completely within 2 min of administration.

It has been reported that improvement is seen in some epileptics treated with mescaline followed by chlorpromazine (Denber, 1964). The effects of mescaline resemble the effects of LSD so closely that it is very difficult to differentiate between the two, and cross-tolerance exists between them (Paton and Pertinee, 1973).

Only about 0.2% of the amount of mescaline injected goes to the brain (Denber and Teller, 1968). Brain level reaches a peak at approximately 30 min after injection. By 120 min after injection, the level has dropped considerably. Mescaline in the brain is bound very loosely to myelin but much more strongly and specifically at nerve endings, leading to the hypothesis that mescaline acts at either the pre- or postsynapse. Therefore there is a parallel between mescaline and LSD, which also appears to be acting postsynaptically.

In avoidance conditioning where the animal is under stress, mescaline, like LSD, causes excitation. In reward situations where no stress is present, it is more likely to cause depression (Smythies and Sykes, 1964).

Many theories have been advanced involving the action of mescaline on norepinephrine and/or dopamine metabolism. However, mescaline causes no significant changes in the levels of these compounds. It does increase the rate of synthesis of serotonin from [^{14}C-]tryptophan, whereas psilocybin and LSD have no effect (Shein, Wilson, Larin, and Wurtman, 1971). If labeled 5-hydroxytryptophan is substituted for the tryptophan, mescaline has no effect. Therefore, it must be assumed that mescaline acts on the tryptophan hydroxylase step. Administration of mescaline and other phenylethylamine hallucinogens, according to Freedman et al. (1970), increased levels of serotonin and 5-hydroxyindoleacetic acid, whereas administration of LSD or other indoleamines also increased the level of serotonin but not that of 5-hydroxyindoleacetic acid. This would permit the attractive theory that mescaline increased the synthesis of serotonin whereas LSD decreased the breakdown of serotonin.

The spasmogenic effect of histamine on guinea pig ileum is enhanced by mescaline (Carlini, Santos, and Lampaio, 1965). This is in contrast to the inhibition by LSD of contraction of uterine muscle by serotonin. Mescaline also potentiates the hypotensive response to histamine. Papaverine and bulbo-capnine have the same effect. The effect is mediated through the inhibition of diamine oxidase activity. This inhibition requires a 4-methoxyphenylethyl residue (Carlini, Sampaio, Santos, and Carlini, 1965a), the same residue Smythies reported necessary for psychotomimetic action. Mescaline has no effect on levels of acetylcholine in rat brain (Graiman and Pepeu, 1962).

The amphetamine-like phenylethylamines produce primarily pressor symptoms but also can act as psychotomimetics (Innes and Nickerson, 1970b). The pressor effects of amphetamines are 0.5 to 1% as potent as those of epinephrine. For the pressor effect, the l-isomer (Benzedrine®) is slightly more potent than the d-isomer (Dexedrine®). The major effects of both are like those of epinephrine. The amphetamines relax smooth muscle to a slight extent, lessen the central depressive effect of other drugs such as barbital, prevent and reverse fatigue, raise the pain threshold, and depress appetite. They depolarize and block cells in the autonomic ganglia. They cause an increase in the levels of epinephrine and norepinephrine. It has been suggested that they may inhibit the breakdown of these compounds by monoamine oxidase. This is very unlikely, however, since they still stimulate subjects who have previously received monoamine oxidase inhibitors. Indications are that they may act on serotonergic receptors so that some of the actions of the drugs may resemble those of LSD. The side effects of the amphetamines are dizziness, tremor, hyperactive reflexes, talkativeness, tenseness, irritability, weakness, insomnia, hyperthermia, euphoria, confusion, assaultiveness, increased libido, anxiety, delirium, panic, suicidal tendencies, either hypertension or hypotension, and if too much is administered death from convulsion or coma. The effects of amphetamines are counteracted by chlorpromazine. Amphetamines are used wisely or unwisely for many conditions ranging from asthma and overweight to hyperkinesis in children. The use of amphetamines is considered to be addicting (Prout, 1964). Too-long use of the drugs quite often gives rise to full-blown psychoses resembling schizophrenia (Connell, 1958; Bell, 1965). There is a great deal of paranoid ideation and numerous hallucinations, although, as in the case of LSD and mescaline, the hallucinations are more visual than aural. The absence of thought disturbance differentiates an amphetamine psychosis from schizophrenia as is also true in the case of LSD psychoses. Withdrawal of amphetamines can produce a catatonic stupor. Because of the paranoid ideation produced by the drug, much assault and homicide is associated with amphetamine abuse (Ellinwood, 1971). The so-called "speed freaks" (amphetamine abusers) frequently clash with the "acid heads" (LSD users) because of the different ideation brought forth by the two types of drugs (Smith, 1969). In almost every case, the "acid heads" are driven off because of their greater passivity as compared to the aggressiveness of the "speed freaks." Of the psychoses induced by amphetamines, 90%

are of the schizophrenic type, but they can also produce extreme anxiety states (McConnell and McIlwaine, 1963).

Hollister has proposed that amphetamines act by releasing bound norepinephrine and dopamine in the brain and that this appears to be the cause of the adrenergic response rather than a blockage of monoamine oxidase. Regardless of the manner of accomplishment, amphetamines quite definitely increase levels of norepinephrine in the brain (Hollister, Noden, and Mayer, 1962). Amphetamines and LSD have no effect on the level of ATP (Wilson, 1967) in the brain even though chlorpromazine, which relieves the effect of amphetamines, causes an increase in ATP and reserpine causes a decrease. Friedhoff and Alpert (1973) proposed that drugs such as amphetamines have an effect on the balance between the dopaminergic and cholinergic systems. Their reasoning is as follows: amphetamine increases dopamine activity, relieves Parkinsonism and produces psychoses. It does not affect the level of acetylcholine. Anticholinergic drugs do not affect dopamine but decrease acetylcholine. They also relieve Parkinsonism and produce psychoses. On the other hand, antidopaminergic drugs decrease dopamine levels, leave acetylcholine levels unaffected, relieve psychoses, but produce Parkinsonism. Chlorpromazine is a good example of this. Cholinergic drugs do not affect dopamine but increase acetylcholine, also relieve psychoses, and produce Parkinsonism.

An interesting antagonism exists between morphine and the amphetamines (Fog, 1970). Morphine produces stereotyped behavior in animals and amphetamine relieves this behavior if administered with morphine. On the other hand, morphine relieves the hyperactivity produced by amphetamine.

There is much speculation as to whether all of the psychotomimetic drugs are acting on the same center and if one could be substituted for another. Are LSD and amphetamine affecting body functions in the same manner, especially since they are so alike structurally, and are mescaline and amphetamine affecting body functions in the same manner? Rosencrans and co-workers devised an experiment that partially answers these questions (Rosencrans and Schechter, 1973). Rats were given a choice of two compartments to enter, one on the left and one on the right. In one of the compartments, they would be given a shock. In the other they would be perfectly safe. The rats were taught that if they were injected with amphetamine the shock would be in the left compartment. However, if they were given an injection of saline, the shock would be administered in the right compartment. From the amphetamine cue, the rats soon learned which compartment to enter and were able to choose the proper compartment without error. When LSD or mescaline was substituted for amphetamine, the rats were no longer able to use it as a cue in choosing the proper compartment. Certainly in this case amphetamine is having an effect quite different from the other psychotomimetic drugs. If d-amphetamine were substituted for l-amphetamine, the rats received the cue, but higher dosages of d-amphetamine were necessary. From this, one can assume that the rats could detect the difference between the effects of amphetamine and other hallucinogens.

3. Cannabis Derivatives

The tetrahydrocannabinols are present in both marijuana and hashish. The seriousness of the effects of these drugs is a very controversial matter at the present time. It is best reconciled by the fact that hashish has always been considered a hard drug and that as far as can be ascertained marijuana is merely a weak form of hashish. A weak form of a hard drug is still a hard drug. On the other hand, much of the marijuana available on the street is often either extremely weak or contains no active ingredients at all so that it is very difficult to say that this particular form of the drug is dangerous. It has already been mentioned that a placebo can cause a stronger psychedelic effect in a sophisticated marijuana user in a psychedelically stimulating setting than genuine marijuana causes when administered in a stark laboratory setting (Caldwell et al., 1969). In fact it has been shown that many people must actually "learn" the response to marijuana (Becker, 1953). On the other hand, Kiplinger, Manno, Rodda, and Forney (1971) showed that subjects could distinguish between marijuana and a placebo on a blind basis. The symptoms of marijuana intoxication have been described many times (Hollister, Richards, and Gullespie, 1968; Tennant and Groesbeck, 1972). The symptoms resemble those of LSD intoxication very closely, but are usually milder. The user sees colors either flowing or in patches. Spatial dimensions are disturbed and confused. Size is distorted. The subject has hot and cold sensations. Time perception is impaired. There are many visual experiences, the more vivid of which could be called hallucinations but probably could better be called dreaming. The subject claims he has increased speed of thought, but attempts to prove this have failed. Depersonalization occurs; the subject can experience euphoria or dysphoria. He becomes drowsy and disinterested. He exhibits signs of drunkenness and uncontrolled laughter. He can show signs of extreme panic. When combined with other drugs, it can lead to panic, toxic psychosis, and schizophrenic reaction. An intake of over 50 g of hashish per month leads to a chronic intoxicated stage including dullness, impairment of judgment, concentration and memory, and usually ending in a psychosis resembling schizophrenia.

Only 10 to 15% of tetrahydrocannabinols ingested are excreted in 24 hr (Burstein, 1973). Some of these are converted to cannabidiol by being oxidized in the 7-position and then are excreted as beta glucuronides; they can also be oxidized to many acid metabolites. As in the case of the previously mentioned psychotomimetic drugs, tetrahydrocannabinol causes an increase of serotonin in the brain (Bose, Saifi, and Bhagwat, 1964); the greatest increase is in the hypothalamus and midbrain (Schildkraut and Effran, 1971).

This probably results from the effect of the cannabinols on preventing the release of bound serotonin (Sofia, Dixit, and Barry, 1971). Here again a sharp parallel is seen to the effect of LSD. In the mouse tetrahydrocannabinol caused an early decrease in norepinephine levels which persisted for about 6 hr. Subsequently the levels increased to far above normal (Holtzman, Lovell, Jaffe, and Freedman, 1969). At the same time serotonin levels increased and the increase was shown to be dose related. The cholinergic nervous system is also affected by the tetrahydrocannabinols. In looking at the metabolic effect of these compounds, it is hard to differentiate them from the other psychotomimetic drugs, except for degree of activity. The fact that no cross-tolerance exists between tetrahydrocannabinol and the other drugs may or may not indicate that their action is on a different center (Teresa, Silba, Carlini, Claussen, and Horte, 1968). Claims that tetrahydrocannabinol speeds up or facilitates thinking, or causes one to perform better on tests of dexterity are completely unsubstantiated scientifically. Most controlled experiments show either no difference or a decrease in dexterity (Caldwell et al., 1969). It has been claimed by users that the effects of marijuana and tetrahydrocannabinols have an erotic component. However, it has also been demonstrated that hashish and therefore probably all of its relatives actually decrease reproductive activity (Miras, 1965). In rats at least, cannabis resin increases the teratogenic activity. After 6 days of administration, the number of abnormal fetuses produced by rats increased fourfold (Persaud and Ellington, 1968).

The relationship of marijuana to the other psychotomimetic drugs is tentative at best, since cross-tolerance cannot be demonstrated (Teresa et al., 1968). However, marijuana can reactivate LSD psychoses that have been previously eliminated by using chlorpromazine (Parr, 1970). Cannabis increases the length of barbiturate sleeping time and therefore may be involved somewhat with this series of drugs. In conclusion it can be said that the tetrahydrocannabinols present symptoms very much like those of the other psychotomimetics, but the symptoms of the milder cannabinol-containing materials, especially marijuana, are not nearly as severe as those of the psychotomimetics. Until more data proves otherwise, it must be said that, even though these drugs may be dangerous, they are not as dangerous as LSD, mescaline, or the amphetamines. This may or may not be akin to saying that, even though lead salts are poisonous, they will not kill nearly as rapidly as cyanide and strychnine.

4. Other Compounds

a. Phencyclidine. Phencyclidine (1-[1-phencyclohexyl] piperidine hydrochloride) is one of the more interesting of the psychotomimetic compounds. Originally manufactured as an anesthetic, it showed marked psychotomimetic properties (Chen, Ensor, Russell, and Bohner, 1959). Of all the psychotomimetic drugs, phencyclidine probably mimics schizophrenia better than any other. Up to 7.5 mg/day of this drug causes blurred vision, visual hallucinations, and delusions. The subject shows rotatory nystagmus, ataxia and altered gait, diminution of pain, touch, position sense, and auditory and visual acuity. Most interesting was the alteration in body image and the repetitive motor behavior. It produced feelings of estrangement, hostility, and negativism. All in all the drug mimicked schizophrenia very closely. Nevertheless most hallucinations were visual rather than aural (Luby, Cohen, Rosenbaum, Gottlieb, and Kelley, 1959). The overall effect of the drug resembled that of sensory isolation more than schizophrenia and led to the theory that either sensory input was impaired or that proprioception was damaged (Rosenbaum, Cohen, Luby, Gottlieb, and Yellen, 1959). In contrast to most of the other psychotomimetic drugs, this one intensified the symptoms of schizophrenic patients (Meyer, Greifenstein, and DeVault, 1959). Sodium succinate antagonizes the stupor caused by phencyclidine without affecting the nystagmus (Levy, Cameron, and Aitken, 1960). This is interesting in that, as with LSD, some compounds that change the psychologic effects do not have the same influence on physical effects. Chlorpromazine antagonizes the psychotomimetic effects of phencyclidine. Although the drug causes loss of sensory discrimination, it increases the deep tendon reflexes (Ban, Lohrenz, and Lehman, 1961).

Phencyclidine causes definite slowing of the EEG and an increase of theta activity (Greifenstein, DeVault, Yoshitake, and Rajeniski, 1958). These changes, however, can be clearly distinguished from those produced by sleep or barbiturates (Rodin, Luby, and Meyer, 1959). The EEG effect changes almost always followed the psychic manifestations. Like LSD, phencyclidine causes an increase in blood pressure (Greifenstein et al., 1958). It also increases the respiratory rate.

The compound has a relatively short duration of action because it is rapidly metabolized (Ober, Gwynn, Chang, McCarthy, and Glazko, 1963) and excreted chiefly as the mono-4-hydroxypiperidine derivative, but quite often it produces a long-lasting psychosis that is difficult to cure. It causes a rather marked increase in body temperature (Cerletti, 1956) and in oxygen consumption (Domino, 1964). Of course, the increase in oxygen consumption could have been brought about by the rise in temperature, since this causes an increase in enzyme activity. This is not the case, as demonstrated by Lees (1962). She showed that 10^{-4} M phencyclidine increased oxygen consumption of rat liver homogenates and mitochondria *in vitro*. The compound increased the oxygen consumption of rat liver homogenates with succinate as a substrate. Alpha-ketoglutarate, beta-hydroxybutyrate or citrate used as substrates also increased the oxygen consumption, but there was no effect when malate was used as a substrate. Along with increasing oxygen consumption, the compound uncoupled oxidative phosphorylation. The action of this compound may be directly on the mitochondria and tricarboxylic acid cycle, and it may inhibit neural transmission.

Administration of phencyclidine caused decrease in the levels of brain norepinephrine and dopamine, but this change may not be related to the psychotomimetic symptoms (Hitzemann, Loh, and Domino, 1972).

The drug is probably one of the more dangerous of the psychotomimetic drugs, causing severe psychotic reactions in many individuals, some of which may have a duration of from 4 to 6 weeks.

b. Other Hallucinogens. Many books have been written on the effects of morphine and heroin. It is unnecessary to repeat these discussions here (see chapter by Ehrenpreis et al., *This volume*). It is interesting to note that morphine does cause catatonia in rats (Stille, 1971). The level of homovanillic acid in the corpus striatum increases in parallel to the catatonic effects. Probably the effects of morphine and heroin should not be strictly considered as psychotomimetic effects. However, some of the derivatives which are considered partial antagonists do have vivid psychotomimetic effects. These effects are seldom seen with morphine, heroin, or naloxone (a typical morphine antagonist). They are found when nalorphine or cyclazocine are administered (Martin, 1967). These compounds are neither specifically agonists nor antagonists to morphine but instead agonize some functions and antagonize others. It is questionable whether the psychotomimetic activity of these compounds is connected with their structural relationship to morphine since their effects are suppressed by pentobarbital but not by morphine. A study of the effect of cyclazocine on continuous discriminated avoidance in rats indicated that psychotomimetic effects were exactly the same as those of LSD, but that naloxone, a true morphine antagonist, had no effects (Wray, 1972). These morphine derivatives apparently would not be compounds of choice to produce model psychoses because of their addictive properties.

Practically all of the anticholinergic drugs act as hallucinogens depending on the concentration and other conditions (Longo and DeCarolis, 1968). Among those reported as causing hallucinations are atropine, scopolamine, benactyzine, trihexyphenydil, caramiphen, adiphenine, and Ditran® (Lakeside Laboratories). These drugs have been used widely clinically and are not abused to a great extent. Their effect is to depress acetylcholine activity (Forrer, 1951).

Scopolamine and atropine have been shown to reduce brain levels of norepinephrine and dopamine. This is believed to be the result of potentiation of the release of norepinephrine and dopamine by acetylcholine and not related to the psychotomimetic symptoms (Hitzmann et al., 1972). The symptoms resemble those of LSD but also differ from those of LSD because of a confusional delirium picture, the diminution of alertness, and isolation from the environment (Pennes and Hoch, 1956). Other than that subjects showed pupillary dilation, dryness of the mouth, and rise in the pulse rate and blood pressure (Innes and Nickerson, 1970a). Subjects felt dizzy or light headed, anxiety and restlessness were a feature of almost all cases, and hallucinations were usually present. The effect on the EEG, as reported in the literature, is confusing. Some workers claim an increase in frequency of the EEG; others claim a decrease in frequency. Sleep spindles have been reported, as have been both desynchronization and synchronization (Longo and DeCarolis, 1968). Many workers claim the effects represent a dissociation between the EEG and clinical symptoms. However, there is not complete agreement on this point. Itil and Fink (1968) claimed that in the presence of psychotomimetic symptoms alpha activity was reduced and delta and theta waves appeared. A great deal of desynchronization was found. Although chemical and EEG effects may be quite different from that of LSD, it is interesting to note that cross-tolerance between LSD and scopolamine has been reported (Isbel, Rosenberg, Miner, and Logan, 1964).

This discussion section cannot begin to cover all of the drugs reported to have caused hallucinations after administration. Certainly ethyl alcohol should be included. Monoamine oxidase inhibitors, imipramine, and many other drugs can be responsible for visual hallucinations. Further discussion of the hallucination problem can be found in the chapter by Mandell and Geyer (*This volume*).

5. Discussion

a. Tolerance. Tolerance to these various chemical compounds is a very interesting subject [See Chap. 23 by Ehrenpreis et al. (*This volume*).] For some of the compounds it is extremely difficult to induce tolerance. DMT is one of the most interesting of the psychotomimetic compounds in this respect. Under ordinary methods, it is virtually impossible to develop tolerance (Kaplan, Stillman, Gillin, and Wyatt, 1973). However, under very special procedures a transitory light tolerance can be developed (Kovacic and Domino, 1974). Tolerance can be developed to most of the other psychotomimetic compounds, but with LSD the tolerance that can be developed is cyclic in nature; it comes and it goes. The length of the cyclic in many cases is around 5 days in the goat and 7 to 8 days in man (Koella and Bergen, 1969).

If cross-tolerance between two psychotomimetic drugs can be demonstrated, i.e., if the subject can be made tolerant to one drug and automatically becomes tolerant to the second, it is an indication that both drugs have the same point of action. There is cross-tolerance between many of the psychotomimetic drugs. LSD and mescaline show cross-tolerance (Appel and Freedman, 1968). The anticholinergic drugs also show cross-tolerance with mescaline and LSD (Cerletti, Schlagen, Spitzer, and Taeschler, 1963). This would indicate that for these three groups of compounds the center of action is the same. On the other hand, no tolerance can be demonstrated between the cannabis derivatives and the other psychotomimetics. Cannabis compounds, then, must be working on a different center.

Most of these hallucinogens must be considered as dangerous drugs since the long-term effect of administration is often cataclysmic. Prolonged use of LSD may, but not necessarily must, lead to schizophreniform psychosis involving spontaneous flashbacks and psychotic episodes that often cannot be differentiated from schizophrenia. Long-term use of phenylethylamines can also lead to schizophreniform psychoses often characterized by catatonia. Even the safety of long-term use of cannabis derivatives is open to question, since it has been claimed that definite personality changes take place. The individual shows lack of drive, lack of interest in surroundings, and introversion. The use of any of these hallucinogens experimentally should take place under only the most controlled situations, where careful attention is paid to long-term effects of drugs.

   b. *Mode of Action.* Phencyclidine presents a picture that resembles schizophrenia more closely than any of the other psychotomimetic drugs. Its action appears to be different from those of the other psychotomimetic drugs. This compound apparently mimics very closely the symptoms produced by sensory deprivation (Luby and Gottlieb, 1971). Because of this, one might imagine that the chief action of the drug is to cut down stimulus input. This fits very reasonably with the chemical findings concerning the drug since it has been shown that it causes uncoupling of oxidative phosphorylation (Lees, 1962). Under such circumstances, energy production in the nerve endings may be reduced to the point that stimuli no longer reach the brain (Luby and Gottlieb, 1971) or that proprioception is severely impaired (Rosenbaum, 1971).

   So little is known of the site of action of marijuana that no definite conclusions can be reached. Undoubtedly, it operates in the synaptic area.

   Most of the other hallucinogenic drugs (LSD, DMT, mescaline, and Ditran®) have been shown to be concentrated at the synapse and in many cases at the postsynaptic membrane. It can be assumed that the action of these drugs may be centered on this structure. The question remains, "What neurotransmission system is affected consistently by these drugs?" Table 1 shows the effect of these drugs on turnover and storage of many of the neurotransmitters operating in the brain. The effect of these drugs on the EEG can be described as completely confusing. Along with their effects on EEG, blood pressure, and temperature, it can be seen at a glance that no effect holds consistently through all the classes of drugs. Indole derivatives decrease serotonin turnover, whereas phenylethylamines increase it. The anticholinergic drugs have no effect. Although indoleamines and phenylethylamines both increase norepinephrine turnover and decrease norepinephrine storage, again, the anticholinergic drugs have no effect. One may question the effect of anticholinergic drugs on norepinephrine turnover since it can be seen that all of the drugs mentioned cause an increase in blood pressure, but whether this is a reaction to the behavior presented by the subject or a direct chemical effect is questionable. All but the anticholinergic drugs increase the levels of dopamine. The anticholinergic drugs and the indoles decrease acetylcholine turn-

TABLE 1. *Effect of hallucinogens on neurotransmitter systems*

| | Point of action | Serotonin | | Norepinephrine | | Dopamine | Acetylcholine | EEG | | |
		Turnover	Storage	Turnover	Storage		Turnover	Frequency	bp	Temp.
Indoles	Post-synapse	→	←	←	→	←	→	←	←	←
Phenylethylamines	Post-synapse	←←	←←	←←	→?	←←←←	↕ ← |	←→→	← |	← |
Cannabinols	Synapse	←	←?	←←	?	←←	←	→→		→
Morphine derivatives	Synapse	→		→→	?	←←	|	→→	←	←←
Phencyclidine	Synapse					←				
Anticholinergics	Synapse	↕	↕	↕	↕	↕	→	→	←	←

over but the phenylethylamines have no effect. It appears clear that if these drugs all act on the same center, they do not single out one particular neurotransmitter system. There are several alternatives to this hypothesis: (1) The drugs are acting on a balance between two neurotransmitter systems such as the cholinergic and the adrenergic (Friedhoff and Alpert, 1973) or between the serotonergic and either the adrenergic or dopaminergic systems (Snyder, 1970). This is of course a very attractive hypothesis since many workers believe that nerve function is dependent upon balance between transmitters rather than levels of one single transmitter. (2) These compounds are acting on specific transmitters in one anatomic location but not all the neurons throughout the brain that use these transmitters are affected. This hypothesis is also somewhat attractive, since it has already been shown that DMT, for example, can inhibit one set of serotonergic neurons while stimulating another (Szara, Morton, and Aikens, 1967). (3) Cross-tolerance between these classes of compounds is not related to their activity on the same center. This is not a very attractive hypothesis since there is no other explanation for cross-tolerance.

Elucidation of the mode of action of these compounds may throw light on the etiology of schizophrenia.

B. Drugs that Produce Depression

Several classes of drugs produce conditions that closely resemble depression. In most cases the production of depression-like symptoms occurs after a long exposure to drugs rather than with a single dose; however, in some instances a single dose can produce them. Since it has been theorized that depressions result from a decrease in catecholamine levels these drugs should affect catecholamine metabolism (Bunney and Davis, 1965). Drugs that produce depression are not as likely to be abused as the hallucinogenic drugs, since depression is not a desirable condition. However, the group of hypnotic drugs (barbiturates, glutethimide, etc.) are often abused. These drugs are abused not because of their ability to produce depression, but because with smaller doses they are likely to produce excitement and euphoria, and with larger doses they can soften painful memories and cause an individual to disregard pain even though he still feels it (Keats and Beecher, 1950). Indeed, they may even increase the physiologic reaction to painful stimuli (Dundee, 1960). It has been established that most of the hypnotics have no analgesic effects.

1. Barbiturates

The barbiturates are the most commonly used of the hypnotics. They are probably the most widely abused of all drugs. The chief action is a relatively nonselective depression of the central nervous system (Wikler, 1945). They apparently involve complex neurotransmission and affect conditioned responses more than unconditioned responses. Barbiturates have a profound effect on the EEG, causing first an increase in the energy of the high-frequency portion of the spectrum, then a decrease in the amplitude with occasional brief periods of electrical silence (Oswald, Berger, Faramillo, Keddie, Olley, and Plunkett, 1963). By the time the subject has fallen asleep, the EEG pattern finally resembles that of sleep with one rather major exception; the amount of time spent in the REM phase of sleep is reduced. This reduction in REM is not permanent and with continued daily administration of the drug, the amount of REM returns to normal. The effect of barbiturates on the central nervous system probably is the result of some of their metabolic effects. The barbiturates primarily depress oxidation and all of the processes involved with oxidation. Many synthetic processes are depressed in the body but not all at the same time. It has been pointed out that functional impairment occurs with lower doses of the barbiturate than would cause a depression of cerebral metabolic rate (Bain, 1952). Respiration of rat brain homogenate is inhibited in the presence of a number of substrates such as glucose, pyruvate, malate, and glutamate (Erwin and Heim, 1963). Particularly important is the inhibition of NADPH oxidoreductase (Guiditta and Diprisco, 1963). Neural transmission then could essentially be affected by a decrease in oxidative phosphorylation. The barbiturates may affect neurotransmitters in many systems. At the neuromuscular junction they cause the postsynaptic membrane to be insensitive to the depolarizing effects of acetylcholine (Thesleff, 1956), therefore causing a decrease in transmission of cholinergic neurons. They also have an effect on transmission of adrenergic systems, causing a release of norepinephrine from storage (Goodman and Gilman, 1956). They cause a marked decrease in norepinephrine turnover and dopamine turnover in the central nervous system (Person and Woldeck, 1971; Lidbrinic, Corrod, Fuxe, and Olson, 1972). This is consistent with the theory that norepinephrine or dopamine may be involved in depression (Bunney and Davis, 1965). Although the barbiturates apparently have an effect on serotonin turnover, they have little effect on serotonin level of rabbit brain (Brody and Bain, 1951). All of these effects could be ascribed to a general decrease in activity. Since depression usually occurs only after repeated administration of barbiturates, it is very difficult to determine this mechanism of action, especially in purely biochemical terms.

Other hypnotics causing depression are glutethimide and methaquolone. Glutethimide inhibits oxidative phosphorylation (Erwin and Heim, 1963). It is also an anticholinergic agent (Tierrian and Gross, 1958). Less work has been done on these two drugs than has been done on the barbiturates because they are newer and less widely used. Glutethimide has been shown to inhibit cerebral NADPH in the same way as barbiturates. Undoubtedly, the production of depression by glutethimide follows the same mechanisms as those of the barbiturates. The analgesic and EEG effects are similar to those of the barbiturates. Methaquolone, in addition to resembling the barbiturates in its properties, produces antihistaminic effects (Malhotra et al., 1960).

2. Tranquilizers

Reserpine, the most commonly used of the rauwolfia alkaloids, is primarily a tranquilizing agent and an antihypertensive agent; however, in addition to these effects, it can produce nightmares and severe psychic depression. Often, continued administration of reserpine can end in hospitalization or even suicide (Quetsch, Achor, Litin, and Faucett, 1959). It produces a state of indifference to environmental stimuli, unaccompanied by ataxia such as is often produced by the barbiturates. It produces catatonia, which is relieved by administering dopamine. Many of the actions of the drugs can be described as trophotropic. These symptoms can be duplicated by increasing cholinergic activity (Brodie, 1958). The results of reserpine administration may come about from the depletion of dopamine and the subsequent rise in the acetylcholine/dopamine ratio (Martin, 1963). The compound has been shown to reduce levels of several transmitter substances. It reduces levels of endogenous serotonin (Pletscher, Shore, and Brodie, 1955), norepinephrine, and dopamine (Carlsson, Rosengran, Bertler, and Nilsson, 1957). It is believed by Costa that the sedative effect of reserpine results from its depletion of catecholamines, whereas the behavioral depression is more closely related to the serotonin depletion, but Carlsson suggested that the deficit in catecholamines was more responsible for the depression (Carlsson et al., 1957; Costa, Gessa, Hirsch, Kuntzman, and Brodie, 1962). The effects of this compound certainly would fit with the involvement of norepinephrine in depression (Bunney and Davis, 1965) but they do not rule out the involvement of serotonin.

The phenothiazines also can produce profound depression. Chlorpromazine, the most commonly used phenothiazine, has a significant effect on the central nervous system, depressing the action of dopaminergic neurons (Domino, 1969). It antagonizes the depression of the transcallosal response produced by epinephrine, serotonin, mescaline, and LSD. It has been shown that chlorpromazine blocks conditioned avoidance responses; however, it does not block unconditioned responses (Cook and Weidley, 1957). In contrast the barbiturates affect both conditioned and unconditioned responses. Again the possibility certainly exists (Domino, 1969) that the compound acts through a depression of norepinephrine.

Alpha-methyl-p-tyrosine depresses norepinephrine and dopamine production to the point where the levels of these transmitters can almost be brought to zero. Like most of the other compounds previously discussed, it depresses the production of catecholamines. If, as Bunney has suggested, depressions result from the depletion of norepinephrine, then alpha-methyl-p-tyrosine should be an excellent agent for producing depression. However, when actually tried, this compound produced no depression in a number of patients

(Gershon, Hekimian, Floyd, and Hollister, 1967). The catatonia induced by alpha-methyl-tyrosine is reversed by the administration of DOPA but not the psychic symptoms (Bedard, Larochelle, Poirier, and Sourkes, 1970).

Also the administration of DOPA should raise catecholamine levels and relieve the symptoms of depression (Weil-Malherbe, 1967). This is not the case. DOPA relieves reserpine sedation but not chlorpromazine sedation. It appears to correct the physiologic effects of the drug but not the psychic (Degwitz, Frowein, Kulenkampff, and Mohs, 1960). These would suggest that the production of depression is considerably more complicated and cannot be explained by reliance on a single simple action such as the depression of norepinephrine production.

IV. CONCLUSION

Of what value are model psychoses? From early times both psychologically and chemically induced model psychoses have been seen as part of religious and semireligious rituals. Sensory isolation has been used to prepare individuals for mystic experiences in religious rituals (Brawley and Pos, 1967). Peyote, cohoba, and teonanacatyl were used as integral parts of rituals. More recently the so-called mind-expanding drugs have been used by individuals for personal pleasure (Farnsworth, 1968). During the Korean War, brainwashing techniques were used to affect man's psychic state (Bexton et al., 1954). Whether any of the above uses of model psychoses can be construed as being for the good of mankind is questionable.

Some of the psychotomimetic drugs have been claimed to be helpful in the treatment of psychotic conditions (Whitaker, 1964). Certainly one cannot discount the usefulness of a number of the psychotomimetic drugs such as the amphetamines, atropine, scopolamine, the morphine derivatives, and the barbiturates. However, whether these medications are always used wisely, can be and is being questioned.

Have the model psychoses helped in the understanding of psychotic conditions? Possibly. The studies on sensory deprivation have given rise to theories that may well apply in existing mental disease. Particularly interesting is the theory of Inglis which blames most of the problem on a paucity of stored information (Inglis, 1956). Inglis theorizes that in problem solving, the central nervous system constantly checks back on stored information to determine if the problem is being solved properly. In the case of information underload, this searching becomes wider and wider, never resulting in the detection of appropriate information. The problem is then solved on the basis of no information or inappropriate information.

In the case of sensory deprivation, the information underload is caused by a lack of sensory stimulation. In the case of sleep deprivation it could be caused by lack of energy production by the neurons, therefore not permitting information to be transmitted to the central core. Phencyclidine also decreases energy production and therefore could cause an information underload. A serious defect in this hypothesis can be seen in the fact that dinitrophenol, one of the most potent uncouplers of oxidative phosphorylation, is not a hallucinogen. In order to overcome this, one must make the unlikely proposal that sleep deprivation and phencyclidine uncouple phosphorylation selectively in some neurons but not in the whole body. There is no experimental evidence to support this.

LSD, mescaline, and many other hallucinogens apparently do not act through simple agonism or antagonism toward the serotonergic or adrenergic systems, since no consistency was found between the effects of the various hallucinogens on either of these systems. There is a possibility that they act on the balance between the cholinergic, adrenergic, and serotonergic systems (Friedhoff and Alpert, 1973). Such an imbalance might prevent information storage and cause an information underload. However, much experimental work needs to be done to determine if such an imbalance exists. It is more likely that the hallucinogens block receptor sites of selected neurons in the central nervous system (Smythies, 1969). This again could cause information underload. But, as in the previous case, more experimental work is necessary to determine if postsynaptic receptor sites are indeed blocked out and if so which specific sites are blocked.

Studies on drugs producing depressions seem to indicate that the adrenergic system as predicted may be involved but that the mechanism by which this takes place is certainly more complicated than the simple depletion of adrenergic transmitters.

Some valuable information has been obtained through the use of model psychoses. Some biologic models of the production of psychoses can be proposed. One such model involving a theory of sensory deprivation (an adaptation of Inglis') was proposed above, but it by no means is presented as the only model. Much more work involving the balances between neurotransmitter systems and the effect of psychotomimetic drugs on receptor sites in single neurons needs to be done to determine the validity of hypotheses such as that proposed.

REFERENCES

Abramson, H. A. (1968): Lysergic acid diethyl amide (LSD-25) XXXVII. Antiserotonin action of lysergic acid derivatives in allergy and neuropsychiatry. *J. Asthma Res.,* 2:257–262.

Aghajanian, G. K., and Weiss, B. L. (1968): Block by LSD of the increase in brain serotonin turnover induced by elevated ambient temperature. *Nature,* 220:795–796.

Appel, J. B., and Freedman, D. X. (1968): Tolerance and cross-tolerance among psychotomimetic drugs. *Psychopharmacologia,* 13:267–274.

Appel, J. B., Lovell, R. A., and Freedman, D. X. (1970): Alterations in behavioral effects of LSD by pretreatment with p-chlorophenylalanine and α-methyl-p-tyrosine. *Psychopharmacologia,* 18:387–406.

Bain, J. A. (1952): Enzymatic aspects of barbiturate action. *Fed. Proc.,* 11:653–658.

Ban, T. A., Lohrenz, J. J., and Lehman, H. E. (1961): Observations on the action of sernyl—a new psychotropic drug. *Can. Psychiatr. Assoc. J.,* 6:150–157.

Beach, F. A., and Janes, J. (1954): Effects of early experience upon the behavior of animals. *Psychol. Bull.*, 51:239–263.

Becker, H. S. (1953): Becoming a marihuana user. *Am. J. Sociol.*, 59:235–242.

Bedard, P., Larochelle, L., Poirier, L. J., and Sourkes, T. C. (1970): Reversible effect of L-DOPA on tremor and catatonia induced by α-methyl-*p*-tyrosine. *Can. J. Physiol. Pharmacol.*, 48:82–84.

Bell, D. S. (1965): Comparison of amphetamine psychoses and schizophrenia. *Br. J. Psychiatry*, 111:701–707.

Bergen, J. R. (1965): Possible relationship of a plasma factor to schizophrenia. *Trans. N.Y. Acad. Sci.*, 28:40–46.

Berger, R. J., and Oswald, I. (1962): Effects of sleep deprivation on behavior, subsequent sleep and dreaming. *J. Ment. Sci.*, 108:457–465.

Bexton, W. H., Heron, W., and Scott, T. H. (1954): Effects of decreased variation in the sensory environment. *Can. J. Psychol.*, 8:70–76.

Bliss, E. L., Clark, L. D., and West, C. D. (1959): Studies of sleep deprivation relationship to schizophrenia. *Arch. Neurol. Psychiatry*, 81:348–349.

Boakes, R. J., Bradley, P. B., Briggs, I., and Dray, A. (1970): Antagonism of 5-hydroxytryptamine by LSD 25 in the central nervous system: A possible neuronal basis for the actions of LSD 25. *Br. J. Pharmacol.*, 40:202–218.

Bose, B. C., Vijayvorgiya, R., Saifi, A. Q., and Bhagwat, A. W. (1963): Chemical and pharmacological investigations of cannabis indica. *Arch. Int. Pharmacodyn. Ther.*, 146:99–105.

Bose, B. C., Saifi, A. Q., and Bhagwat, A. W. (1964): Studies on pharmacological actions of cannabis indica. III The effects of delta 9 tetrahydrocannabinol on the metabolism of norepinephrine in rat brain. *Arch. Int. Pharmacodyn. Ther.*, 147:291–297.

Boszormenyi, A., Der, P., and Nazg, T. (1962): Observations on the psychotogenic effect of N,N diethyltryptamine—a new tryptamine derivative. *Ann. N.Y. Acad. Sci.*, 96:134.

Brawley, P., and Pos, R. (1967): The informational underload (sensory deprivation) model in contemporary psychiatry. *Can. Psychiatr. Assoc. J.*, 12:105–124.

Bridger, W. H. (1968): The interaction of stress and hallucinogenic drug action: Implications for a pathophysiological mechanism in schizophrenia. In: *Schizophrenia Current Concepts and Research,* edited by D. O. Siva Sankar, pp. 470–476. PJD Publications, Hicksville, N.Y.

Brodie, B. B. (1956): Pathways of drug metabolism. *J. Pharm. Pharmacol.*, 8:1–17.

Brodie, B. B. (1958): Interaction of psychoprobic drugs with physiological and biochemical mechanisms in brain. *Mod. Med.*, 26:69–80.

Brody, T. M., and Bain, J. A. (1951): Effect of barbiturates on oxidative phosphorylation. *Proc. Soc. Exp. Biol. Med.*, 77:50–53.

Brown, B. B. (1957): Lysergic acid diethylamide—antagonism of certain drugs. *Ann. N.Y. Acad. Sci.*, 66:677–685.

Brown, W. T., McGeer, P. L., and Moser, I. (1968): Lack of psychotomimetic effect of para methoxyphenylethylene and 3,4 dimethoxyphenylethyl amines in man. *Can. Psychiatr. Assoc. J.*, 13:91–92.

Burstein, S. H. (1973): Labeling and metabolism of the tetrahydrocannabinols. In: *Marijuana,* edited by R. Mechoulam, pp. 167–182. Academic Press, New York.

Bunney, W. E., and Davis, J. M. (1965): Norepinephrine in depressive reactions. A review. *Arch. Gen. Psychiatry*, 13:483.

Caldwell, D. E., Myers, S. A., Domino, E. F., and Merriam, P. E. (1969): Auditory and visual threshold effects of marihuana in man. *Percept. Mot. Skills*, 29:755–759.

Carlini, E. A., Santos, M., and Lampaio, M. R. P. (1965): Potentiation of histamine oxidase by mescaline. *Experientia*, 21:72–73.

Carlini, E. A., Sampaio, M. R. P., Santos, M., and Carlini, G. R. S. (1965a): Potentiation of histamine and inhibition of diamine oxidase by catatonic drugs. *Biochem. Pharmacol.*, 14:1657–1663.

Carlsson, A., Rosengran, E., Bertler, A., and Nilsson, J. (1957): Effect of reserpine on the metabolism of catecholamines. In: *Psychotropic Drugs,* edited by S. Garattini and V. Ghetti, pp. 363–372. Elsevier, Amsterdam.

Cerletti, A. (1956): Lysergic acid diethylamide and related compounds. In: *Neuropharmacology,* edited by H. A. Abramson, pp. 9–84. Josiah Macy Jr. Foundation, New York.

Cerletti, A., Schlagen, E., Spitzer F., and Taeschler, M. (1963): Psychodysleptica. *Schweiz. Apotheker Zeitung,* 101:210–240.

Chen, G., Ensor, C., Russell, D., and Bohner, B. (1959): The pharmacology of 1-(1-phenylcyclohexyl) piperidine-HCl. *J. Pharmacol. Exp. Ther.,* 127:241–250.

Cohen, B. D., Grisell, J. L., and Ax, A. (1962): The effects of voluntary sleep loss on psychological and physiological functions. In: *Proceedings of the Third World Congress of Psychiatry,* pp. 986–991. University of Toronto Press, McGill University Press, Toronto.

Cohen, B. D., and Grisell, J. L. (1963): Some relations between biochemical and psychological phenomena in normal and schizophrenic subjects. In: *Serological Fractions in Schizophrenia,* edited by R. G. Heath, pp. 203–217. Hoeber, New York.

Cohen, M. M., Marinello, M. J., and Baek, N. (1967): Chromosonal damage in human leukocytes induced by lysergic acid diethylamide. *Science,* 155:1417–1419.

Collins, R. L., Ordy, J. M., and Samorajski, T. (1966): Psilocin: Effects on behavior and brain serotonin in mice. *Nature,* 209:785–787.

Connell, P. H. (1958): *Amphetamine Psychosis.* Maudsley Monographs No. 5., London.

Cook, L. and Weidley, E. (1957): Behavioral effects of some psychopharmacological agents. *Ann. N.Y. Acad. Sci.,* 66:740.

Costa, E., Gessa, G. L., Hirsch, C., Kuntzman, R., and Brodie, B. B. (1962): On current status of serotonin as a brain neurohormone and on action of reserpine like drugs. *Ann. N.Y. Acad. Sci.,* 96:118–131.

Cottrell, G. A. (1970): Actions of LSD-25 and reserpine on a serotonergic synapse. *J. Physiol.,* 208:28P–29P.

Curtis, D. R., and Davis, R. (1962): Studies upon neurons of the lateral geniculate nucleus of the cat. *Br. J. Pharmacol.,* 18:217–246.

Daly, J. W., Mauger, A. B., Yonemitsu O., Antonov, V. K., Lapase, K., and Witkop, B. (1967): The synthesis and metabolism of 2,3 dihydro-L-tryptophan and 2,3 dihydro-5-hydroxy-DL-tryptophan. *Biochemistry,* 6:648–654.

Degwitz, R., Frowein, R., Kulenkampff, C., and Mohs, U. (1960): Uber der wickungen des L-DOPA beim Menschenund deren beeinflussung durch Reserpin Chlorpromazin, Iproniazed und Vitamin B-6. *Klin. Wochenschr.,* 38:120–123.

Dement, W. C. (1960): The effect of dream deprivation. *Science,* 131:1705–1707.

Dement, W. C. (1965): Studies on the function of rapid eye movement (paradoxical) sleep in human subjects. In: *Aspects Anatomo—Fonctionnels de la Physiologie du Sommeil,* p. 583. Editions du centre nationel de la Recherche Scientifique, Lyon, France.

Dement, W. C., and Fisher, C. (1963): Experimental interference with the sleep cycle. *Can. Psychiatr. Assoc. J.,* 8:400–405.

Denber, H. C. B. (1964): Studies with mescaline. *Rev. Neurobiol. Supp.,* 10:1157 1168.

Denber, H. C. B., and Teller, D. N. (1968): Studies on mescaline XIX. A new theory containing the nature of schizophrenia. *Psychosomatics,* 9:145–151.

Diab, I. M., Freedman, D. X., and Roth, L. J. (1971): [³H]Lysergic acid diethylamide: Cellular autoradiographic localization in rat brain. *Science,* 173:1022–1024.

Diab, I. M., Roth, L. J. (1972): Cellular autoradiography of ³H-LSD in brain, ³H-thymidine in intestine, WR-2529-¹⁴C in bone utilizing dry mounted, frozen, freeze dried sections. *J. Microsc.,* 96:155–164.

Diaz, P. M., Njai, S. H., and Costa, E. (1968): Factors moderating brain serotonin turnover. *Adv. Pharmacol.,* 68:75–92.

Dixon, A. K. (1968): Evidence of catecholamine mediation in the aberrant behavior induced by lysergic acid diethylamide (LSD) in the rat. *Experientia,* 24:743–747.

Domino, E. F. (1964): Neurobiology of phencyclidine (sernyl) a drug with an unusual spectrum of pharmacological activity. *Int. Rev. Neurobiol.,* 6:303–347.

Domino, E. F. (1969): Pharmacological analysis of the pathobiology of schizophrenia. In: *Schizophrenia Current Concepts and Research,* edited by D. O. Siva Sankar, pp. 148–160. PJD Publications, Hicksville, N.Y.

Dundee, J. W. (1960): Alterations in response to somatic pain associated with anaesthesia II the effect of thiopentone and pentobarbitone. *Br. J. Anaesth.*, 32:407–414.

Elevenon, P., and Boissier, J. R. (1972): LSD effects on signal to noise ratio and lateralization of visual cortex and lateral geniculate during photic stimulation. *Experimentia*, 15:1338–1340.

Ellinwood, E. H. (1971): Assault and homicide associated with amphetamine abuse. *Am. J. Psychol.*, 127:1170–1175.

Ernst, A. M. (1962): Phenomena of the hypokinetic rigid type caused by O-methylation of dopamine in the para-position. *Nature*, 193:178–179.

Erwin, V. G., and Heim, H. Z. (1963): Effects of some hypnotic drugs on respiration and oxidative phosphorylation in rat brain. *J. Pharm. Sci.*, 52:747–751.

Evarts, E. V., Landau, W. M., Freygang, W. H., Jr., and Marshall, W. H. (1955): Some effects of lysergic acid diethyl amide and bufotenine on electrical activity in the cat's visual system. *Am. J. Physiol.*, 182:594–598.

Farnsworth, N. R. (1968): Hallucinogenic plants. *Science*, 162:1086–1092.

Forrer, G. R. (1951): Atropine toxicity in the treatment of mental disease. *Am. J. Psychiatry*, 108:107–112.

Farrow, J. T., and Van Vunakis, H. (1973): Characteristics of d-lysergic acid diethylamide binding to subcellular fractions derived from rat brain. *Biochem. Pharmacol.*, 22:1103–1113.

Fog, R. (1970): Behavioral effects in rats of morphine and amphetamine and of a combination of the two drugs. *Psychopharmacologia*, 16:305–312.

Freedman, D. X., Gottlieb, R., and Lovell, R. A. (1970): Psychotomimetic drugs and brain 5-hydroxytryptamine metabolism. *Biochem. Pharmacol.*, 19:1181–1188.

Freedman, S. J., Grunebaum, H. U., and Greenblatt, M. (1961): Perceptual and cognitive changes in sensory deprivation. In: *Sensory Deprivation*, edited by P. Solomon et al., pp. 58–71. Harvard University Press, Cambridge, Mass.

Friedhoff, A. J., and Hollister, L. E. (1966): Comparison of the metabolism of 3,4 dimethoxyphenylethylamine and mescaline in humans. *Biochem. Pharmacol.*, 15:269–273.

Friedhoff, A. J., and Alpert, M. (1973): A dopaminergic-cholinergic mechanism in production of psychotic symptoms. *Biol. Psychiatry*, 6:165–169.

Friedman, S. A., and Hirsch, S. E. (1971): Extreme hyperthermia after LSD ingestion. *J. Am. Med. Assoc.*, 217:1549–1550.

Gaddum, J. H. (1953): Antagonism between lysergic acid diethylamide and 5-hydroxytryptamine. *J. Physiol.*, 121:15P.

Gershon, S., Hekimian, L. J., Floyd, A., Jr., and Hollister, L. E. (1967): α-methyl-p-tyrosine (AMT) in schizophrenia. *Psychopharmacologia*, 11:189–194.

Goodman, L. S. and Gilman, A. (1956): *The Pharmacological Basis of Therapeutics*, pp. 123–153, 2nd ed. Macmillan, New York.

Graiman, N. J., and Pepeu, G. (1962): The influence of centrally active cholinotic drugs on brain acetylcholine levels. *Br. J. Pharmacol.*, 23:251–262.

Green, H. S., and Sawyer, J. L. (1960): Correlation of tryptamine induced convulsions in rats with brain tryptamine concentration. *Proc. Soc. Exp. Biol. Med.*, 104:153–155.

Greifenstein, F. E., DeVault, M., Yoshitake, J., and Rajeniski, J. E. (1958): A study of a 1-aryl cyclo hexyl amine for anesthesia. *Anesth. Analg.*, 37:283–294.

Guiditta, A., and Diprisco, G. (1963): The inhibition of cerebral NADPH (acceptor) oxidoreductase by barbiturates and nervous depressants: Relation with chemical structure. *Biochim. Biophys. Acta*, 77:394–407.

Guilhaud, G., Benson, J. M., Oliveras, O. L., and Lechkind, O. C. (1973): Suppresion par le LSD de l'effet inhibiteur exence par le noyau dorsul du raphe sur les interneurones de la couchel du couchel de la corne dorsale de lal moelle chez le chat. *C. R. Acad. Sci. (Paris)*, 276:3351–3354.

Hebb, P. O. (1959): *The Organization of Behavior.* Wiley, New York.

Heron, W. (1961): Cognitive and physiological effects of perceptual isolation. In: *Sensory Deprivation*, edited by P. Solomon et al., pp. 6–33. Harvard University Press, Cambridge, Mass.

Heron, W. (1957): The pathology of boredom. *Sci. Am.*, 196:52.

Hitzemann, R. J., Loh, H. H., and Domino, E. F. (1972): Effect of scopolamine on the cerebral accumulation of ^{14}C-catecholamines from ^{14}C-tyrosine. *Pharmacology*, 8:291–299.

Hitzemann, R. J., Loh, H. H., and Domino, E. F. (1973): Effect of phencyclidine on the cerebral accumulation of ^{14}C-catecholamines from ^{14}C-tyrosine. *Arch. Int. Pharmacodyn. Ther.,* 202:252–258.

Hoffer, A., and Osmond, H. (1967): *The Hallucinogens.* Academic Press, New York.

Hollister, L. E., Noden, J. H., and Mayer, H. (1962): Clinical use of amphetamines in psychosomatic medicine. In: *The First Hahnemann Symposium,* p. 577. Lee and Febiger, Philadelphia.

Hollister, L. E. (1964): Chemical psychoses. *Ann. Rev. Med.,* 15:203–213.

Hollister, L. E. (1969): Steroids and moods; correlations in schizophrenics and subjects treated with lysergic acid diethylamide (LSD), mescaline, tetrahydrocannabinol and synhexyl. *J. Clin. Pharmacol.,* 9:24–29.

Hollister, L. E., Richards, R. K., and Gullespie, H. K. (1968): Comparison of tetrahydrocannabinol and synhexyl in man. *Clin. Pharmacol. Ther.,* 9:783–791.

Holtzman, D., Lovell, K. A., Jaffe, J. H., and Freedman, D. X. (1969): 1-D9 tetrahydrocannabinol: Neurochemical and behavioral effects in the mouse. *Science,* 163:1464–1467.

Horita, A., and Hamilton, A. E. (1969): Lysergic acid diethylamide: Dissociation of its behavioral and hyperthermic actions by DL-α-methyl-p-tyrosine. *Science,* 164:78–79.

Hunt, R. R., and Brimblecombe, R. W. (1967): Synthesis and biological activity of some ring-substituted tryptamines. *J. Med. Chem.,* 10:646–648.

Huszti, Z., and Borsy, J. (1964): The effect of diethyltryptamine and its derivatives on monoamine oxidase. *Biochem. Pharmacol.,* 13:1151–1156.

Inglis, J. (1956): Sensory deprivation and cognitive disorder. *Br. J. Psychiatry,* 111:309–315.

Innes, I. R., and Nickerson, M. (1970a): Drugs acting on postganglionic adrenergic nerve endings and structures ennervated by them (Sympathomimetic Drugs). In: *The Pharmacological Basis of Therapeutics,* edited by L. Goodman and A. Gilman, pp. 501–505. Macmillan Co., New York.

Innes, I. R., and Nickerson, M. (1970a): Drugs inhibiting the action of acetylcholine on structures ennervated by postganglionic para-sympathetic nerves. In: *The Pharmacological Basis of Therapeutics,* edited by L. Goodman and A. Gilman, pp. 524–548. Macmillan Co., New York.

Isbel, H., Rosenberg, D. E., Miner, F. J., and Logan, R. L. (1964): Tolerance and cross tolerance to scopolamine, N-ethyl-3-piperidyl benzylate (JB-318) and LSD-25. In: *Neuropsychopharmacology, Vol. 3,* edited by P. B. Bradley, F. Flugel, and P. H. Hoch, pp. 440–446. Elsevier, Amsterdam.

Itil, T., and Fink, M. (1968): EEG and behavioral aspects of the interaction of anti-cholinergic hallucinogens with centrally active compounds. *Prog. Brain Res.,* 28:149–168.

Jacobson, C. B., and Berlin, C. M. (1972): Possible reproductive detriment in LSD users. *JAMA,* 222:1367–1373.

Jouvet, M. (1967): Mechanisms of the states of sleep: A neuropharmacological approach. In: *Sleep and Altered States of Consciousness,* edited by S. S. Kety, E. V. Evarts, and H. L. Williams, pp. 86–126. The Williams and Wilkins Co., Baltimore.

Jouvet, M., and Mounier, D. (1960): Effets des lesions de la formation reticule pontique sur le sommeil de chat. *C. R. Soc. Biol. (Paris),* 154:2301–2305.

Kabes, J., Fink, M., Somtev, A., Urba, J., and Madlo, J. (1972): Some metabolic and behavioral effects of LSD. *Act. Nerv. Super.,* 14:294–295.

Kalir, A., and Szara, S. (1966): Synthesis and pharmacological activity of alkylated tryptamines. *J. Med. Chem.,* 9:341–344.

Kaplan, J., Stillman, R. C., Gillin, J. C., and Wyatt, R. J. (1974): Attempts to evoke tolerance to DMT in man. *New Research, American Psychiatric Association Annual Meeting Abstracts,* May.

Katz, S. E., and Landis, C. (1935): Psychologic and physiologic phenomena during a prolonged vigil. *AMA Arch. Neurol. Psychiatry,* 34:309.

Keats, A. S., and Beecher, H. K. (1950): Pain relief with hypnotic doses of barbiturates and a hypothesis. *J. Pharmacol. Exp. Ther.,* 100:1–13.

Kiplinger, G. F., Manno, J. E., Rodda, B. E., and Forney, R. B. (1971): Dose-response analysis of the effects of tetrahydrocannabinol in man. *Clin. Pharmacol. Ther.,* 12:650–657.

Koella, W. P., and Bergen, J. R. (1969): Cyclic response to repeated LSD administration. In: *Neurophysiological and Behavioral Aspects of Psychotropic Drugs,* pp. 88–101. Charles C Thomas, Springfield, Ill.

Kovacic, B., and Domino, E. F. (1974): Tolerance to behavioral effects of dimethyltryptamine (DMT) in the rat. *Fed. Proc.,* 33:549.

Krus, D. M., Wapner, S., and Casey, T. M. (1963): Differential behavioral responsivity to LSD-25. *Arch. Gen. Psychiatry,* 8:557–563.

Kubie, L. S. (1961): Theoretical aspects of sensory deprivation. In: *Sensory Deprivation,* edited by P. Solomon et al., pp. 208–220, Harvard University Press, Cambridge, Mass.

Lees, H. (1962): The effects in vitro of 1-(1-phenylcyclohexyl) piperidine hydrochloride (Sernyl) on oxidation by liver homogenates and mitochondria of rat. *Biochem. Pharmacol.,* 11:1115–1122.

Leonard, B. E., and Tonge, S. R. (1969): The effects of some hallucinogenic drugs upon the metabolism of norepinephrine. *Life Sci.,* 8:815–825.

Levy, L., Cameron, P. E., and Aitken, R. C. B. (1960): Observation on two psychotomimetic drugs of piperidine derivation—CI 395 (Sernyl) and CI 400. *Am. J. Psychiatry,* 116:843–844.

Lidbrinic, P., Corrod, H., Fuxe, K., and Olson, L. (1972): Barbiturates and meprobamate: Decreases in catecholamine turnover of central dopamine and noradrenaline neuronal systems and the influence of immobilization stress. *Brain Res.,* 45:507–524.

Lilly, J. C. (1956): Mental effects of reduction of ordinary levels of physical stimuli on intact healthy persons. *Psych. Res. Rep. Am. Psych. Assoc.,* 5:1–28.

Lindsley, D. P. (1961): Common factors in sensory deprivation, sensory distortion and sensory overload. In: *Sensory Deprivation,* edited by P. Solomon et al., pp. 174–194, Harvard University Press, Cambridge, Mass.

Longo, V. G., and DeCarolis, A. S. (1968): Anticholinergic hallucinogenics; laboratory results vs clinical trials. *Prog. Brain Res.,* 28:106–112.

Lowe, G., and Williams, P. I. (1972): The effect of LSD-25 on light reinforced behavior in the rat. *Psychopharmacologia,* 27:255–263.

Luby, E. D., Cohen, B. D., Rosenbaum, G., Gottlieb, J. S., and Kelley, R. (1959): Study of a new schizophrenomimetic drug—Sernyl. *AMA Arch. Neurol. Psychiatry,* 81:363–369.

Luby, E. D., Frohman, C. E., Grisell, J. L., Lenzo, J. E., and Gottlieb, J. S. (1960): Sleep deprivation: Effects on behavior, thinking, motor performance, and biological energy transfer systems. *Psychosom. Med.,* 22:182–191.

Luby, E. D., and Gottlieb, J. S. (1971): Model psychoses In: *Lafayette Clinic Studies on Schizophrenia,* edited by G. Tourney and J. Gottlieb, pp. 95–123. Wayne State University Press, Detroit.

Malhotra, O. C., Kohli, R. P., Sareen, K. N., Kissor, K., Amma, M. K., and Gujral, M. L. (1960): Pharmacological study of 2 methyl-3 orthotylquinazol-4 one (D2-2) a new hypnotic. *Indian J. Med. Sci.,* 14:501–507.

Martin, G. J. (1963): The biochemical basis of psychotherapeutics part II. *J. Germantown Hosp.,* 4:23–28.

Martin, W. R. (1967): Opioid antagonists. *Pharmacol. Rev.,* 19:463–521.

Martin, W. R., and Eades, C. G. (1970): The action of tryptamine on the dog spinal cord and their relationship to the agonistic actions of LSD like psychotogens. *Psychopharmacologia,* 17:242–257.

Martin, W. R., and Sloan, J. W. (1970): Effects of infused tryptamine in man. *Psychopharmacologia,* 18:231–237.

McConnell, W. B., and McIlwaine, R. J. (1963): Amphetamine substances and mental illness in northern Ireland. *Br. J. Psychiatry,* 109:218–224.

Meyer, J. S., Greifenstein, F., and DeVault, M. (1959): A new drug causing symptoms of sensory deprivation: Neurological, electroencephalographic and pharmacological effects of Sernyl. *J. Nerv. Ment. Dis.,* 129:54–61.

Miras, C. J. (1965): Effect of hashish on reproductive activity. In: *Hashish: Its Chemistry and Pharmacology,* edited by G. E. W. Wolstenholme and Knight, pp. 37–47. Chushul, London.

Moskowitz, D. (1971): Use of haloperidol to reduce LSD flashbacks. *Milit. Med.,* 136:754–756.

Myers, T. I. (1965): Sensory and perceptual deprivation. In: *Symposium on Medical Aspects of Stress in the Military Climate,* Walter Reed Army Medical Center, pp. 243–251. Government Printing Office, Washington, D.C.

Ober, R. E., Gwynn, G. W., Chang, T., McCarthy, D. A., and Glazko, A. J. (1963): Metabolism of 1-(1 phenylcyclohexyl) piperidine (Sernyl). *Fed. Proc.,* 22:539.

Oswald, I., Berger, R. J., Jaramillo, R. A., Keddie, K. M. G., Olley, P. C., and Plunkett, G. B. (1963): Melancholia and barbiturates: A controlled EEG, body and eye movement study of sleep. *Br. J. Psychiatry,* 109:66–78.

Parr, D. (1970): Delayed psychosis due to LSD. *Lancet,* 2:934.

Paton, D. M., and Pertinee, P. G. (1973): The actions of cannabis in man. In: *Marijuana,* edited by R. Mechoulam, pp. 287–333. Academic Press, New York.

Pennes, H. H., and Hoch, P. H. (1956): Psychotomimetics—Clinical and theoretical considerations; harmine win-2299 and nalline. *Am. J. Psychiatry,* 113:887–892.

Persaud, T. V. N., and Ellington, A. C. (1968): Teratogenic activity of cannabis resin. *Lancet,* 2:406–407.

Person, T., and Woldeck, B. (1971): A reduced rate of turnover of brain noradrenaline during pentobarbitone anaesthesia. *J. Pharm. Pharmacol.,* 23:377–378.

Pletscher, S. F., Shore, P. A., and Brodie, B. B. (1955): Serotonin release as a possible mechanism of reserpine action. *Science,* 122:374–375.

Prout, C. T. (1964): Reactions to use of amphetamines as observed in a psychiatric hospital. *N.Y. S. J. Med.,* 64:1186–1192.

Quetsch, R. M., Achor, R. W. P., Litin, E. M., and Faucett, R. L. (1959): Depressive reactions in hypertensive patients: A comparison of those treated with rauwolfia and those receiving no specific anti-hypertensive treatment. *Circulation,* 19:366–375.

Rodin, E. A., and Luby, E. D. (1966): Effects of LSD-25 on the EEG and photic evoked response. *Arch. Gen. Psychiatry,* 14:435–441.

Rodin, E. A., Luby, E. D., and Gottlieb, J. S. (1962): The electroencephalogram during prolonged experimental sleep deprivation. *Electroencephalogr. Clin. Neurophysiol.,* 14:544–551.

Rodin, E. A., Luby, E. D., and Meyer, J. S. (1959): Electroencephalographic findings associated with Sernyl infusion. *Electroencephalogr. Clin. Neurophysiol.,* 11:796–798.

Randic, M., and Padjen, A. (1971): Effect of N,N dimethyltryptamine and D-lysergic acid diethylamide on the release of 5-hydroxyindoles in rat forebrain. *Nature,* 230: 532–533.

Rauzzino, F. J., and Siefter, J. (1967): Potentiation and antagonism of biogenic amines. *J. Pharmacol. Exp. Ther.,* 157:143–148.

Rosencrans, J. A., and Schechter, M. D. (1973): *d*-Amphetamine as a discriminative cue; drugs with similar stimulus properties. *Eur. J. Pharmacol.,* 21:212–216.

Rosenbaum, G., Cohen, B. D., Luby, E. D., Gottlieb, J. S., and Yellen, D. (1959): Comparison of Sernyl with other drugs I: Attention, motor function and proprioception. *AMA Arch. Gen. Psychiatry,* 1:651–656.

Rosenbaum, G. (1971): Feedback mechanisms in schizophrenia. In: *Lafayette Clinic Studies on Schizophrenia,* edited by G. Tourney and J. Gottlieb, pp. 163–185. Wayne State University Press, Detroit.

Rosenberg, D. E., Isbel, H., and Miner, E. J. (1963): Comparison of a placebo, N-dimethyltryptamine, and 6-hydroxy-*N*-dimethyltryptamine in man. *Psychopharmacologia,* 4:39–42.

Rosenberg, D. E., Isbel, H., Miner, E. J., and Logan, C. R. (1964): The effect of N,N dimethyltryptamine in human subjects tolerant to lysergic acid diethylamide. *Psychopharmacologia,* 5:217–227.

Sackler, A. M., Williams, A. S., and Sparber, S. B. (1963): Effects of lysergic acid diethylamide on the total leukocytes and eosinophils of the female rat. *Nature,* 199: 1194–1195.

Schildkraut, J. J., and Effran, D. H. (1971): The effects of delta-nine-tetrahydrocannabinol on the metabolism of norepinephrine in rat brain. *Psychopharmacologia,* 20:191–196.

Shagass, C., and Schwartz, M. (1964): Evoked potential studies in psychiatric patients. *Ann. N.Y. Acad. Sci.,* 112:526–542.

Shein, H. M., Wilson, S., Larin, F., and Wurtman, R. J. (1971): Stimulation of

(^{14}C) serotonin synthesis from (^{14}C) tryptophan by mescaline in rat pineal culture. *Life Sci.,* 10:273–282.

Siva Sankar, D., and Domjan, M. (1973): Release of particulate norepinephrine by d-LSD-25 and reserpine. *Res. Commun. Chem. Pathol. Pharmacol.,* 5:205–214.

Smith, D. E. (1969): Speed freaks vs acid heads. Conflict between drug subcultures. *Clin. Pediatr.,* 8:185–188.

Smythies, J. R., and Antun, F. (1969): Binding of tryptamines and allied compounds to nucleic acids. *Nature,* 223:1061–1063.

Smythies, J. R., Johnston, V. S., Bradley, R. J., Bennington, F., Morin, R. D., and Clark, L. C. (1967): Some new behaviour-disrupting amphetamines and their significance. *Nature,* 216:128–129.

Smythies, J. R., Johnston, V. S., and Bradley, R. J. (1969): Behavioural models of psychosis. *Br. J. Psychiatry,* 115:55–68.

Smythies, J. R., and Sykes, E. A. (1964): The effects of mescaline upon the conditioned avoidance response in the rat. *Psychopharmacologia,* 6:163–172.

Snyder, S. H. (1970): Catecholamines, brain function and how psychotrophic drugs act. In: *Principles of Psychopharmacology,* edited by W. G. Clark, pp. 115–125. Academic Press, New York.

Sofia, R. D., Dixit, B. N., and Barry, H. (1971): The effect of delta-1-tetrahydrocannabinol on serotonin metabolism in the rat brain. *Life Sci.,* 10:425–436.

Sparkes, R. S., Melnyk, J., and Bozzett, L. P. (1968): Chromosonal effect *in vivo* of exposure to lysergic acid diethylamide. *Science,* 160:1343–1345.

Stille, G. (1971): Zur Pharmakologie Katatonigener Stoffe. *Arzneim. Forsch.,* 21:997–1003.

Szara, S., Rockland, L. H., Rosenthal, D., and Handlon, J. H. (1966): Psychological effects and metabolism of N,N diethyltryptamine in man. *Arch. Gen. Psychiatry,* 15:320–329.

Szara, S., Morton, D. M., and Aikens, A. (1967): Comparison of hallucinogenic congeners on regional serotonin metabolism in brain. *Pharmacologist,* 9:250.

Szara, S., and Faillace, L. A. (1968): Hallucinogenic drugs; influence of mental set and setting. *Dis. Nerv. Syst.,* 29:124–126.

Tennant, F. S., and Groesbeck, C. J. (1972): Effects of hashish. *Arch. Gen. Psychiatry,* 27:133–136.

Teresa, M., Silva, A., Carlini, E. A., Claussen, U., and Horte, F. (1968): Lack of cross tolerance in rats among (−) Δ9- trans tetrahydrocannabinol (Δ9-THC), cannabis extract, mescaline and lysergic acid diethylamide (LSD-25). *Psychopharmacologia,* 13:332–340.

Thesleff, S. (1956): The effect of anesthetic agents on skeletal muscle membrane. *Acta Physiol. Scand.,* 37:335–349.

Tonge, S. R. (1969): The effects of some hallucinogenic drugs upon the metabolism of 5-hydroxy-tryptamine in the brain. *Life Sci.,* 8:805–814.

Tierrian, H., and Gross, F. (1958): Anti-cholinergische eigenschaften hypnotisch und anti-konvulsiv wirkender glutarsaureimide. *Helv. Physiol. Pharmacol.,* 16:208–221.

Tyler, P. B., Goodman, J., and Rothman, T. (1947): The effect of experimental insomnia on the rate of potential changes in the brain. *Am. J. Physiol.,* 149:185–193.

Weil-Malherbe, H. (1967): The biochemistry of the functional psychoses. *Adv. Enzymol.,* 29:479–540.

West, J. W., Janszer, H. H., Lester, B. K., and Cornelison, F. S., Jr., (1962): The psychosis of sleep deprivation. *Ann. N.Y. Acad. Sci.,* 96:66–70.

Whitaker, L. H. (1964): Lysergic acid diethylamide in psychotherapy. *Med. J. Aust.,* 1:36–41.

Wikler, A. (1945): Effects of morphine, nembutal, ether and eserine on two-neuron and multi-neuron reflexes in the cat. *Proc. Soc. Exp. Biol. Med.,* 58:193–196.

Williams, H. L., Lubin, A., and Goodnow, J. (1959): Impaired performance with acute sleep loss. *Psychol. Monogr.,* 73 (484):1–26.

Wilson, W. S. (1967): The effects of phenobarbitone, leptazol, dexamphetamine, iproniazid, imipramine, LSD, chlorpromazine, reserpine and hydroxyzine on the in vivo levels of adenine nucleotides in the rat brain. *Br. J. Pharmacol.,* 36:448–457.

Wray, S. R. (1972): A correlative evaluation of cyclazocine LSD and naloxone on continuous discriminated avoidance in rats. *Psychopharmacologia,* 26:29–43.

Biological Foundations of Psychiatry,
edited by R. G. Grenell and S. Gabay.
Raven Press, New York © 1976.

Psychochemotherapy

Arthur K. Shapiro

Department of Psychiatry, Special Studies Laboratory, Payne Whitney Clinic, New York Hospital, Cornell University Medical College, New York, New York 10021

I. PLACEBO EFFECTS IN MEDICINE

A. Historical Background

Psychologic factors in illness and treatment have always been important in medicine and were recognized by Hippocrates and also by Galen who insightfully observed, "He cures most successfully in whom the people have the greatest confidence." He then estimated that 60% of patients had emotional rather than physical symptoms, a figure that is close to the contemporary estimate of 50 to 80%. Despite the psychologic sensitivity of Galen and Hippocrates, all of the drugs used in their treatment were placebos.

Treatment was primitive, unscientific, for the most part ineffective, and often shocking and dangerous. Patients were given every known organic and inorganic substance including blood from almost every animal and nearly all excretions from humans and animals.

Some famous treatments used for centuries bore unique names such as the royal touch, Egyptian mummy, bezoar stone, mandrake, Theriac (with 37 to 63 ingredients) and mattioli (with 230 ingredients), the last two requiring several months to concoct, and a unicorn's horn which sold for as much as the equivalent of $250,000. Galen's elaborate pharmacopoeia contained 820 animal, vegetable, and mineral substances all of which were worthless. Medical reasoning was primitive: lung of the long-winded fox was given to consumptives; fat of a hirsute bear was prescribed for baldness; mistletoe, a plant that grows on the oak which cannot fall, was specified for the falling sickness; a wounded person was treated with sympathetic powder which was applied to the bloodstained garment, and by sympathetic ointment applied to the inflicting implement. Throughout medical history patients were purged, puked, poisoned, punctured, cut, cupped, blistered, bled, leeched, heated, dehydrated, frozen, sweated, and shocked.

Useful drugs or procedures appeared infrequently in medical history and even then were usually forgotten by succeeding generations. For thousands of years physicians prescribed what we now know were useless and often dangerous medications. This would not have been possible were it not for the fact that physicians did in some way help their patients. Today we know that the effectiveness of these procedures was due to psychologic factors that are often referred to as the placebo effect. Since almost all medications until recently were placebos, the history of medical treatment can be characterized largely as the history of the placebo effect.

B. The Placebo as Adaptive Mechanism

The tendency to react with placebo effects is probably a built-in adaptive mechanism that has helped mankind survive. Man's survival could have been impaired by realistic reactions to the unpredictable and overwhelming phenomena to which he was exposed. His capacity, need, and ability to explain the unknown by projection of internal fantasy onto his environment provided adaptive psychologic outlets in the form of externalization of fantasy, catharsis, control over internal and external environment, and other psychologic mechanisms. This process would decrease anxiety, depression, despair, and hopelessness, and liberate energies for adaptation to realistic problems.

Man has always reacted to unknown stressful stimuli with unrealistic fantasies of optimism, pessimism, and a combination of both. This was reflected in primitive periods by elaborate mythologies and magic in which the world was populated by benevolent and malevolent forces, devils and gods. In such a setting, optimistic fantasy might provide an adaptive denial of an otherwise unmanageable world, a pessimistic fantasy would prepare for adversity, a capacity for reality testing would modify unrealistic fantasy, and a propitious combination of these factors would be used for survival, adaptation, and increased control of the environment.

As the world became more known and manageable, diffuse fantasy and projection were less necessary, and the witch doctor–priest–scientist became more specialized. Today the scientist has a methodology to deal with the unknown; religion has become institutionalized and increasingly restricted to vague spiritual aspects of man's existence; and, although medicine has made great advances in its understanding and treatment of disease, illness still can provoke fantasy because of its importance to the individual.

Man's greater success in conquering his physical environment than in furthering his psychological understanding has increasingly led to a preoccupation with psychological problems. Previously, the physical environment was inexplicably intertwined with psychological problems and resolutions. With increasing control of the physical environment, somatic displacement and projection of psychological problems became a less adequate and necessary outlet. Psychological problems now could be approached directly. But man's comprehension of his impulses, conflicts, and relationship with others, and psychologic insight into himself, is not adequate. With failure of traditional, religious, and other explanations, man's capacity for fantasy and projection has focused increasingly on self-understanding, and psychotherapy has become the institutionalized outlet for the expression and resolution of conflict. Placebo effects, primarily associated with physical treatment in the past, can now be expressed and experienced through psychological treatment in the form of psychotherapy or psychochemotherapy.

C. Definition of Placebo and Placebo Effect in Modern Medicine

A placebo is any component of therapy that is deliberately or knowingly used for its nonspecific, psychologic, or psychophysiologic effect, or that is used unknowingly for its presumed or believed specific effect on a patient, symptom, or illness, but which, unknown to patient and therapist, is without specific activity for the condition being treated.

A placebo, when used as a control in experimental studies, is a substance or procedure that is without specific activity for the condition being evaluated. The placebo effect is the nonspecific psychologic or psychophysiologic result produced by placebos.

In other words, a therapeutic procedure may be used with or without the knowledge that it is a placebo. This includes treatments given in the belief that they are not placebos, but which actually are placebos by objective evaluation. The placebo may be inert or active and may include, therefore, all medical treatment, no matter how specific or how administered. It may take the form of oral or parenteral medication, topical preparations, inhalents, and all mechanical, surgical, psychotherapeutic, and other therapeutic techniques. It would include any treatment which produced symptoms or side effects which were not specific for that treatment. A placebo may or may not result in a placebo effect, and the effect may be favorable or unfavorable, that is, positive or negative.

D. Placebo Effect in Contemporary Medicine

Modern medicine no longer relies chiefly on psychologic factors, placebo effects, or the doctor-patient relationship. Today there is an increasing number of specific and predictable drugs and medical procedures. However, although psychologic factors may be minimized, they can never be excluded. It is true that if the dosage of a drug is too high, all patients will react with toxicity or even death, regardless of psychologic factors. But such predictability is unimportant because the majority of clinically useful drugs are prescribed in dosages which are far below the toxic level, and are in a range in which psychologic factors or placebo effects are important.

Despite scientific advances, the placebo effect is an important component of modern medicine. The incidence of placebo reactions approaches 100% in some studies. Placebos can mimic the effect of active drugs, have profound effects on organic illnesses, and can be more powerful than, or reverse the action of, potent active drugs. Drugs are reported effective four to five times more frequently in uncontrolled studies than in controlled studies. If placebo effects are not reported in controlled studies, the studies are considered unreliable. Perhaps a major medical achievement of the past 20 years is the development of methodology and controlled experimentation to test the efficacy of treatment.

However, the importance of the placebo effect is always underestimated because it is easier to recognize the shortcomings of others than of ourselves. Three studies have demonstrated that physicians attribute the use of placebos to other physicians three times as often as they attribute their use to themselves (Hofling, 1955; Shapiro and Struening, 1973a, b, 1974). In addition, in a series of questions on what should be included in a definition of placebo, physicians tended to exclude their own therapies from the definition. Surgeons excluded surgery, internists excluded active medication, psychotherapists and psychoanalysts excluded psychotherapy and psychoanalysis. These defensive attitudes about placebo effects are also reflected in the history and definition of the word *placebo*.

Placebo Effects in Psychochemotherapy

Periodically in the history of medicine the pharmacopoeia expands and contracts. The high point was probably Galen's 820 animal, vegetable, and mineral substances which was used for over 1,000 years. The process is usually more rapid in recent medical history and was observed in the 19th century by Trousseau who admonished: "You should treat as many patients as possible with the new drugs while they still have the power to heal."

Drugs used for psychologic problems have always been particularly susceptible to fashion, but the period preceding the psychochemotherapy era of the last 25 years also had its share of now almost forgotten remedies. There were stomachics such as cimicufuga nigra, condurango blanco, Carter's Little Liver Pills, and drugs "for man or beast." Popular surgical procedures included hysterectomies, tonsillectomies, and thymectomies. Tincture of strychnine, valerian, and gentian were extensively used as tonics for the body.

In the modern psychochemotherapy era of the past 25 years, many remember mephenesin (Tolserol®) for neurotic tension, azocyclonal (Frenquel®) for hallucinations, nialamide (Niamid®), a monoamine oxidase (MAO) inhibitor without side effects, that was used initially at a dosage of 10 mg b.i.d., later at a dosage of 150 mg b.i.d. or q.i.d. and finally, still without side effects, discontinued.

This theme in the history of medicine—increase in faddish placebos when older placebos stop working, followed by rash of newer placebos—tends to disappear when a specific remedy for an identifiable illness becomes available. For example, appendectomy replaced abdominal massage for appendicitis, thyroid treatment became specific for myxedema madness, antibiotics for general paresis, and niacin for pellegra. Unfortunately, we have not reached that degree of specificity in psychiatry.

The etiology and treatment of most psychiatric illnesses have not been clearly specified. The illnesses are often vague, influenced by many subtle psychosocial factors, spontaneously remit, and do not have a precise predictable course and outcome. Psychiatric treatment, although today often more effective than placebo, continues to be too unpredictable, imprecise, and nonspecific. Such observations throughout medical history prompted America's leading medical historian, Fielding Garrison, to observe that "whenever many different remedies are used for a disease, it usually means that we know very little about treating that disease, which is also true of a remedy when it is vaunted as a panacea or cure-all for many diseases."

Therapy will be impaired if physicians are unaware of placebo effects. Therapeutic effects will be attributed to specific procedures which, unknown to the physician, are caused by nonspecific or placebo effects. The therapist's credulity about the efficacy and specificity of the procedure will be exaggerated, and it will encourage the use of one procedure or technique for all patients. Therapists who rely on one technique will be unable to treat many patients; some may be hurt because of inappropriate treatment, and specific indications for a therapeutic procedure will be obfuscated. Awareness of placebo effects will enable clinicians better to evaluate the effects of therapy, contribute to the development of more flexible and appropriate procedures, and make therapy more comprehensive, resourceful, and effective. The recognition that these factors contribute to the treatment process will improve studies by investigators, and may help clarify unsolved problems of specificity in many therapies.

Evaluation of Therapies

These considerations and the recognition and study of the placebo effect have contributed to improved methodology in clinical evaluation of therapies. Although many of the problems and difficulties in evaluation remain unsolved, major advances have been achieved, especially through the use of the following experimental procedures.

Single-blind procedure. Methods of clinical evaluation have had a varied and checkered history. One of the earliest techniques has been referred to as the single-blind procedure. In this method, the physician or investigator knows that control substances are being used and which patients are receiving them. The patient alone is unaware and the control substance is usually an inert placebo. Single-blind studies frequently produce spurious results because of bias that occurs when investigators know to which groups patients have been assigned. The double-blind procedure was thus evolved.

Double-blind procedure. Here neither patient nor physician (nor others treating or evaluating) knows to which groups patients have been assigned. Although the earliest use of such a procedure dates back to the beginning of the twentieth century, it became popular only recently. Since 1960, the double-blind procedure has been the norm for most well designed studies.

Triple-blind procedure. The triple-blind procedure (a title more euphemistic than descriptive) has been used in two ways. Some investigators have attempted to exclude or minimize placebo effects by conducting a preliminary study with placebos. Placebo reactors are then excluded from the definitive study which follows. But placebo effects may occur in as high a percentage of cases in the subsequent study as in the preliminary study. Another way of using this type of study is one in which only investigators who do not treat patients or evaluate outcome are aware of the design of the study.

In all of these procedures, it is important for the placebo control to be identical to the experimental substance. Patient, physician, or investigator might uncover the code if the placebo does not visually resemble the experimental drug, have the same taste, consistency, rate of dissolving in water, and other features in common.

In addition, the placebo control should mimic all the telltale side effects of the experimental substance. Thus, a sophisticated study would employ an active placebo. A placebo control into which active but incidental ingredients are introduced (such as atropine to produce xerostomia) is referred to as an active placebo. Without an active placebo, physician and staff usually are able to distinguish between experimental and control groups, and the double-blind procedure then actually becomes a single-blind procedure.

If a drug becomes established as specifically effective for an illness, it can then be employed as a control, comparison, or standard drug for the new agent being evaluated. Advantages of this design are the lessening of ethical conflicts about using inert substances as a control, and the providing of information about the usefulness of the new drug in comparison with the established older drug.

Limitations of the double-blind procedure. The use of the double-blind procedure limits the possibility of erroneous acceptance of a drug as effective when in fact it is not. However, the opposite may also occur and this procedure may result in rejection of a drug as ineffective when it is actually effective. This occurs because physicians or staff may be too conservative or anxious about their evaluations and thus fail to recognize true differences between placebo and active drug response.

Some investigators believe that objective experiments do not exist. This has prompted suggestions that every experiment be done by an enthusiast and a skeptic and that the investigator's bias be specified with the published results.

Many suggestions about how to make methodology more rigorous and fool-proof have appeared in the literature. These have led to the pragmatic principle that before a new treatment be generally accepted as specific, several studies by different investigators should report similar results.

II. RECENT TRENDS IN PSYCHOCHEMOTHERAPY

As in previous medical history, we seem to be in another period of an expanding pharmacopoeia. A recent text on psychochemotherapy reviewed and discussed 44 antipsychotic, 42 antidepressant, and 40 antianxiety agents. Many others, introduced since 1969 and not included in this list, could be added. Recent surveys of many facets of the epidemiology and treatment of mental illness have underscored the magnitude of this development. The cost of mental illness in 1968 has been estimated at four billion dollars for treatment and prevention and 17 billion dollars for reduced productivity—a staggering total of 21 billion dollars. Of a total 1.26 billion prescriptions written by American physicians in 1970, 17% were for psychotropic prescriptions at a cost of 972 million dollars. These psychotropic drugs were used by 50% of American adults at least once by 1965, and by 25% in 1967 alone. Between 1958 and 1965 prescriptions increased 21% for all types of drugs and 31% for psychotropics.

In 1970, about one out of every three American adults used prescription psychotropic drugs and one of 10 used over-the-counter psychotropic drugs. Of the 214 million prescriptions for these drugs, 40% were prescribed by general practitioners, 20% by internists, 23% by other physicians, and only 17% of the total by neurologists and psychiatrists. Eighty-five percent of users had never seen a psychiatrist.

Considering the vast array of available psychotropic medications, the impossibility of effectively mastering their use, the likelihood that most of the drugs are prescribed in placebo dosages by physicians inadequately trained to use them, I would estimate that at least 95% of these drugs are being used primarily for their placebo effect. Psychotropic drugs have become the glorious placebos of our generation.

Psychotropic treatment has become overly complicated and confusing. Few of the drugs now in use will survive the test of time and the practical pharmacopoeia will be restricted and become more manageable. The following review of guiding principles is based on the author's experience of 18 years of clinical use, teaching, supervision, and research. Its purpose is to provide a rational and pragmatic guide for psychochemotherapy for psychiatrists and nonpsychiatrists who do not specialize in the use of psychopharmaceuticals. The author believes that 95% of the needs in psychochemotherapy can more than adequately be covered by mastering use of perhaps eight or nine drugs. Thorough mastery of a minimal number of psychotropic drugs will more than offset the shortcomings of a limited, and inevitably incomplete, mastery of psychochemotherapy in general.

A. Principles of Treatment

Psychochemotherapy can be simplified by following four guiding principles:

1. The physician should familiarize himself thoroughly with the indications, contraindications, effective dosage ranges, cautions, and side effects of a few drugs in each psychotropic drug category. Adequate knowledge of a drug results in increased confidence that is communicated to the patient, enhancing the overall effectiveness of the total treatment. In addition, thorough knowledge of the expected side effects and of their treatment will decrease premature discontinuation of potentially effective drugs.[1]

2. New and inadequately evaluated drugs should be avoided until knowledge of efficacy and side effects has accumulated. It is impossible to keep up with the flood of new psychopharmacologic agents. They exceed all other pharmaceuticals in sales during the summer months. Over 500 psychopharmaceutic drugs have been investigated or introduced in the modern era, and more than 100 are currently used throughout the world.

Avoiding indiscriminate use of newly introduced drugs may avoid calamities such as that following the use of Germany's most popular sleeping tablet and tranquilizer, thalidomide. Other drugs that have been withdrawn are etryptamine (Monase®) and amphenidone (Dornwal®) because of blood dyscrasia, iproniazid (Marsilid®) because of hepatitis, and pheniprazine (Catron®) because of hepatitis and optic atrophy. It is apparent that various side effects will become known only after long-term use. For example, we know that phenothiazines produce tardive dyskinesia, dermatologic pigmentation, and ocular opacities; antianxiety drugs can cause development of tolerance and addiction, tricyclic antidepressants produce toxic confusional states, MAO inhibitors produce hypertensive crises; phenothiazine-tricyclic-antiparkinson drug combinations produce cardiac toxicity from cumulative atropinic effects; and various drug combinations produce inhibition or enhancement of metabolism.

Because the risk of serious side effects must be balanced against the expected advantages of new drugs over alternative methods of treatment, and since there is little probability that newly introduced drugs will be more effective than older ones, evidence for a therapeutic breakthrough in psychochemotherapy should consist of more than just the clinical reports appearing in various journals. Especially recommended for periodic reviews of the drug

---

[1] Drug companies monitor side effects associated with their drugs in extensive files that are made available to physicians. Thus, if a physician has a question about the possibility of teratology in the second trimester, the manufacturers of the drug should be called and the information will be provided from their files.

literature are *The Medical Letter, Drugs of Choice,* and *Rational Drug Therapy.*

Although the recent Food and Drug Administration (FDA) regulations have established careful criteria, which include evidence for efficacy and safety, and have contributed to minimizing the haphazard use of ineffective and inadequately evaluated drugs, not all problems have been solved. These regulations require only proof of efficacy and safety but do not require evidence supporting the superiority or advantages of one drug over another, nor is it necessary to describe all of the possible untoward reactions from drug combinations. In addition, the recommended dosages are generally too conservative for maximally effective use.

3. Psychopharmacologic agents should not be used knowingly as placebos. Placebo dosages for psychopharmacologic drugs are frequently recommended by drug manufacturers. Examples are trifluoperazine (Stelazine®) 1 to 2 mg b.i.d., meprobamate 200 mg q.i.d., and chlordiazepoxide (Librium®) 5 mg t.i.d. Such dosages, even though placebo, should be avoided since some may cause serious complications, such as agranulocytosis, hepatitis, dermatitis, and some may accumulate over time.

The dosage ranges recommended in this paper were derived from an extensive review of the literature. Although dosages are higher than those recommended by drug manufacturers and customarily used by nonpsychiatrists who use drugs infrequently, they are suggested as the potentially active and effective dosages for meaningful, nonplacebo treatment.

Needless to say, the decision about an appropriate initial dosage must be left to the clinician. The patient's potential idiosyncracy, sensitivity to lower dosages, previous medical history, concomitant medical conditions, and the physician's discomfort with high initial dosages may be factors in the decision.

Some patients may improve on low dosages of psychopharmacologic drugs because of placebo effects which are inevitable in treatment situations. Another group may not respond to an inactive dosage of a drug, which may be an inadequate placebo stimulus, but may improve because of physiologic side effects which may be produced by an active drug. A third group may improve only on a much higher, nonplacebo, and specific dosage. In other words, if patients do not improve on a minimal starting dosage, the possibility of their responding to higher dosages must be considered.

Medication should not be discontinued prematurely. A readiness to change medication before an effective dosage is reached may result in ineffective undertreatment. Psychochemotherapy is somewhat analogous to treatment with digitalis, because there is no predetermined dosage for all patients, and the dosage for every patient has to be determined empirically from the level of response (dose response principle). The dosage of most psychopharmacologic drugs should be titrated against an endpoint of symptom relief or the development of side effects which cannot be tolerated by the patient or counteracted by the physician.

High dosages should be used if necessary despite side effects, since they are generally not serious. Psychopharmacologic agents, unlike most other sedatives, have a wide therapeutic dosage range, making for ease of management. Many complications and side effects of major tranquilizers and antidepressant drugs are not dose-related. In addition, side effects may be necessary for effective treatment of some patients because of indirect psychologic effects or because side effects may be an indication of effective dosage levels.

If the physician restricts his use of psychopharmaceuticals to a few drugs in each category, he can become familiar with the effective dosage ranges, usual or possible side effects, their intensity, time necessary for patients to adapt to them, and their management. With this knowledge, treatment becomes more effective because of the potential use of all the therapeutic factors contributing to clinical improvement.

4. The fourth principle encompasses the clinical basis for choice of drugs. Psychochemotherapy generally is not more complicated than the schemata in Figs. 1 and 2. The diagrams illustrate the different indications for the use of drugs for psychotic and neurotic conditions.

The diagnosis should provide the primary indication for selection of drugs

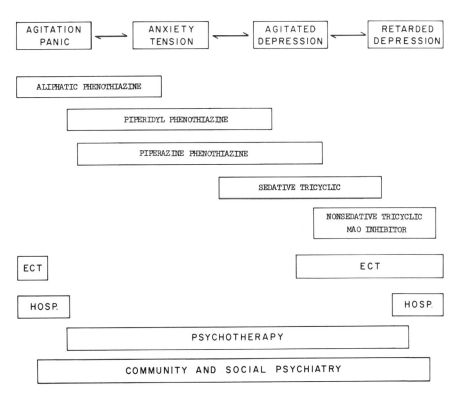

FIG. 1. Psychochemotherapy for psychoses.

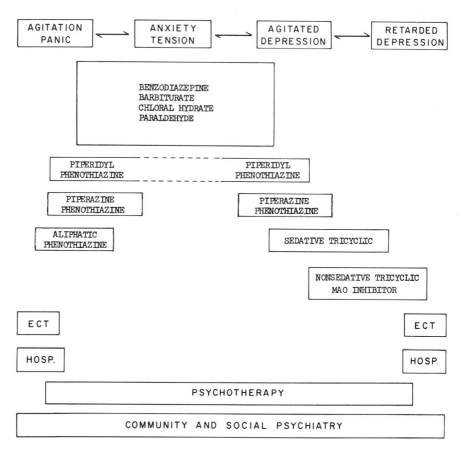

FIG. 2. Psychochemotherapy for neuroses.

since the evidence from controlled studies indicates, for example, that pheno-thiazines are effective for schizophrenia, antidepressants for depression, lithium for manic-depression, and so on. In addition to diagnosis, the clinical basis for choice of drug in treatment of both neurotic and psychotic condi-tions is related to the amount of anxiety and depression as indicated in Figs. 1 and 2. Anxious patients require quieting and depressed patients require stimulation. Symptoms may vary from marked agitation and panic at one end of a continuum, to marked withdrawal, inhibition, blocking, and retarded depression at the other end. Between these extremes are varying degrees of anxiety (tension, nervousness, jitteriness, agitation) and depression (anergia, neurasthenia, hypochondria, anorexia, insomnia, sadness, blueness, moodi-ness, feelings of inferiority, inadequacy, guilt, and suicidal rumination). For example, a sedative-type phenothiazine would be indicated in agitated schizo-phrenic patients and a phenothiazine without sedative properties would be indicated in anergic schizophrenic patients, although both drugs are equally effective in ameliorating schizophrenia. Similarly, for depression, a sedative antidepressant would be indicated for an agitated depressed patient, and a nonsedative antidepressant would be indicated for an anergic depressed patient. Thus, treatment can be based both on diagnostic indications and the need for modifying presenting symptomatology.

The application of the fourth principle will be further amplified in subsequent discussion of the various drug categories.

III. ANTIPSYCHOTIC DRUGS

Drugs in this category, primarily phenothiazine derivatives, are generally referred to as antipsychotic drugs because they ameliorate psychotic conditions, especially schizophrenia.

A. Effectiveness

The ameliorative effect of phenothiazines for psychotic conditions, especially schizophrenia, has been established by the evidence of 200 to 300 double-blind studies. This evidence is more extensive than for any other medical treatment. In several large studies in which phenothiazines were compared with intensive psychotherapy, group psychotherapy, milieu therapy, electroconvulsive therapy, and insulin coma therapy, psychochemotherapy was clearly superior in all. When other therapies were combined with psychochemotherapy, the results were not better than with psychochemotherapy alone. Effectiveness has not been established for most other conditions and usage depends on clinical impression and experience.

Many controlled studies have established that there are no significant differences in effectiveness among commonly used phenothiazines in use today; in other words, they are all equally effective. Many attempts have been made, including the use of complicated computer analyses, to delineate specific indications for the various antipsychotic drugs. Despite some initial success, none of the studies has been successfully replicated.

On this basis, there would be no need for a clinician to use more than one drug. However, several controlled studies have indicated that a significant proportion of patients may not respond to a phenothiazine in one subgroup (for instance, an aliphatic) and may improve when given a phenothiazine in another subgroup (for instance, a piperazine).

Controlled studies have established that maintenance treatment with phenothiazines significantly decreases the chance of relapse for at least 6 months, and several studies indicate protection against relapse for as long as 4 years.

B. Indications

The use of phenothiazines is best substantiated in treating patients with acute and chronic psychoses, and in maintenance treatment of patients with compensated psychoses. Other possible indications include overactivity, severe anxiety, agitation, panic, depression, and marked agitation, manic phase of manic depressive illness, and history of addiction or potential addiction to sedative drugs. Phenothiazines may be indicated for prolonged hiccup and nausea and vomiting from carcinomatosis, acute infections, nitrogen mustard therapy, irradiation, motion sickness, or after operation, although for these conditions, it is questionable whether these drugs are better than barbiturates and antihistamines.

C. Contraindications

General contraindications include: symptomatic sedation, most neurotic conditions, anergic and withdrawn depression, impaired renal and hepatic function or a history of previous agranulocytosis, stupor and concurrent large dosages of sedatives, narcotics, and alcohol. Other contraindications are: cerebral thrombosis, toxic delirium, circulatory collapse, and altered states of consciousness. Phenothiazine drugs should be withdrawn 48 hours prior to surgery, and before spinal and regional anesthesia, because of potentiation of anesthetic agents and alteration of physiologic functioning. They should be used cautiously in patients who are elderly and who have a history of allergy, epilepsy, and brain damage. They should not be used routinely as postoperative medication, especially in older patients who may become disoriented. Phenothiazines should not be administered intravenously.

D. Complications and Side Effects

Many of the complications and side effects of phenothiazine drugs vary in incidence and intensity, and with individual susceptibility. These complications can be grouped under (1) allergic reactions, (2) central, and (3) autonomic nervous system effects, and (4) metabolic, endocrine, and (5) miscellaneous effects.

Allergic Reactions

Allergic reactions include agranulocytosis, jaundice, systemic or dermatologic drug sensitivity, and photosensitivity. Photosensitivity includes phototoxic, dermatologic, and severe sunburn after even brief exposure to sunlight, usually occurring during the summer months of the year, and prolonged high dosage of medication may cause cutaneous or ocular pigmentation and ocular opacities.

It might be useful to remember that jaundice and agranulocytosis occur infrequently and that jaundice usually occurs in the first five weeks of treatment and agranulocytosis in the 5th to 10th week of treatment. Agranulocytosis cannot be anticipated by serial blood counts, and is usually diagnosed by the sudden appearance of an overwhelming, usually oral or pharyngeal, infection. It is important to stop the medication immediately because mortality increases to 40% with continued use. Although the jaundice is usually benign, and patients recover whether the medication is continued or not, change of medication is probably indicated.

In the Central Nervous System

In the central nervous system the following extrapyramidal syndromes may occur: akathisia, akinesia, parkinsonism, and dyskinesia. Persistent dyskinesia, convulsion, and photosensitivity, a light exhaustion syndrome, occur infrequently.

Because extrapyramidal side effects are common, these complications will be described and suggestions will be made about their management.

Akathisia is characterized by restlessness, may mimic anxiety, and can range from a mild form of jitteriness, the need to keep in motion, an inability to concentrate on anything for longer than moments, and insomnia, to severe pacing. Akathisia can be differentiated from anxiety or agitation because the symptoms are caused by extrapyramidal stimulation and it affects the motor system but not the cortex. These symptoms are subjectively different from the symptoms of anxiety or the side effects of amphetamines. The symptoms occur frequently during the first weeks of therapy, last for periods of hours, and often subside with continued treatment. However, the symptoms may be severe. Symptoms are related to dosage, but do not depend on high dosage. They occur more frequently with high potency phenothiazines such as the piperazine subgroup, mildly with the aliphatic subgroup, and are absent with the piperidyl subgroup. The treatment is reassurance if the symptoms are mild, and a trial on antiparkinson agents although they are usually ineffective. With severe akathisia, when it is necessary to keep the patient on medication, barbiturates or benzodiazepines might be considered. Another alternative is to substitute or combine the medication with another phenothiazine which does not have these untoward effects. Akathisia usually disappears within 3 months of treatment.

Akinesia is characterized by muscular weakness and fatigue. Patients are aware of the weakness of a limb used for repetitive muscular acts, such as walking or writing. They may complain of muscular or joint aches and pains, become extremely apathetic, disillusioned, disinclined to initiate or expend energy and appear depressed, regressed, and dependent. Akinesia is often erroneously attributed to sedation from medication, or to a depressive psychological reaction. The differential diagnosis is related to the understanding that the symptoms are due to extrapyramidal stimulation. The patient usually experiences this state as different from being tired, sedated, or depressed. The patient is alert and complains not of drowsiness but of weakness and fatigue. Symptoms usually occur within the first week of treatment, are related to dosage, but may occur on small dosages. Akinesia occurs frequently with the piperazine subgroup, occasionally with the aliphatic subgroup, and is absent with the piperidyl subgroup. It may be extremely profound in 20 to 40% of patients taking the antidepressant amitriptyline. Akinesia usually decreases and disappears with continued treatment, and is responsive to antiparkinson agents.

Parkinsonism is frequent, temporary, reversible, and related to dosage. It occurs more frequently in older patients and in females. The symptoms are tremors, rigidity, masked facies, drooling, shuffling gait, loss of associated movements, and cogwheeling. Early onset can be detected by change in handwriting which becomes constricted and jerky. The symptoms are infrequent in the piperidyl subgroup, common in the aliphatic subgroup, and frequent in the piperazine subgroup. These symptoms are responsive to dosage reduction and to antiparkinson agents, and frequently decrease or disappear after 3 to 4 months of treatment.

Dyskinesia, also referred to as sporadic, dyskinetic, or dystonic syndrome, involves contraction of lateral or bilateral muscles of the upper extremities, particularly of the neck, head, and back, resulting in mandibular tics, oculogyric spasms, speech difficulties, swallowing difficulties, torticollis, hyperextension of the neck and trunk, and torsion spasms. Typically, the symptoms have rhythmic periodicity. They begin imperceptably, reach a maximum muscular contraction within a minute, decrease and disappear within a minute, and then return at irregular intervals. The symptoms are uncommon, affect 2 to 3% of patients, occur frequently in males under the age of 30, and infrequently in children. The symptoms can occur with very small doses of phenothiazines and usually appear within 48 to 72 hr of initial treatment. Parenteral administration is more likely to produce these symptoms. The prevalence is higher with the halogenated piperazines, infrequent in the aliphatic subgroup, and nonexistent in the piperidyl subgroup. The symptoms may be accompanied by profuse diaphoresis, pallor, inability to talk, and great fear in the patient. Fatalities are extremely infrequent. The condition has been confused with hysteria, tetanus, meningitis, encephalitis, other central nervous system disorders, and concurrent psychotic symptoms. However, these symptoms are so typical that the diagnosis can easily be made, especially if it is known that the patient just started phenothiazine medication. The symptoms can be relieved immediately and dramatically by the use of an antihistamine or an antiparkinson agent, but perhaps most predictably by 60 to 90 mg of a barbiturate, followed by an oral antiparkinson agent for a week without discontinuing phenothiazine medication. Dyskinesia will not return, and after one week the antiparkinson agent can be discontinued.

Persistent dyskinesia, grimacing, and masticatory movements of the mouth, may occur in patients who are elderly and have some evidence of previous brain damage. The symptoms are related to high dosage given over a prolonged period of time. Because the symptoms are frequently irreversible and usually persistent after discontinuation of the medication, high doses over prolonged periods should be avoided in older patients with organic brain damage. Oral dyskinesia is more frequent in patients over 50 years, and the choreiform type, choreoathetoid movements of the extremities, is more common in patients under 40.

Autonomic Nervous System

In the autonomic nervous system complications include anticholinergic actions which predominate and are manifested by tachycardia, xerostomia, mydriasis, pallor, constipation, paralytic ileus, bladder paralysis, nasal congestion, hypotension, and orthostatic hypotension. Adrenergic and histaminogenic blocking actions are of secondary clinical importance.

Metabolic or Endocrine Complications

These include weight gain, hyperglycemic and feminizing effects, menstrual irregularities, lactation in females, gynecomastia in males, false positive pregnancy tests, polyphagia, polydipsia, and polyuria.

Miscellaneous Complications

Sedation and drowsiness, hypothermia, unexpected deaths from asphyxia during a seizure, ventricular fibrillation, or respiratory or vascular collapse, variable potentiation of barbiturates, narcotics, anesthetics, and alcohol, and pigmentary retinopathy are all possible complications.

E. Dosage and Route of Administration

The therapeutic daily dosages recorded in this chapter are those recommended for oral administration. Occasional indications for higher dosages are recorded in parentheses.[2]

Intramuscular administration is indicated for patients who cannot take or who resist oral medication or who require rapid control of symptoms, for example, those with nausea, vomiting, catatonia, and disorganized panic reactions. Manufacturer information should be consulted for intramuscular dosages, which are usually one-half to one-fourth those recommended for oral use. Parenteral psychopharmaceuticals should be given cautiously and

---

[2] Drug Package Insert Rules, recently established by the Food and Drug Administration, restrict the condition for which a drug is used and the drug dosage to the conservative recommendations of the drug company package insert. This ruling has been protested as arbitrary, inappropriate, and ill-advised. Paradoxically, this ruling, ostensibly aimed at improving treatment, will result in establishing ineffective placebo dosages and deprive many patients of appropriate treatment. The ultimate fate of this contentious ruling awaits further developments.

only if no other route or drug can be substituted. Intramuscular administration can cause subcutaneous necrosis and severe hypotension. Blood pressures should be recorded prior to each injection. Injection should be given in the gluteal muscles. Great caution is necessary in elderly or emaciated patients. Oral medication should be substituted as soon as possible. Intravenous use of psychopharmaceuticals is contraindicated because of the danger of periphlebitis and severe hypotension. Barbiturates are a safer substitute. Delayed, or sustained, release drugs are not recommended because the amount of released or absorbed medication is unpredictable.

Drug Combinations

Drug combinations are not recommended because increased effectiveness has not been demonstrated and because of the dangers inherent in polypharmacy.

Occasional combinations may be indicated when a particular phenothiazine produces side effects, and it is clinically necessary to increase the total dosage of phenothiazine. For example, thioridazine does not cause extrapyramidal side effects, but may cause sedation; trifluoperazine does not cause sedation, but extrapyramidal symptoms are frequent, and so on. Based on clinical impression, although not experimentally demonstrated, the pattern of side effects associated with specific phenothiazines can be combined to minimize specific side effects.

Combinations of a phenothiazine and antidepressant, such as perphenazine and amitriptyline (Triavil®, Etrafon®), have yielded significantly better results than either agent alone in approximately 50% of controlled studies. This combination may be effective when the diagnosis is unclear and when anxiety, depression, or schizophrenia unknowingly coexist.

Maintenance Dosages

Maintenance dosage should be as low as is necessary to maintain therapeutic gains. Studies show an increasing relapse rate up to 55% for as long as 6 months after discontinuation of medication. One study showed a significant difference lasting 4 years between patients treated with chlorpromazine and placebo. Such data have led to the general recommendation that patients continue on maintenance phenothiazine treatment for at least 6 months. The patient may be given a trial off medication for the next 6 months, but should be carefully followed so that psychochemotherapy can be reinstituted as soon as possible after signs of relapse appear. Some patients, with regular periodic exacerbations, sometimes occurring every 4 months, 16 months, and so on, should be advised to stay on medicine for longer periods, such as 3 years, and some for the rest of their lives.

F. Phenothiazines

Aliphatic Subgroup

Chlorpromazine (*Thorazine®*). Chlorpromazine has a wide therapeutic dosage range of 200 to 2,500 (4,000)[3] mg, and a small incidence of minor but often bothersome side effects. The major disadvantage is probably the slightly greater frequency of agranulycytosis and jaundice compared with other phenothiazines. Less important is the higher incidence of hypotension, spontaneous seizures, potentiation of epileptic seizures, dermatitis, photosensitivity, and pigmentary and ocular changes. Tolerance and addiction do not develop with chlorpromazine. Since patients have recovered after taking as much as 10 g of this drug, it is a poor suicidal agent. The sedative properties may be useful for extremely anxious patients. Because the effects of epinephrine may be reversed by all phenothiazines, norepinephrine should be used for hypotensive reactions.

Triflupromazine (*Vesprin®*). The dosage of triflupromazine, an alternative drug in the aliphatic subgroup, varies between 50 and 200 (400) mg. Reports of agranulocytosis, seizures, and jaundice, have been infrequent, and it produces less sedation than chlorpromazine but more than drugs in the piperazine and piperidyl subgroups.

Promazine (*Sparine®*). Promazine is probably less effective than chlorpromazine. The incidence of agranulocytosis is the same as with chlorpromazine but higher than with other phenothiazines. The highest incidence of seizures and hypotension occurs with promazine. Since other phenothiazine drugs in this category are probably more effective therapeutically and have fewer side effects, promazine is not recommended.

Piperazine Subgroup

Compared with other phenothiazines, this group is characterized by high potency and low incidence of agranulocytosis, jaundice, convulsions, hypotension, dermatitis, and potentiation. These drugs produce less drowsiness or sedation, a higher incidence of akathisia, akinesia, and other extrapyramidal reactions, and have a smaller therapeutic dosage range.

Since piperazines are as effective as other phenothiazines, and cause fewer serious complications, especially agranulocytosis and jaundice, they are the drugs of choice, especially during early treatment of new patients.

Extrapyramidal reactions are troublesome, but can be controlled by reducing dosage or frequently (for akinesia, dyskinesia, and parkinsonism) by administering antiparkinson agents such as biperiden (Akineton®, 2 to 6 mg), benztropine (Cogentin®, 1 to 4 mg), procyclidine (Kemadrin®, 10 to

---

[3] Indications for higher dosages are recorded in parentheses.

20 mg), and trihexyphenidyl (Artane®, 4 to 8 mg). Side effects or toxic effects caused by anticholinergic drugs include xerostomia, mydriasis, bladder or bowel paralysis, and mental confusion. Accordingly they should be used only when necessary, at the lowest possible dosage, and discontinued when possible, frequently three or four months after initiation of treatment.

Trifluoperazine (Stelazine®). Because of minimal sedative effects (drowsiness, lethargy, and so on), trifluoperazine, used in therapeutic daily doses of 10 to 40 (80) mg, is frequently the drug of choice when a major tranquilizer is indicated for patients with anergic and withdrawn psychoses, depression, agitated depression, and severe underlying depression. Sedative phenothiazines may exacerbate depression. Agranulocytosis, jaundice, convulsions, hypotension, dermatitis, photosensitivity, autonomic effects, and potentiation of other drugs are infrequent or absent. The major side effects are extrapyramidal reactions which occur over a small dosage range.

Perphenazine (Trilafon®). The indications for perphenazine, which is given in therapeutic daily doses of 12 to 96 mg, are the same as for trifluoperazine.

Fluphenazine (Prolixin®, Permitil®). An advantage of fluphenazine, which is similar to perphenazine and trifluoperazine, is the development of an intramuscular depot form of the drug (Prolixin enanthate® or decanoate) which lasts two to four weeks. These long-acting phenothiazines may be of considerable use in patients who are reluctant to, or unreliably, take their medication unless periodically visiting their physicians, or when the expense of daily medication is a factor. The dosage for both oral and parenteral forms may vary from 1 to 100 mg (or even more) and should be determined by clinical requirements and appearance of side effects, as previously described. For parenteral long-acting fluphenazine, initial dosage is about 25 mg (1 cc), and frequency of administration may vary from 1 to 4 weeks. Additional oral dosages of the same or other phenothiazines may be required during acute exacerbation of an illness.

Prochlorperazine (Compazine®). The efficacy, indications, complications and side effects of prochlorperazine are roughly similar to those of other piperazine drugs, with these exceptions: agranulocytosis, jaundice, and sedation occur less frequently than with chlorpromazine but more frequently than with perphenazine and trifluoperazine. Extrapyramidal symptoms occur more frequently than with the aliphatic subgroup and perhaps less frequently than with other piperazine derivatives. Dosage varies between 15 and 150 mg/day.

Less frequently used piperazine drugs are acetophenazine (Tindal®) and carphenazine (Proketazine®).

Piperidyl Subgroup

Thioridazine (Mellaril®). Thioridazine, given in therapeutic daily doses of 100 to 800 mg, is the only drug recommended in this category. Based on controlled studies it is effective and has a small incidence of side effects and complications. Pigmentary retinopathy, a serious complication, may occur on dosages over 1,500 mg/day or with low dosages over a long period, but it is infrequent, usually reversible, and probably does not occur when the dosage is limited to a daily maximum of 800 mg. Orgasm without ejaculation or incomplete erection, both of which occur frequently, may be upsetting to patients, and should be inquired about because patients are often reluctant to mention them. Thioridazine may be tolerated by patients who react adversely to side effects of other phenothiazines; clinical experience suggests that patients often tolerate this drug better than others. Sedative and hypotensive effects occur as frequently as with chlorpromazine. Extrapyramidal effects, such as akathisia, akinesia, dyskinesia and parkinsonism occur less frequently than with any other group of drugs, and may account for greater tolerance by many of the patients. Other advantages are that it is not an antiemetic, and dermatologic pigmentation and ocular opacities have not been reported. It may be more useful than other drugs in treating organically impaired, confused, and agitated senile patients who may respond to low dosage, such as 10 to 25 mg q.i.d. It has been reported to be more effective than imipramine in depressed patients with anxiety. The major disadvantage is that the maximum daily dosage is limited to 800 mg and the drug may not be effective in severely agitated patients who may require two to three times this dosage.

Advantages of thioridazine are less frequent extrapyramidal symptoms, infrequent or absent agranulocytosis, jaundice, skin pigmentation, photosensitivity, lenticular opacities, and antiemesis.

Newer piperidine derivatives, with inadequately evaluated advantages over older drugs, include mesoridazine (Serentil®) and piperacetazine (Quide®).

G. Butyrophenones

Haloperidol (Haldol®)

This is the only FDA approved butyrophenone used in the United States at the present time although many others have been used in Europe and several thousand have been synthesized since 1957. The chemical structure appears to differ from the phenothiazines, but butyrophenones are phenothiazine equivalents as indicated by the X-ray crystallography, chemistry, therapeutic indications, and pattern of side effects. They resemble the high-potency piperazine subgroup and have the same pattern of side effects. Extrapyramidal effects may be more severe than for other antipsychotic drugs. The dosage varies from 1 to 200 (occasionally 500) mg. In many controlled studies haloperidol has been established as an effective antipsychotic drug, equivalent to other antipsychotic agents. Although it has been described as more effective for aggressive, manic, and geriatric patients, many more controlled comparative studies will be necessary to establish these claims. Haloperidol is conveniently available as a tablet, liquid, and parenteral injection.

Major success has been achieved with haloperidol in the treatment of Gilles de la Tourette's syndrome. Dosage may vary between 1 and 200 (500) mg/day, the higher dosages being used only at the beginning of treatment to control the symptoms, and very low maintenance dosages are usually possible as treatment progresses. The usefulness of other butyrophenones used in Europe, such as pimozide and penfluridol, will require further evaluation.

H. Thioxanthenes

Thioxanthenes resemble phenothiazines except for substitution of a carbon atom for the central nitrogen atom. The most frequently used thioxanthene drugs in the United States are thiothixene (Navane®) and chlorprothixene (Taractan®) which appear to be effective antipsychotic agents. However, various claims about antidepressant activity, stimulatory properties, fewer side effects, and other advantages over older drugs have not been substantiated.

I. Rauwolfia Alkaloids

Rauwolfia alkaloids are infrequently used in psychiatry because phenothiazines act more rapidly and are more effective. Rauwolfia alkaloids may exacerbate or cause peptic ulcer and depression.

J. Other Treatment for Psychoses

Before introduction of psychochemotherapy, prefontal lobotomy, insulin coma treatment, and electroconvulsive treatment were used frequently for psychotic conditions. Lobotomy, probably used more frequently than warranted, is used infrequently today because of serious neurologic and psychologic scquelae, ineffectiveness for most patients, and the greater effectiveness of psychochemotherapy. Lobotomy, however, may be indicated in carefully selected chronic patients who have not responded to all other available modalities.

Insulin coma treatment, although believed by many to be an effective treatment for schizophrenia during extensive use for about 25 years, was probably a complicated nonspecific but powerful placebo treatment. Phenothiazines have completely replaced insulin coma treatment as a treatment for schizophrenia in most parts of the world.

Electroconvulsive treatment is generally not useful in the long-term treatment of schizophrenia or psychoses, although it is predictably effective in aborting an acute episode of such disorders and is occasionally useful in chronic patients.

Carbon dioxide inhalation therapy, narcosis (sleep) therapy, and megavitamin (nicotinamide) treatment have not been substantiated as effective.

IV. ANTIANXIETY-SEDATIVE-HYPNOTIC DRUGS

Drugs commonly used and referred to as antianxiety agents should be more properly designated as antianxiety-sedative-hypnotic (ASH) drugs because of the essential similarity of their neuropharmacology.

The distinction between antianxiety, sedative, and hypnotic effects are unclear and are largely associated with the dosage of the administered drug. Antianxiety effects refer to the alleviation of mild to moderate anxiety and tension without inducing drowsiness, sluggishness, sleepiness, loss of alertness, clarity of consciousness, and psychomotor performance. This definition was previously used to define sedative effects before the appearance of antianxiety agents. Since then, sedative effects tend to refer to slight interference with higher cortical functioning, mild drowsiness, and desirable soporific actions. Hypnotic effects refer to drowsiness, sluggishness, interference with cortical functioning, and sleep. Higher dosage causes anesthesia, coma, and death.

A. Classification

A common method of classifying these drugs is based on clinical structure and is outlined in Table 1. Despite the chemical differences, most of the compounds have essentially similar pharmacologic properties. Clinical use is based on subtle differences among them.

Chloral hydrate, first synthesized in 1832, our oldest hypnotic, and bromides, introduced in 1857 for epilepsy, were both used by about 1870 for various nervous diseases and as hypnotics. Paraldehyde was introduced in 1882. These drugs were largely replaced by barbiturates which were introduced as barbital in 1903, followed by phenobarbital in 1912, and subsequently by hundreds of other compounds.

The first glycol derivative, mephenesin, which was introduced in 1946, was largely replaced in 1954 when meprobamate was introduced. The first benzodiazepine derivative was introduced in 1959 as chlordiazepoxide, followed by diazepam in 1963.

Discussion of ASH drugs will be confined largely to barbiturates, glycol derivatives, and benzodiazepines since most of the controlled studies have included these compounds.

B. Effectiveness

The most widely used and most effective agent for anxiety is probably the ubiquitous placebo, which may be an inert substance, a camouflaged compound without specific effects, or an active substance without specific activity for the condition being treated. Evidence from double-blind studies, however, indicate that specific effects can be obtained from various ASH drug categories. Although the clinical effectiveness may be only slightly superior to those obtained from placebo effects, a conclusion indicated by the difficulty of obtaining statistically significant differences, and by the small incidence of negative studies, the consensual evidence from many studies demonstrates statistically significant differences between several ASH drug categories and placebos.

An adequate number of studies have demonstrated that barbiturates and benzodiazepines are more effective than placebos. However, the evidence from controlled studies suggests that no one benzodiazepine is more effective than any other. In addition, because there have been very few double-blind studies comparing benzodiazepines and barbiturates, and because significant differences cannot be readily demonstrated in the few comparative studies that exist, it is likely that the effectiveness of benzodiazepines and barbiturates is not significantly different. Because meprobamate was better than placebo in only five of 26 double-blind studies, and better than barbiturates in only one of 10 double-blind studies, the usefulness of this category of drug is questionable. Most of the other categories listed in Table 1 can be omitted from further consideration either because of various well-known limitations and contraindications, or because of inadequate evidence about their effectiveness. In addition, the important ASH drugs are benzodiazepines, glycol derivatives, and barbiturates, which account for about 60% of all prescriptions for psychotropic medication.

From this brief review, pharmacotherapy for anxiety can be narrowed to benzodiazepines and barbiturates. If price alone were the only consideration, barbiturates would be the drugs of choice, since at present the wholesale cost of barbiturates is about $2.50 for 1,000 tablets or about $10.00 for 25,000 tablets, compared with a cost of about $7.50 to $12.00 for 100 tablets of diazepam, which is a potential ratio of 24 to 300 times the cost per tablet.

However, before considering other factors that will contribute to a more rational choice of drug, the pharmacology of barbiturates should be reviewed.

C. Barbiturates and Benzodiazepines

Lipid solubility is an important attribute of both barbiturates and benzodiazepines. Increased lipid solubility results in rapid absorption from the gastrointestinal tract and crossing of the blood-brain barrier, leading to more rapid onset of action and increased hypnotic potency. In the barbiturate series, lipid solubility can be increased by an increase in one or both alkyl side chains at C_5, up to a total of six or seven carbon atoms, a substitution of an S atom for O at C_2, as in thiopental, and by N_1 methylation.

Figure 3 contains the formulas for several well-known barbiturates in order of decreasing lipid solubility. The lipid solubility of methdiphenylbarbital should be increased by the methylation at N-1 and decreased by replacing the usual C_5 aliphatic substitutions with the two phenyl groups. The last

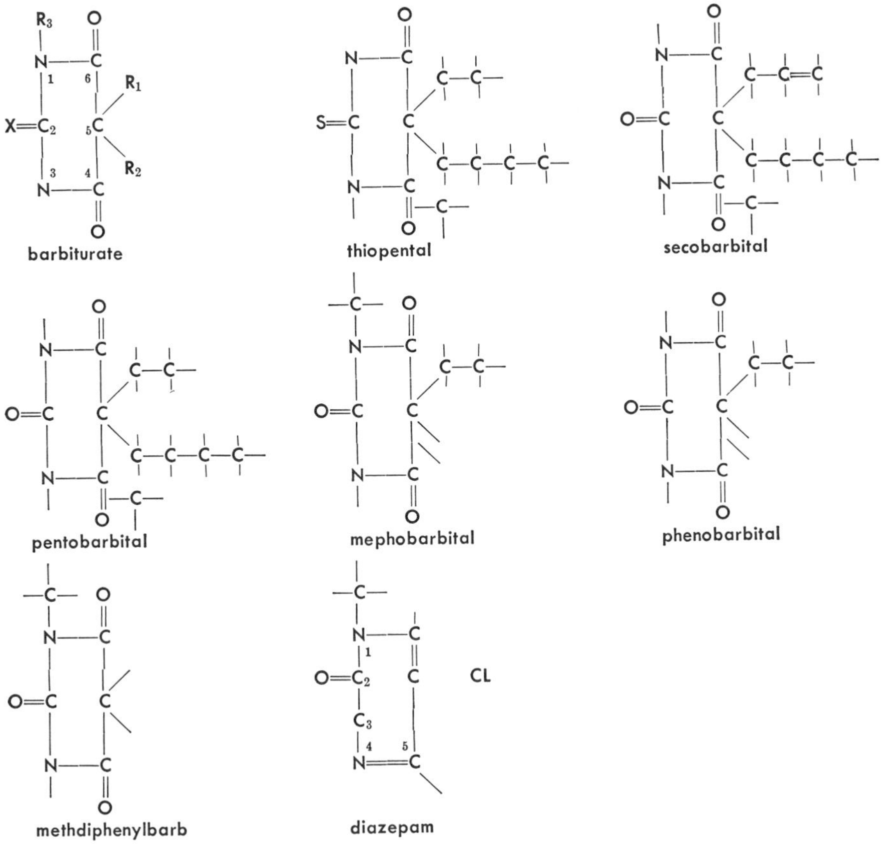

FIG. 3. Barbiturates.

formula is similar in structure to methdiphenylbarbital. There is a methyl group at N-1, O at C-2, and two phenyl groups at C-5. This is the formula for diazepam.

The similarity between the barbiturate and benzodiazepine formulas suggest similar neuropharmacologic patterns of activity for both. The principal effect for both compounds in general is sedation at low dosages and depression at higher ones. More precisely, both have a similar sequence of dose-related effects: sedation, hypnosis, anesthesia, coma, and death. Both are anticonvulsants. On chronic use, both can cause dependency, tolerance development, addiction, and withdrawal effects that include hyperexcitability and convulsions. Both can suppress the withdrawal syndrome due to barbiturates and other depressants and alcohol. Both can cause paradoxical excitement. The EEG shows an arousal pattern at low dosages and a suppression of arousal at higher dosages. The latter probably results from depression of the reticular activating system with both drugs. Both have little effect, except at very high dosages, on neuromuscular transmission and striated muscle contraction. Both reduce after discharge in the limbic system and have similar depressant effects on transmission in polysynaptic pathways. Both drugs can impair fine motor tasks, judgment, and induce drowsiness if the sedative dosage is exceeded. They have additive effects with other depressants. They can cause confusion in older patients. Both have similar contraindications, such as porphyria, allergy, concomitant use of anti-coagulants, and severe renal or hepatic disease.

These observations lead to the conclusion that with few exceptions benzodiazepines and barbiturates are alike in their actions. The many cited differences are associated with species differences, rate of absorption, patterns of distribution in the body, and effective doses. The major difference between benzodiazepines and older sedatives is the superior safety margin of the former. The ratio of the lethal to a selected therapeutic dose is much larger for the benzodiazepines than for other sedatives. Thus for benzodiazepines there is a wide margin between the dose required for sedation and that causing depression of the vital centers, making suicide difficult to achieve.

Some observations on the pharmacokinetics and metabolism of benzodiazepines may explain these important differences. Because of its lipid solubility, diazepam will cross the blood-brain barrier rapidly. This also means that it will leave the brain as readily as it enters. Considering that the brain receives 70% of the cardiac output, it follows that the onset of the diazepam action is prompt following either parenteral or oral dosing. Conversely, the same considerations explain the rapid offset of the diazepam action. The lean tissues (muscle, connective tissue, and others) provide a sizeable pool for its redistribution. The fast redistribution of diazepam therefore serves as a means for protecting the brain from overdosing. This is supported by the observation that the mouse LD_{50} by vein is about 20 times an experimental "therapeutic" dose (ED_{50} for inclined screen). In comparison this same ratio for phenobarbital is about two.

From the foregoing facts, it becomes apparent that the margin of safety for diazepam will be even greater with oral dosing in contrast to the parenteral route. The slower build-up of a diazepam blood concentration after oral dosing would allow ample time for the fast redistribution of the drug. Therefore, a lethal effect by oral administration would be difficult to achieve.

Another important factor is the complex metabolism of the benzodiazepines. The biotransformation of diazepam occurs through dimethylation to form N-desmethyldiazepam or oxidation to form 3-OH-diazepam, and when diazepam is both demethylated and oxidized, oxazepam is formed. Chlordiazepoxide is demethylated to demoxapam and then enters the previously described cycle as N-desmethyldiazepam. All of these metabolic products are active benzodiazepines with different half-lives. Inactivation of the benzodiazepines occurs by glucuronide conjugation or acetylation of the OH metabolites, especially oxezapam. The conjugated metabolites are excreted in the kidney. The role of this drug biotransformation in the overall pharmacology of diazepam could be as follows: because of its high lipid solubility diazepam would enter and leave the brain rapidly, as the blood concentration first rises and then falls. Diazepam, with a half-life of about 7 to 10 hr, redistributes to viscera, lean tissue, and fat depots. The active metabolic products, such as N-desmethyldiazepam, 3-OH-diazepam, and oxazepam, are less lipid soluble and cross the blood-brain barrier less readily; they also redistribute to viscera, lean tissue, and fat depots. The half-lives and peak concentrations of these active metabolites are much longer than that of diazepam, extending up to 95 hr. Therefore, with repeated daily dosages of either diazepam or chlordiazepoxide, it is not surprising that these long-lived and active metabolites will accumulate.

Thus, benzodiazepines, beginning either as diazepam or chlordiazepoxide, enter and leave the central nervous system rapidly, then form three to four other less lipid soluble active products which in turn enter and leave the brain more slowly as their blood concentration rises, and in turn are redistributed. As each successive active metabolite peaks and declines more slowly the overall result is a longer and smoother pharmacologic effect. This can be advantageous. However, the major advantage of the benzodiazepines is the very wide therapeutic to toxic ratio that makes them relatively safe drugs and substantially lowers the suicidal risk.

For example, patients who ingested 1,000 to 2,250 mg of chlordiazepoxide were drowsy, sedated, and arousable. The toxic dosage for a short-acting barbiturate is approximately 3,000 mg and for a long-acting barbiturate is about 5,000 mg. Thus, 30 to 50 100-mg tablets of a barbiturate can lead to death, but 100 to 225 10-mg tablets of chlordiazepoxide are probably not toxic.

Considering that in the United States there are annually 25,000 successful suicides, probably 25,000 concealed suicides, and 125,000 to 250,000 attempted suicides (an annual incidence of 0.5 to 1.0 attempted, concealed, and successful suicides per physician), the safety margin provided by benzodiazepines is an important basis for their being the drugs of choice for minor anxiety and tension. The barbiturates are probably indicated where expense is a problem and suicide and addiction potentials are absent.

Benzodiazepines, like barbiturates, may be indicated in seizures, status epilepticus, myoclonic epilepsy, and acute dystonia because of their high potency, fast acting properties, and immediate effects, followed by lower potency and long acting actions. Other claimed advantages, such as absence of hepatic microsomal enzyme induction which can decrease plasma levels of oral anticoagulants and tricyclic antidepressants, and absence of effect on REM sleep, requires further study and evaluation. Withdrawal effects may be less intense because the long acting multiple metabolic products help the body to slowly withdraw itself.[4]

---

[4] I wish to thank Dr. Walter F. Riker, Jr., Professor of Pharmacology, Cornell University Medical College, for his advice and helpful discussions on the pharmacology of barbiturates and benzodiazepines.

The major benzodiazepines used in the United States are diazepam (Valium®), chlordiazepoxide (Librium®), oxazepam (Serax®), chlorazepate (Tranxene®), and flurazepam (Dalmane®). Controlled studies indicate that they are more effective than placebo, not more effective than barbiturates, and that no one benzodiazepine is more effective than another. The dosage, as with all psychotropics, varies with the illness, genetics, metabolism, and other variable factors which differ in each patient. The lower dosages, such as 5 mg t.i.d. of chlordiazepoxide, or 2 mg t.i.d. of diazepam, are probably placebo dosages since controlled studies do not demonstrate differences when compared with placebos. The effective dosage of chlordiazepoxide can vary between 30 and 80 (300) mg/day; diazepam 10 to 40 (60) mg/day. The dosage of oxazepam is about three to four times that of diazepam and the dosage of chlorazepate is about two times the dosage of diazepam. The dosage should be low at the beginning of therapy, perhaps in the placebo range, but if ineffective, they should be increased until clinical effect is achieved or side effects appear.

Safe dosages below the threshold for addiction have not been established, although 100 to 600 mg/day of chlordiazepoxide can cause addiction and withdrawal effects. Withdrawal effects may be attenuated but subtly present and lead to confusion between preexisting anxiety and withdrawal symptoms and needless continuation of medication. Withdrawal symptoms seldom appear until the third or fourth day; seizures may occur on the eighth day. Gastric lavage is not useful in recovering swallowed drug.

D. Glycol Derivatives

The major drugs in this category are meprobamate (Equanil®, Miltown®, tybamate (Salacen®, Tybatran®), and phenaglycodal (Ultran®). As previously described, a recent careful review of the controlled studies of meprobamate resulted in the conclusion that the evidence for efficacy was inadequate. However, this review did not consider the effect on the results of favorable therapeutic and research settings, which are important variables contributing to successful treatment. Some disadvantages of these drugs are that they are more expensive, often not markedly more effective, may be more toxic, and likely to produce as much addiction as the barbiturates. Although the use of meprobamate will probably decrease following the success of benzodiazepines, is still accounts for about 6.5% of all psychotropic prescriptions.

The therapeutic dosage is between 1,600 and 3,200 mg/day; the frequently prescribed dosage of less than 400 mg q.i.d. is probably a placebo dosage for most patients.

A common and preventable complication of meprobamate is the onset of withdrawal reactions after sudden cessation of treatment on dosages of 2,400 mg or higher. These reactions are principally anxiety, muscle twitching, insomnia, nausea, vomiting, anorexia, ataxia, hallucinations, electroencephalographic changes, and major convulsions. Such symptoms can be erroneously attributed to a return of the original symptoms and thus lead to needless continuation of medication. Withdrawal reactions can be prevented by giving one-half the dosage on successive days for variable periods, depending on the length of treatment and dosage (for example, 8, 4, 4, 2, 2, 1, 1, 0 tablets). The half-life of meprobamate is 24 hr.

Although meprobamate is possibly less effective than barbiturates as a suicidal agent, deaths have been reported with as little as 20 g (50 400-mg tablets), but doses up to 40 g (100 400-mg tablets) have been tolerated.

Other glycol derivatives are not recommended because evidence of efficacy and knowledge about side effects are less well known.

E. Miscellaneous Drugs

Chloral hydrate and barbiturates, most often used in hospitalized medical patients, are often useful for sedation, helpful for insomnia, and safer than

TABLE 1. *Classification of antianxiety-sedative-hypnotic drugs*

Type	Generic	Proprietary
Tertiary alcohols	Ethchlorvynol	Placidyl
Other alcohols	Ethanol	—
Piperidinediones	Methyprylon	Nodular
	Glutethimide	Doriden
Carbamates	Ethinamate	Valmid
Chloral derivatives	Chloral hydrate	Notec, Somnos
	Chloral betaine	Beta-Chlor
Cyclic ether	Paraldehyde	—
Bromides	—	—
Glycol derivatives	Meprobamate	Equanil, Miltown
	Phenaglycodol	Ultran
	Hydroxyphenamate	Listica
	Tybamate	Salacen, Tybatran
Antihistamines	Hydroxyzine	Atarax, Vistaril
	Methapyrilene	Over-the-counter
	Pyrilamine Maleate	Over-the-counter
	Doxylamine	Decapryn
Anticholinergics	Benactyzine	Suavitil
	Adiphenine	Transentine
	Scopolamine	—
Miscellaneous	Methaqualone	Quaalude
	Chlormezanone	Trancopal
	Ectylurea	Levanil
	Oxanamide	Quiactin
Benzodiazepines	Chlordiazepoxide	Librium
	Diazepam	Valium
	Oxazepam	Serax
	Flurazepam	Dalmane
	Chlorazepate	Tranxene
Barbiturates	—	—

many other minor tranquilizers. Paraldehyde is often useful for delirium tremens. Most of the other ASH drugs listed in Table 1 are not recommended for routine use primarily because their effectiveness or side effects have not been as adequately demonstrated or evaluated compared with the afore-mentioned more popular drugs.

Suicide attempts are an unfortunate consequence of increased popular use of ASH drugs. The management of overdosage is less understood and more difficult with these drugs than with barbiturates and older sedative agents. For example, glutethimide (Doriden®) may cause prolonged coma, and the sequellae may be permanent brain damage or death.

Tolerance and addiction develop with all the ASH drugs. They are contraindicated in patients with a history of or potentiality for addiction. Such patients may be treated with phenothiazine and antidepressant drugs, however, because uncomfortable side effects such as extrapyramidal effects, orthostatic hypotension, and so on, preclude dosage increase and therefore development of tolerance, and addiction.

V. ANTIDEPRESSANTS

A. Antidepressant Treatment

Prior to 1935 effective treatment for depressed patients was unavailable. A popular estimate for treatment of hospitalized depressed patients in the 1920s and 1930s was that 44% recovered or socially improved within one year, with a rise to 54% after longer periods. A small but significant portion of patients became chronically depressed and were hospitalized for prolonged periods or died because of inanition, overcrowded conditions, inadequate medical care, or suicide.

The first treatments for depression were the convulsant therapies initiated by the introduction of pentylenetetrazol (Metrazol®) in 1935, followed by electroconvulsive treatment (ECT) in 1938, modified ECT in 1955, and indoklon in 1956. Lobotomy, developed in 1936, was increasingly used in the 1940s. Amphetamines were used by 1950, followed by dextroamphet-amine combined with amobarbitol, and methylphenidate in the 1950s. Pheno-thiazines were first used in the United States in 1954, from which tricylic antidepressants were developed in 1958. Monoamine oxidase (MAO) in-hibitors were first used for depression in 1957 with the introduction of iproniazid. Lithium carbonate began to be used for manic stages of manic depressive illness by 1970. The psychotherapies, in one form or another, have always been used, but have been most extensively used since World War II.

The total annual cost for treatment, prevention, and reduced productivity of depressive illness in the United States has been estimated at about 1.0 to 3.1 billion dollars. The incidence of depression in the United States is about

15%; 75% of psychiatric hospitalizations are for depression, and 20% of medically hospitalized patients are significantly depressed. The expectation of depression during the lifetime of males is 8 to 10% and is 16 to 20% in females. Only about 50% of morbid depressions are treated.

Antidepressant drug prescriptions accounted for 9% of all psychotropics in 1970, costing about 86.6 million dollars. The number of prescriptions for all psychotropics increased 44% between 1964 and 1970, compared with an increase of 108% for antidepressant drug prescriptions.

B. Classification

There are two principal groups of antidepressant drugs: (1) tricyclic antidepressants, closely related to phenothiazine drugs, include imipramine (Tofranil®), desipramine (Norpramin®, Pertofrane®), amitriptyline (Elavil®), nortriptyline (Aventyl®), and doxepin (Sinequan®); (2) the MAO inhibitors available in the United States include the hydrazide derivative phenelzine (Nardil®), and the nonhydrazide tranylcypromine (Parnate®). Iproniazid (Marsilid®), isocarboxazid (Marplan®), nialamide (Niamid®), pheniprazine (Catron®), and etryptamine (Monase®) have been withdrawn from the market because of toxicity, side effects, or comparative ineffectiveness.

C. Effectiveness

Evidence about the comparative effectiveness of antidepressant treatment has accumulated in the literature so that recommendations can now be made which are based on carefully controlled studies.

In a recent review of controlled studies, tricyclic antidepressants were better than placebo in 69 of 106 studies (65%). In 40 studies comparing imipramine with other tricyclic antidepressants, imipramine was better than the others in six, inferior in six, and as effective in 28. In 44 studies comparing amitriptyline with other tricyclic antidepressants, amitriptyline was better in 10, inferior in five, and as effective in 29.

MAO inhibitors were better than placebo in 13 of 33 studies (39%) and not more effective in 20 studies. Phenelzine and tranylcypromine were more effective than other MAO inhibitors. Of 26 studies comparing imipramine with MAO inhibitors, imipramine was better in nine, and as effective in 17.

ECT was better than placebo in one study, better than phenelzine in three studies, better than imipramine in three, and as effective in four studies. Lithium has been demonstrated in many studies as highly effective for manic phases of manic depressive illness. Several studies have demonstrated that phenothiazines are more effective in anxious depressed patients and tricyclics are more effective in anergic depressed patients. Several studies suggest that diazepam is more effective than amitriptyline in the first week or two of treatment, but that amitriptyline is more effective after two weeks. Lithium was evaluated as effective as imipramine in one chronic maintenance treatment study.

Combination treatments such as perphenazine and amitriptyline (Triavil®, Etrafon®), which together make up the sixth most frequently prescribed psychotropic, are more effective than placebo or either drug alone in about 50% of studies. Subjects in these studies include heterogeneous groups of patients who are anxious and depressed, either hospitalized or nonhospitalized, and psychotic or nonpsychotic. This combination may be an appropriate "if-in-doubt"-type medication for patients whose diagnosis is unclear. Careful study of types of patients who may respond to this combination will be necessary for further clarification of the specific indications for this and other drug combinations.

These results may be said to indicate that after spontaneous remissions and placebo effects, the best treatment for acute depression is ECT. Tricyclic antidepressants are less effective than ECT but more effective than MAO inhibitors. Depressed patients with considerable anxiety may respond better to a phenothiazine or a phenothiazine-tricyclic combination drug. Depressed patients who are anergic, blocked, and retarded respond better to tricyclic drugs. Benzodiazepines may be indicated in some categories of depressed patients, but only in the first two weeks. Lithium is clearly indicated in manic-depressive illness.

The effectiveness of maintenance therapy with antidepressants has been resolved recently by four studies which included treatment of over 700 patients for periods extending from 4 months to 2 years. The results demonstrated that maintenance treatment with imipramine and amitriptyline consistently decreased the relapse rate by 50% compared to treatment with placebo. Imipramine was better than a no drug control in two studies and better than diazepam in one study. In two studies imipramine was better than weekly psychotherapy or group psychotherapy. Psychotherapy, in one study, although never as effective as imipramine, tended to improve social and family interpersonal relationships after 6 months. Drug treatment did not interfere or have a negative effect on psychotherapy. In one study, lithium was superior to imipramine and placebo for manic-depressive patients, and in another study both lithium and imipramine were better than placebo for depressed patients.

These results suggest that relapse can be substantially reduced with maintenance tricyclic-antidepressant treatment. Treatment should continue for about 6 months and then be reevaluated. Diazepam is not useful for maintenance treatment. Lithium may be as useful as imipramine for depressed patients. Drug therapy has a primary effect on depressive symptomatology and does not interfere with psychotherapy which may have a delayed effect on improving interpersonal functioning.

D. Indications

Antidepressant drugs are used in treating withdrawn depression, involutional depression, mild reactive depression, neurotic, psychotic, and senile depression, depressive phase of manic-depressive reaction, and patients with depressive symptoms and history of or potential for addiction to sedative drugs.

E. Contraindications

Antidepressant drugs are contraindicated in patients with serious suicidal or homicidal tendencies. The side effects are often difficult for hypersensitive patients to tolerate. Hypotension and orthostatic hypotension may be unimportant in young patients, but are serious in elderly patients, especially those with very high, low, or labile blood pressures and cardiovascular disease. These complications may lead to fatal falls, fractures, and cardiovascular thromboses. Antidepressants can potentiate stimulant, sedative, hypnotic, narcotic, anesthetic, and hypotensive drugs, such as ether, merperidine, cocaine, procaine, insulin, phenylephrine, ephedrine, epinephrine, histamine, bee venom, methyldopa, alcohol, amphetamine, barbiturate, and phenothiazine drugs.

F. Complications and Side Effects

Many of the complications and side effects of antidepressant drugs vary in incidence and intensity, and with individual susceptibility. Complications may affect the central or autonomic nervous system and may have allergic and miscellaneous other effects. However, it should be remembered that negative placebo effects, which are as ubiquitous as positive placebo effects in medical treatment, should not be confused with physiologic side effects of treatment. Confusion between placebo and nonplacebo effects, both positive and negative, will impair effective treatment.

In the central nervous system, antidepressant drugs increase sympathetic activity. Central nervous system depressants are frequently potentiated. They may also cause dizziness, vertigo, weakness, ataxia, slurred speech, hyperreflexia, peripheral neuropathy, dysarthria, headache, peripheral edema, tremors, and mild Parkinsonism. Toxic confusional episodes occur in 20 to 40% of patients but can be differentiated from symptoms of schizophrenia, psychotic exacerbations of the depression, and so on, by a careful check of mental status. These toxic episodes can be precipitated by comcomitant use of sympathomimetics and atropinics (including antiparkinson agents), and occur more frequently but not exclusively in aged patients with preexisting brain damage. The clinical belief that schizophrenia or underlying psychosis can be exacerbated has not been verified, and when observed may have been confused with toxic confusional episodes.

In the autonomic nervous system, antidepressant drugs may cause xerostomia, hyperhidrosis, vomiting, constipation, hypotension, orthostatic hypotension, tachycardia, palpitations, mydriasis, increased ocular tension, urinary retention, delayed ejaculation, and impotence.

Allergic reactions are infrequent but may include cholestatic jaundice and agranulocytosis caused by dibenzapine derivatives, and hepatocellular jaundice (but not agranulocytosis) with hydrazide MAO inhibitors.

The nonhydrazide MAO inhibitors, such as tranylcypromine (Parnate®), and less frequently the hydrazide MAO inhibitors, potentiate the effects of sympathomimetic amines which cause hypertension, with symptoms of severe headache, neck pain, and occasionally cause brain hemorrhage and fatalities. This side effect can be caused by sympathomimetics such as methylphenidate and ephedrine, which are often present in many over-the-counter nasal or sinus decongestants, and pressor amines, such as tyramine, contained in Chianti wine, certain beers, chicken liver, tomato juice, broad beans, normite (a dietary supplement containing yeast), and aged cheeses such as camembert, stilton, emmenthaler, gruyère, New York State cheddar, and processed American cheese.

G. Dosage and Route of Administration

The therapeutic daily dosages recorded here are those recommended for oral use. Occasional indications for higher dosages are recorded in parentheses. Parenteral use of antidepressant drugs is not indicated at the present time.

H. Maintenance Dosages

Current practice is to continue antidepressant medication, usually at dosages lower than therapeutic dosages for at least 6 months, and indefinitely in some patients with recurrent depression. There is evidence that ECT is superior to antidepressant drugs for acute depression, and current clinical belief is that ECT is inferior to antidepressants for prevention of recurrent depression.

I. Drug Combinations

As described previously, there is some evidence that using antidepressants along with major tranquilizers, either in various fixed dosage combinations available on the market or individually, is more effective than either agent given alone. Controlled studies are essential for further clarification of the types of patients for whom combination treatment is indicated. In addition, when dibenzazepine derivatives and MAO inhibitors are combined, a synergistic, toxic, atropine-like effect may occur causing tremors, hyperpyrexia, convulsions, and sometimes death. Although a few clinicians have combined these drugs in certain dosage ratios without serious sequelae, their general use is not justified because the combination has not been substantiated as effective, may be potentially dangerous, and is not recommended at this time. Concurrent use of drugs with atropinic properties, such as phenothiazines, tricyclic antidepressants, and antiparkinson drugs, may precipitate toxic confusional episodes, adynamic ileus, acute glaucoma, urinary retention, cardiac toxicity, and other signs and symptoms of atropine overdosage.

Evidence is accumulating about various interactions among drugs caused by stimulation or inhibition of hepatic microsomal enzymes, and other mechanisms. Some of the known interactions include decreased tricyclic serum levels caused by barbiturates, antianxiety agents, chloral hydrate, alcohol, lithium, and contraceptive pills, and increased serum levels caused by methylphenidate, high-dose estrogens, and thyrotropic releasing hormone.

J. Tricyclic Antidepressants

There are two major categories of tricyclic compounds. Considering only the drugs marketed in the United States, (1) the iminodibenzyls include imipramine (Tofranil®) and desipramine (Norpramin®, Pertofrane®), and (2) the dibenzocycloheptenes include amitriptyline (Elavil®), nortriptyline (Aventyl®), protriptyline (Vivactil®), and doxepin (Sinequan®). Because imipramine and amitriptyline are the oldest, most extensively used, and often served as a standard for comparison with other tricyclic antidepressants, discussion will be confined to these drugs as a prototype for the others. Controlled studies tend to indicate that they are all equipotent, except that amitriptyline is reported effective more often than the others, and that none of the drugs is more rapid acting than others.

Although amitriptyline and imipramine have the same general chemistry, indications, contraindications, side effects, range of action and dosage, the indications for the two drugs differ because of the sedative-hypnotic properties of the former. Particularly at the beginning of treatment, 20 to 40% of patients respond to amitriptyline with varying degrees of mild to profound sedation. The sedation is probably an akinetic effect similar to the extrapyramidal effect of the phenothiazines, which are chemically related to the tricyclic dibenzazepine derivatives, because the symptoms are largely anergia of the musculoskeletal system rather than sedation of the cortex. Imipramine does not cause this side effect and may be useful for patients who require stimulation for such symptoms as retardation, blockage, inhibition, and anergia. Patients with agitation and insomnia associated with depression formerly required a phenothiazine or sedative to control these symptoms. Hyperactivity, anxiety, agitation, and insomnia frequently are more difficult to tolerate than are other depressive symptoms. Use of two drugs may increase side effects as described earlier. Amitriptyline often can be used instead of phenothiazines or sedatives to control agitation. Based on clinical experience, but not experimentally verified, amitriptyline can often be used for insomnia associated with depression as well as for intractable insomnia without depression. It is very effective for nighttime sedation when used in doses of 50 to 250 mg. Sedation is markedly potentiated by concurrent use of sedatives and tranquilizers such as barbiturates, benzodiazepines, ethyl alcohol, thioridazine, and so on. Many patients with intractable insomnia who have become habituated and addicted to barbiturates have been able to substitute amitriptyline successfully. Although daytime akinesia or sedation, if it occurs, almost always disappears between the first and 10th day of treatment, insomnia does not recur. Patients can be assured that the initial akinesia will disappear within ten days. Another clinical impression, again unconfirmed by controlled study, is that if insomnia can be controlled within 10 to 14 days, the patient will improve shortly thereafter. Amitriptyline and imipramine can be combined safely. This combination may be useful for patients with anergia during the day and insomnia at night. Imipramine will stimulate during the day; amitriptyline will sedate at night. Both drugs can be used safely in patients who have become habituated, tolerant, and addicted to amphetamines for daytime stimulation and to barbiturates for nighttime sedation.

The usual side effects encountered with both drugs, especially on a dosage of 150 mg, which for many patients is probably near the minimum effective dosage (which may range from 75 to 350 mg/day), are xerostomia, constipation, tachycardia, hypotension, and orthostatic hypotension. Hyperhidrosis occurs frequently with imipramine and infrequently with amitriptyline. These side effects may be troublesome but generally are not serious except in older patients, in whom treatment should be initiated with small doses followed by gradual increase. Blood pressure should be recorded in a supine, sitting, and standing position before each dosage increase. Mydriasis, loss of accommodation, acute glaucoma, or aggravation of existing glaucoma, and delayed micturition may also occur. Cholestatic jaundice similar to that with chlorpromazine is unusual but has been reported.

MAO Inhibitors

As previously discussed together with other MAO inhibitors, phenelzine antidepressants are less effective than tricyclic antidepressants. Phenelzine has been reported to be more effective than other MAO inhibitors. Another possible indication for the use of MAO inhibitors is the clinical impression, unverified by controlled study, that a patient who is unresponsive to one treatment may respond to an MAO inhibitor. Among the MAO inhibitors only phenelzine is marketed in the United States; all others have been withdrawn because of comparative ineffectiveness or toxicity. The therapeutic dosage of phenelzine is 45 to 90 mg/day.

Side effects are similar to the dibenzapine derivatives, except for the absence of hyperhidrosis and sedation. Agranulocytosis is absent; hepatocellular jaundice is infrequent; hypertensive crises are serious and frequent when MAO inhibitors are combined with sympathomimetics. MAO inhibitors require about 2 weeks of treatment before effective dosage are reached and require about 1 to 2 weeks for excretion.

K. Other Antidepressants

Few controlled studies warrant the routine use of other antidepressants. Tranylcypramine (Parnate®), a nonhydrazide MAO inhibitor, is not recommended because of inadequate evidence of effectiveness and because it sometimes unpredictably precipitates acute hypertensive crises. This reaction is infrequent, but at least 21 deaths have been reported. Although it is not known if tranylcypramine causes this complication more frequently than other MAO inhibitors, its routine use is not recommended except after other psychotropics have been tried. Benactyzine combined with meprobamate (Deprol®) and deonal (Deaner®) is considered ineffective. Lithium carbonate can now be considered the most effective treatment for the manic stage of manic-depressive illness and in bipolar depression. Tricyclic antidepressants are a better choice for depression because lithium has only occasionally been reported as effective.

Based on several controlled studies, thioridazine (Mellaril®), a major tranquilizer, might be more effective than imipramine (Tofranil®) in the treatment of depression with anxiety, but not in retarded depression.

L. Stimulant Drugs

Amphetamines, after many years of use, have not proven to be effective. Some of the frequently used amphetamines are: dextroamphetamine (Dexedrine®), methamphetamine (Desoxyn®, Methedrene®), phenmetrazine (Preludin®), benzphetamine (Didrex®), pipradrol (Meratran®), methylphenidate (Ritalin®), and mephentermine (Wyamine®). Disadvantages are that they cause anorexia and jitteriness, and that tolerance and addiction develop rapidly. Intravenous use of high doses of amphetamines has recently become a problem. Toxic psychotic episodes are frequent on high dosages. If amphetamines are employed for anorexia or mild depressive symptoms, they should be used only for brief periods. In contrast, a major advantage of antidepressant drugs is that patients do not become tolerant or addicted to them because side effects prevent increases in dosages. The use of amphetamines with barbiturates, totally unsupported by controlled studies, is unwarranted.

M. Lithium Carbonate

Although acute and severe manic-depressive illness may require hospitalization, mild manic symptoms or illness and possibly selected patients with cyclothymic characteristics can be treated with lithium as outpatients. A screening laboratory work-up includes urinalysis for protein and casts, blood glucose, BUN, Na, K, Cl, EKG in cardiac patients, and EEG in patients with history of alcoholism, drug abuse, or central nervous system pathology. Pulmonary and cardiac status should be evaluated. If patients are on diuretics or salt restricted diets, serum K and Na should be monitored as therapy proceeds. Otherwise the only important laboratory determination would be periodic plasma lithium levels. For less severe symptoms requiring less intense treatment, plasma lithium levels can be checked every week until adequate blood levels of between 0.5 and 1.5 mEq/liter plasma are reached, and once every month thereafter. Outpatient treatment can be initiated with 300 mg lithium carbonate t.i.d., and subsequently titrated, up or down, to the appropriate plasma level of about 1.0 mEq/liter. For acutely ill patients who are to be treated more intensively, usually in the hospital, initial dosage of lithium should be about 4 to 5 300 mg/day. Plasma lithium should be checked every 2 days for 2 weeks, weekly for the next month, and monthly thereafter. Response to treatment usually occurs in 7 to 10 days.

Toxic side effects may occur when plasma lithium levels reach levels greater than about 1.5 to 2.0 mEq/liter (usually 1.5 mE/liter), and may include nausea, coarse tremor, and vomiting. These may be followed by diarrhea, marked drowsiness, weakness, difficulty walking, dizziness, slurred speech, confusion, and other symptoms of organic brain syndrome. If nausea or diarrhea develop, lithium should be stopped, plasma levels determined, and dosage adjusted accordingly.

Lithium is excreted by the kidneys and its half-life is about 24 hours. Adequate plasma level is dependent on normal fluid intake and output. Lithium levels should be determined about 8 to 12 hr after the last dosage of lithium. Manic symptoms may return as promptly as 1 to 2 days after discontinuing lithium.

N. Electroconvulsive Treatment (ECT)

The use of ECT decreased markedly after the introduction of the antidepressant drugs. During the past ten years, with increased experience and after many controlled clinical trials, ECT is considered quicker, more predictable, and generally more effective than drugs. The advantages and disadvantages of ECT and the antidepressant drugs are summarized in Tables 2 and 3.

TABLE 2. *Electroconvulsant treatment*

Advantages	Disadvantages
More rapid and higher remission rate; serious suicidal or homicidal risk; may improve insomnia unresponsive to sedatives; often ineffective after inadequate responses to other treatment.	Expensive and complicated procedure; may result in fractures; causes reversible memory impairment and retrograde amnesia; psychologic treatment interrupted or of minimal importance discontinuation of work usually necessary; does not prevent recurrences.

TABLE 3. *Antidepressant drugs*

Advantages	Disadvantages
Less complicated and expensive than ECT; no amnesia; more readily accepted by patients; permits continuation of work and psychotherapy; may be better for mild, moderate, or neurotic depressions, and in low dosages for some physically ill and senile patients; maintenance psychochemotherapy may prevent recurrences.	Slower remission, may take 3 to 6 weeks; may cause toxic confusional episodes; long follow-up usually necessary; other side effects, although infrequent, may be serious, such as liver and blood dyscrasias, acute glaucoma, urinary retention, hypotension and orthostatic hypotension (dangerous in patients who are elderly and have cardiovascular disease and require careful management and follow-up).

O. Psychedelic Drugs

Most of the psychedelic drugs, also referred to as psychotomimetics, psychodysleptics, hallucinogens, and so on, are derived from plants. Lysergic acid diethylamide hydrochloride (LSD) was synthesized in 1943. It causes symptoms somewhat similar to but not identical with schizophrenia, and toxic delirium similar to symptoms caused by atropine or scopolamine.

Not enough controlled studies have been reported to substantiate the claims that LSD is useful in conditions resistant to more conventional therapy, such as chronic alcoholism, sociopathic conditions, childhood schizophrenia, character neuroses, and terminal cancer.

Although definitive evidence is not available about the safety or danger of LSD, there are documented incidents of suicide or homicide and precipitation of psychotic episodes in predisposed individuals who had taken the drug, almost always when not under medical supervision. It has been claimed, but not demonstrated, and unlikely in the author's belief, that occasional use of LSD can cause permanent chromosomal or genetic abnormalities, alter personality, or induce other organic changes. Permanent effects are more likely with unsupervised, indiscriminate, chronic use of large dosages of LSD. LSD is available legally only to special investigators who are trying to evaluate its possible clinical usefulness.

In contrast to LSD, more than 15 other psychedelic drugs, such as peyote (mescaline), marihuana (tetrahydrocannabinol), teonanactyl mushroom (psilocybin), DMT (dimethyltrypamine), STP (methyl dimethox-methyl phenylethylamine), and so on, are used, not for medical purposes, but primarily for experimental, religious, and euphoriant purposes.

VI. PSYCHOTHERAPY

Most of the evidence from comparative studies indicates that psychochemo-therapy alone is much better than psychotherapy alone, that drugs and psychotherapy are much better than psychotherapy alone, and that drugs and psychotherapy are slightly better than drugs alone. These findings are fairly consistent for most diagnostic entities and strongly favor psychochemotherapy in schizophrenia, psychotic depression, and manic-depressive illness. In addition, the past 15 years of research have demonstrated fairly well the untenability of the old belief that superficial treatment like psychochemotherapy leads to symptom substitution, more serious psychopathology, or interferes with intensive psychotherapy. Psychotherapy is often facilitated by appropriate psychochemotherapy and combined treatment is increasingly used by psychiatrists.

However, definitive conclusions about the value of psychotherapy must be held in abeyance for several reasons. The effectiveness of psychochemotherapy may be easier to demonstrate because of its rapid effect on symptoms which are easier to measure. Psychotherapeutic effectiveness, because its main effect may be on nonsymptom criteria such as social effectiveness and interpersonal relationships, may be more difficult to demonstrate in general, and measurable only after longer periods of treatment.

It is obvious that because psychotherapy has not been clearly demonstrated as a strongly effective therapy, one cannot conclude that it is ineffective. Further research is warranted, currently in progress at many centers, and should yield clarifying data in the near future. It is probable that without supporting evidence from controlled studies in the next 10 to 20 years, the usefulness of psychotherapy as a viable therapy will be questionable.

Until further available study about this issue, and others such as the indications for drugs alone, psychotherapy alone, or their combination, it is probably clinically wise to always consider psychotherapy as a possible concomitant of psychochemotherapy. Such therapy may include: brief or long psychotherapy; supportive, suggestive, persuasive, reeducative, group, insight-oriented, dynamic, or psychoanalytic psychotherapy; hypnosis; behavior therapy; milieu, social, and community therapy; vocational rehabilitation, and so on.

VII. SUMMARY

Thorough knowledge of a minimal number of psychotropic drugs will more than offset the shortcomings of a limited mastery of psychochemotherapy.

Over 95% of psychochemotherapy can be more than adequately covered by mastering the use of eight (at most 16) drugs.

For the psychoses (see Fig. 1), for patients in panic or with severe agitation in whom sedation may be desirable, an aliphatic phenothiazine is recommended, with a piperidine and piperadyl as second and third choices. For patients with milder anxiety, piperidyl and piperazine phenothiazines are recommended. For depressed patients, a sedative tricyclic antidepressant or phenothiazine is indicated when anxiety or agitation is present; a non-sedative tricyclic is the drug of choice when anxiety or agitation is absent. An alternative choice is an MAO inhibitor, such as phenelzine, which may be useful when response to other drugs is inadequate. When anxiety and depression coexist and the diagnosis is unclear a phenothiazine and tricyclic antidepressant might be useful. Lithium is indicated in manic phases of manic-depressive illness. Not to be ignored are psychotherapy, social psychiatry, and for severe depressions associated with suicidal or homicidal tendencies and symptoms not responding to other treatment, ECT.

In the neuroses (see Fig. 2) the schema is similar to the psychoses except for the following: most neurotic patients are not extremely agitated or depressed, and are best treated with benzodiazepine derivatives or barbiturates. For more severe anxiety symptoms, a piperadyl or piperazine phenothiazine may be useful. Similarly for more severe depressive symptoms, a tricyclic antidepressant followed possibly by an MAO inhibitor are possible alternatives. Neurotic patients rarely require ECT and are usually treated with forms of psychotherapy and social psychiatry.

This summary is one possible way of achieving simplicity and mastery of psychopharmacology. Although not all of the complexities and subtleties could be covered, this summary provides a pragmatic outline for effective treatment for the vast majority of patients.

REFERENCES

Psychochemotherapy
Clark, W. G., and Giudice, J. (1970): *Principles of Psychopharmacology*. Academic Press, New York.
Hollister, L. E. (1973): *Clinical Use of Psychotherapeutic Drugs*. Charles C Thomas, Springfield, Ill.

Abstracts and newsletters
American Society for Pharmacology and Experimental Therapeutics: *Rational Drug Therapy* published monthly, W. B. Saunders, Philadelphia.
Ayd Medical Communication Ltd.: *International Drug Therapy Newsletter* published monthly.
Drug and Therapeutic Information Inc. *The Medical Letter on Drugs and Therapeutics*, New York.
Modell, W. (ed.): *Drugs of Choice*. C. V. Mosby, St. Louis.
U.S. Dept. of Health, Education, and Welfare, Public Health Administration, NIMH: *Psychopharmacology Abstracts*, published monthly, 5454 Wisconsin Ave. Chevy Chase, Maryland 20015.

Side effects

Shader, R. I., and DiMascio, A. (1970): *Psychotropic Drug Side Effects: Clinical and Theoretical Perspectives.* Williams and Wilkins, Co. Baltimore.

Antipsychotic drugs in schizophrenia

Grinspoon, L., Ewalt, J. R., and Shader, R. I. (1968): Psychotherapy and pharmacology in chronic schizophrenia. *Amer. J. Psychiatry,* 124:67–74.

Karon, B. P., and Vandenbos, G. R. (1972): The consequences of psychotherapy for schizophrenic patients. *Psychother. Theor. & Pract.,* 9:111–119.

May, P. (1968): *Treatment of Schizophrenia.* Science House, New York.

Tobias, L. L., and MacDonald, M. L. (1974): Withdrawal of maintenance drugs with long-term hospitalized mental patients: A critical review. *Psychol. Bull.,* 81:107–125.

Antidepressant drugs

Beck, A. T. (1973): *The Diagnosis and Management of Depression.* University of Pennsylvania Press, Philadelphia.

Mindham, R. H. S., Howland, C., and Shepherd, M. (1973): An evaluation of continuation therapy with tricyclic antidepressants in depressive illness. *Psychol. Med.,* 3:5–18.

Secunda, S. K. (1973): *The Depressive Disorders.* U.S. Department of Health, Education, and Welfare, NIMH, Rockville, Maryland.

Smith, A., Targanza, E., and Harrison, G. (1969): Studies on the effectiveness of antidepressant drugs. *Psychopharmacol. Bull,* March.

Special Section: Drug Treatment of Affective Disorders, papers by Raskin, A.; Klerman, G. L. et al; Covi, L. et al; Prien, R. F. et al. *Am. J. Psychiatry,* 131:181–203, 1974.

Electroconvulsive treatment

Kalinowski, L. B., and Hoch, P. N. (1961): *Somatic Treatments in Psychiatry,* 2nd ed., Grune and Stratton, Inc., New York.

Antianxiety-sedative-hypnotic drugs

American Medical Association (1971): *AMA Drug Evaluations,* Chapters 27,28,29,32. Chicago, Illinois.

Elliot, H. W. (1973): Drug therapy of anxiety. *Postgrad. Med.,* 54:159–164.

Garattini, S., Mussini, E., and Randall, L. O. (1973): *The Benzodiazepines.* Raven Press, New York.

Goodman, L. S., and Gilman, A. (1970): *The Pharmacologic Basis of Therapeutics.* Chapters 9,10,12. Macmillan Co., New York.

Goth, A. (1972): *Medical Pharmacology.* Sections 3 and 4, pp. 211–261. C. V. Mosby Co., St. Louis.

Greenblatt, D. J., and Shader, R. I. (1971): Meprobamate: A study of irrational drug use. *Am. J. Psychiatry,* 127:1297–1303.

Outpatient psychotherapy and phychochemotherapy

Koegler, R. R., and Brill, N. Q. (1967): *Treatment of Psychiatric Outpatients.* Appleton-Century-Crofts, Inc., New York.

Luborsky, L., Singer, B., and Luborsky, L. (1975): Comparative studies of psychotherapies. *Arch. Gen. Psychiatry,* 32:995–1008.

Epidemiology and psychotropic statistics

Conley, R. W., Conwell, M., and Arrill, M. B. (1967): An approach to measuring the cost of mental illness. *Am. J. Psychiatry,* 124:63–70.

Manheimer, D. I., Davidson, S. T., Balter, M. B., Mellinger, G. D., Cisin, I. H., and Parry, H. J. (1973): Popular attitudes and beliefs about tranquilizers. *Am. J. Psychiatry,* 130:1246–1253.

Mellinger, G. D., Balter, M. B., and Manheimer, D. I. (1971): Patterns of psycho-therapeutic drug use among adults in San Francisco. *Arch. Gen. Psychiatry,* 25:385–394.

Parry, H. J., Balter, M. B., Mellinger, G. D., Cisin, I. H., and Manheimer, D. I. (1973): National patterns of psychotherapeutic drug use. *Arch. Gen. Psychiatry,* 28:769–783.

Secunda, S. K. (1973): The Depressive Disorders. US Dept Health, Education, and Welfare, NIMH, Maryland.

Placebo effect

Honigfeld, G. (1964a): Non-specific factors in treatment. *Dis. Nerv. Syst.,* 25:145–225.

Honigfeld, G. (1964b): Non-specific factors in treatment: Review of social-psychological factors. *Dis. Nerv. Syst.,* 25:225–239.

Shapiro, A. K. (1960): A contribution to the history of the placebo effect. *Behav. Sci.,* 5:109–135.

Shapiro, A. K. (1968): Semantics of the placebo. *Psychiat. Quart.,* 42:653–695.

Shapiro, A. K. (1971): Placebo effects in psychotherapy and psychoanalysis. In: *Handbook of Psychotherapy and Behavior Change,* edited by A. E. Bergin and S. L. Garfield. Aldine Publishing Co., New York.

Shapiro, A. K., and Struening, E. L. (1973a): Defensiveness in the definition of placebo. *Comp. Psychiat.,* 14:107–120.

Shapiro, A. K., and Struening, E. L. (1973b): Ethical attitudes toward the use of placebos in medicine. *Psychiat. Med.,* 4:17–29.

Shapiro, A. K., and Struening, E. L. (1974): A comparison of the attitudes of a sample of physicians about the effectiveness of their treatment and the treatment of other physicians. *J. Psychiat. Res.,* 10:217–229.

Hofling, C. K. (1955): The place of placebos in medical practice. *G. P.,* 11:103.

Biological Foundations of Psychiatry,
edited by R. G. Grenell and S. Gabay.
Raven Press, New York © 1976.

Kinetics of Antipsychotic and Antidepressant Drugs in Man

Leo E. Hollister

Veterans Administration Hospital and Stanford University School of Medicine, Palo Alto, California
94304

For purposes of this discussion, antipsychotic drugs will include the few whose kinetics have been studied to any extent in man, specifically chlorpromazine, thioridazine, butaperazine, and haloperidol. Only tricyclic antidepressants will be considered, such as amitriptyline and imipramine, their demethylated metabolites, desipramine and nortriptyline, and protriptyline. Study of the kinetics of the tricyclic antidepressants has advanced faster than for the antipsychotics. As will become evident, the body of knowledge presently available for both classes of drugs is fragmentary and controversial.

I. ANTIPSYCHOTIC DRUGS

A. Clinical Criteria of Dosage

During the two decades of widespread use of antipsychotic drugs, the principal rule for determining the dose of drug has been: give as much as is needed to produce desired therapeutic results with as little cost in unwanted effects as is possible. This empiric approach has not worked too badly. Using ordinary clinical criteria to assess improvement in schizophrenic symptoms and signs, a careful clinician can usually titrate dosage to the individual patient's needs. That the latter may vary widely is evident when one considers that reported effective doses of antipsychotic drugs have varied over a 50-fold range between individual patients. This high degree of variation, coupled with the generally conservative advice given in regard to dosage, has probably resulted in some patients being undertreated. Probably many more are chronically overtreated because of a disconcerting tendency not to establish the lowest possible effective maintenance dose.

Besides the criterion of amelioration of schizophrenia, the desired effect of the drug, some clinicians have also used an undesired effect of antipsychotic drugs as a gauge of dose. For many years the concurrence of two such diverse and novel pharmacologic effects as amelioration of schizophrenia and production of extrapyramidal motor reactions was a mystery. Now we believe that these two unique attributes of antipsychotic drugs are mediated through the same pharmacologic mechanism, a postsynaptic block of dopamine receptors (Hollister, 1973). As the two effects are not highly correlated (some schizophrenics improve with little extrapyramidal reactions and conversely), one posits two functionally separate dopaminergic systems in the brain, one that serves a psychic function (amelioration of schizophrenia) and another that serves a motor function (production of extrapyramidal motor reactions). The fact that both clinical effects are mediated through a common pharmacologic mechanism can be employed to estimate the proper dose of drug. If a patient has shown no change in his schizophrenic psychosis and no sign of extrapyramidal motor reactions, one can be almost certain that a proper amount of drug has not been delivered to those sites in his brain at which the important pharmacologic actions occur. As has just been suggested, one can not use the presence of extrapyramidal motor reactions to infer that an ideal therapeutic dose has been attained; one may have to treat the unwanted pharmacologic effect and proceed to augment dose to obtain the desired therapeutic effect.

To depend on such criteria, subject as they are to the vagaries of clinical observation, is not wholly satisfying. Other areas of pharmacology have shown excellent correlations to exist between plasma levels of drugs and their clinical effects (Nies, 1972). One might assume that such would be the case with psychotherapeutic drugs. Were a reliable measure of plasma concentrations of drug available, one might assume that a therapeutic range could be determined and that determinations of plasma concentrations could lead to a more precise system of regulating doses of a drug. This goal is the impetus for current efforts to study the kinetics of these drugs in man.

B. Plasma Concentrations of Drugs

1. *Various methods.* Most of the literature pertaining to plasma concentrations of antipsychotic drugs in man has appeared within the past few years.

As successive new techniques became available, the inadequacies of those that preceded them became clearly evident. Due to differences in the techniques employed, as well as other problems, many studies are contradictory.

The three techniques most often employed for measuring plasma concentrations of antipsychotic drugs are radioderivation (only chlorpromazine), gas-liquid chromatography (GLC), possibly combined with mass-spectrometry, and fluorescence (Usdin, 1971). Thin-layer chromatography (TLC) and spectrophotometry have been more often used to detect urinary excretion of drug or metabolites, lacking the requisite degree of sensitivity to detect the small amounts available in plasma, but some use of these techniques has been made for the latter purpose.

Radioderivation is based on an *in vitro* reaction of primary or secondary amines with the labeling material. Hydrogen-3 acetic anhydride and $[^{14}C]CH_3I$ were used to label chlorpromazine and sulfoxide metabolites (Efron, Manian, and Harris, 1970). The specificity of radio-labeling of this sort is low and the complexity of the technique is high. Consequently this approach has not been widely adopted.

At the moment, GLC is most widely employed. Various detection systems including flame ionization, microcoulometry, or electron capture have their proponents (Hammar and Holmstedt, 1968; Curry, 1968). Although GLC provides suitable sensitivity for determinations of plasma concentrations (down to 10 ng/ml of chlorpromazine), the reliability of these techniques still leaves much to be desired.

Attempts are being made to make fluorescent derivatives of chlorpromazine and its metabolites. Ordinarily fluorometry would not be sensitive enough to detect the small amounts of drug present in plasma. Primary or secondary amino groups or metabolites with one or more hydroxyl groups can be reacted with 5-dimethylaminonaphthalene-1-sulfonyl chloride (DANSYL) to produce fluorescent derivatives (Forrest and Green, 1972; Kaul, Conway and Clark, 1974). Fluorescein isothiocyanate also can be reacted with primary or secondary amines. These techniques are still in a developmental stage and are fraught with considerable difficulty.

The spectrophotometric technique for measuring plasma concentrations of chlorpromazine was limited to a sensitivity of 150 ng/ml (March, Donato, Turano, and Turner, 1972). This technique has limited clinical application as one would be working fairly close to the limits of sensitivity for most levels of drug likely to be attained on therapeutic dosage.

2. *Nontechnical Difficulties.* Besides the technical difficulties mentioned above, others are peculiar to the measurement of chlorpromazine. The strong protein-binding of this drug (almost 99% in man) makes the efficiency of the extraction technique of critical importance. Unless stored in the dark or protected by nitrogen, chlorpromazine is especially photolabile. Both *S*- and *N*-oxides may be formed, creating misleading artifacts. Few available assays measure free chlorpromazine, although this may not be the only active material in plasma.

All things considered, one must take most presently available data on plasma concentrations of these drugs with reservation. Only a handful of laboratories in the world can make these determinations with the accuracy and dependability that one should demand from a research determination. Furthermore no attempts have yet been made to cross-validate different techniques that purport to measure the same thing. Until this has been done, it may be difficult to interpret much of the data being published.

C. Correlations between Plasma Concentrations and Clinical Effects

1. *Can a Range of Therapeutic Levels Be Defined?* Many familiar factors affect the plasma concentrations of antipsychotic drugs: rate of absorption, pharmaceutical preparation in which administered, and rate of metabolism. Rate of excretion is not too important, as little chlorpromazine is excreted in the unmetabolized state. Confounding problems in relating plasma concentrations of antipsychotic drugs to clinical effects are their high binding to protein and to fat, the latter property leading to accumulation in tissues; the selective concentration in brain against a plasma gradient; and the tendency for chlorpromazine at least to be metabolized or degraded in the gut (Curry, Davis, Janowsky, and Marshall, 1970).

Plasma concentrations of chlorpromazine reach peak levels in 2 to 4 hr after most forms of administration. Following almost any oral dosage form, one is likely to get some instances of extremely poor absorption; intramuscular administration always provides prompt availability of the drug, with measurable plasma levels evident in 15 min. The latter form of dosage also provides plasma concentrations approximately three to four times as high as equivalent oral doses of the drug (Hollister, Kanter, and Wright, 1963; Hollister, Curry, Derr, and Kanter, 1970).

Determination of plasma disappearance rates is made somewhat difficult by the tendency for successive plasma levels of chlorpromazine to fluctuate widely, with sharp increases following an apparent progressive decline. The causes of such fluctuations are only speculative, but enterohepatic circulation or release of drug from tissue stores have been most frequently offered as explanations. Disappearance rates following single doses have shown a two-phase curve of the type characteristic for highly lipid-soluble drugs. An initial rapid phase with a half-life of 2 hr was followed by a slow phase with a half-life of 16 hr. Most patients show plasma concentrations less than 50% of peak levels at 6 hr, about 20% at 12 hr, and about 16% of peak levels at 24 hr following a single dose. Even in the presence of definite liver damage, as in patients with compensated Laennec's cirrhosis, these rates of disposition still hold (Maxwell, Carrella, Parker, Williams, Mould, and Curry, 1972).

When chlorpromazine is administered in an ordinary divided dose schedule, diurnal variations of five- to 10-fold may be observed in plasma concentrations within a single patient, even in steady-state conditions (24 and 53 days of treatment). Such variations in plasma concentrations might be more related to side effects, such as drowsiness, than to the desired clinical effects (Cooper, Albert, Hillet, and Caille, 1973). Almost all investigators have observed a wide interpatient variability in plasma concentrations attained during chronic treatment with equal doses of chlorpromazine. Such variations are due to a variety of influences, including different genetic patterns of drug metabolism and different prior histories of drug exposure. A somewhat puzzling feature, regularly observed in one study, was that plasma concentrations increased to a peak at 2 weeks of treatment and thereafter slowly declined. Clinical improvement therefore could be correlated with plasma concentrations only during the first 2 weeks of treatment and not thereafter. The subsequent decline in prevailing plasma levels strongly suggested the induction of drug-metabolizing enzymes induced by chronic exposure to chlorpromazine (Sakalis, Curry, Mould, and Lader, 1972). Possible induction of drug-metabolizing enzymes was suggested by prior work indicating a gradually increasing peak of glucuronide excretion over a 3-week period. (Forrest, Forrest, Bolt, and Serra, 1966). On the other hand, glucuronide excretion in man was not much higher after chronic treatment than after initial doses of drug. (Hollister and Curry, 1971). If drug-metabolizing enzymes are induced, it is quite possible that they may primarily involve other pathways than glucuronidation.

A recent study attempting to define a therapeutic range for plasma concentrations of chlorpromazine found that patients with negligible levels (less than 30 ng/ml; level of sensitivity, 10 ng/ml) were unlikely to improve. On the other hand, major toxicity was associated with levels of 750 to 1,000 ng/ml. The ideal therapeutic range seemed to be between 150 and 300 ng/ml or higher (Rivera, Calimlim, Castenada, and Lasagna, 1973). A particularly interesting aspect of this study was that plasma concentrations were lower in patients receiving concurrent anti-Parkinson drugs, such as trihexyphenidyl. The latter delay gastrointestinal motility and could presumably allow more metabolism or degradation of chlorpromazine to occur during the longer sojourn of the drug in the gut.

It is surprising how little we know of the influence of other drugs in the gastrointestinal tract that may affect the absorption of any drug. One might assume that other drugs that delay gastrointestinal motility, such as tricyclic antidepressants or sympathomimetics, would also impair absorption of unchanged chlorpromazine. Colloidal antacids are known to adsorb phenothiazines and impair their absorption (Forrest, Forrest, and Serra, 1970). We know even less about the effects of concurrent food in the gut or the effects of physical activity.

Plasma concentrations of thioridazine have been measured most often in studies concerning its bioavailability in various dosage forms, possibly because of a great commercial interest in establishing a delayed-action dosage form. Measurements have used a spectrophotometric method, which has produced disconcertingly high levels of thioridazine as compared with equal doses of chlorpromazine. Levels of thioridazine are reported up to 5,000 ng/ml as contrasted to only rare instances in which chlorpromazine levels exceed 1,000 ng/ml. The most likely explanation is that the spectrophotometric method is nonspecific and detects metabolites as well as unchanged drug. Thioridazine, as well as most other phenothiazines, is less subject to glucuronidation than is chlorpromazine. Thus more unconjugated metabolites are likely to be found in plasma.

The data available for thioridazine suggest that the time span of plasma concentrations following oral doses is similar to that from chlorpromazine. The drug appears to be as extensively metabolized, only 12% being recovered unchanged in the urine, the principal metabolite being either ring or sidechain sulfoxide derivatives, or their combinations (Buyze, Eggberts, Muusze, and Poslavsky, 1973). Levels tend to be dose related, and an apparent steady state is reached in 3 to 4 days regardless of the frequency of daily doses (Mellinger, Mellinger, and Smith, 1965). Generally it has not been possible to discern any major differences in plasma concentrations attained following regular or delayed-action tablets, accumulation of drug obliterating the slightly lesser availability of the delayed-action dosage form (Viukari and Salmimies, 1973).

Peak levels of thioridazine following single 100-mg oral doses were reached in 1.5 to 4 hr and concentrations varied between 0.13 and 0.52 μg/ml. The serum half-life of thioridazine in volunteer subjects was 9 to 10 hr. Patients receiving doses of 5 mg/kg or less showed good correlations between dose of drug and plasma concentrations, but higher doses showed much more variation. Plasma concentrations, given equivalent doses, were higher as patients were older. No relationship between plasma concentrations and thioridazine doses has been clearly established (Martensson and Roos, 1973).

One study, using thioridazine in depressed patients rather than schizophrenics, attempted to relate clinical results to prevailing plasma concentrations. Sixteen patients considered treatment failures had higher mean plasma concentrations than 41 successfully treated (3.3 versus 2.0 μg/ml). These results seemed to indicate that failure to respond could not be attributed to inadequate levels of drug, the higher levels in the failed patients undoubtedly representing attempts of clinicians to increase the doses to obtain maximal therapeutic benefits (De Jonghe and van der Helm, 1970). As will be made clear later on, depressed patients represent a more heterogeneous group in terms of their response to drugs than do schizophrenics, so one can not extrapolate these findings to the latter patients.

The most extensive study of the relationship between thioridazine plasma concentrations and clinical effects involved 25 acute schizophrenic patients. Following 6 days of placebo therapy and baseline observations, they were given a dose of oral liquid concentrate in the amount of 4 mg/kg and followed for 4 additional days. Plasma thioridazine concentrations were measured primarily by a fluorometric method and verified by a GLC method. The latter correlated significantly ($r = 0.61$) with the former method in measuring plasma levels 4 hr after drug administration, although levels from GLC were generally lower. The average half-life for all patients was 24 hr (standard deviation, 8 hr); no differences were noted between men and women, but the latter showed more variability. Peak plasma concentrations ranged between 2.5 and 13.2 μg/ml, the mean being 6 μg/ml; these occurred from 30 min to 8 hr after the dose. Even following a single dose a number of clinical measurements of psychotic disturbance showed lessening that correlated to varying degrees with various indices of thioridazine concentrations, such as half-life, total area under the curve, and peak level (Gottschalk, Biener, Noble, Birch, Wilbert, and Heiser, 1974). It is most unusual to find such good clinical correlations following single doses of drug in psychotic patients; inferences about correlations between steady-state levels and plasma correlations await further work. An intriguing possibility might be that a single-dose study, such as this, could predict those patients who might respond preferentially to this drug.

It should be noted that in the last three studies cited, concentrations of thioridazine were orders of magnitude different from those cited earlier. The last three studies used GLC techniques rather than spectrophotometric methods of measurement, the former undoubtedly being more specific. Once again, one must emphasize the vast importance of the technique of measurement in determining the results obtained.

A study of butaperazine levels following single doses given to man showed that they were related to the size of the dose, peak levels of 150 ng/ml following a 20-mg dose with twice that following a 40-mg dose. Peak plasma concentrations following single doses were thought to predict rather well the levels ultimately attained during steady-state conditions. The predictable wide interpatient variations were found. As with chlorpromazine, a two-phase disappearance rate was observed, the rapid phase having a half-life of 4 to 6 hr and the slow phase having a half-life of 10 to 15 hr (Davis, Janowsky, Scherke, Manier, and El-Yousef, 1974).

A separate study of plasma concentrations of butaperazine was largely concerned with differences in pharmaceutic preparations. What was most puzzling is that following 40-mg doses of the drug, these investigators reported plasma concentrations of 18 to 27 μg/ml. A fluorometric technique for measurement was also used in this study, but the reported concentrations from identical doses varied from those reported above by almost two orders of magnitude. Once again, the imperfections of existing techniques for measuring plasma concentrations of these drugs should be clearly evident. Contrary to most other experience, including that based on clinically observable effects, this study reported lower plasma concentrations of drug following intramuscular administration than from oral doses. Patients who responded to treatment best tended to have somewhat higher plasma concentrations than others, but in view of the questionable meaning of the reported plasma concentrations, it would be impossible to attempt to establish any therapeutic range (Simpson, Lament, Cooper, Lee, and Bruce, 1973).

Perphenazine plasma concentrations were measured by a GLC technique following 100-mg intramuscular doses of the enanthate ester. Peak plasma concentrations of 21 to 47 ng/ml were attained on the 1st or 2nd day after injection with a slow decline over an interval of 14 days. No conclusions could be drawn about the relationship of such levels to clinical response (Kragh-Sorensen, Larsen, Hansen, and Naestoft, 1973).

No studies of the kinetics of haloperidol in man have yet been reported, as the GLC technique for its determination is of fairly recent origin. The drug is rapidly absorbed following subcutaneous administration in rats, and rapidly disappears from the plasma. Penetration into the brain is rapid and brain concentrations of the drug may exceed plasma concentrations by a factor of 10. On the basis of these data, one might expect that the kinetics of haloperidol will resemble those of chlorpromazine to a great extent when it is finally studied in man (Marcucci, Airoldi, Mussini, and Garattini, 1972).

2. *Are Differences in Routes of Metabolism Important?* Chlorpromazine potentially can form over 160 different metabolites, of which only a minority have yet been identified and still fewer tested for pharmacologic activity. In general sulfoxide metabolites lose activity while 7-hydroxy metabolites retain activity until conjugated. One small clinical study of this matter has come up with a provocative result. Patients who responded best to chlorpromazine were found to have relatively high levels of chlorpromazine or the active 7-hydroxy metabolite, whereas those who responded poorly tended to have a preponderance of sulfoxide metabolites (Sakalis, Chan, Gershon, and Park, 1973). It remains to be seen whether such determinations can be used to predict clinical responses to the drug. One might speculate that the well-known phenomenon that patients who fail to respond to one drug may respond well to another is due to different patterns of metabolism between drugs.

D. Urinary Excretion of Unchanged Drugs or Metabolites

1. *Urine Tests to Monitor Compliance with Therapeutic Programs.* Simple colorimetric urine tests have long been used to measure qualitatively for metabolites of chlorpromazine and other phenothiazines. These tests have been most valuable to monitor compliance of patients in taking the prescribed drug-treatment program. They were most extensively validated in a large scale collaborative study involving three groups of patients, one maintained on their customary doses of chlorpromazine or thioridazine, another who received doses on 3 days of the week, and the third who were discontinued from treatment (Caffey, Forrest, Frank, and Klett, 1963). The test was quite adequate to reflect these various conditions. As these tests are most sensitive with drugs taken in large doses, such as chlorpromazine and thioridazine, they have become less widely used as more potent agents became popular.

2. *Quantitative Measures of Urinary Excretion of Metabolites for Determining Bioavailability.* Spectrophotometric techniques can be rather simply applied to the quantitative estimation of unchanged drug and of conjugated and nonconjugated metabolites. Prior to the advent of measurements of plasma concentrations of chlorpromazine and thioridazine, such tests were employed to test the bioavailability of various dosage forms. Timed urine specimens and simple clinical tests were adequate to demonstrate the far greater potency of intramuscularly administered drug as compared with oral doses and the inadequacies of delayed-action dosage forms. The latter were generally not much different in the pattern of release than conventional oral tablets but delivered somewhat less total drug (Hollister, Kanter, and Wright, 1963). These findings have recently been confirmed in a study that used both urinary excretion patterns and plasma concentrations. Disparity betweeen plasma concentrations of unchanged chlorpromazine and the urinary excretion of metabolites when the drug was given by mouth as compared with intramuscular injection suggested that oral doses of the drug were extensively metabolized in the gut as well as by the first pass through the liver as compared with doses that had direct access to the circulation (Hollister and Curry, 1971). Although it seems reasonable that the amount of drug or metabolites excreted reflect the total amount absorbed, patterns of metabolism might differ between different pharmaceutic preparations. For comparing similar preparations, quantitative measurement of urinary excretion should be an adequate test of bioavailability, circumventing the more difficult plasma concentration techniques or the less sensitive clinical assessments.

3. *Urinary Excretion of Drug or Metabolites and Clinical Effects.* Attempts to relate the pattern of excretion of chlorpromazine and its metabolites to clinical results have been generally unfruitful. A recent attempt found no difference in rates of excretion of urinary metabolites between resistant and nonresistant patients (Sved, Perales, and Palaic, 1971). Although one might conclude that different patterns of metabolism are not related to different types of clinical responses, it should be recalled that studies of metabolites in plasma suggested the opposite. So the issue is not yet settled. Following withdrawal of medication, metabolites of chlorpromazine disappeared from urine in about 4 weeks, which seemed to coincide with relapse. The ability of patients to maintain improvement for long periods after withdrawal from drug may very likely be attributed to the extensive accumulation of drug in body stored following chronic treatment. Judging by urinary excretion following resumption of treatment, steady-state conditions were reached after 10 days of treatment on a fixed dose.

E. Present Pharmacokinetic Model for Chlorpromazine

As chlorpromazine has been the drug whose fate in the body has best been determined, its pharmacokinetic model may be pertinent for other antipsychotic drugs. Preliminary evidence supports the hope that such is the case.

An orally administered dose of chlorpromazine is primarily absorbed in the upper gastrointestinal tract. During its transit through the intestine, the drug can be metabolized by enzymes in the intestinal wall or degraded by the action of other chemicals or bacteria that may be present. Very little drug or intestinal products of the drug passes intact through the intestine, without first reaching the circulation.

After delivery to the liver by the portal system, drug is subject to further metabolism during the first pass through the liver. Unchanged drug entering the systemic circulation from the liver is highly bound to plasma proteins (as high as 99%). Free drug upon reaching the brain is avidly taken up by brain tissue, so that eventually the brain accumulates concentrations severalfold that which were maximally present in plasma. Similarly peripheral tissues concentrate this highly lipophilic substance. The rapid initial disappearance of the drug from the plasma is followed by a much slower second phase, a pattern of redistribution from blood to tissues so characteristic of highly lipophilic drugs.

Upon further passes through the liver, more metabolism of the drug occurs. Metabolized drug is excreted in the bile, some to pass through the intestine for fecal excretion, the majority to be reabsorbed into the circulation for renal excretion. Possibly a small portion of conjugated metabolites is reconstituted and recirculated in the blood. The kidney excretes the more polar metabolites, although the maximal daily rate of excretion from single doses does not exceed 30% of the total dose. Only small fractions of the amount excreted represent unchanged drug, approximately 80% being conjugated metabolites.

Following a parenteral dose, such as from intramuscular administration, increased amounts of unchanged drug reach the circulation, the initial metabolism in the gut and liver having been avoided. Subsequently the pattern outlined above would hold.

Considering the considerable attack to which oral doses of drug are exposed, it is little wonder that rather large daily doses of chlorpromazine must be used to attain clinical effects. Nor should it be strange that the drug is so much more potent when administered parenterally. We are not yet sure how more potent phenothiazines attain their advantage, whether through higher affinity for tissue or receptors or by virtue of less susceptibility to metabolic attack.

F. Further Questions

The initial three underlying assumptions about the utility of measuring plasma concentrations of antipsychotic drugs are still far from proven. First, the methods are far from established as highly accurate or reproducible. Different techniques measure different portions of drug or metabolites. We are not even sure what is important to measure, only unchanged drug or that plus specific active metabolites. Finally, with the exception of chlorpromazine and thioridazine, few other antipsychotic drugs are currently amenable to such measurement. It may be to our great disadvantage that chlorpromazine was the first antipsychotic drug to appear; it is difficult to imagine any other having a more complex metabolism.

Second, establishment of a definite therapeutic range of plasma concentrations, analogous to other drugs that are monitored by such measurements, is still uncertain. One can infer that minimal levels of drug are not therapeutic, but this conclusion might more quickly and easily be reached by clinical observations. The same situation applies to toxicity seen with extraordinarily high plasma concentrations. The apparent wide diurnal oscillations in plasma levels subsequent to separate doses may not necessarily be discouraging, for it should be possible to establish a postabsorptive plasma concentration range. Still past experience has revealed that the most satisfactory use of plasma concentrations for guiding treatment have been with drugs that produce rather small diurnal variations around the steady-state level.

Third, improved management of patients through monitoring plasma concentrations compared with clinical criteria for dose has not yet been tested. Very likely attempts to prove this point should await more definite confirmation of the validity of the various techniques employed for such measurements.

Other interesting problems for future study have been brought out by the work done so far. The problem of interpatient variability in attaining plasma levels from identical doses of drug should be examined further in respect to genetic influences and the activity of drug-metabolizing enzymes prior to treatment. On the other hand, the idea that a single dose might be used to predict ultimate steady-state levels or clinical response has great appeal; it could provide a rather simple method for estimating the individual dose requirement of patients or the proper choice of drug. Whether or not these drugs induce enzymes that accelerate their metabolism is an important question. Tolerance for some pharmacodynamic effects, such as drowsiness, hypotension, or anticholinergic actions, has been commonly noted clinically, but the antipsychotic effects are thought to be unabated. The nature and degree of tolerance to these drugs needs further exploration to see if it might have a metabolic basis. The provocative notion that different patterns of metabolism of these drugs may presage different clinical results is an old one that has never been settled. As more metabolites are identified and synthesized, we may get a better idea of their clinical importance, either in regard to therapeutic or toxic effects. Finally we should begin to explore more systematically the various factors influencing the availability of drugs, whether they be the type of pharmaceutic preparation, the presence of food in the gastrointestinal tract, or the concurrent use of other drugs that might interact in one way or another with the antipsychotic drug to alter its availability.

II. TRICYCLIC ANTIDEPRESSANTS

A. Clinical Criteria of Dosage

As with antipsychotic drugs, doses of tricyclic antidepressants have been largely determined empirically. The desired effect, amelioration of depression, is weighed against the undesired effects, usually excessive sedation or peripheral and central anticholinergic manifestations. Tolerance to the sedative effects of tricyclics may develop fairly rapidly. Tolerance is less apparent to the anticholinergic side effects, but these do not necessarily increase linearly with dose. Thus usual dosage patterns start with small doses increased by frequent increments, either until the desired therapeutic effect has been achieved or the presence of unwanted effects makes further increases in dose intolerable.

Effective doses have ranged between 50 and 600 mg daily, depending upon many factors. Few clinicians have felt compelled to increase doses higher as seizures or cardiac toxicity become more likely complications. More often than not, failures of suitable patients to respond to treatment may be traced to inadequate doses, the unwanted pharmacologic effects limiting dosage more than might have been really necessary. Success in treatment also depends on the key phrase, "suitable patients." Almost all clinical studies of tricyclic antidepressant drugs, including the very first, have emphasized that these drugs are most suitable for patients with endogenous depressions (Hollister, 1973). They may indeed be a highly specific form of treatment for such types of depressed patients, which are a minority among the whole clinical spectrum of depressive illness. This rather selective indication for tricyclics must be borne in mind when considering the relationship between plasma concentrations of these drugs and clinical effects.

B. Plasma Concentrations of Drug

1. *Various Methods.* Measurements of plasma concentrations of tricyclics have been achieved only in recent years. Although a variety of techniques have been used, consistency between various methods is generally higher with these drugs than with the antipsychotics. Still disagreements have occurred in the literature accumulated to date.

The most sensitive and specific technique for measurement is GLC combined with mass spectrometry. Using this technique it is possible to identify in plasma a number of metabolites of nortriptyline; besides the parent drug, the 11-hydroxy metabolite and the 11-hydroxy demethylated metabolite could be identified (Hammer, Alexanderson, Holmstedt, and Sjoquist, 1971). Others have used similar techniques for determination of plasma concentrations of imipramine (Frigerio, Belvedere, De Nadai, Fanelli, Pantarotto, Riva, and Morselli, 1972). The availability of the sophisticated and expensive instrumentation required for these analyses rather limits their widespread application at the moment.

GLC alone has been used to identify and measure a number of tricyclic drugs, including imipramine, desipramine, clomipramine, and trimipramine (Viala, Cano, Gola, and Gouezo, 1971). Although having the advantage of being much simpler than the combined technique, even GLC alone is not an easy technique to import into one's laboratory.

Fluorometry has been widely used to measure tricyclics, most recently being applied to determinations of protriptyline levels. Concentrations of the latter drugs at steady-state conditions (3 weeks of treatment) varied from 89 to 292 ng/ml among patients receiving doses of 0.25 to 1.04 mg/kg. Plasma concentrations were poorly correlated with dose (Moody, Whyte, and Naylor, 1973).

A still simpler technique employed TLC separation of imipramine and desipramine with quantification being accomplished by densitometric scanning. As is usually the case, large variations in plasma concentrations were found between different patients. The ratio between the parent drug, imipramine, and its major active metabolite, desipramine, also varied enormously, the desipramine/imipramine ratio ranging from 0.3 to 15.0 (Nagy and Treiber, 1973). Available evidence suggests that both compounds possess pharmacologic activity, so it has generally been the custom to measure both and use the sum of the two as it is not certain that one is more active than the other as the criterion against which clinical response is measured. The same considerations apply in the case of amitriptyline and nortriptyline.

Formation of radiolabeled derivatives of imipramine and desipramine, using the procedures described earlier for chlorpromazine, has also been accomplished. For the same reasons of low specificity and high complexity, this technique has not caught on widely (Harris, Gaudette, Efron, and Manian, 1970).

2. *Nontechnical Difficulties.* Protein-binding of tricyclics is quite high, just as with phenothiazines. Using an ultrafiltration technique with labeled compounds, the binding was estimated to be 96% for imipramine and amitriptyline, 90% for desipramine, 95% for nortriptyline, and 92% for protriptyline (Borga, Azarnoff, Forshell, and Sjoquist, 1969). Thus careful extraction techniques are required. Fortunately most of these compounds are more stable than chlorpromazine, so that deterioration during the handling process is less of a problem.

Plasma binding may vary nonetheless between individuals and this variation may explain in part some of the difficulties encountered in trying to make correlations between plasma concentrations and clinical results. The percentage of free imipramine varied from approximately 5 to 24% among 25 consecutive patients (Glassman, Hurwic, Kanzler, Shostak, and Perel, 1974). Children showed substantially less binding and higher blood concentrations of imipramine than did adults. Consequently toxic reactions might be expected more often in this group when given equivalent doses (Winsberg, Perel, Hurvic, and Klutch, 1974).

C. Plasma Concentrations and Clinical Effects

1. *Can a Range of Therapeutic Levels Be Defined?* The same factors affect the plasma concentrations of these drugs as others. Consequently wide inter-patient variations might be expected. In one study wide variations in plasma concentrations were found between different patients given desipramine. Steady-state levels varied over a 30-fold range (only an eightfold range if two extreme cases are omitted). The same was true for nortriptyline, where a 14-fold variation was encountered. Plasma concentrations were related to dose and disappearance time from plasma related to peak levels. Individual patients tended to handle different drugs of the same class in much the same fashion (Sjoquist, Hammar, Borga, and Azarnoff, 1969).

Similar wide variations were found among 30 women in-patients with endogenous depressions treated with 150 mg/day of nortriptyline for 4 weeks. The steady-state levels varied between 48 and 230 ng/ml. Plasma levels correlated weakly with the rating of depression ($r = 0.42$) only at the 4-week rating. The authors thought that poor results were obtained with plasma concentrations over 175 ng/ml (Kragh-Sorensen, Asberg, and Eggert-Hansen, 1973). A somewhat similar study in 15 patients receiving 150 mg/day of amitriptyline for 6 weeks found the usual wide variations in the plasma levels of amitriptyline and nortriptyline. The 4-week clinical ratings showed a good correlation between plasma concentrations and clinical response, but not with the occurrence of side effects. These authors thought that levels of the combined drugs of less than 120 ng/ml were associated with poor clinical results (Braithwaite, Goulding, Theano, Bailey, and Coppen, 1972). A rather narrow optimal therapeutic range of plasma concentrations is suggested by both these studies.

Other data indicate a wider therapeutic range of plasma levels. In the case of 29 patients with endogenous depression treated with nortriptyline, best responses were observed when the steady-state level was between 50 and 139 ng/ml. At lower or higher doses, responses were poorer (Asberg, Cronholm, Sjoquist, and Tuck, 1971). Another study, which measured the plasma concentrations of imipramine following treatment with this drug, found that all patients responding to treatment had levels above 20 ng/ml. To a lesser extent, side effects and plasma concentrations were correlated (Walter, 1971). Treatment of 32 heterogeneous depressed patients with 150 mg/day of nortriptyline produced no correlation between plasma concentrations and clinical response at either four or six weeks. Mean levels in the group were 193 ng/ml (SE 25) at 2 weeks and 171 ng/ml (SE 19) at 4 weeks (Burrows, Davies, and Scoggins, 1972). Besides the use of consecutive admissions, many of whom may not have been patients for whom tricyclic antidepressants were the preferred drug, if indeed any drug was needed, many of these patients attained plasma concentrations higher than those usually considered to be optimal.

At the moment it is impossible to delineate with any great precision what an optimal plasma concentration should be for any of the tricyclic antidepressants or their active metabolites. One can say that levels that are too low are associated with poor results, whereas those that are too high may also be associated with increased side effects. In view of the great difficulty in making these measurements for clinical purposes, it remains to be proven that laboratory monitoring of plasma concentrations will improve the results of treatment over clinical monitoring as has been done in the past. Currently all patients on antidepressant drugs in Sweden are subjected to laboratory monitoring; it will be interesting to hear the final conclusions of this large-scale clinical experience.

2. *Are Differences in Routes of Metabolism Important?* The apparent difficulties in finding an optimal range of plasma concentration for therapy and the varying correlations found between these and clinical response may be caused by failure to consider separately levels of the secondary and tertiary amine forms. Secondary amines, such as desipramine and nortriptyline, are thought to be primarily important for blocking uptake of norepinephrine, whereas tertiary amines, such as imipramine and amitriptyline, may preferentially block uptake of serotonin. Thus depending upon whether the biochemical disturbance in the depressed patient involves primarily serotonin or norepinephrine (something still impossible to determine), correlations might better be made with levels of one or the other substance rather than with their sum (Braithwaite, Goulding, Theano, Bailey, and Coppen, 1973). Unfortunately one can not predict how a patient will metabolize tricyclics that are tertiary amines to produce secondary amine metabolites. If any meaningful clinical experiment is to be done, it may be restricted to the secondary amine type of drug given to patients with a presumed decrease in norepinephrine transmission as the basis for their depression.

3. *Other Aspects of the Kinetics of Tricyclics.* Protriptyline persistence in man has been studied using labeled drug. The peak of radioactivity in plasma following an oral dose occurred in 8 to 12 hr; some radioactivity could be measured as long as 37 days afterward. The cumulative urinary excretion was 50% of the label over a 16-day period (Charalampous and Johnson, 1967).

Plasma clearance of desipramine was twice that of nortriptyline, reflecting the differences in degree of plasma-binding (Alexanderson, 1972a). The steady-state plasma levels of desipramine, nortriptyline, and oxyphenbutazone were either similarly high or low in individual patients. Each of the three drugs probably is acted upon by the same hydroxylating enzymes (Hammar, Martens, and Sjoquist, 1969). The kinetics of nortriptyline appear to be controlled also by genetic factors. Twenty-nine relatives of three propositi with high nortriptyline levels were compared with 20 random subjects. Doses of 75 mg/day were given for 8 days with plasma concentrations measured on days 4, 5, 6, and 8. The steady-state levels were related to body weight, but not to age or sex when adjusted for body weight differences. There was no tendency for bimodality in the distribution of plasma levels between the two groups, suggesting polygenic control (Asberg, Price-Evans, and Sjoquist, 1971).

Single doses of 1 mg/kg of nortriptyline produced peak levels of 24 to 61 ng/ml, whereas doses of 0.4 mg/kg every 8 hr for 2 weeks produced steady-state levels of 52 to 111 ng/ml. The apparent volume of distribution (Vd) varied between 21 and 31 liters/kg. Plasma clearance was the same after single and multiple doses, indicating that nortriptyline does not alter its own metablism (Alexanderson, 1972b). Single-dose kinetics were found to predict steady-state levels. A greater similarity in half-life and Vd was found in monozygotic than in dizygotic twins pairs, suggesting that these aspects are under genetic control. The half-life varied between 18 and 93 hr, the Vd, between 21 and 57 liters/kg (Alexanderson, 1973).

4. *Bioavailability.* Three subjects were given identical intramuscular and oral doses of nortriptyline. The total area under the curves of plasma concentrations was similar with either preparation and calculations indicated the availability to vary between 56 and 79%. Gastrointestinal absorption is assumed to be complete. The major metabolite, 10-hydroxynortriptyline, was present in the same amount with either route of administration (Alexanderson, Borga, and Alvan, 1973). In this respect tricyclics may differ from phenothiazines, which produce higher plasma concentrations of unchanged drug following intramuscular administration.

D. Further Questions

The technical problems in measuring plasma concentrations of tricyclics are less those of reliability than availability. Existing techniques often require either very expensive apparatus or considerable labor or both. To bring such determinations to the clinic will require that either some simplification or automation of existing techniques be accomplished.

Prior to establishing laboratory monitoring of plasma concentrations of these drugs as a routine part of clinical practice, a definite correlation must be established between a range of plasma concentrations and good clinical results. Such correlations are at present rather tenuous. Furthermore one must prove that laboratory monitoring of dose is more efficient than clinical monitoring based on observed pharmacologic effects of the drugs.

Research questions regarding the relative importance and indications for the tertiary versus the secondary amine-type antidepressants and what factors may determine the rate and degree of appearances of secondary amines following treatment with tertiary amines are of some interest. Such studies may require extensive biochemical work to answer the clinically important question of whether the two types of drugs affect different biochemical substrates of depression; urinary excretion of catecholamine or indoleamine metabolites, or their accumulation in the cerebrospinal fluid, should be measured concomitantly.

III. SUMMARY

Measurement of plasma concentrations of antipsychotic drugs is still a difficult and apparently inexact procedure. With available techniques, it is impossible to make definite clinical correlations between the plasma concentrations of these drugs and the responses of schizophrenic patients. Nonetheless the unpredictable responses of patients to drugs, so that they may respond to one drug but not to another, have not been satisfactorily explained on the basis of the various constellations of presenting symptoms and signs. It seems more likely that the explanation for these different responses may be found in further study of the kinetics of drugs producing poor or indifferent results in a patient versus those producing good results. Differences in metabolism of a drug have long been suspected as a partial explanation, but the issue is as yet unsettled.

Measurements of plasma concentrations of tricyclics are more accurate than those for antipsychotic drugs, but still far from being a widely practical clinical procedure. The definition of optimal plasma levels for clinical response, or their correlation with side effects, is still uncertain. In the case of depressed patients, a more important determinant of clinical response may be the type of depression being treated rather than the specific handling of a drug by that patient.

ACKNOWLEDGMENTS

Research by this author was supported by U.S. Public Health Service Grant MH-03030 from the National Institute of Mental Health.

The author would like to acknowledge the assistance of his esteemed colleague Dr. I. Forrest in the preparation of this manuscript.

REFERENCES

Alexanderson, B. (1972a): Pharmacokinetics of desmethylimipramine and nortriptyline in man after single and multiple oral doses—A cross-over study. *Eur. J. Clin. Pharmacol.*, 5(1):1–10.

Alexanderson, B. (1972b): Pharmacokinetics of nortriptyline in man after single and multiple oral doses. Predictability of steady-state plasma concentrations from single-dose plasma-level data. *Eur. J. Clin. Pharmacol.,* 4(2):82–91.

Alexanderson, B. (1973): Prediction of steady-state plasma levels of nortriptyline from single oral dose kinetics: A study in twins. *Eur. J. Clin. Pharmacol.,* 6:44–53.

Alexanderson, B., Borga, O., and Alvan, G. (1973): The availability of orally administered nortriptyline. *Eur. J. Clin. Pharmacol.,* 5:181–185.

Asberg, M., Price-Evans, D. A., and Sjoquist, F. (1971): Genetic control of nortriptyline kinetics in man; A study of relatives of propositi with high plasma concentrations. *J. Med. Genet.,* 8(2):129–135.

Asberg, M., Cronholm, B., Sjoquist, F., and Tuck, D. (1971): Relationship between plasma level and therapeutic effect on nortriptyline. *Br. Med. J.* 3:331.

Borga, O., Azarnoff, D. L., Forshell, G. P., and Sjoquist, F. (1969): Plasma protein binding of tricyclic antidepressants in man. *Biochem. Pharmacol.,* 18(9):2135–2143.

Braithwaite, R. A., Goulding, R., Theano, G., Bailey, J., and Coppen, A. (1972): Plasma concentration of amitriptyline and clinical response. *Lancet,* 1:1297–1300.

Braithwaite, R. A., Goulding, R., Theano, G., Bailey, J., and Coppen, A. (1973): Clinical significance of plasma levels of tricyclic antidepressant drugs in the treatment of depression. *Lancet,* 1:556–558.

Burrows, G. D., Davies, B., and Scoggins, B. A. (1972): Plasma concentration of nortriptyline and clinical response in depressive illness. *Lancet,* 2:619–623.

Buyze, G., Egberts, P. F. C., Muusze, R. G., and Poslavsky, A. (1973): Blood levels of thioridazine and some of its metabolites in psychiatric patients. A preliminary report. *Psychiatr. Neurol. Neurochir.,* 76:229–239.

Caffey, E. M., Jr., Forrest, I. S., Frank, T. V., and Klett, C. J. (1963): Phenothiazine excretion in chronic schizophrenics. *Am. J. Psych.,* 120:578–582.

Charalampous, K. D., and Johnson, P. C. (1967): Studies of C^{14}-protriptyline in man: Plasma levels and excretion. *J. Clin. Pharmacol.,* 7(2):93–96.

Cooper, S. F., Albert, J. M., Hillel, J., and Caille, G. (1973): Plasma-level studies of chlorpromazine following administration of chorpromazine hydrochloride and chlorpromazine embonate in chronic schizophrenics. *Curr. Ther. Res.,* 15:73–77.

Curry, S. H. (1968): Determination of nanogram quantities of chlorpromazine and some of its metabolites in plasma using gas-liquid chromatography with an electron capture detector. *Anal. Chem.,* 40:1251.

Curry, S. H., Davis, J. M., Janowsky, D. S., and Marshall, J. H. L. (1970): Factors affecting chlorpromazine plasma levels in psychiatric patients. *Arch. Gen. Psych.,* 22:209–215.

Davis, J. M., Janowsky, D. S., Sekerke, H. J., Manier, H., and El-Yousef, M. (1974): The pharmacokinetics of butaperazine in serum. In: *Advances in Biochemical Psychopharmacology, Vol. 9, Phenothiazines and Related Drugs,* edited by I. S. Forrest, C. J. Carr, and E. Usdin, pp. 457–461. Raven Press, New York.

De Jonghe, F. E. R. E., and van der Helm, H. J. (1970): Plasma concentrations of thioridazine in patients with depression. A preliminary report. *Acta Psychiatr. Scand.,* 46:360–364.

Efron, D. H., Manian, A. A. and Harris, S. R. (1970): The simultaneous measurement of chlorpromazine, chlorpromazine sulfoxide and their demethylated analogs in plasma by radioactive derivative formation. *Psychopharmacol. Bull.,* 6:73.

Forrest, I. S., Forrest, F. M., Bolt, A. G., and Serra, M. T. (1966): An attempt to correlate urinary chlorpromazine excretion with response during drug therapy. *Proceedings of the Vth International Congress of the Collegium Internationale Neuropsychopharmacologicum,* Excerpta Medica International Congress Series No. 129, p. 1186. Excerpta Medica, Amsterdam.

Forrest, F. M., Forrest, I. S., and Serra, M. T. (1970): Modification of chlorpromazine metabolism by some other drugs frequently administered to psychiatric patients. *Biol. Psychiatry,* 2:53–58.

Forrest, I. S., and Green, D. E. (1972): Phenothiazines: Metabolism and analytical detection. *J. Forensic Sci.,* 17:592–617.

Frigerio, A., Belvedere, G., De Nadai, F., Fanelli, R., Pantarotto, C., Riva, E., and Morselli, P. L. (1972): A method for the determination of imipramine in human plasma by gas-liquid chromatography-mass fragmentography. *J. Chromatogr.*, 74:201–208.

Glassman, A. H., Hurvic, M. J., Kanzler, M., Shostak, M., and Perel, J. M. (1974): Imipramine steady-state studies and plasma binding. *Advances in Biochemical Psychopharmacology, Vol. 9, Phenothiazines and Related Drugs*, edited by I. S. Forrest, C. J. Carr, and E. Usdin, pp. 457–461. Raven Press, New York.

Gottschalk, L. A., Biener, R., Noble, E. P., Birch, H., Wilbert, D. E., and Heiser, J. F.: Thioridazine plasma levels and clinical response. *Arch. Gen. Psychiatry, in press.*

Hammar, C. G. and Holmstedt, B. (1968): The identification of chlorpromazine metabolites in human blood by gas liquid chromatography. *Experientia* 24:98–100.

Hammar, C. G., Alexanderson, B., Holmstedt, B., and Sjoquist, F. (1971): Gas chromatography-mass spectrometry of nortriptyline in body fluids of man. *Clin. Pharmacol. Ther.*, 12(3):496–505.

Hammer, W., Martens, S., and Sjoquist, F. (1969): A comparative study of the metabolism of desmethylimipramine, nortriptyline, and oxyphenylbutazone in man. *Clin. Pharmacol. Ther.*, 10(1):44–49.

Harris, S. R., Gaudette, L. E., Efron, D. H., and Manian, A. A. (1970): A method for the measurement of plasma imipramine and desmethylimipramine concentrations. *Life Sci.*, 9:781–788.

Hollister, L. E. (1973): *Clinical Use of Psychotherapeutic Drugs*, pp. 192. Charles C Thomas, Springfield, Ill.

Hollister, L. E., Curry, S. H., Derr, J. E., and Kanter, S. L. (1970): Studies of Delayed-Action medications. V. Plasma levels and urinary excretion of four different dosage forms of chlorpromazine. *Clin. Pharmacol. Ther.*, 11:49–59.

Hollister, L. E., Kanter, S. L., and Wright, A. (1963): Comparison of intramuscular and oral administration of chlorpromazine and thioridazine. *Arch. Int. Pharmacodyn.*, 144:571–573.

Hollister, L. E., and Curry, S. H. (1971): Urinary excretion of chlorpromazine metabolites following single doses and in steady-state conditions. *Res. Commun. Chem. Pathol. Pharmacol.*, 2:330–338.

Kaul, P. N., Conway, M. W., and Clark, M. L. (1974): Pharmacokinetics of chlorpromazine metabolites—A colossal problem. In: *Advances in Biochemical Psychopharmacology. Vol. 9. Phenothiazines and Related Drugs*, edited by I. S. Forrest, C. J. Carr, and E. Usdin, pp. 391–398. Raven Press, New York.

Kragh-Sorensen, P., Larsen, N. E., Hansen, C. E., and Naestoft, J. (1973): Gas chromatographic measurement of perphenazine in whole blood. *Acta Psychiatr. Scand. Suppl.*, 246:15–17.

Kragh-Sorensen, P., Asberg, M., and Eggert-Hansen, C. (1973): Plasma-nortriptyline levels in endogenous depression. *Lancet*, 1:113–115.

March, J. E., Donato, D., Turano, P., and Turner, W. J. (1972): Interpatient variation and significance of plasma levels of chlorpromazine in psychiatric patients. *J. Med.*, 3:146–162.

Marcucci, F., Airoldi, L., Mussini, E., and Garattini, S. (1972): Distribution of haloperidol and trifuperidol in brain and blood of rats. *Chem. Biol. Interact.*, 4:427–430.

Martensson, E., and Roos, B. E. Serum levels of thioridazine in psychiatric patients and healthy volunteers. *Eur. J. Clin. Pharmacol.* 6:181–186.

Maxwell, J. D., Carrella, M., Parkes, J. D., Williams, R., Mould, G. P., and Curry, S. H. (1972): Plasma disappearance and cerebral effects of chlorpromazine in cirrhosis. *Clin. Sci.*, 43:143–151.

Mellinger, T. J., Mellinger, E. M., and Smith, W. T.: Thioridazine blood levels in patients receiving different oral forms. *Clin. Pharmacol. Ther.*, 6:486–491.

Moody, J. P., Whyte, S. F., and Naylor, G. J. (1973): A simple method for the determination of protriptyline in plasma. *Clin. Chim. Acta*, 43:355–359.

Nagy, A., and Treiber, L. (1973): Quantitative determination of imipramine and desipramine in human blood plasma by direct densitometry of thin-layer chromatograms. *J. Pharm. Pharmaco.*, 25:599–603.

Nies, A. S. (1972): Cardiovascular disorders: In: *Clinical Pharmacology. Basic Prin-*

ciples in Therapeutics, edited by K. L. Melmon and H. F. Morelli, pp. 142–216. Macmillan, New York.

Rivera-Calimlim, L., Castaneda, L., and Lasagna, L. (1973): Effects of mode of management on plasma chlorpromazine in psychiatric patients. Clin. Pharmacol. Ther., 14:978–986.

Sakalis, G., Curry, S. H., Mould, G. P., and Lader, M. H. (1972): Physiologic and cilinical effects of chlorpromazine and their relationship to plasma level. Clin. Pharmacol. Ther., 13:931–946.

Sakalis, G., Chan, T. L., Gershon, S., and Park, S. (1973): The possible role of metabolites in therapeutic response to chlorpromazine treatment. Psychopharmacologia, 32:279–284.

Simpson, G. M., Lament, R., Cooper, T. B., Lee, J. H., and Bruce, R. B.: The relationship between blood levels of different forms of butaperazine and clinical response. J. Clin. Pharmacol., 13:288–297.

Sjoquist, F., Hammer, W., Borga, O., and Azarnoff, D. L. (1968): Pharmacological significance of the plasma level of monomethylated tricyclic antidepressants. In: The Present Status of Psychotropic Drugs. Pharmacological and Clinical Aspects. p. 128. Excerpta Medica, Amsterdam.

Sved, S., Perales, A., and Palaic, D. (1971): Chlorpromazine metabolism in chronic schizophrenics. Brit. J. Psychiatry, 119:589–596.

Usdin, E. (1971): The assay of chlorpromazine and metabolites in blood, urine, and other tissues. CRC Crit. Rev. Clin. Lab. Sci., 2:347–391.

Biological Foundations of Psychiatry,
edited by R. G. Grenell and S. Gabay.
Raven Press, New York © 1976.

Drug Tolerance and Dependency

Seymour Ehrenpreis, David N. Teller, and Abel Lajtha

New York State Research Institute for Neurochemistry and Drug Addiction, Ward's Island, New
York, New York 10035

This chapter discusses those aspects of addictive drugs that are concerned with the mechanisms of development of tolerance and dependence, as well as the symptoms of withdrawal from such drugs and the treatment of these symptoms. The reader is referred to standard texts for details of the pharmacology of these drugs (26). The drugs discussed here include barbiturates, opiates, alcohol, cocaine, anxiolytics, and amphetamines. Wherever possible we will describe drug effects in humans, although most of the laboratory results are from animal experiments. Among the groups of drugs causing addiction, most of the research and theories of tolerance and dependence pertain to narcotics. Accordingly more attention is given to these than to the other classes of drugs.

I. THEORIES OF TOLERANCE DEVELOPMENT

The major problem involved in determining the mechanism of tolerance is that most of the data about tolerance was obtained in whole animal experiments. The complexity of elucidating mechanisms on such a basis is enormous. Tolerance development has recently been demonstrated in an isolated tissue, the guinea pig ileum, and this may permit the study of basic biochemical or molecular mechanisms in a simplified system (18,19). The major mechanisms proposed for development of tolerance are discussed below.

A. Changes in Biotransformation of the Drug

Although this mechanism has proved to be highly successful in terms of explaining tolerance to other drugs, there is little evidence to suggest an altered metabolism of opiates when the drugs are administered chronically. Axelrod appeared to obtain evidence that narcotic antagonists inhibit enzymes required for N-demethylation of many narcotic drugs and proposed that this could account for tolerance (3). However, as pointed out by a number of investigators, there are many inconsistencies in this hypothesis. Mulé has stated quite emphatically that "neither distribution nor metabolism of morphine provides any further insight into the mechanism of tolerance development" (36). This was based on the fact that an examination of excretion of metabolites of various analgesics showed that neither the pattern nor the amounts of metabolites changed significantly in tolerant animals. Indeed long-term treatment with analgesics caused a decrease in enzymatic activity. This is the opposite of what would be expected if these enzymes were involved in tolerance, i.e., enzyme induction has frequently been postulated to be the mechanism of tolerance for other drugs (cf. barbiturates).

B. Immunological Response

Immunological response is another proposed mechanism (see Cochin, 12). In this mechanism the opiate acts as an antigen, causing elaboration of an antibody. The antibody neutralizes the subsequently administered opiate, thereby explaining the development of long-term tolerance. However, attempts to transfer this immunity from one animal to another have failed. Other transfer experiments involving various "brain factors" were proposed and have also not been successful.

C. Possible Role of Protein or Nucleic Acid

This is an area that has received intense investigation, particularly since rather specific inhibitors of synthesis of protein and nucleic acids have become available. Evidence from many laboratories suggests that inhibitors of either type can attenuate tolerance.

One problem in assessing the effects of these drugs is their great, generalized toxicity. A substantial percentage of animals receiving inhibitors of protein or nucleic acid synthesis become very sick or die. Accordingly there may be a reduced ability of such animals (as controls) in a test of analgesia to respond to a painful test stimulus, and thus there is a great difficulty in evaluating the effectiveness of any added analgesic. Moreover it is not sufficient to use controls consisting of animals given the inhibiting drug alone since there appears to be a synergistic effect between opiates and inhibitors of nucleic acid or protein synthesis.

D. Neurotransmission and Tolerance

There are several interrelated hypotheses that attempt to correlate events occurring at synapses to the development of tolerance:

1. For example morphine interacts with a neuronal receptor to produce at least one well-defined effect: inhibition of release of acetylcholine. The receptor appears to be highly specific for opiates as can be demonstrated by various techniques. One mechanism of tolerance states that the opiate remains associated with this specific type of receptor for very extended periods of time, i.e., there is a high degree of *receptor occupancy,* which extends past the mean systemic (total body) peak concentrations of the drug (42). Accordingly the next quantity of drug administered will find a smaller statistical fraction of these receptors available for interaction. Hence the drug effect will be diminished, and therefore tolerance has begun. Eventually the degree of receptor occupation becomes so great that the receptors are fully saturated with the drug; any drug administered subsequently has essentially zero effect. In other words tolerance is complete. What this hypothesis fails to explain is that tolerance must reflect an adaptation of the particular synapse to the action of the drug. If all sites of action of morphine are fully occupied, then the maximum effect must be observed, hence analgesia must be complete. (This would occur if a very large dose of the drug were given and complete analgesia was observed.) However, the reverse is observed: no analgesia is actually obtained when the dose of drug is increased. Presumably under such conditions all receptors are occupied. However, the paradox remains that this situation would also be obtained in a naive animal given a large dose of the drug. The two final states are opposite. Accordingly the receptor occupancy hypothesis of tolerance does not seem to be highly satisfactory.

2. Tolerance must reflect a change in some receptor molecule, and indeed this has been proposed by several workers (28). The *receptor disuse* hypothesis of Collier (13) and of Sharpless and Jaffe (44) is of considerable interest. In this hypothesis an opiate interrupts certain pathways by inhibiting release of a neurotransmitter. This results in a state similar to that of denervation with accompanying supersensitivity of the postsynaptic effector. Although the amount of transmitter may be somewhat diminished, the supersensitivity of the postsynaptic elements increases to a far greater extent and thus the response of the effector is exaggerated. This hypothesis has some factual basis, since the sensitivity of the guinea pig ileum for example is somewhat increased to acetylcholine and serotonin when tissues from addicted animals are examined. Moreover we have shown that transmission in such ilea does show some of the aspects of increased sensitivity (18).

3. Another explanation for tolerance has been suggested: We have shown for the first time that the guinea pig ileum itself can develop tolerance to the blockade of electrically induced transmission produced by injected opiates (18). Tolerance is visualized as occurring because of the elaboration

of additional nerve terminal receptors that bind and inactivate the opiate and in this way prevent the drug from blocking the transmission process. This concept has application to explaining some of the symptoms of opiate withdrawal as discussed below.

4. A newer concept of tolerance involving receptors has developed from studies *in vitro* with amphetamines and alcohol. As discussed in the sections concerning those drugs, metabolites of the original agent may produce "false transmitters," substances that the cell handles in a similar fashion to endogenous neurotransmitters. However, the false transmitters may bind tightly to storage sites or may be inactive in neurotransmission. By combining with physiological receptor sites, such false transmitters deplete the number of inactive binding points for any remaining natural transmitter and increase the functional activity of the transmitter. After a period of time, the false transmitter may displace the natural one from various functional receptors and perhaps produce some of the chronic toxicity effects. The response of the tissue may be a gradual increase in the synthesis of the partially blocked natural neurotransmitter, as the endogenous synthesis of these is under feedback control. Thereafter, when the dosage producing the false transmitter stops, the tissue may be overabundantly supplied with both neurotransmitter synthesis and a reappearance of original receptors as the false transmitter concentration declines. Such tissue, neuronal or otherwise, would then be supersensitive and respond erratically.

In addition the possible false transmitter may possess peculiar psychopharmacological activity as a new agent taken up into storage and released by normal processes. The tetrahydroisoquinoline alkaloids produced from alcohol may affect dopaminergic receptors on which alcohol itself has no marked effect.

II. DEFINITION OF DRUG DEPENDENCE

A chemical is considered to be a drug if it is used for the relief of symptoms, cure of a disease, or to alter an abnormal body state. Accordingly many addictive chemicals, such as cocaine, amphetamines, etc., which have little or no medical use, should not strictly be considered as addictive "drugs." However, in view of the widespread use of such substances as "drugs," we are including them in the present discussion.

Drug dependence has two well-defined components—psychological and physical—and these vary greatly for most classes of drugs. The psychologically dependent state is characterized by the overriding and repeated seeking of a drug or drugs; the entire behavior of the addict may be dictated by the overwhelming craving for the drug. Positive reinforcement plays an important role in the psychological component of addiction. It is difficult, if not impossible, to distinguish between psychological dependency and habituation with a variety of abused drugs or chemicals that do not also produce physi-

TABLE 1. *Drugs of abuse*

Frequency of use	Type of drug
Occasional	Hallucinogens (LSD),[b] marijuana
Constant, at infrequent intervals	Alcohol,[a] cocaine,[b] hashish
Long term, interspersed with drug-free intervals	Barbiturates,[a] amphetamines,[b] cocaine[b]
Regular, daily	Alcohol,[a] barbiturates,[a] anxiolytics[a]
Chronic almost continuous	Alcohol,[a] barbiturates,[a] heroin,[a] amphetamines[b]

[a] Withdrawal produces physiologic dependency syndromes.
[b] Withdrawal may precipitate evidence of psychologic dependency—psychotic episodes or depression.

ological symptoms of withdrawal when their intake stops. Such compounds are found among the hallucinogens (LSD, mescaline, psilocybin, and marihuana) and anorexigenic amphetamines (fenfluramine). However, other drugs in the same classes may produce definite physiological signs of withdrawal and can be definitively assigned the term, addicting, or dependency producing.

Several degrees of drug use may be discerned leading to a greater or lesser state of dependency, as can be seen in Table 1.

III. THEORIES OF THE MECHANISM OF PHYSICAL DRUG DEPENDENCY

A. Disuse Supersensitivity

This theory, proposed by Sharpless and Jaffe (44), was considered applicable not only to opiates but to barbiturates as well. They were able to show that after chronic barbiturate administration the threshold for convulsions (induced by metrazole) was lowered. The threshold reverted to normal levels with time as the barbiturate was withdrawn. They seem to have obtained similar evidence in terms of a nonnarcotic antagonist interaction, whereby the antagonism of pilocarpine by scopolamine was progressively reduced with chronic administration of the scopolamine. This represents a development of tolerance to classic cholinergic drugs.

B. Pharmacological Redundancy

The pharmacological redundancy hypothesis (34) is a complex mechanism based on the postulate that there are two types of important pathways in the central nervous system: the primary and the redundant pathways. These are differential sensitivities of both pathways to drugs, the primary being perhaps more sensitive to drugs producing dependency. If the primary pathways are blocked, the redundant pathways become successively more functional, and eventually they may even become hypersensitive. One aspect of the redundant circuit is that it is controlled by a negative feedback from the primary circuit. Accordingly, as the primary circuit is depressed by the drug, its influence on the redundant circuit decreases and the latter begins to take over to a greater extent. As the redundant pathway takes over, the effect of the drug gradually decreases since it is acting more or less selectively on the decreasingly active primary pathways. Accordingly tolerance would be demonstrated. When the drug is withdrawn or removed by an antagonist the following sequence of events is said to occur: the primary pathways now become activated to act on effectors; the redundant pathways that had hypertrophied also are working; and together both serve to overstimulate the effectors. Accordingly there is an exaggerated response, what is termed the abstinence syndrome. Evidence for such pathways has been obtained for various systems, mainly of a reflex nature.

Attractive as this hypothesis may be, it still does not explain the findings that a withdrawal-type phenomenon has been observed to occur in the guinea pig ileum (18). The redundancy hypothesis postulates new pathways with perhaps different kinds of neurotransmitters being involved. Neither of these obviously occurs in the ileum.

C. Receptor Theory

The concept of a receptor for narcotic analgesic action is the theoretic basis for much of the current research on the mechanisms of narcotic action and antagonism, and now also for explanation of the development of tolerance (18, 32). This concept states that a drug combines in a physically definable fashion with one or more specific macromolecular sites in the neuron in such a way that the normal functions of those cellular areas that contain these macromolecules are altered. The problems of identifying such sites, of determining whether they are unique for individual classes of drugs, whether such sites are active enzyme centers or exert remote effects on, for example, general membrane functions are some of the challenging, current research goals in the pharmacology of many drugs besides narcotics (19, 23).

The isolated guinea pig ileum has provided the means of attacking the problem of tolerance in a living *in vitro* system. The tissue can be shown to develop tolerance to the effect of morphine on cholinergic transmission as shown by the following: A very large dose of morphine (750 mg/kg) injected into a naive guinea pig causes almost complete block of contractions elicited by electrical stimulation of the tissue. The same dose injected into an animal given morphine chronically is essentially ineffective, i.e., electrical stimulation produces normal contractions. Ten days of morphine administration (100 mg/kg twice daily) is required for complete tolerance to develop. The only major change in the properties of the ileum during chronic morphine administration is that it contracts when naloxone is added *in vitro,* i.e., to the tissue in the organ bath. Naloxone has no effect on ileum from a normal animal. The contracture has been shown to result from the outpouring of acetylcholine from the tissue as a consequence of the displacement of morphine from a new receptor located within the postganglionic nerve terminals, termed internal or "I" receptor. (18). Ehrenpreis and coworkers have postulated that this "I" receptor can best account for the phenomena of tolerance and withdrawal. It has been proposed that tolerance results from induction of such "I" receptors during the course of chronic administration of morphine. These receptors, which increase progressively in number, bind and inactivate drug molecules within the nerve terminal thereby reducing the amount available to combine with the receptor which is ordinarily involved with the action of morphine on transmission, termed "T" receptor. Thus, greater amounts of the drug would be required to produce the acute effect, i.e., tolerance develops. Reduced affinity of the "T" receptors for morphine does not occur, so a change in this receptor cannot account for tolerance. Precipitated withdrawal, observed in particular when an antagonist is administered, is caused by a massive displacement of opiate from the "I" sites accompanied by outpouring of acetylcholine. This excess transmitter, coming in contact with structures that are rendered supersensitive during the course of opiate administration, results in intense cholinergic stimulation throughout the body, both in the CNS and periphery.

This is of course only a working hypothesis and there are other explanations of tolerance but there is additional independent evidence for involvement of two separate receptors with morphine tolerance in the CNS (see ref. 22 for a review).

Enzymes and Dependence. The Shuster enzyme derepressant theory (46) is of considerable interest, and the following is a brief description of this theory:

(1) A drug, such as morphine, inhibits an enzyme involved in the synthesis of a neurotransmitter. This inhibition results in the primary effects of morphine, e.g., analgesia, sedation, etc. (2) Morphine also derepresses the synthesis of an enzyme that is involved in the synthesis of the neurotransmitter or inhibits synthesis of an enzyme that metabolizes (destroys) the transmitter. In either event the concentration of the transmitter progressively increases, thereby counteracting the action of the opiate. (3) When the drug is withdrawn, the increased level of neurotransmitter, as well as of the enzyme required for its synthesis, results in excessive transmission at the particular synapse and an exaggerated response of the effector.

There is some experimental evidence that in the brain of the morphine-tolerant mouse, the optimal synthesis and turnover of ^{14}C-labeled catecholamines is dependent upon the continued administration of morphine (41). Such effects are difficult to interpret for several reasons, although at first they appear to confirm the enzyme-derepressant theory, because the effects of drugs on enzyme systems *in vivo* markedly vary with conditioning (45), animal strains (22, 25), and even ethnic background (50). These subjects are often not considered by neuropharmacologists or biochemists in evaluating the biochemical data. There is also some evidence against this theory. For example nalorphine, which has both agonist and antagonist properties toward morphine and is an equally potent, albeit dysphoric, analgesic, does not produce significant dependence, although *in vivo* and *in vitro* a high degree of tolerance does develop.

IV. CHEMISTRY OF NARCOTIC ANALGESICS

A. Structure and Analgesic Potency

There are thousands of synthetic analgesics. Many are far more potent than morphine, although this remains the most widely used potent analgesic today. Many excellent reviews have been published on structure-activity relationships among the various analgesics and the interested reader is referred to these (10, 14, 35). The most important classes of substances with potent analgesic activity are shown in Table 1 with a few important representatives from each class.

B. Morphine and Derivatives

Morphine is basically a phenanthrene derivative containing a six-membered piperidine ring. The A ring is fully aromatic and contains a phenolic OH group (Fig. 1a). Only the levo-enantiomorph is active as an analgesic. When the phenolic OH group is esterified the potency is greatly reduced, as exemplified by codeine. Acetylation of the two hydroxyls of morphine produces heroin, which is somewhat more potent and toxic than the parent compound. Hydromorphine (Dilaudid®) and oxymorphine (Numorphan®) are derivatives that are used clinically. Other derivatives of morphine such as etorphine can be several hundred to several thousand times as potent in terms of analgesia in animals.

C. Morphinan and Benzomorphan Derivatives

It is of interest that removal of the oxygen bridge in morphine produces compounds that can be more potent than morphine, e.g., levorphanol (Fig. 2a). Changes in the remainder of the molecule cause changes in potency similar to those that occur when morphine is modified, e.g., methylation of the phenolic OH group in morphinans and morphine change the potency. In the benzomorphan series the C ring is completely absent (Fig. 2b). Examples of benzomorphans are metazocine, phenazocine, pentazocine, and cyclazocine.

D. Phenylpiperidines

Meperidine is the best known of this group (Fig. 3a). It is perhaps the most widely used synthetic analgesic and in terms of potency is considerably

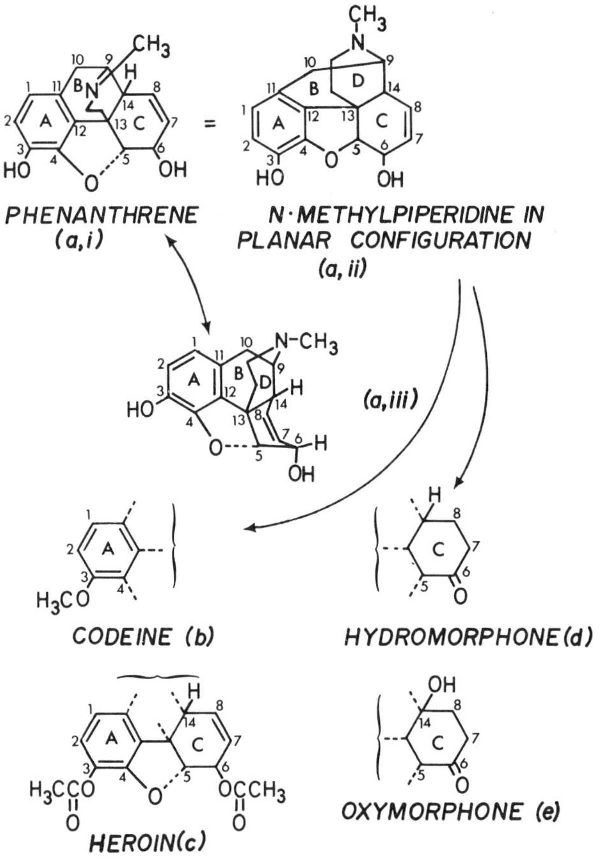

FIG. 1. Morphine and derivatives. The phenanthrene nucleus (a,i) is labeled A, B, C, but the D-ring (N-methyl piperidine ring) is "above" the surface. When this is flattened out, the structure a,ii develops. Current views of the shape of morphine indicate a folded configuration as shown in a,iii. However, it is easier to visualize the chemical substitutions with reference to the a,ii configuration.

weaker than morphine but stronger than codeine. These compounds are far simpler in structure than morphine. Many have been synthesized; the reader is referred to various reviews (9, 27) for a detailed discussion of their pharmacology. Among the piperidine derivatives that are used are ethoheptazine (Zactane®) (Fig. 3b) and pyrrolidine (prodilidine) (Fig. 3c).

E. Diphenylpropylamines

Methadone (Fig. 4a) is more addictive than morphine and longer acting, but the withdrawal symptoms are less severe than those from morphine. Methadone has both antitussive and spasmolytic properties. Normethadone is used primarily as an antitussive (Ticarda) but has an addiction liability greater than that of codeine. Of considerable interest is the finding that the

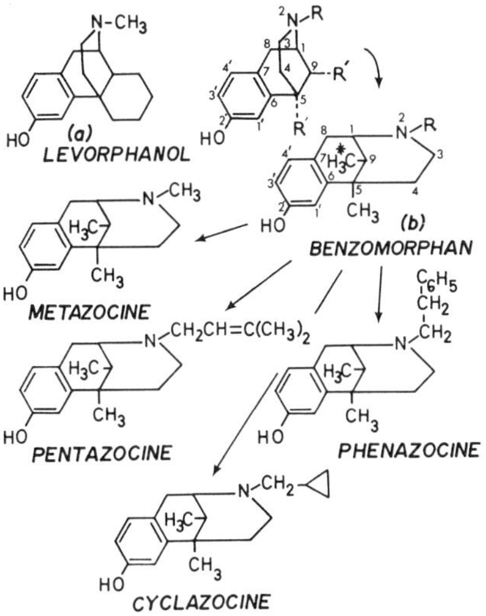

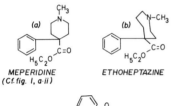

FIG. 2. Levorphanol and benzomorphans. The starred methyl group in the benzomorphan nucleus (b) has interesting properties: in the α-orientation (away from N 2) it produces lower analgesia and much less toxicity than in the β-orientation (toward N 2).

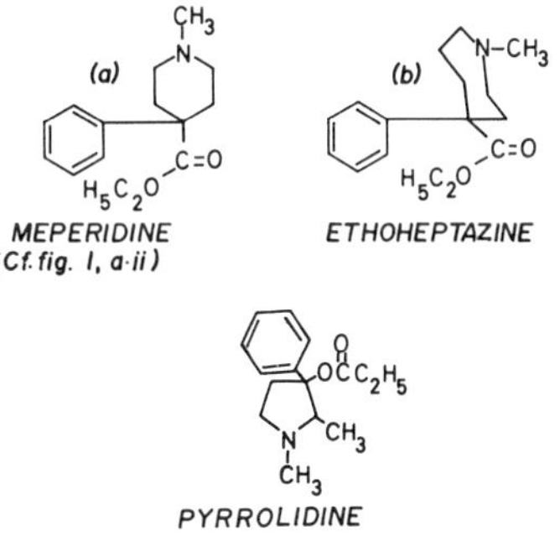

FIG. 3. Meperidine and phenylpiperidines. Meperidine is arranged for comparison to Fig. 1,a,ii and to methadone (Fig. 4).

dextro compound of a derivative related to methadone (Dextromoramide) has high analgesic potency. This is one instance in which the levo-isomer is far less potent than the dextro. In contrast, the dextro-isomer of methadone has only 1/10–1/20 the potency of the levo form.

V. CHEMISTRY OF NARCOTIC ANTAGONISTS

A. Morphine Analogs

Changing the alkyl group on the piperidine nitrogen can result in an antagonist e.g., nalorphine (Fig. 5). However the alkyl derivatives (amyl and hexyl) are not antagonists, but are fairly potent analgesics. The well-known antagonist naloxone is an N-allyl derivative in the oxymorphone series.

Morphinan Analogs consist of compounds in which the furan ring of morphine is removed. Replacement of the N-methyl group by an allyl group results in the rather potent antagonist levallorphan.

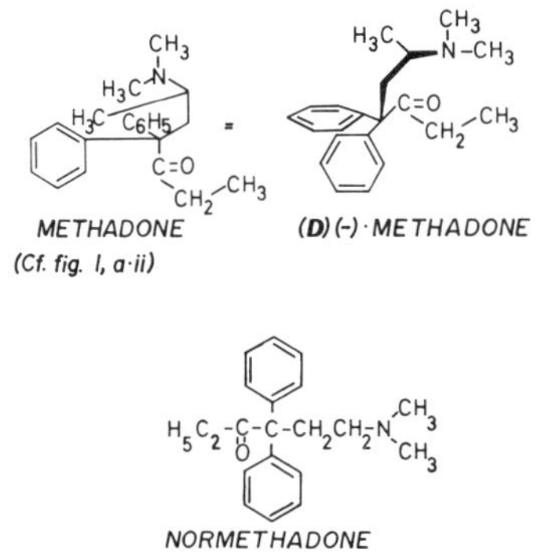

FIG. 4. Methadone and derivatives. Note that this compound's series has a phenylalkyl amino-dimethyl chain (spread out in normethadone representation), which is very similar to that of the neuroleptics. Spatially, the configuration is quite different, as shown for D-methadone.

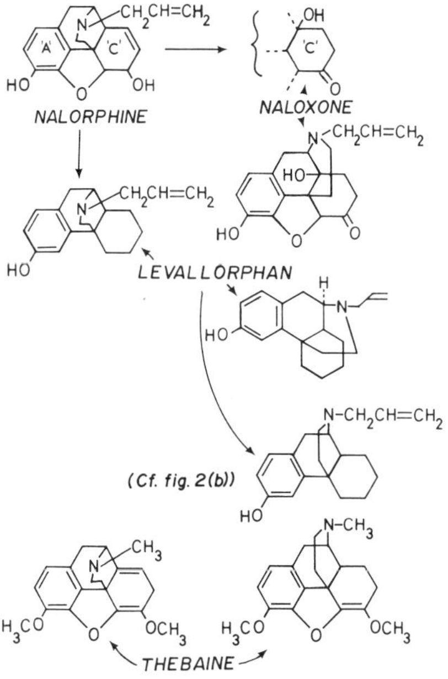

FIG. 5. Nalorphine, levallorphan, and thebaine. Removal of the oxygen bridge (furan ring) changes nalorphine (primarily antagonist activity) to levallorphan (very potent antagonist). Naloxone has the furan bridge but has only antagonist activity. The basic structures of these compounds originate from thebaine, a natural product derived from opium, for which no satisfactory synthetic route exists. Thus at present production of the antagonists requires production of the base (alkaloids) from which the abused narcotics are also derived.

B. Benzomorphan Derivatives

Again N-allyl derivatives are potent antagonists, while the N-amyl derivative has almost pure analgesic activity. Cyclazocine is both a potent antagonist as well as a psychotomimetic.

C. 4-Phenylpiperidines

In this series allyl derivatives do not seem to possess antagonistic activity but instead, behave as agonists.

D. Thebaine Derivatives

Some of these have analgesic potency which is several thousand times that of morphine. On the other hand N-allyl derivatives of some thebaine derivatives have proven to be highly potent antagonists.

VI. TOLERANCE TO NARCOTICS

A. Criteria of Tolerance

The usual criteria for determining tolerance to opiates depend on standard tests for analgesia, respiratory rate, or body temperature regulation. Either the same dose is repeatedly given to an animal to determine the response (as a fraction of the response to an initial dose) or the dose is increased to achieve the initial end point. In animals it is possible to observe tolerance 24 hr after giving large amounts of an opiate. This can be done either by giving the drug intravenously or by using an implanted pellet. Tolerance to physiological effects of narcotic analgesics is summarized in Table 2.

TABLE 2. Development of tolerance to physiologic effects of narcotic analgesics*

Development of high-grade tolerance	Minimal or no tolerance
Analgesic	
Euphoria-dysphoria	
Narcosis	
Respiratory depression	Miosis
Inhibition of REM sleep	Convulsions
Hypotension	Constipation
Anorexia	Nausea and vomiting
Hypothermia	Antagonistic effect of nalorphine, cyclazocine
Alteration of spinal cord reflexes	
Increased motor activity (mouse)	
Lenticular opacities (rodents)	
Antidiuretic action	

* After Hug (28).

Possible distinctions between acute and chronic tolerance are discussed below. According to Hug, "In most cases there does not seem to be a fundamental difference between acute and chronic tolerance in terms of the tissues affected or the degree of tolerance that can be produced" (28).

B. Onset

At times even a single narcotic dose may be sufficient to produce significant tolerance, e.g., 10 or 20 mg/kg of morphine can produce tolerance in the rat lasting for several days or even several weeks. However, in most instances tolerance develops only upon continuous administration of the drug. If a drug-free period intervenes, most aspects of the tolerance rapidly disappear, however, as noted below, some sensitivity or long-term effects have been observed in various species.

C. Degree

In some instances tolerance appears to be an all or none phenomenon, i.e., there is no slow development of drug resistance. Thus tolerance to emetic and hypertensive actions of morphine in man once established does not revert. However, tolerance to the analgesic and respiratory action is only proportional to dosage. Thus an analgesic or respiratory depression effect of the drug can be achieved again simply by raising the dose. The same is true for lethal and euphoric actions of the drug. An addict constantly increases the size and frequency of intake in order to achieve a state of euphoria. This of course serves to enhance the tolerance to the drug.

D. Rate of Disappearance

This has been a subject of some controversy. Tolerance disappears within 24 hr or a few days after cessation of drug intake in most animal species studied as well as in addicts. On the other hand, a number of investigators (28) have reported the persistence of tolerance to some actions of morphine for 6 months to 1 year following administration of even a single dose. This is particularly true in the rat, although some aspects of long-term tolerance have also been observed in man. In contrast the monkey shows a type of hypersensitivity that has been observed several months after chronic administration of morphine. Thus a dose of morphine given several months later produced an exaggerated response or an increased sensitivity to the drug.

E. Cross Tolerance

It is generally agreed that the potent analgesics show cross tolerance, i.e., tolerance development to the effects of one of these drugs causes tolerance to other related drugs. This is said to occur regardless of the chemical formula of the particular narcotic (see Table 3). However, careful evaluation of the various chemical types of narcotic analgesics has revealed that there are specific differences among them (28) for which cross tolerance does not develop.

TABLE 3. *Potent analgesics*

Class of analgesic	Representative compound
1. Opium alkaloids and their derivatives	Morphine, oxymorphone, oxycodone, nalorphine,[a] naloxone,[b] etorphine
2. Morphinans	Levorphanol, levallorphan[a]
3. Benzomorphans	Phenazocine, pentazocine,[a] cyclazocine[a]
4. 4-Phenylpiperidines	Meperidine, pethidine, anileridine, piminodine, fentanyl
5. Diphenylpropylamine	Methadone, dipipamone

[a] Has both analgesic as well as antagonistic activity.
[b] Has only antagonistic activity.

VII. NARCOTIC DEPENDENCY

A. Opiate Dependence

Physical dependence is described in terms of what occurs when the particular drug is withdrawn. This state is characterized by the abstinence syndrome of which the major sign is a physiological hyperexcitability upon abrupt discontinuance of the drug or upon the administration of an antagonist in the case of opiates (Table 4).

Perhaps the best test as to whether a drug causes dependency in the same manner as other opiates is the substitution procedure. Morphine is given to a group of addicts for several days at doses to 250 mg/day. The drug is then discontinued and 14 hr later either a placebo or the drug in question is administered to the individual for a period of 24 hr. The intensity of withdrawal symptoms is then noted. The withdrawal syndrome is potentiated by various disorders including cirrhosis of the liver, hepatitis, and congestive heart failure. All previously synthesized and naturally occurring drugs that

TABLE 4. *Abstinence syndrome to opiates in various animals*

Mice	Rats	Dogs	Man
Jumping	Teeth chattering	Yawning	Pain in abdomen and muscles
Loss of weight	Weight loss	Lacrimation	Cold sweat
Diarrhea	Diarrhea	Fever	Diarrhea
Tremors	"Wet dog" shakes[a]	Rhinorrhea	Nausea and vomiting
		Restlessness	Goose flesh
		Tremors	

[a] The animal shakes itself many times in a manner similar to a dog that has just come out of the water.

suppress the abstinence syndrome produce the same kind of addictive liability as any other opiate.

An alternative way to test whether a drug is addicting or not is simply to administer it to the subject for a period of time and then challenge with an antagonist, such as naloxone or nalorphine. However, certain drugs that can substitute for opiates in the withdrawal type of experiment do not show abstinence signs when challenged with an antagonist. For example, naloxone will not produce a typical withdrawal syndrome during the initial stages of maintenance treatment with cyclazocine or pentazocine (after morphine or heroin).

It should be noted that the abstinence syndrome due to certain narcotic antagonists, particularly nalorphine, cyclazocine, and pentazocine, may be absent, or if it occurs it is generally far less severe than that of the pure agonists. Nevertheless these antagonists do possess dual actions in that they also produce analgesia, and this may account for their slight to moderate addicting properties. Table 5 summarizes the dependence liability among a large series of opiates and opiate antagonists.

TABLE 5. Activity of narcotic analgesics and agonist-antagonists in mice and man[a]

International nonproprietary name	Trade and common names	ED$_{50}$ Mouse (mg/kg)	ED$_{50}$ Man (mg)	Dependence liability in man
Morphine	—	1.2	10	High
Oxymorphone	Numorphan	0.08	1.12–1.15	High
Oxycodone	Nucodan, Eucodal, Eumorphal, Eucosan, Percodan	0.3	10–15	High
Hydrocodone	Dihydrocodeinone, Dicodid, Hycodan	1.6	15	Intermediate
Hydromorphone	Dihydromorphinone, Dilaudid, Hymorphan, Dimorphid, and Dimorphone	0.15	2–4	High
Heroin	—	0.45	2–10	High
Nalorphine	Nalline	4.8	10	Low
Etorphine	M-99	0.001	0.05	High
Pethidine	Meperidine, Demerol, Isonipecaine, Dolantin	4.7	80	High
Anileridine	Leritine	1.6	30	High
Piminodine	—	0.5	10	High
Phenoperidine	—	0.032	0.3–2	High
Alphaprodine	Nisentil, Prisilidine	0.9	40–60	High
Fentanyl	Subrimaze	0.008	0.05	High
Methadone	Amidone, Dolophine, Panalgen	0.8	5–10	High
Dipipanone	Diconal	1.4	20–25	High
Levorphanol	Dromoran	0.25	2–3	High
Levallorphan	—	—	10	—
Phenazocine	Narphen, Prinadol, NIH 7519	0.1	2–3	Intermediate
Pentazocine	Talwin	4.7	20–40	Low
Cyclazocine	—	0.08	0.025	Intermediate
1-Etazocine	NIH 8178	1.17	8	Intermediate
1-Metazocine	NIH 7569	0.85	10	Intermediate

[a] (After Jacobson, ref. 30.)

B. Dependence on Narcotic Antagonists Produced in Laboratory Animals

From the few studies in this area, evidence appears to indicate that chronic administration of cyclazocine, naloxone, or nalorphine did not cause a typical abstinence syndrome in these animals when they were challenged later with naloxone. In particular the jumping syndrome was absent. This suggests that, although evidence for dependence with these drugs (with the exception of naloxone) has been established, it must be of a different nature from that produced by the opiates themselves.

VIII. TREATMENT OF NARCOTIC DEPENDENCY STATES

A. Methadone

This treatment is called methadone maintenance and was begun by Dole and coworkers (17). The procedure for treating an addict with methadone is as follows: (1) Withdraw from heroin or other opiate. (2) Give methadone at doses sufficient to control withdrawal but so small as to not produce effects of the narcotic. The dose is about 20 mg twice a day. (3) Increase the dose of methadone to a level of 80 to 120 mg/day over a period of 1 to 2 months. The maintenance dose is usually given as a single dose in the morning. (4) Place patient on laxative in order to counteract constipating effect of methadone. Note: some of the side effects of methadone include constipation, impotence, excessive sweating, or anxiety. Tolerance generally develops to these. (5) The patient is maintained on this dose for at least 1 year. (6) The patient is rehabilitated by psychiatric means. In addition help with job training and employment, enrollment in school, etc. are important adjuncts to rehabilitation. (7) Testing of urine for drugs of abuse is an important part of the program.

It should be noted that methadone, even in the long-term treatment process, does not result in a cure of addiction. Almost invariably the addict once withdrawn from the methadone reverts back to his previous ways. This reversion is a result of "heroin hunger." However, in examining the question of the success of the program, the following statistics may be cited as supporting this approach (16): Of 2,200 heroin addicts admitted to the program, about 80% remained for the treatment and this was accompanied by a marked reduction in the crime rate and a high rate of employment among those in the program. Gessa, Vargiu, Biggio, and Tagliamonte (22a) have recently reviewed proposed mechanisms by which methadone might act in the CNS. It appears to meet the structural requirements of a sympathomimetic agent (it has a phenylalkylamino structure) and may exert an amphetamine-like effect at dopamine (DA) nerve terminals in addition to inhibiting DA receptor sites. Thus methadone shares several pharmacological and biochemical actions common to phenothiazine and butyrophenone neuroleptics: induction of catalepsy and hypothermia in rats; blockade of apomorphine-induced gnawing; increase of brain homovanillic acid without increasing 5-hydroxy-indoleacetic acid; stimulation of DA synthesis.

B. Narcotic Antagonists

Use of narcotic antagonists to prevent the particular euphoric effect of heroin and thereby block its psychological appeal to recidivism could prove to be the most satisfactory method of treating addicts to opiates. These antagonists successfully neutralize the actions of large amounts of the drug. Complete withdrawal from the opiate is not required nor is it even desirable, since the antagonist could well precipitate a full-blown withdrawal syndrome. At present the ideal antagonist is naloxone, a drug essentially devoid of any intrinsic pharmacological activity when used at a reasonable dosage. However, the antagonism of opiates by this drug is very short, lasting only 4 to 6 hr. Indeed the fact that it is nonaddicting is somewhat of a drawback; any time the addict chooses to, he may cease taking naloxone, wait a reasonable period of time, and resume his habit. In this regard it may be desirable that the antagonist be at least somewhat addicting in order to have a "hold" on the addict. All other antagonists, even nalorphine and pentazocine, do produce some addiction in man and animals. The somewhat stronger dependence due to cyclazocine is characterized by loss of appetite, tachycardia, mydriasis, increase in body temperature, and insomnia if the drug is withdrawn. In addition the drug produces dysphoria in man. It is of interest that despite the evident dependence-liability of cyclazocine, nalorphine does not precipitate withdrawal after a cyclazocine course of treatment. Originally nalorphine was reported to be nonaddicting, i.e., withdrawal symptoms were not observed upon abrupt cessation. However, more recently there have been observations of some symptoms similar to those noticed after withdrawal of morphine.

IX. CHARACTERISTICS OF ALCOHOL TOLERANCE AND DEPENDENCE

Recent reviews which attempt to organize a great deal of information into fertile areas of investigation are those by Kalant, LeBlanc, and Gibbins (31), and by Lieber (33). These two excellent reviews present details of pharmacology and biochemical effects of ethanol and related agents beyond what can be presented here.

A. Alcohol Intoxication: Characteristics

Low blood levels result in depressed inhibitions, loss of judgment, efficiency, and logical thought; euphoria may occur. At blood levels of 100 to 200 mg%, ataxia occurs with slurred speech, prolonged reaction time, loss of control over emotions, e.g., silliness, viciousness. At 300 mg% there is loss of consciousness, pupillary light reflex is sluggish or absent, respiration is irregular; there is a fall in temperature and blood pressure and possibly coma. Blood levels of 400 mg% may result in death due to medullary paralysis.

Primary direct effects of ethanol on CNS neuronal activity may be localized at the level of membranal sodium conductance and active ion transport. Inhibition of these processes by ethanol in excitable membranes of specific cell types has been demonstrated (see ref. 49 for review). The anatomical site of action may be the lateral hypothalamus in *alcoholism,* although other areas may be affected initially. Subsequent effects of chronic alcohol intake, such as the possible condensation of an ethanol metabolite (acetaldehyde) with normal cell constituents to produce false neurotransmitters or psychotomimetic agents, to alter biogenic amine metabolism, and to produce alkaloid derivatives *in vivo,* are subjects of current intensive research.

B. Withdrawal Syndrome

Depending on the length of time on alcohol as well as on the level of intake, the characteristics of alcohol withdrawal are entirely different. After moderate drinking, e.g., one drinking episode followed by sleep, nausea, perhaps apprehension and insomnia may follow. These symptoms can be reversed by taking a drink of alcohol.

After severe drinking, vomiting, diarrhea, tachycardia, fever, delirium tremens (DT; hallucinations which may be visual, tactile, or auditory) may ensue.

DT usually has an onset 2 to 4 days after cessation of drinking, although it may not occur until as long as a week afterward. Incidence is about 5%. It is believed that DT may be related to suppression of REM sleep by alcohol. There have been several proposals to explain DT. Perhaps it is due to the excessive liberation of catecholamines that reaches its highest level during withdrawal. Another possible cause is magnesium ion loss occurring during chronic alcoholism. This would have a destabilizing effect on the entire nervous system. As a result of both effects, there are profound alterations of neuromuscular transmission mechanisms, with the excessive output of transmitter producing intense muscular activity. The sensitivity to photic stimulation in the alcoholic may also be related to reduced magnesium levels.

C. Characteristics of Tolerance to Alcohol

Tolerance to the effects of alcohol can develop extremely rapidly, i.e., even after a single dose is given. Almost all of the effects of alcohol show tolerance in man with the exception that the LD_{50} is increased only two- to fourfold. EEG effects show that tolerance develops in a few days in monkeys. Rat behavior shows tolerance to ethanol in the same period. In man development of tolerance often requires 2 to 3 weeks of chronic ethanol administration. Obviously the rate of appearance of tolerance depends on the dosage. The tolerance that does develop is low-grade tolerance, i.e., a pharmacological effect of ethanol can be achieved simply by increasing the dosage. In several animal studies, chronic administration of alcohol resulted in a shift in the dose-response curve to the right. This is similar to what is observed when a competetive antagonist is given. However, the degree of tolerance to alcohol is not great, because the ED_{50} is increased only two- to threefold.

D. Reversal of Tolerance

In animals disappearance of tolerance to chronic ethanol administration often requires several days or weeks. It is of interest that once tolerance had worn off in rats the induction of tolerance to a second course of administration of alcohol was increased. In other words the first exposure of the animals to the drug caused a sensitization mechanism responsible for the development of tolerance. The time required to produce the tolerant state diminished progressively with each series of alcohol treatments and withdrawals during which the alcohol administration was stopped, until the animals appeared to be restored to their normal state of sensitivity.

E. Mechanism of Tolerance Development and Withdrawal

One way of explaining tolerance to ethanol is by the induction of metabolizing enzymes. The rate of breakdown of alcohol increases with progressive administration. The precise mechanism of the augmented metabolism is somewhat in dispute. Moreover the enhanced rate of ethanol metabolism is at most only 100% above that of untreated animals. This relatively small increase in the ethanol oxidation rate is considered by some to be inadequate to explain the ability of chronically treated animals to survive increasing doses, which may reach three to 25 times the initially lethal dose.

Although the activity of alcohol dehydrogenase in brain is less than that of liver, the brain enzyme does show adaptive changes to ethanol within 8 days in mice (40), increasing to twice its initial level, then decreasing when the alcohol stops. The product of the reaction, acetaldehyde, shows cross-tolerance with ethanol, and mice exposed to either ethanol or acetaldehyde exhibit changes in brain catecholamines and similar withdrawal behavior (37). Methanol is produced endogenously, is metabolized by the same enzyme, and during chronic alcohol metabolism it accumulates significantly. When the ethanol stops, the withdrawal syndrome may also be caused by the rapid metabolism of methanol to formaldehyde by the activated dehydrogenases. Formaldehyde or acetaldehyde can react with normal precursors of neurotransmitters to produce psychotomimetic agents or inactive false neuro-transmitters. As Goldstein (24) has shown, normal levels of catecholamines suppress the withdrawal reaction to ethanol. Treatment of alcoholic animals with reserpine to deplete endogenous catecholamines produces an intensified withdrawal reaction. Thus acetaldehyde or formaldehyde might produce in-active neurotransmitters and a prolongation or intensification of withdrawal symptoms. In these studies atropine, physostigmine, *p*-chlorophenylalanine, and 5-hydroxytryptophan, substances affecting cholinergic or serotonergic pathways, did not affect the withdrawal syndrome, while reserpine, α-methyl-tyrosine, phentolamine, and propanolol intensified the seizures. Amino-oxyacetic acid, a precursor of γ-aminobutyrate, suppressed the convulsions. Thus functional γ-aminobutyric acid (GABA) and catecholamine pathways tend to suppress the hyperexcitability of the alcohol-withdrawal state (24). In addition there may be some similarities of the ethanol and morphine tolerance development; chronic treatment with either drug raises the dopamine level—alcohol in the caudate nucleus (38), morphine in striatum and hy-pothalamus (11).

These alterations in CNS metabolism may be responsible for many of the diverse effects of ethanol. Formerly it was believed that ethanol had diffuse and generally nonspecific effects on the CNS, but the results of recent research indicate a high degree of specificity for many of ethanol-induced changes in CNS physiology and biochemistry. Sorting out the various alterations into cause and effect for the sequelae of acute or chronic intoxication, habituation to, or abrupt abstinence from alcohol remains a formidable but possible task (43). We have summarized examples of some of the variety of effects due to ethanol on CNS function in Table 6.

TABLE 6. *Various effects of ethanol on CNS functions*

State of ethanol intoxication[a]	Test system	Response
A 40 mg i.v.; 10 min	Cat, lateral hypothalamus	Na^+-sensitive interneurons stop = disinhibition
A 0.6–2.24 g i.p.; 10 min	Hamster, brain glucose	increased
A 4g i.p.; 0.5–2 hr	Rat brain serotonin, 5HIAA	increased
A Blood levels 150 mg%	Human short-term memory	blackout
B 400 mg p.o.; q.i.d./10 days	Human plasma 17-hydroxy-corticosteroids	increased, suppresses CNS (peptide) hormone releasing factors
B 10% p.o.; free choice/42 days	Rat brain serotonin	increased
B 10% p.o.; 10–46 days	Leucine incorporation into brain proteins	30% decrease
B 10% p.o.; 24 days	Formation of U^{14}C-leucyl-tRNA	5% decrease
C 10% p.o. 9 months/24 hr.	Rat, lateral hypothalamus	spontaneous activity returns to normal
C 10% 20 days; 48 hr.	Mouse C57BL/6J; brain pH5, protein synthesizing enzyme	up to 50% loss

[a] A, Acute, dose in mg or g/kg and time interval before test. B, Chronic, dose range in mg/kg and dura-tion of treatment. C, Withdrawal, final dose in mg/kg (or % in food or water) and interval prior to test measurement.

X. CHARACTERISTICS OF BARBITURATE INTOXICATION TOLERANCE AND DEPENDENCE

A. Characteristics of Barbiturate Intoxication

At the physiological pH range (6.0 to 8.0), most of the barbiturates (with pK_a from 7.4 to 8.0) exist primarily in nonionized, lipid soluble forms. Such solubility correlates well with their degree of hypnotic activity and is important in determining their entry into the CNS. In addition the form of substituent groups on positions C-5 and N-1 of the hexahydropyrimidine nucleus (Fig. 6) produces four classes of these CNS depressants: ultrashort, short, intermediate, and long acting.

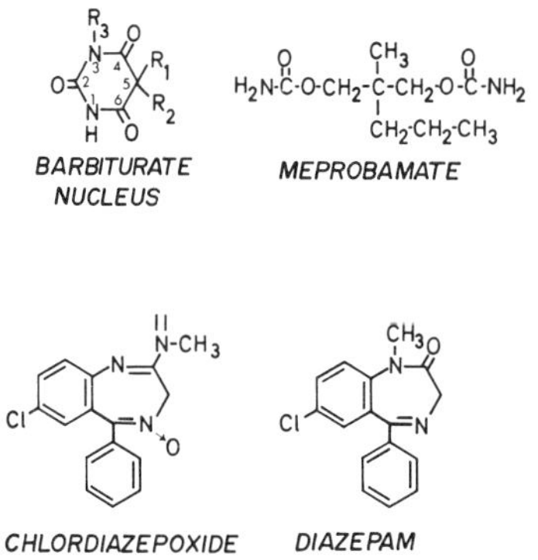

FIG. 6. Barbiturates and common "tranquilizers" that produce physical dependency.

Barbiturates depress polysynaptic reflexes. They block neuromuscular transmission by inhibiting release of acetylcholine. They also prevent contractions of smooth and striated muscle in response to acetylcholine, probably by combination with muscarinic receptors as well as extra-junctional elements (19). Barbiturates also decrease response to electrical stimulation, by a direct inhibition of Na^+ conductance by uncoupling of ion pumps from the energy-producing (ATPase) or transducing (NADH reductase) systems, via insertion of the barbiturate into the presynaptic membrane. Such effects also occur with phenothiazines and alcohol, and may also involve delocalization of Ca^{2+}, so that the membrane becomes more fluid and is less capable of maintaining (electrical) potential differences. This effect is often referred to as membrane stabilization, which simply means that the barrier is less likely to break down under the influence of the stimulus because it has an internal fluidity and an increased capability for molecular relaxational movement.

Severe, acute poisoning with barbiturates involves all of the above effects, which combine to produce a hypoxic condition and demise caused by respiratory failure. Through a similar mechanism, chronic heavy usage of barbiturates produces cortical atrophy due to neuronal degeneration without any accompanying gliosis.

B. Barbiturate Tolerance

It is considered that the development of tolerance to barbiturates is qualitatively similar to that of alcohol. Indeed cross-tolerance exists between these two types of drugs. As in the case of alcohol, acute tolerance can develop to barbiturates in experimental animals. A single dose is sufficient in dogs, rats, and rabbits. It may be noted that different modalities of tolerance have been observed, e.g., ataxia, anesthesia, behavioral effects, etc.

The duration of tolerance has been determined in a few species. It lasts about 48 hr in rats for pentobarbital; a similar time course was obtained in monkeys and dogs, possibly in humans as well. Characteristics of tolerance and dependency due to barbiturates are outlined in Table 7. The reverse of

TABLE 7. *Characteristics of barbiturate dependence and withdrawal*

Dependence	Symptoms of withdrawal
Requires more than 500 mg/day for perhaps 60 days Tolerance develops Cross tolerance to ethanol and other CNS supressants	Delirium Auditory and visual hallucinations (psychosis) Anxiety Grand mal seizures Tremors Autonomic effects: increased heart rate, blood pressure, and rectal temperature ncreases response to sensory stimulation INausea and vomiting.

tolerance, i.e., hypersensitivity to barbiturates, has been noted in several species. Thus chronic administration of a barbiturate to dogs first resulted in tolerance, but with continued administration of increasing doses the animals demonstrated a reaction that was characterized as intoxication to the drug. Shortly thereafter the animals died.

C. Mechanism of Tolerance Development

Induction of enzymes by barbiturates has been investigated extensively and appears to be one of the established, if not the main, mechanism for tolerance production. This has been extensively reviewed by Misra (35a). An increased rate of metabolism of barbiturates upon chronic administration has been demonstrated *in vivo* as well as with isolated microsomal metabolizing enzymes. It is this factor that has been widely cited to explain cross-tolerance among drugs that are known to be metabolized in a similar fashion to the barbiturates.

However, Hug (28) has raised questions as to whether metabolism alone could fully account for tolerance. Perhaps his most compelling argument against this is that barbiturates, when applied directly to the brain, also produce tolerance. On the other hand, there is no evidence that such drugs are not also metabolized in brain tissue. Hug concluded that there must also be an adaptation of the nervous system functions to the effect of the barbiturate in order to fully account for tolerance. This view is also partially supported by experiments with barbital, which is metabolized very poorly. In this case chronic administration produced little change in tissue concentration, although tolerance to the hypnotic action developed. Such tolerance disappeared 7 to 14 days after the drug was stopped (see Misra, 35a, and Hug, 28, for reviews).

D. Mechanism of Dependency Development

Little information is available concerning the factors controlling dependency on barbiturates. The withdrawal reaction may be caused by increased metabolism of neurotransmitter precursors by the barbiturate-induced enzymes that have been suddenly depleted of drug substrate. Subsequent hypersensitivity to a withdrawn barbiturate has been reported, but this does not appear to occur through CNS mechanisms (28). Rapid withdrawal after chronic barbiturate treatment changes the EEG; seizures, irritability, and tremors occur with development of beta-spindling in the 18 to 26 Hz EEG frequency bands. Both alcohol and barbiturates depress glucose utilization in brain and they may thereby decrease the synthesis rate or pool size of modulatory neurohormones such as GABA, which control and inhibit neuronal excitability. These speculations are currently under investigation in the authors' laboratories. Additional theories relating to this subject have been reviewed by Essig (20, 21). Cortical activity is involved with the convulsive withdrawal state, but ablation of the cortical and cerebellar mantles does not prevent seizures, thus suggesting that brainstem and spinal cord be examined for changes in neurotransmitters after barbiturates, alcohol, or anxiolytics have been withdrawn. Attempts to modify GABA metabolism, to increase GABA levels, etc., in the CNS have been successful in ameliorating the withdrawal syndrome (20, 21).

XI. CHARACTERISTICS OF ANXIOLYTIC TOLERANCE AND DEPENDENCE

A. Tolerance to Anxiolytics

Meprobamate (Fig. 6): tolerance develops to effects on EEG and behavior in rats and cats; meprobamate increases microsomal enzyme activity.

Benzodiazepine (Fig. 6): tolerance develops to the depression of righting reflex in mice and rats, to changed performance on inclined plane and rotating rod and reduction in motor activity, to increase in seizure threshold, and to depression of avoidance-escape in mice.

Development of tolerance appears to be accompanied by enhanced activity of microsomal enzymes of CNS depressants. It is widely held that cross-tolerance exists between such agents as alcohol, barbiturates, and anxiolytics. Actions of these drugs on metabolizing enzymes and microsomes appear to be the most widely accepted mechanism for such cross-tolerance. Hug (28) is of the opinion that cross-tolerance "is an alteration in the sensitivity of the nervous system, while drug-metabolizing systems are probably involved minimally, if at all." At the present time, there are few hard data to support Hug's hypothesis. This hypothesis would probably require that the sites of action of these various drugs are quite similar, i.e., perhaps they share a common receptor. This now seems unlikely, particularly in the case of ethanol, for which the existence of a receptor is still highly questionable.

B. Dependence and Anxiolytic Agents

There have been a number of reviews on the quality of dependence to these agents (2, 20, 48). The reader is referred to these for details. (See the previous section on barbiturates.) All of these drugs resemble barbiturates in several respects: Pharmacologically they are CNS depressants, although it is well recognized that the anxiolytics act in more discrete regions of the CNS than do the barbiturates. All of the drugs produce toxic symptoms that resemble those of barbiturates, e.g., drowsiness, ataxia, confusion, impaired memory, double vision, rage reactions, and coma after very high dosage. The signs of withdrawal from this group of compounds resemble those due to barbiturates. These include nausea and vomiting, increased sympathetic nervous system activity, convulsions, and delirium when withdrawal follows

TABLE 8. *Characteristics of withdrawal syndrome from anxiolytics*

Propanediol (Meprobamate)[a]	Piperidinedione (Glutethimide)	Benzodiazepine (Chlordiazepoxide, Diazepam)
Grand mal seizures	Abdominal cramps	Nausea
Nervousness	Vomiting	Vomiting
Paranoia and hallucination	Tremor	Anorexia
Tremor	Hyperpyrexia	Insomnia
High fever	Tachycardia	Depression
Psychotic behavior	Delirium (confusion, hallucination, etc.)	Grand mal seizure and delirium
		Tachycardia

[a] Chlordiazepoxide withdrawal symptoms appear to be milder than those from drugs of the meprobamate type.

prolonged heavy use of the drugs. Characteristic withdrawal symptoms caused by commonly used anxiolytics, including those of the propanediol, piperidinedione, and the benzodiazepine group, are listed in Table 8.

XII. CHARACTERISTICS OF TOLERANCE AND DEPENDENCE BY CNS STIMULANTS

The stimulants with the greatest potential for production of psychological dependency problems are cocaine and amphetamine. Although a variety of other stimulants produce some pharmacological effects that are similar to those produced by these two drugs, the others are not generally considered

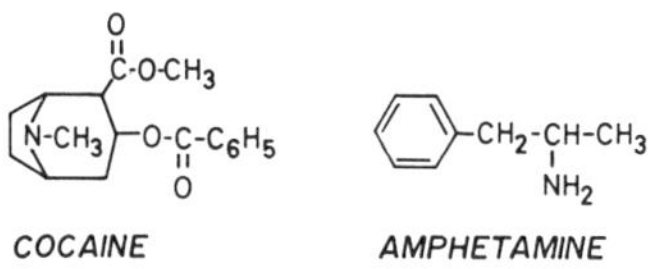

FIG. 7. Cocaine and amphetamine.

COCAINE   AMPHETAMINE

to be dependency forming ("hard") drugs. Among these are caffeine, theophylline, other xanthines, and nicotine. There is some question whether caffeine and nicotine are addictive drugs, and they are not discussed here. Those interested in these two common agents are referred to recent reviews (5, 7, 8). Moreover, as Snyder (47) has pointed out for both cocaine and amphetamines (Fig. 7), there are no prominent physiological withdrawal symptoms, except for depression.

A. Cocaine

Cocaine has the following characteristic pharmacological CNS actions:

1. reversal of fatigue and abolition of hunger, particularly in depressed states;
2. state of excited euphoria that may differ from that caused by alcohol;
3. a heightened degree of alertness and lack of appreciation of fatigue, both of which can last for many hours;
4. insomnia;
5. greater muscular power;
6. enhanced sexual activity, particularly in women;
7. chronic stereotyped behavior, which can be compulsive;
8. possibility of paranoid psychosis, particularly after long-term use;
9. possibility of auditory and visual hallucinations;
10. psychological dependence is accompanied by tolerance; as much as 50 times the amount of drug is required by the chronic user to achieve the same effect as the novice.

B. Amphetamines

Amphetamines have the following characteristics of CNS effects:

1. paradoxical calming of hyperactive children;
2. euphoria;
3. psychotic episodes (tolerance seems to develop to 2 and 3);
4. anorexia (loss of appetite);
5. rebound depression following euphoria (mainly among addicts);
6. psychosis develops that resembles that of paranoid schizophrenia;
7. compulsive stereotypic behavior.

It has been suggested that the central stimulant effects of amphetamine are due to direct effects on dopaminergic neurons. The mechanisms of amphetamine's action in the CNS have been described as follows:

1. it releases dopamine and blocks the reuptake of dopamine;
2. this leads to stimulation of dopamine receptors by increasing the availability of dopamine at postsynaptic receptor sites;
3. the increased receptor stimulation then initiates a neuronal feedback inhibition of other dopaminergic neurons.

Recently Bunney, Aghajanian, and Roth (6) have obtained evidence that extremely small systemic doses of *d*-amphetamine (0.25 to 1.6 mg/kg) *decrease* the firing rate of cells in the substantia nigra, zona compacta, and ventral tegmental areas; such blockade was reversed by systemically administered chlorpromazine and haloperidol. Thus *d*-amphetamine, loosely referred to as a central stimulant, is in fact, a depressant of certain CNS neurons.

It should be noted that both cocaine and amphetamines show two similar, but separate, behavioral effects that are distinguishable by the dosage or frequency of administration required to elicit (I) mild euphoria or (II) stereotyped, compulsive, and psychotic behavior. (It is possible that other CNS stimulants, i.e., caffeine, nicotine, also may have two dose or usage ranges, with quite different symptoms in each range.) However, the attempts to interpret amphetamine or cocaine actions for all dose levels and frequency of usage through a single mechanism is misleading and is no more appropriate for understanding the pharmacology of stimulants than it is for the depressants (e.g., alcohol and barbiturates).

Cocaine, a peripheral nerve anesthetic with effects similar to procaine, probably affects CNS function by a different mechanism. It has been shown to block the uptake of catecholamines into the presynaptic nerve ending. Whether this occurs by blockade of the Na^+ flux into electrically stimulated tissue (the activity of such ion flux determines the high affinity uptake of certain neurotransmitters) as reported by Quastel (39) or if a stabilization by cocaine of the (exocytic) membranes forming the neurotransmitter storage vesicles noted by Dewhurst (15) is responsible for the direct action of cocaine on the CNS, is still an unsolved problem. This question is particularly intriguing because, in addition to amphetamine and cocaine, ethanol has also been shown to block Na^+ flux (Israel, Carmichael, and MacDonald, 29) and norepinephrine uptake. All three of these addictive compounds have one common dependency-producing effect, a transient production of euphoria. Each of the three drugs is pharmacologically distinctive (particularly in the peripheral, autonomic, and sympathetic nervous systems) and to attempt such a relation now appears hazardous. However, similarity of the inhibitory effect on Na^+ flux in the CNS catecholamine uptake mechanism in different brain regions might be experimentally tested as the origin of the euphoria component common to these three drugs. Of course such a test would recognize the boundaries of the proposal, i.e., restriction of observations and dosage to the initial low-dosage "rush" or "lift" period, because with chronic or intensive dosage other mechanisms, including the development of tolerance, might obscure any similarities among these compounds.

Tolerance develops rapidly to all stimulant actions of cocaine (47).[1] Tolerance develops to the following effects of amphetamines: euphoria, acute lethal effects, pupillary dilation, suppression of REM sleep, increased activity in animals, some aspects of behavior, hyperthermia, cardiovascular stimulation, and sympathomimetic effects on smooth muscle, and perhaps to the anorexigenic action. Amphetamines are *not* cross-tolerant with cocaine (28).

XIII. MECHANISMS OF TOLERANCE

The amphetamines are known to release catecholamines, and depletion of catecholamine stores has been attributed at least to the tolerance observed to amphetamine's cardiovascular effects. Another alternative is the possible conversion of amphetamine to a metabolite that acts as a false transmitter. The evidence that this mechanism applies in the CNS is very limited, i.e., in this region amphetamines appear not to act by releasing catecholamines but by direct effects upon receptors (4).

Tolerance to many of amphetamine's effects can be shown to be functional, i.e., due to changes in the physiological activity of affected tissue, rather than dispositional, i.e., due to the sequestration or accumulation of the drug or its metabolites, for the following reasons:

1. depletion of norepinephrine and accumulation of p-hydroxynorephedrine as a false transmitter accompanies development of behavior tolerance;

2. subsequent withdrawal of amphetamine produces an unexpected stimulation of additional stereotyped behavior ("hoarding" of food by rats), which has a characteristic lag phase and persistence for up to 2 weeks.

---

[1] However, Hug (28) cites some compelling arguments against the concept of tolerance to cocaine's effects, particularly to its excitatory activities, and mentions that *increased sensitivity* to stimulant effects of cocaine have been observed in four species.

This is perhaps one of the first experimental demonstrations of a functional dependency upon amphetamine. Prior to this only a slight increase in sleeping time and food intake was shown in amphetamine-withdrawn rats and a small increase in REM-sleep in humans (32,*a*).

In contrast withdrawal of cocaine has not been reported to produce any physiologic abstinence syndrome. Simon (46,*a*) has compared cocaine, amphetamine, and imipramine and summarized cocaine's activity as follows:

1. Cocaine is weaker than amphetamine except for reversal of neuroleptic-induced catalepsy and antagonism of reserpine effects.

2. These strong effects are also seen after imipramine-like drugs. However, cocaine can be differentiated from amphetamine by dissimilar behavioral effects after inhibition of catecholamine synthesis by such agents as *p*-chlorophenylalanine and α-methyltyrosine.

REFERENCES

1. Ariens, E. J., van Rossum, J. M., and Simonis, A. M. (1957): Affinity, intrinsic activity, and drug interactions. *Pharmacol. Rev.,* 9:225–228.
2. Aston, K. (1972): Barbiturates, alcohol, and tranquilizers. In: *Chemical and Biological Aspects of Drug Dependence,* edited by S. J. Mule and H. Brill, pp. 37–63. CRC Press, Cleveland.
3. Axelrod, J. (1956): Possible mechanism of tolerance to narcotic drugs. *Science,* 124:263.
4. Banerjee, U., and Lin, G. S. (1973): On the mechanism of central action of amphetamine: The role of catecholamines. *Neuropharmacology,* 12:917–931.
5. Bradshaw, P. W. (1973): The problem of cigarette smoking and its control. *Int. J. Addict.,* 8:353–371.
6. Bunney, B. S., Aghajanian, G. K., and Roth, R. H. (1973): Comparison of effects of L-DOPA, amphetamine and apomorphine on the firing rate of rat dopaminergic neurones, *Nature [New Biol.],* 245:123–125.
7. Burg, A. W., and Stein, M. E. (1972): Urinary excretion of caffeine and its metabolites in the mouse. *Biochem. Pharmacol.,* 21:909–922.
8. Burg, A. W., and Stein, M. E. (1972): Tissue distribution of caffeine and its metabolites in the mouse. *Biochem. Pharmacol.,* 21:923–936.
9. Casy, A. F. (1970): Analgesics and their antagonists: Recent developments. In: *Progress in Medicinal Chemistry, Vol. 7,* edited by G. P. Ellis and G. B. West, pp. 229–284. Butterworths, London.
10. Casy, A. F. (1971): The structure of narcotic analgesic drugs. In: *Narcotic Drugs: Biochemical Pharmacology,* edited by D. Clouet, pp. 1–16. Plenum Press, New York.
11. Clouet, D. H., and Ratner, M. (1970): Catecholamine biosynthesis in brains of rats treated with morphine. *Science,* 168:854–856.
12. Cochin, J. (1972): Some aspects of tolerance to the narcotic analgesics. In: *Drug Addiction, Vol. 1, Experimental Pharmacology,* edited by J. M. Singh, L. H. Miller, H. Lal, pp. 365–375. Futura Publishing Co., Mt. Kisco, New York.
13. Collier, H. O. J. (1968): Supersensitivity and dependence. *Nature,* 220:228–231.
14. Deneau, G. A., and Seevers, M. H. (1964): Pharmacological aspects of drug dependence. *Adv. Pharmacol.* 3:267–283.
15. Dewhurst, W. G. (1970): The blood-brain barrier and other membrane phenomena in psychopharmacology. In *Principles of Psychopharmacology,* edited by W. G. Clark and J. del Giudice, pp. 105–112. Academic Press, New York.
16. Dole, V. P. (1971): Blockade with methadone. In: *Narcotic Drugs: Biochemical Pharmacology,* edited by D. Clouet, pp. 478–483. Plenum Press, New York.
17. Dole, V. P., Nyswander, M. E., and Warmu, A. (1968): *JAMA,* 2703.

18. Ehrenpreis, S., Light, I., and Schonbuch, G. H. (1972): Use of electrically stimulated guinea pig ileum to study potent analgesics. In: *Drug Addiction, Vol. 1, Experimental Pharmacology,* edited by J. M. Singh, L. H. Miller, H. Lal, pp. 319–342. Futura Publishing Co., Mt. Kisco, New York.

19. Ehrenpreis, S., and Teller, D. N. (1972): Interaction of drugs of dependence with receptors. In: *Chemical and Biological Aspects of Drug Dependence,* edited by S. J. Mule and H. Brill, pp. 178–217. CRC Press, Cleveland.

20. Essig, C. F. (1968): Addiction to barbiturate and non-barbiturate sedative drugs. *Res. Publ. Assoc. Res. Nerv. Ment. Dis.,* 68:188.

21. Essig, C. (1970): Barbiturate dependence. In: *Drug Dependence, Advances in Mental Science, Vol. 3,* edited by R. T. Harris, W. M. McIsaac, and C. R. Schuster, Jr., pp. 129–140. University of Texas Press, Austin.

22. Fraser, H. F. (1974): Certain theoretical and practical considerations involved in evaluating the overall abuse potential of opiate agonists and antagonists. In: *Narcotic Antagonists,* edited by M. C. Braude, L. S. Harris, E. L. May, J. P. Smith, and J. E. Villareal, pp. 439–453. Raven Press, New York.

22a. Gessa, G. L., Vargiu, L., Biggio, G., and Tagliamonte, A. (1974): Effect of methadone on brain dopamine metabolism, *Biochemical Pharmacology,* Supplement Part 2, IIIrd International Catecholamine Symposium, Strasbourg, pp. 841–844.

23. Goldstein, A. (1974): Opiate receptors: Minireview. *Life Sci.,* 14:615–623.

24. Goldstein, D. B. (1973): Alcohol withdrawal reactions in mice: Effects of drugs that modify neurotransmission. *J. Pharmacol. Exp. Ther.,* 186:1–9.

25. Goldstein, D. B. (1973): Inherited differences in intensity of alcohol withdrawal reactions in mice. *Nature [New Biol.],* 245:154–156.

26. Goodman, L. S., and Gilman, A. (1970): *The Pharmacological Basis of Therapeutics,* pp. 237–272. Macmillan, New York.

27. Harris, L. S. (1974): Narcotic antagonists—Structure-activity relationships. In: *Narcotic Antagonists,* edited by M. C. Braude, L. S. Harris, E. L. May, J. P. Smith, and J. E. Villareal, pp. 13–20. Raven Press, New York.

28. Hug, C. L. (1972): Characteristics and theories related to acute and chronic tolerance development. In: *Chemical and Biological Aspects of Drug Dependence,* edited by S. J. Mulé and H. Brill, pp. 307–398. CRC Press, Cleveland.

29. Israel, Y., Carmichael, J. F., and Macdonald, J. A. (1973): Effect of ethanol on norephinephrine uptake and electrically stimulated release in brain tissue. *Ann. N.Y. Acad. Sci.,* 215:38–48.

30. Jacobson, A. E. (1972): Narcotic analgesics and antagonists. In: *Chemical and Biological Aspects of Drug Dependence,* edited by S. J. Mule and H. Brill, pp. 101–118. CRC Press, Cleveland.

31. Kalant, H., Le Blanc, A. E., and Gibbins, R. J. (1971): Tolerance to, and dependence on, some non-opiate psychotropic drugs. *Pharmacol. Rev.,* 23:135.

32. Kosterlitz, H. W., Waterfield, A. A., and Berthoud, V. (1974): Assessment of the agonist and antagonist properties of narcotic analgesic drugs by their actions on the morphine receptor in the guinea pig ileum. In: *Narcotic Antagonists,* edited by M. C. Braude, L. S. Harris, E. L. May, J. P. Smith, and J. E. Villareal, pp. 319–334. Raven Press, New York.

32a. Lewander, T., Moliis, G., and Brus, I. (1974): On amphetamine tolerance and abstinence in rats. *Biochemical Pharmacology,* Supplement Part 2, IIIrd International Catecholamine Symposium, Strasbourg, pp. 819–821.

33. Lieber, C. S. (1972): Alcohol. In: *Chemical and Biological Aspects of Drug Dependence,* S. J. Mule and H. Brill, pp. 135–161. CRC Press, Cleveland.

34. Martin, W. R. (1970): Pharmacological redundancy as an adaptive mechanism in the central nervous system: *Fed. Proc.,* 29:13–18.

35. May, E. L. (1973): Agonist and antagonistic actions of narcotic analgesic drugs. Chemistry. Synthetic compounds. In: *Agonist and Antagonist Actions of Narcotic Analgesic Drugs,* edited by H. W. Kosterlitz, H. O. J. Collier, and J. E. Villareal, pp. 17–22. University Park Press, London.

35a. Misra, A. L. (1972): Disposition and metabolism of drugs of dependence. In:

   Chemical and Biological Aspects of Drug Dependence, edited by S. J. Mulé and
   H. Brill, pp. 220–276. CRC Press, Cleveland.
36. Mulé, S. J. (1969): The relationship of the disposition and metabolism of morphine
   in the CNS to tolerance. In: *The Scientific Basis of Drug Dependence,* edited by
   M. Steinberg, pp. 97–109. Underhill, London.
37. Oritz, A., Griffiths, P. J., and Littleton, J. M. (1974): A comparison of the effects
   of chronic administration of ethanol and acetaldehyde to mice: evidence for a
   role of acetaldehyde in ethanol dependence. *J. Pharm. Pharmacol.,* 26:249–260.
38. Post, M. E., and Syn, A. Y. (1973): The effect of chronic ethanol administration on
   the levels of catecholamines in different regions of the rat brain. *Res. Comm. Chem.
   Pathol. Pharmacol.,* 6:887–894.
39. Quastel, J. H. (1970): Metabolic effects of some psychopharmacological agents in
   brain *in vitro.* In: *Principles of Psychopharmacology,* edited by W. C. Clark and
   J. del Giudice, pp. 141–155. Academic Press, New York.
40. Raskin, N. H., and Sokoloff, L. (1974): Changes in brain alcohol dehydrogenase
   activity during chronic ethanol ingestion and withdrawal. *J. Neurochem.,* 22:427–
   434.
41. Roseman, S. J., and Smith, C. B. (1972): ^{14}C-catecholamine synthesis in mouse
   brain during morphine withdrawal. *Nature,* 240:153–155.
42. Seevers, M. H. (1958): Termination of drug action by tolerance development.
   Fed. Proc., 17:1175–1181.
43. Seixas, F. A., and Aggleston, S., editors (1973): Alcoholism and the central
   nervous system. *Ann. N.Y. Acad. Sci.,* 215.
44. Sharpless, S., and Jaffe, J. (1969): Withdrawal phenomena as manifestations of
   disuse supersensitivity. In: *Scientific Basis of Drug Dependence,* edited by H. Steinberg, pp. 67–76. Grune and Stratton, New York.
45. Sherman, A. D., and Mitchell, C. L. (1972): Effects of morphine and pain on brain
   intermediary metabolism. *Neuropharmacology,* 11:871–877.
46. Shuster, L. (1971): Tolerance and physical dependence. In: *Narcotic Drugs:
   Biochemical Pharmacology,* edited by D. Clouet, pp. 408–423. Plenum Press, New
   York.
46a. Simon, P. (1974): Psychopharmacological profile of cocaine. *Biochemical Pharmacology* Supplement Part 2, IIIrd International Catecholamine Symposium,
   Strasbourg, pp. 871–872.
47. Snyder, S. H. (1972): CNS stimulants and hallucinogens. In: *Chemical and Biological Aspects of Drug Dependence,* edited by S. J. Mulé and H. Brill, pp. 55–63.
   CRC Press, Cleveland.
48. Stolman, S. (1972): Barbiturates and minor tranquilizers. In: *Chemical and Biological Aspects of Drug Dependence,* edited by S. J. Mulé and H. Brill, pp. 119–
   134. CRC Press, Cleveland.
49. Wayner, M. J. (1973): Effects of ethyl alcohol on lateral hypothalamic neurons.
   Ann. N.Y. Acad. Sci., 215:13–37.
50. Wolff, P. H. (1972): Ethnic differences in alcohol sensitivity. *Science,* 175:449–450.

Biological Foundations of Psychiatry,
edited by R. G. Grenell and S. Galay.
Raven Press, New York © 1976.

Stress, Anxiety, and Endocrine Function

Arthur Yuwiler

Neurobiochemistry Laboratory, Brentwood Veterans Administration Hospital, Los Angeles, California 90023; and Department of Psychiatry, University of California at Los Angeles, Los Angeles, California 90024

I. INTRODUCTION

Concepts are no more free of their histories than are men, and the broad range of scientific activity subsumed under the name stress research reflects its diverse origins. Just as men were aware of gravity before Newton specifically formulated his universal Laws of Gravitation, so men were generally aware that life was beset with troubles, that troubles wreak a toll, that higher organisms learn from experience, and that early experience sometimes leaves enduring marks. Expressions akin to "life is one damn thing after another" or "as the twig is bent so grows the tree" permeate nearly all cultures in recorded history. The codification and introduction of these general views into science, however, was made somewhat independently by the behavioral sciences (especially psychiatry) on one hand and by physiology on the other, and contemporary research bears the marks of these two parental disciplines.

Psychiatric research centered around trauma. Clinical observations suggested that psychologic trauma, especially in childhood, could lead to overtly maladaptive physiologic and psychologic responses both in childhood and in later life. These maladaptive responses were laid to an inappropriate or arrested psychic development initiated by the traumatic event. Research was directed at exposing the critical internal and external conditions for such maladaptation, the mechanisms by which such maladaptive responses became manifest and the therapeutic procedures most efficacious in promoting more realistic restructuring of self and world. Thus, in this tradition, the stressor was invariably traumatic and was subjectively defined. The magnitude and form of the effects of the stressor were dependent on the internal strengths and resources of the individual. Therefore, they were both individualistic and age dependent. The consequences of the trauma were regarded as invariably maladaptive.

The second great tradition of stress research stems from the work and ideas of Claude Bernard, Walter Cannon, and especially Hans Selye. Bernard stressed the importance of maintaining a constant internal environment as a condition of life. Cannon introduced the term homeostasis for the coordinated physiologic processes maintaining the steady states of the organism and explicated the emergency role of epinephrine in immediate flight or fight responses. Selye discovered the ubiquitous adrenocortical activation in response to a wide array of stimuli. Together these provided the basic physiologic framework for stress research.

Briefly, it was postulated that survival required organisms to develop processes maintaining a constant internal environment in the face of changing external stimuli. One process of particular importance was the antagonistic interplay between the sympathetic and parasympathetic branches of the autonomic nervous system. Disturbances of physiologic equilibrium by external forces initiated a series of reactions designed, on the one hand, to meet the exigencies of the moment and, on the other hand, to restore or approximate the initial physiologic state. These processes were in continuous operation to meet the continual micro changes in the external environment. Superimposed on these ongoing responses were other processes designed to meet more serious challenges. Faced by an immediate threat, discharge of the sympathetic nervous system and release of epinephrine from the adrenal medulla, prepared the organism for flight or fight, by such physiologic alterations as increasing heart rate, heart stroke, arterial pressure, blood glucose, and blood flow through the musculature. Almost concomitantly, the adrenal cortex releases adrenal corticoids, which both facilitated some of the emergency processes and initiated a series of incompletely defined restorative processes.

Of the two emergency responses, the adrenocortical response is the more general and is elicited by an astonishing variety of both pleasant and unpleasant stimuli. Because of its generality, and in accordance with Selye's definition of the stress response as the nonspecific response common to all stressors, adrenocortical activation has become the operational definition of stress in physiologically oriented stress research.

In addition, Selye proposed that stressors (defined as stimuli of sufficient magnitude to disturb physiologic equilibrium) acting over time first elicit an alarm reaction, then a second stage of resistance characterized by apparent adaptation to the stressor, and finally, a stage of exhaustion culminating in death. This triad of responses constitutes Selye's General Adaptation Syndrome.

Thus, in contrast to the subjective definition of stress in the behavioral tradition, stress is operationally defined in the physiologic one. Whereas the behavioral tradition regards stress as necessarily traumatic, stress may either be appetitive or aversive in the physiologic tradition. Finally, although the consequences of stress are regarded as maladaptive in the one tradition, it is regarded at least as initially adaptive and restorative in the other.

In the early stages of stress research, these two approaches remained relatively distinct, like two separate branches of a river. The psychologic tradition naturally devoted itself to psychologic phenomena, e.g., fear, anxiety, rage, and despair. The physiologic tradition explored the physiologic changes accompanying hunger, cold adaptation, surgical shock, and so on. Slowly, however, as it became clear that some psychologic stressors elicited physiologic responses, such as ulcers, and some physiologic stressors were accompanied by such psychologic variables as fear and pain, these two traditions were forced to merge. Given their conceptual divergences, this fusion was not easy and it is still far from complete. It is still reflected in research orientation and in interpretation of data and is most marked in comparisons of human and animal investigation.

Indeed the fusion of these two traditions is further hampered by the deceptive familiarity of the terms used. The term stress itself is one of the more stressful aspects of stress research for everyone knows what it means and, therefore, it is used to mean many different things. Gradually, however, the term stressor for the stimulus and stress response for adrenocortical activation, have come into general usage and are employed here. It should be obvious, however, that such usage does not suggest that animals without functional adrenals, by reason of evolution or surgery, are therefore unaffected by stressors but rather that other indices of the stress response are required. Furthermore, adrenocortical activation is but a part of a chain between receipt of stimulus and adaptive response, being a result of complex neural and endocrine changes on the one hand and the activators of complex metabolic adjustments on the other.

Despite the limitations in using adrenocortical activation as the operational definition of stress, any understanding of the stress literature requires at least a general familiarity with adrenal physiology.

II. HYPOTHALAMIC-PITUITARY-ADRENAL INTERRELATIONSHIPS

Some basal secretion of adrenal corticoids occurs in the hypophysectomized rat. However, glucocorticoid secretion by the adrenal cortex is under the trophic control of the pituitary, and release of glucocorticoids from the adrenal by the stressor is secondary to release of adrenocorticotropic hormone (ACTH) from the pituitary. Indeed, it is likely that ACTH measurements will soon replace glucocorticoids as the referent in stress studies.

Although the broad outlines of ACTH action on the adrenal are clear, the details are still obscure. ACTH does not appear to enter the cell itself but rather binds to a specific binding site on the cell membrane. This binding site is likely an adenylcyclase site since cyclic adenosine monophosphate (cAMP) rises within 10 sec after exposure of the gland to ACTH. The adenylcyclase is fluoride stimulated, has a calcium requirement, and responds selectively to ACTH and not to other polypeptide hormones. Activity is inhibited by phenothiazines.

All of the major actions of ACTH can be simulated by cAMP but the precise sequence of events in cAMP regulation has yet to be defined. cAMP is reported to activate an adrenal protein kinase, which, by analogy with other systems, might phosphorylate and remove repressor nuclear histones or non-histone acidic proteins blocking nuclear DNA. Removal of the repressor would then lead to stimulation of specific DNA-directed messenger RNAs and then to specific protein synthesis. Phosphorylation and stimulation of ribosomal proteins by cAMP has also been suggested. Studies with inhibitors of protein synthesis suggest that enhanced specific protein synthesis may accompany ACTH stimulation of 20, 22-demolase and conversion of cholesterol to pregnenolone (see Fig. 1). However, no specific evidence has yet been obtained for ACTH or cAMP stimulation of general protein synthesis in the adrenal.

Prostaglandins also appear to be involved in ACTH activation of the adrenal, although their role is even more obscure than that of cAMP. ACTH stimulation of the adrenal leads to release of prostaglandins E and F and a decrease in adrenal content of prostaglandins E_2, F, F_2, whereas prostaglandin E_2 produces a brief transient stimulation of glucocorticoid synthesis by a mechanism inhibited by cycloheximide and, therefore, presumably involves protein synthesis.

Just as ACTH appears to control release and synthesis of corticoids by the adrenal, control of ACTH release appears to be mediated by the central nervous system. In particular, the median eminence region of the hypothalamus, a region rich in nerve terminals but essentially devoid of cell bodies,

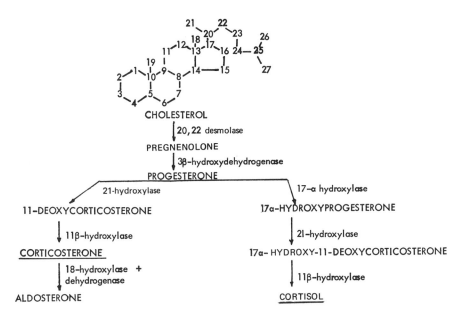

FIG. 1. Adrenal steroid biosynthesis.

is intimately involved in ACTH release. Stimulation of this region increases, whereas lesions decrease ACTH production. Median eminence control of ACTH formation appears to be humoral rather than neural, however, and exerted through the release of another trophic hormone, corticotropin-releasing factor (CRF), secreted by neurosecretory cells in the superoptic and periventricular nuclei of the hypothalamus and discharged at axonal terminals into the region of the median eminence. Synaptosomal and granular fractions from median eminence homogenates have been isolated and shown to possess CRF activity. Such discharged CRF is carried to the anterior pituitary by the rich venous network of the posterior portal system, where it stimulates ACTH production.

Although strong evidence exists to support this picture of neural regulation of CRF release, the chemical nature of CRF is undefined. At least three hypothalamic peptides with CRF properties have been obtained from the median eminence, but their certain identification as CRF has been hindered by the lack of adequate test systems.

CRF is not alone in stimulating ACTH release, however. Large doses of vasopressin, the antidiuretic hormone of the posterior pituitary, also stimulates ACTH release from the anterior pituitary both *in vitro* and *in vivo* but its contribution to the physiologic release of ACTH is a matter of some debate. Although vasopressin and ACTH release appear to be regulated by separate hypothalamic mechanisms and are under different peripheral controls, it has been suggested that, under certain conditions, vasopressin might act by releasing CRF from the hypothalamus, that it may act in concert with CRF to promote ACTH release, that it may function as a separate mechanism for ACTH release, or that the effect of vasopressin on ACTH release is only of pharmacologic rather than physiologic importance. The bulk of evidence suggests that vasopressin release of ACTH *in vivo* is not dependent on the hypothalamus or the forebrain and instead appears to act at the level of the pituitary itself.

Despite considerable effort, definition of the central neurophysiologic pathways regulating ACTH release is still sketchy. Existing methods have both technical and theoretical limitations and problems, and both electrical stimulation studies and lesion studies often suffer from parallel difficulties in interpretation. Thus, in studies using macroelectrode stimulation, it is often difficult to distinguish whether effects are due to stimulation of the nuclei of interest or to stimulation of adjacent passing axons. Destruction of nuclei by gross lesioning similarly may also destroy adjacent axons, again leaving interpretation ambiguous. Microelectrode and lesioning studies are complicated by both sampling problems and the differences in activity and functions of neurons within a small region. By dint of rather rigorous stimulation and response criteria, however, much progress has been made.

In addition to methodologic problems, definition of such pathways is further complicated by the intricately interwoven factors influencing ACTH release and by the possibility that different neuroanatomical pathways may be involved in regulating response to different stressors, in maintaining normal basal secretion, and in mediating circadian rhythmicity in this system. For example, the corticoid response to a leg break is blocked by contralateral deafferentation of the basal hypothalamus, but even complete deafferentation fails to block the response to a limb tourniquet, which, however, can be blocked by transection of the spinal cord. Similarly, constriction of the carotid arteries of the vagotomized dog leads to adrenocortical activation, whereas denervation of vascular receptors in the carotid sinuses and in the thyrocarotid junction blocks this activation and decreases adrenal sensitivity to ACTH. A mapping of the neural systems involved in one of these responses may not necessarily shed information on the others, except perhaps at final common pathways in the hypothalamus.

As mentioned above, limited response to stressors is retained by medial hypothalamic islands; after partial deafferentation of the hypothalamus, however, complete deafferentation of the basal medial hypothalamus leads to abolition of response to neurogrenic stressors (although not to stressors such as tissue injury) as well as to abolition of the circadian rhythm of adrenal corticoids and increases basal steroid levels. These data suggest two important points. First, the abolition of responses indicates that the hypothalamus receives both stress and circadian information from sites outside the hypothalamus itself. Second, the elevation in corticoid levels after deafferentation indicates that tonically active CRF-containing cells are under inhibitory control from nuerons outside the hypothalamic islands. The first point is further supported by data from both lesion and stimulation studies that uniformly indicate that control of ACTH release is not discretely localized in any hypothalamic site but rather that adrenocortical stimulation can be elicited from many sites over the ventral medial hypothalamus from the prepotic area to the posterior median eminence. Anatomical and physiologic studies have instead implicated a number of extrahypothalamic brain regions in ACTH control. Chief among these are the amygdala, septum, and hippocampus, although stimulation in the reticular formation, rhinencephalon, temporal cortex, and occipital cortex all modify the pituitary response to stress.

The pattern is both anatomically and functionally complex. Feedback control in regulating basal secretion appears to involve inhibitory influences from septum, nucleus accumbens, diagonal band of Broca, and the mesencephalic reticular formation. On the other hand, some stresses seem to involve stimulation of the amygdaloid-basal septum-cingulate gyrus complex, the rostral mesencephalic reticular formation, and the medial forebrain bundle. The corticoid diurnal rhythm appears to be mediated by a pathway projecting from the hippocampus to the septum through the anterior hypothalamus and the periventricular arcuate nucleus. Several nuclei within these broad circuits have complex effects on corticoids. Animal studies indicate that the basal and medial amygdala affect the ventromedial hypothalamus differently, although amygdala stimulation generally increases plasma adrenal steroid levels. Amygdala stimulation in man also elicits a rise in adrenal corticoids. On the other hand, hippocampal lesion studies implicate the hippocampus as a possible site for ACTH inhibitory control. Indeed, low-frequency hippocampal stimulation leads to a decrease in blood corticoids, but high-frequency stimulation leads to an increase in corticoids. Inhibition of plasma corticoids following hippocampal stimulation has been reported in man. Septum, like amygdala, appears to contain at least two electrophysiologically distinct systems, but stimulation in this region generally enhances plasma corticoid concentrations.

In addition to these suggested sites for inhibitory and stimulatory control of CRF and thereby ACTH release, an interaction between basal steroid levels and stimulation effects have been reported for some brain regions. Thus stimulation of the rostral pons or caudal midbrain regions of the reticular formation reportedly alters the secretion of corticoids in different directions depending on the basal corticoid level. Corticoid excretion is elevated when the basal level is low and decreased when the basal level is high. Similarly, hippocampal stimulation during stress inhibits ACTH secretion but, during rest, ACTH secretion is stimulated. Whether these reflect altered sensitivity of the target neurons or alterations in signal is unknown. In addition, temporal responses to stimulation are not uniform between sites. For example, stimulation of the amygdaloid septal complex and stimulation of the medullary reticular formation or medial midbrain all lead to increases in plasma ACTH, but amygdaloid-septal stimulation elicits a fast adrenocortical response and midbrain stimulation elicits a slow response.

These changes in response as a function of instantaneous blood steroid concentrations, if verified, may help define the mechanism and physiologic significance of the phenomena of feedback control of glucocorticoid secretion. That is, it is now well known that systemic administration of natural or synthetic corticoids, or direct implantation of corticoids into the hypothalamus or the reticular formation, decreases spontaneous ACTH secretion, decreases the response of the adrenal to exogenous ACTH, and decreases the adrenal response to some, but not all, stressors. This strongly suggests a feedback between central or circulating glucocorticoids and pituitary responsivity. Furthermore, because stressors do differ in their ability to override such feedback inhibition, it has been suggested that there may exist both a corticoid-sensitive and -insensitive neural pathway mediating ACTH release. Alternately, the ability to overcome feedback inhibition may indicate differences in stressor intensity. Thus, following pretreatment with the synthetic steroid dexamethasone, the steroid response to tourniquet injury is fully blocked, the response to urethane anesthesia, intestinal traction, hemorrhage, and 50 mU of vasopressin is partially blocked and the response to 5,000 mU of vasopressin is essentially unaffected. On the basis of this data, hemorrhage or intestinal traction could be regarded as more severe stressors than tourniquet injury, or as having greater ACTH-releasing capacity. Also to be considered in interpreting these observations, however, are studies that two types of feedback may occur: one sensitive to the absolute rate of increase in circulatory glucocorticoids, and the other a delayed feedback system, sensitive to the absolute level of corticoids. This latter system appears to affect ACTH release rather than synthesis but interestingly enough may also involve protein synthesis. Very severe stressors appear to override this type of inhibition.

The need to consider both the rate of corticoid increase and the absolute level of corticoids in feedback control complicates, but does not obviate, the possibility of qualitatively ranking stressors by their ability to overcome inhibition. It does, however, offer an alternate to the hypothesis of a dual system of both a steroid-sensitive and -insensitive neural pathway regulating ACTH production. Appropriate manipulations of time and steroid concentration may be sufficient to explain apparent stimulus strength, whereas corticoid rise time, together with basal steroid level, may account for the apparent differences between stressors in overriding steroid feedback blockade.

If both rate-sensitive and concentration-sensitive feedback mechanisms exist, then the search for the site of feedback inhibition is complicated at least twofold. Certainly numerous studies have confirmed that adrenocorticoid administration leads to adrenal atrophy unless ACTH is administered simultaneously; this constitutes strong evidence that corticosteroids can directly inhibit the ACTH-releasing processes of the pituitary. In addition, however, implants of dexamethasone into the pituitary decreases pituitary ACTH and adrenal weight but increases median eminence CRF. Implantation of dexamethasone into the median eminence decreases median eminence CRF, pituitary ACTH, and adrenal weight. This suggests that corticoids may exert negative feedback effects on brain structures preceding the hypothalamus at the hypothalamic level and at the pituitary level. The hypothalamus does contain corticoid-sensitive cells that respond to administered steroids with altered firing rates and selective, saturable, nuclear binding of corticosterone by cells in the hippocampus has been demonstrated. Such binding appears to involve a macromolecular nucleic acid protein complex suggesting that corticoid-directed protein synthesis may occur in this region. A high molecular weight, saturable, corticosterone-binding protein has also been demonstrated in the cytosol of hippocampal neurons, which may function to carry corticosteroids from the cell membrane to the nucleus. As previously indicated, the hippocampus has been implicated as a possible site involved in concentration-sensitive feedback inhibition.

If glucocorticoids have a negative feedback effect on ACTH formation and release, it seems conceivable that ACTH might exert a negative feedback on CRF formation and release. Evidence to support this possibility is minimal but it has been demonstrated that administered ACTH increases pituitary levels of ACTH and inhibits the fall in ACTH following stress. This is consistent with the possibility that ACTH levels may have a feedback effect on CRF release.

Although feedback inhibition has been rather conclusively demonstrated at several levels, the extent to which each, or any, of these levels are operative during normal physiologic function is unclear. However, it is certainly conceivable that changes in feedback sensitivity may underlie some of the changes in stress responsivity that accompany stress experience specifically and aging more generally.

An additional complicating phenomena in stress studies is the normal circadian rhythmicity in corticoid secretion. It is now well recognized that blood and adrenal corticoid levels vary systematically over the day. In the rat, this rhythmic pattern appears at 21 to 25 days of age and, depending on the lighting cycle, normally peaks in the late afternoon at about 6 P.M. and has its nadir in the early morning. This circadian change in plasma and adrenal corticoids appears paralleled by a circadian change in steroid-binding proteins in brain and especially in hippocampus. This establishes a connection between brain and plasma levels. The rat of course is a nocturnal animal and, in diurnal animals, such as man, the pattern is inverted with peak values in the early morning. This diurnal rhythm appears as a smooth cyclic phenomenon. However, in man at least, measurements over short time periods indicate that rather than a smooth continuous release of adrenal steroids, steroids are released in short bursts beginning at about 4 A.M. and usually coincident with rapid eye movement (REM) sleep. The apparently smooth cycle is thus the integrated form of these bursts of activity.

The diurnal rhythm in corticoid secretion, as might be expected, is accompanied by a corresponding rhythmic change in plasma ACTH, and it seems reasonable to assume that the corticoid rhythm is under ACTH control. Adrenalectomy does not abolish this ACTH rhythm but does appear to shift the time of the peak apparently because of abolition of adrenocorticoid feedback inhibition. Since ACTH release is presumably controlled by CRF, a rhythm in hypothalamic CRF might also be expected. Results to date are somewhat ambiguous. On the one hand, it has been reported that hypothalamic CRF levels are relatively constant over the 24-hr period but precipitously drop at about the time of the peak in ACTH and corticoids. On the other hand, a circadian rhythm in hypothalamic CRF has been reported with a peak 1 to 2 hr before the corticoid peak and a drop thereafter. This discrepancy may be due to difficulties in CRF determinations and in distinguishing between CRF and vasopressin but also may be due to more subtle differences in the state of experimental animals since tissue concentrations of CRF, or ACTH for that matter, are the result of both the rate of formation and rate of removal, and both are sensitive to environmental factors. Despite disagreement on the form of the CRF rhythm, there is general agreement that adrenalectomy slightly enhances the level of hypothalamic CRF, whereas hypophysectomy markedly elevates it. This is taken as evidence for a short feedback loop, whereby ACTH inhibits CRF release.

The rhythmic activity and stress response activities of the hypothalamic-pituitary-adrenal axis appear to be under different central controls and can be dissociated in a number of ways. Specific lesions can be made that abolish the rhythm without abolishing stress responsivity. During development adrenocorticoid rhythms appear at 21 to 25 days of age, the circadian rhythm in CRF activity appears at 14 to 21 days of age, and stress responsivity appears at 9 days. Finally, the adrenocortical rhythm is susceptible to disruption by environmental changes in lighting. Thus the rhythm is abolished in rats under conditions of constant light or darkness or after blinding. In the human the rhythmic pattern is altered by modifying light-dark cycles and the rhythm is shifted or attenuated in the blind. Indeed, in the absence of light as the zeitgiber, sleeping and eating patterns appear to determine circadian phasing. Stress responsivity is not abolished by these procedures, although some data suggests that the magnitude of the stress response may be altered.

Although clearly dissociable from stress responsivity, awareness of rhythmicity is of some importance to stress research both to avoid confusing normal circadian changes with stress responsivity and to minimize experimental variables. In addition, the magnitude and duration of stress-induced changes may be altered by the temporal relationship between stress exposure and circadian phasing.

The general picture to this point is that stressors initiate a series of neural events leading to discharge of CRF from neural endings in the median eminence. The released CRF enters the pituitary through the pituitary portal system and stimulates the synthesis and release of ACTH. Blood-borne ACTH then activates the adrenal cortex to synthesize and release adrenal corticoids. Although CRF is the usual mediator of these events, vasopressin may also stimulate ACTH production in some instances. At each step in this sequence, feedback inhibition may occur such that CRF production and/or release may be altered by circulating corticoids (long-loop feedback) or by ACTH (short-loop feedback), and ACTH release also may be directly modified by circulating corticoids. The neural sequence of events appears somewhat different for different stressors with the hippocampus perhaps playing an inhibitory role in modulating CRF release. Superimposed upon these various changes in an ongoing circadian rhythm in the activity and/or synthesis and release of various components. Thus, although neural control of ACTH has been amply demonstrated, the exact pathways involved in regulating the basal secretion, circadian rhythmicity, and stress responsivity of the hypothalamic-CRF-releasing neurons are still only vaguely defined. The neurotransmitters involved in these processes are also unclear. Considerable pharamacologic evidence has implicated the ventral ascending pathway of the noradrenergic system in inhibition of CRF release by stressors and, thereby, ACTH release. This pathway arises in the medulla and pons and projects to the ventral diencephalon. Elevations in norepinephrine following administration of DOPA, the precursor of dopamine and norepinephrine, or dihydroxyphenyl-serine, which is directly converted to norepinephrine, or inhibition of mono-amine degradation with monoamine oxidase inhibitors, generally inhibit 17-hydroxycorticoid production in response to stressors. Direct intraventricular infusion of large amounts of norepinephrine or dopamine have a similar effect, although the concentrations employed are more pharmacologic than physiologic. Conversely inhibition of tyrosine hydroxylase, the rate-limiting enzyme in catecholamine biosynthesis, leads to an increase in plasma corticoids as does intraventricular, but not systemic, administration of the catecholamine depletor guanethadine, which does not cross the blood-brain barrier. Although the bulk of the literature appears to implicate norepinephrine in inhibition of ACTH release, there is by no means universal agreement that this is so or that the action of norepinephrine is through its role as a putative transmitter directly acting on hypothalamic CRF neurons rather than by its action on other systems such as the hypothalamic-hypophyseal vasculature.

In a similar vein, serotonin has been implicated in modulating the circadian rhythmicity of the ACTH system. Serotonin content of the hippocampus and amygdala exhibit circadian rhythmicity, which parallels that of plasma corticosterone, whereas disruption of this system with p-chlorophenylalanine, a blocker of tryptophan hydroxyase activity (and, perhaps, destroyer of serotoninergic terminals), lead to a marked decrease in serotonin and a disruption of corticoid rhythmicity. Similarly, lesions of the midbrain raphe system, the site of serotoninergic cell bodies, also disrupts the corticoid rhythm. However, since corticoid rhythmicity is dependent upon light as zeitgeber, it is difficult to know whether these serotonin effects are directly on the neural systems affecting corticoid rhythmicity or those involved in processing environmental information.

As described above, ACTH initiates steriodogenesis in the adrenal cortex and this may be mediated by adenylcyclase. The general metabolic steps in synthesis of adrenal steroids are shown in Fig. 1. Although these steps will not be discussed in detail here, some special features need be mentioned.

The adrenal is rich in cholesterol esters, and adrenal steroids are synthesized either *de novo* from acetate or from these cholesterol esters. Stimulation of corticoid biosynthesis after ACTH is accompanied by a fall in adrenal cholesterol content, and this has been employed as an indirect marker for stress.

The conversion of cholesterol to pregnenolone involves oxidative cleavage of the cholesterol side chain between carbons 20 and 22. This is a NADPH-requiring process, as are the hydroxylations at carbons 11 (e.g., formation of corticosterone), 17, and 21 (formation of 17 hydroxyprogesterone). Each of these require specific hydroxylase and molecular oxygen. The NADPH for these reactions comes from the breakdown of glycogen to glucose-1-phosphate by phosphorylase a, conversion to glucose-6-phosphate, and subsequent metabolism of the glucose-6-phosphate through the hexose monophosphate shunt. Because one of the actions of cAMP in muscle is to initiate a series of reactions culminating in conversion of inactive phosphorylase b to active phosphorylase a, it seemed reasonable to assume that cAMP indirectly stimulates steriodogenesis in the adrenal cortex by increasing the availability of NADPH by enhanced glycogenolysis. However, this does not appear to be the case. Rather cAMP appears to stimulate steriodogenesis more directly. Thus cAMP facilitates cleavage of cholesterol esters and stimulates the conversion of cholesterol to pregnenolone. This latter action appears to involve protein synthesis since it is blocked by protein synthesis inhibitors such as puromycin or cycloheximide. Considering the rapidity of the rise in corticoids after ACTH, this involvement of protein synthesis is rather surprising. cAMP also appears to stimulate hydroxylation at the 11 position and inhibit the conversion of pregnenolone to progesterone. Two enzymes are required for this conversion and cAMP is competitive with NAD, the cofactor required for the oxidation.

As seen in Fig. 1, adrenocortical steroids can be divided into those with oxygen on position 11 (e.g., corticosterone and cortisone), which affect carbohydrate and protein metabolism but have little effect on salt and water regulation, and those without oxygen at position 11, which affect electrolyte and water metabolism but have little influence on protein or carbohydrate metabolism (e.g., 11-deoxycosticosterone) and aldosterone, which has a hydroxyl group at position 11 but is the most potent of the electrolyte regulating hormones. The 11 hydroxyl group in aldosterone is probably normally in hemiacetal linkage with the aldehyde group at position 18 thereby partly explaining this anomalous structure-activity relationship. A hydroxyl group on position 21 seems required for an effect on carbohydrate metabolism and generally enhances sodium retention and a hydroxyl group at position 17 enhances actions on carbohydrate metabolism.

Although there is considerable species difference in the ratio of steroids secreted by the adrenal gland, it is nonetheless remarkable that of the 30 or more steroids isolated from adrenal tissue, cortisol, corticosterone, and possibly 18-hydroxycorticosterone are the major glucocorticoid components in the blood of all vertebrates. This consistency is all the more marked considering the enormous differences in anatomic localization and gross appearance of corticoid tissue between various species. Indeed the very preservation of this system throughout evolution would seem to attest to its biologic importance. Furthermore, aldosterone is the major mineralocorticoid across phyla, although its presence has not been detected in some species, especially those salt-water forms in which the ionic composition in plasma appears at equilibrium with the surrounding sea water. In others, such as the toad, aldosterone concentration is an order of magnitude greater than in mammals indicating the importance of external ionic milieu to this species.

The lability of the adrenocortical system is both the *raison de etre* and the despair of workers in stress research. The simple recaging of an unhandled animal for 30 sec can lead to a fourfold rise in ACTH, which peaks in 3 min and returns to near baseline within 6 min, whereas adrenal corticoids double their value within 5 min and return to baseline within 15 min. Stronger stressors increase both the amplitude and duration of these elevations. The magnitude of these changes is dependent upon stressor, sex, prior experience, caging conditions, and time of day. Thus female rats generally have higher basal corticoid levels than males and are more responsive to stressors. Rats less than 8 days of age fail to respond to most stressors, whereas postweaning young rats generally are more responsive than older ones. Prior handling attenuates both the peak and duration of responses and singly housed animals are generally more responsive than group-housed animals. Finally it has been reported that animals subjected to mild stressors have a greater change in the amplitude of response if stressed during the nadir of the circadian period but that stress-induced elevations persist longer, if animals are stressed at the peak of the circadian cycle.

Human peripheral blood (see Table 1) contains approximately 10 to 40 μg of adrenal glucocorticoids per 100 ml. Approximately 80% of this is cortisol, and the remainder is largely corticosterone. Steroid ratios have been shown to shift in some animals in response to different stressors so that these percentages cannot be taken as invariant. Approximately 30% of secreted adrenocortical hormones circulates as free steroid, 50% is bound to a low-affinity high-capacity carrier associated with albumin and 20% is bound to a

TABLE 1. *Steroids in adrenal venous blood*

Steroid	Dog	Human	Cat	Rat	Guinea pig
Cortisol	+	+			+
Cortisone			+		+
Corticosterone	+	+	+	+	+
11-Deoxycortisol	+	+			
11-dehydrocorticosterone			+		+
Δ^4-Androstenedione	+	+			
Dehydroepiandrosterone		+			
17-Hydroxyprogesterone	+	+			
17-Hydroxypregnenolone	+	+			
11-β-OH-Δ^4-Androstenedione	+	+			
18-Hydroxy-11-deoxycorticosterone				+	
11-Ketoprogesterone	+				
11-β-Hydroxyprogesterone	+				
Progesterone	+				
Aldosterone	+				
Pregnenolone			+		

high-affinity low-capacity 52,000 molecular weight globulin named transcortin or corticoid-binding globulin (CBG). It is generally believed that the biologically active steroid component is the freely circulating steroid and that bound steroid is a reserve buffer in equilibrium with free steroid. Various factors alter the steroid-protein binding and these factors may be of some physiologic importance. For example, binding affinity is decreased by small increases in temperature so that circulating free corticoid is increased in systemic hyperthermia such as fever, or in local hyperthermia related to tissue damage. Furthermore, changes in steroid blood levels may result from changes in transcortin concentration rather than changes in corticoid output per se. Thus elevations in Porter Silber chromogens in pregnancy, for example, may be due to increases in synthesis of transcortin, rather than the stress of pregnancy.

Corticoids disappear from blood in a biphasic manner with an initial sharp fall in concentration, presumably reflecting removal of free steroid, followed by a more gentle fall, presumably reflecting loss of bound steroid. The initial rate of decline appears to be age dependent and turnover is slower in the infant than in the adult. The concentration of CBG in the blood is also lower in infancy so that the delayed disappearance in the immature animal more likely reflects the maturational changes of steroid catabolizing enzymes than protection of steroid by binding. In the adult rat, corticosterone has a half-life of 20 to 30 min.

Corticoids are catabolized primarily in liver by reduction of the unsaturated ketone in position 3 and often, as well, by loss of the ketol at position 17, and are excreted usually after conjugation at position 21 as glucuronides or as sulfate esters. The loss of the 17-ketol group results in conversion to a ketosteroid and 5 to 10% of urinary ketosteroids are of adrenal origin, the remainder arising from androgen catabolism. Adrenal ketosteroids can be partly distinguished from gonadal ketosteroids in having an oxygen at position 11 and the ratio of 17-keto-11-oxyketosteroids to 17-keto-deoxysteroids has sometimes been used in man to assess the relative contributions of these two endocrine systems to the ketosteroid pool. Measurement of 17-hydrocorti-coids is a more direct estimate of adrenocortical activity and is to be preferred over measurement of 17-ketosteroids. Even this may be inaccurate, however, for what is generally measured in the common Porter-Silber procedure is tetrahydrocortisone and tetrahydrocortisol, which together account for only 25% of the glucocorticoid derivatives excreted. Elimination is largely through the urine, although some is lost in the feces.

Not only is the adrenocortical system extremely labile but adrenal corticoids seem essential to survive in a stressful environment, although they are not essential for the maintenance of life in a placid one. The adrenalecto-mized animal survives so long as there is access to salt and the environment is constant and unchallenging. However, sudden temperature changes, short-term fasting, mild exposures to physical or psychologic trauma, infections, hemorrhage, or other stressors, which would only mildly affect endocrinologi-cally intact animals, can be fatal to adrenalectomized ones. Because the biologic importance of adrenocorticoids is state dependent and because of some of the properties of these hormones, the view has arisen that adreno-corticoids function in a permissive manner by initially facilitating physiologic and metabolic processes to meet the immediate emergency and subsequently facilitating process to restore or establish homeostatic equilibrium.

If the adrenocortical system indeed functions in such a regulatory manner, then adrenal corticoids should affect many different systems and adreno-cortical actions might not be invariant but rather would depend upon the metabolic state of the entire organism and of particular target tissues. The physiologic and biochemical effects of glucocorticoids then should be many and complex; this is illustrated in Table 2. On the other hand, the basic operating principles of this system, or any other effective control system, must be few and precise, since even minor pertubation in a biologic control system may become dangerously magnified. This last statement is still one of faith, but the former expectations are certainly true.

Glucocorticoids appear to mediate between immediate catabolism and subsequent anabolism, and in the process they affect protein, carbohydrate, and lipid metabolism, water and mineral balance (and thereby neuromuscular irritability and circulatory hemodynamics), blood cytology, inflammatory responses and the immune response, secretion of pancreatic trypsinogen, and secretion of gastric pepsinogen and hydrochloric acid.

The various actions of adrenocortical hormones are tissue specific, and changes in one tissue may be quite different from those in another. In liver, for example, glucocorticoids increase urea formation by increasing amino acid uptake and gluconeogenesis from amino acids while inhibiting protein syn-

TABLE 2. *Biochemical effects of glucocorticoids*

A. General effects
    Brain
        Increased glucose
        Increased glycogen
    Liver
        Increased glycogen
        Increased glucose production
        Increased ketone body production
        Increased urea production
        Increased amino acid uptake
        Increased RNA synthesis
        Increased protein synthesis
    Adipose tissue
        Increased FFA release
        Decreased glucose utilization
    Muscle
        Decreased glucose utilization
    Lymphatic tissue
        Decreased glucose utilization
        Decreased nucleic acid synthesis

B. Enzymatic effects
    Brain
        Tryptophan-5-hydroxylase
        α-Glycerolphosphate dehydrogenase
        5-Hydroxytryptophan decarboxylase (?)
        Tyrosine hydroxylase
        Glutamine synthesis
    Adrenal
        Phenethanolamine-N-methyltransferase
        Dopamine-β-hydroxylase
    Liver: in carbohydrate metabolism
        Aldolase
        Fructose-1,6-diphosphatase
        Glucose-6-phosphatase
        Glycogen synthesis
        Phosphoglyceraldehyde dehydrogenase
        Pyruvate carboxylase
    Liver: in amino acid metabolism
        Alanine aminotransferase
        Glutamic acid dehydrogenase
        5-Hydroxytryptophan decarboxylase (?)
        Serine dehydratase
        Tryptophan-5-hydroxylase
        Threonine dehydratase
        Tryptophan aminotransferase
        Tryptophan oxygenase
        Tyrosine aminotransferase
    Liver: In urea cycle
        Arginosuccinase
        Arginase
        Ornithine transcarbamylase

thesis in muscle and other tissues and increasing loss of amino acids from them. Liver protein nitrogen increases as does liver RNA without altering DNA. The increase in hepatic protein following corticoid administration is due, in part, to hormonal induction of a variety of enzymes important in gluconeogenesis, glycolysis, urea formation, and amino acid catabolism. Induction of these enzymes is preceded by an increase in liver RNA nucleiotidyl transferase, increased RNA polymerase, increased RNA turnover, and an increase in the absolute amount of RNA.

Glucocorticoids strongly affect liver glucose metabolism, and such effects may be primary to their adaptive function. Glucocorticoids *in vitro* inhibit liver glycogen formation. However, *in vivo* this is overcome by gluconeogenesis derived primarily from amino acids as well as from lactate, pyruvate, succinate, etc. This increased gluconeogenesis is not dependent upon new enzyme formation even though synthesis of many key gluconeogenic enzymes (glucose-6-phosphatase, fructose-1, 6-diphosphatase, phosphoenolpuruvate carboxykinase, and pyruvate carboxylase) is enhanced by glucocorticoid treatment. It has been suggested that glucocorticoids act somewhere between pyruvate and triose phosphate in gluconeogenesis and sufficiently enhance glucose formation to elevate blood glucose and increase liver glycogen deposition despite the inhibitory action of the glucocorticoids themselves on glycogen formation. This increase in glycogen represents true gluconeogenesis and not simply reduced glucose utilization although glucocorticoids do inhibit peripheral utilization of glucose.

Glucocorticoids, *in vitro* at least, appear to inhibit DPNH oxidation. This would *in vivo* lead to decreased oxidative decarboxylation of pyruvate, increasing its availability for glucose synthesis and decreasing acetyl coenzyme A (CoA) availability. Glucocorticoids release free fatty acids from fat pads and increase peripheral lipogenesis, perhaps indirectly through the increase in insulin release accompanying the elevation in blood glucose.

What holds true for liver, however, is not necessarily true for other tissues. Whereas liver RNA and protein concentration are increased by corticoids, RNA in both thymus and spleen is decreased, and protein is decreased in thymus but not in spleen. The marked involution of thymus and lymphatic tissue generally following increased glucocorticoids dramatically demonstrates the tissue selectivity of these hormones. Glucocorticoid-induced involution of these tissues involves destruction of immature thymocytes and lymphocytes, suppressed DNA synthesis, and inhibited mitosis. The concentration of circulating lymphocytes decreases. Eosenophiles also decline, apparently because of destruction of these cells in bone marrow. On the other hand, polymorphonuclear neutrophiles increase despite depressed mitotic activity possibly by increased cellular half-life.

These hemocytologic changes, which can be conveniently detected in both experimental animals and man, have been widely used in stress studies, particularly in the older literature. Advantage has also been taken of the ionic effects of adrenocorticoids. Although aldosterone is the most important regulator of water and ion metabolism, some glucocorticoids are also active. Glucocorticoids lower blood calcium by inhibiting calcium uptake from the gastrointestinal tract and also inhibit bone formation, although this is probably caused less by changes in calcium uptake than by direct inhibition of the synthesis of the mucopolysaccharides that comprise the ground substance of the bone. Urinary phosphate excretion is also increased by glucocorticoids, probably by decreasing resorption in the renal tubules. Like aldosterone, glucocorticoids in small doses reduce sodium excretion and increase potassium excretion. However, whereas aldosterone affects all mechanisms of sodium uptake, the active glucocorticoids appear to stimulate primarily sodium-potassium exchange. These effects of glucocorticoids on ion metabolism are rather general among tissues and the entrance of sodium into, and potassium out of, intracellular compartments is facilitated by these hormones. Cortisol and cortisone both enhance water diuresis.

It should be mentioned that aldosterone secretion is primarily regulated by a complex chain involving release of the proteolytic kidney enzyme, renin, into the bloodstream, and reaction of renin with the α_2 globulin angiotensinogen to produce angiotensin I, which is pharmacologically inert, but which is then enzymatically changed to active angiotensin II. Angiotensin II, together with plasma sodium and potassium concentration, then exerts a major regulatory role in aldosterone release. ACTH also appears to be involved despite earlier reports that it was without influence.

This brief tabulation of adrenocortical actions on liver metabolism, blood cytocomposition, and ion metabolism encompasses most of the peripheral changes that have been used experimentally to detect adrenocortical activation. Numerous other actions exist, however, that are important to stress reactions which can be mentioned only briefly here. Thus adrenocorticoids increase gastric secretion, uropepsin excretion, and produce or reactivate gastric ulcers. Autonomic reactivity is potentiated, cardiac output is increased, circulatory responses to norepinephrine and epinephrine are potentiated and capillary resistance is increased. Corticoids have been implicated in microregulation of capillary beds by inducing histidine decarboxylase and thereby increasing local formation of histamine, while simultaneously potentiating catecholamine vasoconstriction. In addition adrenocorticoids inhibit inflammatory reactions, and they are widely used therapeutically for this purpose, although the detailed mechanisms involved are not fully understood. They also inhibit antibody production, impair migration of phagocytic cells, and impair phagocytosis itself. As might be expected, resistance to infections is often decreased.

Information regarding the direct effects of pituitary-adrenal hormones on the central nervous system is fragmentary and tantalizing. Behavioral, neurochemical, and neurophysiologic changes accompany alterations in hormonal status but there is as yet no comprehensive picture of the interrelationships between the phenomena observed at these various levels of observation.

ACTH and corticoids enter brain as mentioned earlier and are somewhat selectively concentrated in specific regions. Again as mentioned earlier ACTH and corticoids are taken up generally by brain in proportion to their concentration in blood. Septum and hippocampus in particular appear to have specific low-capacity high-affinity uptake sites for corticoids and highly specific nuclear binding of corticosterone has been demonstrated with high nuclear retention, particularly in hippocampus. Uptake occurs primarily in pyramidal neurons of the hippocampal areas CA 1 and CA 2 as well as by granule cells of the dentate gyrus. The movement of corticoids from cell wall to nucleus is presumably mediated by macromolecular protein corticoid-binding proteins that are found in the cytosol and are particular richly distributed in hippocampus, amygdala, septum, and hypothalamus. As already indicated the hippocampus in particular has been implicated as a key site for glucocorticoid feedback regulation and modulation of circadian rhymicity.

Not only do corticoids enter brain, they also undergo active metabolism. Most of these reactions are presumably detoxification reactions and are largely carried out by glia. Some, however, may have functional importance. Thus cortisol and corticosterone are interconverted by NAD-requiring redox reactions, cortisone and cortisol are acetylated, cortisone is converted to 11-dehydrocortisone, corticosterone to 11-dehydrocorticosterone, and 11-β-hydroxyandrostenedrone to adreonstene.

The neurophysiologic responses to topically or systemically administered pituitary adrenal hormones are mixed. For example, as mentioned above hippocampus appears to somewhat selectively accumulate corticosterone, and some studies suggest the hormone is concentrated in neurons rather than glia. Corticosterone depresses single unit activity in the hippocampus particularly when topically applied to Ammons horn hippocampal cells, and in massive doses may cause atropic changes in hippocampal neurons. In contrast, ACTH has the opposite effect of increasing single unit activity in this region in both normal and hypophysectomized animals. Similarly, activity of neurons in the anterior-medial region of the hypothalamus (one of the presumed sites of CRF neurons) is biphasically first stimulated and then depressed by ACTH application, but is generally depressed by the synthetic glucocorticoid dexamethasone.

More grossly, cortisol decreases electroshock seizure threshold if administered to adult rats, but if administered to young rats before day 8 cortisol elevates the seizure threshold. Thus there seems to be a biphasic age-dependent effect of glucocorticoid administration. Interestingly the pituitary adrenocortical system of the neonatal rat during the 1st week of life is remarkably resistant to activation by stressors, even though the pituitary contains ACTH and the adrenal is capable of responding to exogenous ACTH. Presumably this stress nonresponsiveness period reflects incomplete maturation of the central processes controlling CRF release and corresponds to the period of life before rapid myelinization occurs.

The behavioral effects of corticoids are complex and somewhat controversial. In man adrenocortical insufficiency, such as in the adrenocortical degeneration of Addison's Disease, is accompanied not only by such somatic changes as hypotension, muscular weakness, and gastrointestinal upset but also by anorexia and in some subjects a peculiar increase in sensory acuity. Gustatory, auditory, and olfactory modalities all seem to be involved. Thus the olfactory sensitivity of Addison's patients is reported to be an order of magnitude greater than that of normals. Increased sensitivity does not necessarily indicate increased performance, however. For example, auditory acuity is enhanced but so is the error rate in word discrimination. This supersensitivity, together with reports of a reciprocal relationship between circadian changes in sensory acuity and glucocorticoid levels, suggests that the supersensitivity is not simply secondary to general physiologic changes in Addison's disease but rather reflects a direct influence of corticoids on sensory threshold.

On the other hand, depression, apathy, melancholia, anxiety, and instability are common both to adrenal insufficiency in Addison's disease and to excessive 11-oxy steroid production in Cushings syndrome. These behavioral changes are also sometimes observed after chronic ACTH or glucocorticoid treatment, although more generally the behavioral response is one of euphoria.

The personality changes accompanying adrenal pathology in man are difficult to detect in animals where personality can only be inferred from performance. The effects of pituitary adrenal hormones on performance are mixed and task dependent. Adrenalectomy seems to have little influence on acquisition of avoidance behavior or on other learned responses. On the other hand, hypophysectomy is reported to severely interfere with acquisition of an avoidance response and ACTH administration reverses this interference. The decapeptide (ACTH 1–10) and heptapeptide (ACTH 4–10) analogues of ACTH as well as α-melanocyte-stimulating hormone (α-MSH) also reverse the effects of hypophysectomy. ACTH administration to intact animals generally has little effect on acquisition of conditioned avoidance behavior, although a few reports of facilitation have appeared. However, considerable data now indicates that ACTH administration delays extinction of the conditioned avoidance response. Again the first 10 amino acids of ACTH seem essential for eliciting this response and both MSH and the synthetic peptides mentioned above are effective.

In contrast to the effects of ACTH on delaying extinction of the conditioned avoidance response, glucocorticoids hasten the extinction of the response. Therefore the action of ACTH is not mediated through stimulation of the adrenal but is more direct. On the other hand, glucocorticoid facilitation of extinction does not seem to be caused by suppression of ACTH. This conclusion is based upon structure-activity relationships and the persistence of corticoid facilitation in hypophysectomized animals. It is further supported by the observation that cortisol implants in the reticular formation (which do not induce ACTH release) are potent in facilitating extinction of the avoidance response.

The effects of glucocorticoid treatment on acquisition of avoidance responses is less clear and depends critically on experimental conditions. Some studies have indicated a positive correlation between plasma corticoid levels and passive avoidance learning, and a negative correlation between corticoid levels and active avoidance learning. It has been proposed that this reflects the different behavioral consequences of fear in these two situations.

The site of action of ACTH and the steroid in eliciting these behavioral changes has been studied by lesion and implantation procedures and generally appears to be in the nuclei parafascicularis in the posterior thalamus. Adrenal steroids also seem to have additional behavioral actions at the level of the anterior hypothalamus. The special localization in the thalamic reticular formation, that great funnel of converging information, suggests that these hormones may modulate activity at this node of sensory integration.

A general framework with which to view the direct behavioral effects of adrenocortical hormones has been proposed by Weiss and de Weid. They have suggested that ACTH increases and maintains central arousal in ambiguous and potentially dangerous situations, whereas the subsequent rise in corticoids opposes this activation and tends to restore central nervous system excitability to its prestressor condition.

Less well established are the effects of pituitary adrenal hormones on other behaviors. Some evidence for corticoid effects on aggressive behavior have been reported, but it is unclear whether these represent differences in arousal or aggressivity per se. Thus males of some mouse strains show increased aggressive behavior following isolation. Adrenal weights of such animals have been reported both to be the same as, or smaller than, those of grouped controls depending upon the time of isolation and the number of animals in the grouped condition. Adrenalectomy is reported to suppress this isolation-induced aggression, corticoid administration to enhance it, and ACTH administration to ameliorate it. In contrast to mice, isolated rats are generally more anxious than aggressive, and isolated rats are reported to have larger adrenals than grouped controls and to be more responsive to mild stimuli as evidenced by adrenocortical activation. Hydrocortisone treatment to normal rats reportedly leads to an increase in mouse-killing behavior. Attempts have also been made to relate dominance to adrenocortical activity with mixed results. In one study dominant monkeys were found to have lower adrenocortical responses to ACTH than submissive monkeys, and ACTH responsivity was found to be changed when dominant monkeys were added to, or removed from, the colony. On the other hand, dominant monkeys have been reported to show higher excretion of urinary 17-hydroxycorticosterone when shocked than did less dominant animals and to show greater response to other stressors as well.

The detailed biologic mechanism underlying the behavioral effects of either insufficient or excess corticoids is not known. Those related to adrenal insufficiency or occurring after adrenalectomy may be caused by ionic changes reflecting difficulties in regulating salt balance in the absence of mineral corticoids. Brain sodium appears to be increased in salt-maintained adrenalectomized animals and sodium distribution between extra- and intracellular spaces may be altered. Potassium content seems to be unchanged, although some conflict exists over whether potassium turnover is increased. Glucocorticoids do play some role in these changes. Both chronic and acute administration of glucocorticoids or ACTH to intact animals lowers seizure threshold, the effect being minimal with corticosterone and maximal with cortisone or 17-hydroxycorticosterone, and this alteration in seizure threshold may reflect altered sodium compartmentalization produced by these compounds. Although ionic shifts occur in adrenalectomy, activities of such ion sensitive enzymes as brain sodium-potassium activated ATPase are not altered.

Glucocorticoids have remarkably few known metabolic effects on brain itself. Neither ACTH nor corticosterone appear to alter oxygen consumption in man although hydrocortisone may inhibit oxygen uptake by rat brain mitochondria *in vitro*. Cortisone administration to adrenalectomized animals increases whole brain carbohydrate and/or glycogen content, but these effects are less clear in intact animals and depend somewhat upon the route of administration and dosage. Subcutaneous hydrocortisone at doses of 100 mg/kg elevates brain glucose twofold, slightly increases creatine phosphate, glucose-6-phosphate, and adenosine triphosphate (ATP), but does not alter glutamate or glycogen. However, infusion of cortisol, together with glutamate, does increase brain glycogen as does acutely or chronically administered hydrocortisone at a dosage of 3.0 mg/kg. Continuous hydrocortisone treatment for 12 days decreases brain ATP and creatine phosphate while increasing glycogen. The rise in glycogen precedes the fall in ATP.

Glucocorticoids are effective inducers of many peripheral enzymes, particularly in liver, but corticoids have few such effects in brain. The best documented enzymes change is that of α-glycerolphosphate dehydrogenase, which is elevated by ACTH or cortisol both in intact animals and in glial cell cultures and which, in animals, is decreased by adrenalectomy or hypophysectomy. This is a relatively specific change, and other dehydrogenases such as isocitric dehydrogenase, malate dehydrogenase, and lactate dehydrogenase are unaffected. The metabolic significance of this enzymic change is not clear but likely involves alterations in brain lipid composition, since α-glycerolphosphate dehydrogenase is intimately involved in phospholipid biosynthesis and corticoids enhance myelenization.

Glucocorticoids promote the premature appearance of glutamine synthetase in the chick neural retina and of ATPase in the developing chick brain. Continuous hydrocortisone treatment has been reported to increase brain and peripheral tissue 5-hydroxytryptophan (5-HTP) decarboxylase activity in young animals, but this has not been confirmed by all investigators. Although this is an important enzyme, catalyzing the decarboxylation of both 5-HTP and DOPA, normal enzymic activity appears well in excess of need. Conceivably, however, alterations in the activity of this enzyme could have significance under very special conditions.

Tryptophan hydroxylase is normally the rate-limiting enzyme in serotonin synthesis and this enzyme is decreased in brainstem following adrenalectomy but restored by administration of glucocorticoids. Chronic administration of glucocorticoids has also been reported to elevate liver tryptophan hydroxylase activity. Early studies suggested that adrenalectomy and hypophysectomy decreased cerebral serotonin. However, other studies report an increase in serotonin and still others fail to find changes following adrenalectomy.

The influence of administered adrenal corticoids on serotonin levels is also unclear. Chronic administration of hydrocortisone has been reported both to increase brain serotonin levels and to be without effect. Chronic corticoid treatment has also been reported to block the increase in serotonin normally following tryptophan administration, whereas acute hydrocortisone administration causes a fall in brain serotonin. The synthesis of brain serotonin is dependent upon brain tryptophan hydroxylase activity, upon blood tryptophan concentration, and upon tryptophan passage through the blood-brain barrier. Complex interactions between these factors probably contribute to these conflicting findings. Thus, if handling stress elevates adrenal epinephrine, free fatty acids may be released from adipose tissue and plasma free fatty acids may increase. These in turn can displace tryptophan from albumin-binding sites, increase free blood tryptophan, and thereby increase brain tryptophan and serotonin formation. On the other hand, tryptophan pyrrolase activity is elevated by hydrocortisone, as are liver tyrosine and tryptophan transaminases. These would tend to decrease blood tryptophan, brain tryptophan, and thereby serotonin. Hormonal induction of these enzymes in turn can be influenced by diet and by other hormones such as glucagon and growth hormone released by specific stressors. Balances between different catabolic routes by tryptophan metabolism may be in constant flux, and this flux may partly account for the circadian rhythms of serotonin in some tissues. Finally, as mentioned previously, serotonin may be involved in regulation of corticoid rhythmicity and in feedback control on this rhythmicity. These factors in serotonin formation, even in the relatively uncomplicated pharmacologic condition, underline the complexity of metabolic changes that are inherent in studying the biologic effects of the more complex signal of a stressor.

Glucocorticoids per se have little direct effect on whole brain catecholamines, their metabolic turnover, or their metabolic enzymes despite pharmacologic evidence linking catecholamines to mediation of the stress response and despite changes in catecholamine turnover following some stressors. Recent evidence, however, indicates that local catecholamine metabolism may be influenced by manipulation of the adrenocortical system. Thus tyrosine hydroxylase activity has been reported to be decreased by adrenalectomy and stimulated by dexamethasone. These changes occur only in the median eminance, however, and not in other nuclei. Brain dopamine-β-hydroxylase (DBH) is unaffected by these treatments. However, serum DBH is increased after hypophysectomy, and ACTH, but not dexamethasone, causes a fall in activity.

Brain levels of dicarboxylic acids and γ-aminobutyric acid (GABA) are influenced by glucocorticoids. These changes are age dependent and may be relevant to the altered seizure thresholds of adrenalectomized and corticoid-treated animals. Cortisone or cortisol treatment of intact adult rats produces a fall in GABA and glutamic acid. Glutamine remains constant or increases. Although glutamic acid decreases upon a single injection of glucocorticoids, its concentration is increased upon chronic glucocorticoid treatment. This may reflect its role as an energy source in the acute conditions and as an intermediary in gluconeogenesis in the chronic one but may also have implications in moderating the level of excitability. Glutamic acid is an excitatory transmitter, whereas GABA has been shown to be an inhibitory transmitter in some systems. These amino acid changes following adrenalectomy are not simply the reverse of changes produced by glucocorticoids. Glutamic acid, aspartic acid, glutamine, GABA, and free amino acid pools in brain all decrease after adrenalectomy. Glutamic acid decarboxylase and GABA transaminase activities also decrease. These changes reflect the general alterations in cerebral metabolism and protein synthesis accompanying adrenalectomy. Deoxycorticosterone, or cortisol, replacement therapy reverses some of these changes. For example, both hormones prevent the slight fall in glutamine following adrenalectomy, but only deoxycorticosterone reverses the fall in GABA and partly restores glutamic acid levels.

Perhaps the most dramatic effect of glucocorticoids are the marked changes in brain size and composition following corticoid treatment of the neonate. A single injection of corticoids on the first day of life markedly retards whole body growth and brain size, especially cerebellar size. These weight changes are accompanied by decreases in brain DNA, indicating a reduction in cellular content, brain RNA, protein, and cholesterol. The ratio of intracellular to extracellular potassium is raised (in contrast to the reverse change in the adult), and brain oxygen consumption is decreased. Functional changes accompany these changes in cell number and composition. Corticoid treated animals have premature eye opening but a delay in development of the evoked response to light. The decrease in body growth may be caused by decreased cellular sensitivity to growth hormone and is of some clinical importance, since chronic corticoid treatment of children with status asmaticus also leads to growth retardation.

Corticoids and ACTH can pass the placental barrier, and maternal stress could conceivably effect the developing fetus. The influence of neonatal corticoid administration has been reviewed by Schapiro.

III. ADRENAL CATECHOLAMINES

By definition, stressors disturb homeostatic peace. Although adrenal corticoids seem to act to both restore equilibrium and prepare for future onslaughts, their major biologic actions are relatively slow and less geared to the crisis of the moment than to those of the immediate future. Responses to the immediate threat are largely governed by other systems. The most important of these are the autonomic nervous system and the adrenal medulla. Cannon is largely responsible for drawing attention to these systems in emergency fight-or-flight reactions.

The adrenal medulla is a modified ganglion consisting of masses of cells containing fine, dense core, chromaffin granules interspersed with sympathetic ganglion cells all in close association with preganglionic fibers. The dense core granules contain catecholamines bonded to ATP by ionic interaction between the amino groups of the former and the phosphate groups of the latter. The molar ratio of catecholamine to ATP is approximately $1:3$ to 4. The granules also contain a protein, chromogrannin, and lipid. Whether more than one type of granule is involved in the storage of the amines is uncertain, although histochemical and quantitative differences in the relative quantities of amines under certain conditions suggest that this may be the case.

The chromaffin granules contain a magnesium-dependent ATPase and avidly take up and concentrate catecholamines in a process stimulated by magnesium and ATP. This stimulated uptake is relatively specific for the catecholamines and serotonin. The existence of a relatively stable and a labile pool of adrenal catecholamines has also been posited. Norepinephrine is stored in granules in sympathetic nerve endings, but these granules differ from those in the adrenal medulla; however, ATP and the catecholamines seem to exist in the same stoichiometric relationship in both sympathetic nerve endings and the adrenal medulla.

The ratio of epinephrine to norepinephrine and the absolute level of catecholamines in the adrenal medulla appears to differ between species. Epinephrine predominates in all cases. In the rabbit the ratio of epinephrine to norepinephrine is $50:1$, in the rat $10:1$, in man $5:1$, and in the cat $5:2$. Total catecholamine content of the adrenal is about 1.2 mg/g in the rat and about 0.6 mg/g in man.

All of the enzymes required for catecholamine biosynthesis are present in the sympathetic nerve endings. Tyrosine hydroxylase, the rate-limiting enzyme in norepinephrine synthesis converts tyrosine to DOPA, which is in turn decarboxylated to dopamine by 5-HTP-DOPA decarboxylase. Dopamine is transported to cytoplasmic particles containing dopamine-β-hydroxylase, which converts it to norepinephrine. In addition some vesicles in the adrenal appear to contain the enzyme phenethanolamine-N-methyl transferase, which methylates norepinephrine to form epinephrine. At least two sets of controls exist on this system. Tyrosine hydroxylase is inhibited by its end-product norepinephrine to provide a negative-feedback control. *In vivo* this control is probably exercised by free rather than particle-bound norepinephrine. Second, glucocorticoids, insulin, and glucogon stimulate phenethanolamine N-methyltransferase, thereby permitting some regulation of the epinephrine to norepinephrine ratio. This is of interest both because it relates catecholamine synthesis and hormonal status and also because glucogon and insulin, which are normally considered to act in opposition, both exhibit the same action on this enzyme, as they do also in inducing liver tyrosine aminotransferase.

Upon neural stimulation both epinephrine and norepinephrine are released into the circulation by a process involving influx of calcium into the storage vesicle. This is accompanied by release of ATP and dopamine-β-oxidase. Once released the catecholamines are rapidly bound by peripheral tissue, degraded, or excreted as either free or conjugated catecholamine. The major urinary product is 3-methoxy-4-hydroxymandelic acid (VMA), which is normally excreted at a level of about 5 mg/day. The remaining urinary products are present in much lesser amounts: 3,4-dihydroxymandelic acid, 100 μg/day; normetanephrine, 100 μg/day; conjugated norepinephrine, 100 μg/day; and conjugated epinephrine 15 μg/day. Degradation after release takes place primarily in liver by reaction with liver catechol-O-methyltransferase to produce metanephrine and normetanephrine, which is then oxidized by monoamine oxidase.

Catecholamines taken into tissue appear to go to two pools: one turns over rapidly and produces O-methylated derivatives, and a slower one that produces deaminated derivatives. The faster pool is believed to represent metabolically active amine, which is degraded by catechol-O-methyl transferase in the synaptic space, whereas the slower pool is thought to be inactivated within the tissue by mitochondrial monoamine oxidase.

Blood norepinephrine levels are tonically maintained at a very low level (about 0.3 μg/liter) by a continual secretion and loss from noradrenergic neurons. Epinephrine levels wax and wane as a function of periodic bursts from the adrenal medulla. Although many of the pharmacologic actions of epinephrine resemble the physiologic responses in acute stress, it is only in very extreme stress that epinephrine really contributes to these responses. Instead increased heart rate, heart stroke, the rise in systolic pressure, and the diversion of blood flow to the muscles are manifestations of activation of the sympathetic nervous system. Epinephrine exerts its primary influence on stress adaptation by metabolic means.

One of the most important of these metabolic actions is to stimulate the formation of glucose from glycogen. In common with various other hor-

mones, epinephrine stimulates adenylcyclas activity and the production of cyclic 3'5'-AMP. This occurs in many tissues, including brain. In liver, adenyl
cyclase activates diphosphorylase kinase, which phosphorlates phosphorlase
a to form phosphorylase b. Phosphorylase b then acts to convert glycogen to
glucose. In muscle similar reactions occur, but this tissue lacks glucose-6-
phosphatase so that lactic acid accumulates. The end result of these reactions
is an increase in blood glucose and blood lactic acid. The circulating lactic
acid is picked up by the liver and converted to glucose by epinephrine-
stimulated gluconeogenesis. Furthermore, epinephrine stimulates release of
free fatty acids from adipose tissues, heart, and diaphragm. In adipose tissue
this release of fatty acid is also thought to be mediated by cAMP activation
of lipase. The effectiveness of epinephrine in stimulating release of free fatty
acids from adipose tissue is markedly reduced by adrenalectomy and restored
by administration of adrenal corticoids, but only if given prior to administration of epinephrine.

The catecholamines, then, serve in acute stresses to prepare the organism
for action by activation of the noradrenergic sympathetic system, and to provide the energetic resources to carry out such actions by the metabolic effects
of epinephrine.

IV. OTHER HORMONAL SYSTEMS

Science, as an inferential system, continuously grows and changes as new
techniques reveal new phenomena to be incorporated into the existing scientific rubric. The wealth of information that accumulated following development of isotopic and immunologic techniques for assessing circulating hormones has revealed that the complexity of adrenal responses and metabolic
reactions in stress is matched by those of other hormones as well. It was of
course obvious that such complexity must exist. Stressors vary enormously
in their initial demands on the organism and even more on the subsequent
accommodations necessary to restore or approximate the initial state. Recovery from tissue damage requires different processes than recovery from
fright. Cold differs from fasting, and both differ from anticipatory dread.
Were corticoids to act alone and in an invariant manner, metabolic rigidity,
not flexibility, would result. Not only is it self-evident that flexibility does exist
but a number of studies have indicated that pharmacologic responses to
corticoids are not identical to physiologic responses to stressors. In good part
this flexibility results from complex interactions between the effects of
adrenocortical hormones and those of other hormones elicited by the stressor.

A detailed accounting of the properties of the hormones that now appear
to respond to different stressors is beyond the scope of this chapter. All of
the hormones of the anterior pituitary; ACTH, growth hormone (Somatotropin, STH), prolactin, thyrotropin (TSH), lutenizing hormone (LH), and
follicle-stimulating hormone (FSH), have been shown to be influenced by one

TABLE 3. Hormone changes in stress

Stress	FSH	LH	PRL	GH Primate	RAT	CAT	TSH	Glucagon
1. Physiologic								
Hunger			±	±	−	o		+
Thirst								
Infection				+				
Exercise			+	+	−			
Cold			+	o	−		+	
Heat			±		−		±	
Injury		o	+	+				
Hypoglycemia				+	−	o		
Anemia	+	+	+	+	+			
Sex								
2. Psychologic								
Novelty			+				+	
Noise				+	−			
Threat					−			
Immobilization			+	o				
Shock				±			±	
3. Pharmacologic								
Epinephrine				+	−			
Chlorpromazine				+				
Ether	+	+	+	+	−			
DOPA					−			

+ Increase, − decrease, o no change.

or another stressor. In addition insulin and especially glucagon secretions are altered by some stressors. Thus blood loss elevates LH, FSH, prolactin, and growth hormone in man, whereas cold elicits a rise in prolactin, growth hormone (in man), and thyrotropin. An admittedly incomplete tabulation of the hormonal responses to some stressors is given in Table 3, and only some of the more important are discussed.

A. Prolactin

It can be seen that a wide variety of stressors increase circulating prolactin levels. Evidence suggests that pituitary prolactin, like other hormones of the anterior pituitary, is under hypothalamic control. Evidence for both a hypothalamic releasing factor (PRF) and an inhibitory factor (PIF) has been obtained. The latter may be under the control of dopaminergic fibers of the tuberoinfundibular tract arising from dopaminergic neurons in the arcuate nucleus. Dopaminergic control appears to be by tonic release of PIF at the hypothalamic level and by direct dopamine inhibition of prolactin release at the pituitary level. This picture is complicated, however, in that vasopressin may increase plasma prolactin under some conditions, thyroxine may inhibit prolactin release by the pituitary *in vitro* and increase pituitary prolactin *in vivo*, and thyroid releasing factor stimulates prolactin secretion in sheep, monkey and man but not in rats. Prolactin release thus appears to be influenced by a number of factors that may interact to produce its ubiquitous increase following stressors.

The significance of the stress-induced prolactin release to stress adaptation is unknown as indeed is the function of prolactin in general. As its name implies, prolactin was initially thought to stimulate lactation of the mammary glands and proliferation of the mucosa of the crop sac of doves and pigeons. It certainly does the latter and in addition elicit regurgitation feeding behavior and suppression of sexual activity. Its role in lactation is less clear because growth hormone also elicits lactation. However, elevated serum prolactin and low growth hormone levels have been demonstrated in nursing mothers so that it is likely that prolactin does participate in this process. Prolactin seems to stimulate progesterone secretion in the newly formed corpus lutea of rats and mice but it does not appear to be leuteotropic in most mammals including man. In many species prolactin administration causes regression of the gonads. In addition to being released by many stressors, plasma prolactin undergoes a circadian variation, which peaks shortly before waking and is dissociated from the circadian rhythm of growth hormone. Breast stimulation in some but not all women leads to an increase in serum prolactin similar to that after postpartum suckling, and an orgasm-related rise in prolactin has been reported in some women following sexual intercourse. Males have not shown such a change.

Beyond this, very little is known about the physiologic role of prolactin in man, especially with regard to stress adaptation. Human prolactin does have remarkable structural similarities to human growth hormone, and it has been suggested that both have a common evolutionary origin and may have arisen from repeated tandem duplication of a gene coding for a smaller peptide. Furthermore prolactin does have potent somatotropic properties in some invertebrates and stimulates glucose uptake and lipogenesis. Whether these relate to stress adaptation in higher organisms is uncertain.

B. Growth Hormone

Growth hormone is also remarkably responsive to stressors and pituitary release of this hormone also appears to be under both positive and negative neural control although basal secretion appears to be independent of either. Indirect evidence suggests the existence of both a releasing factor and an inhibitor of the releasing factor in hypothalamic extracts, although they have not yet been characterized. A hypothalamic peptide inhibiting growth hormone release has been isolated from ovine hypothalamus as have several peptides from hypothalami of other species having growth hormone releasing properties in some systems. In part the difficulties in clear identification of these controlling peptides are caused by technical problems in relevant assays and assay systems. Radioimmunoassay of growth hormone often does not correspond to estimates obtained by bioassays based on tibia growth or on results obtained by pituitary electrophoresis. Furthermore purified growth hormone from different species vary considerably. Human growth hormone has some 200 amino acid residues in a single polypeptide chain, a molecular weight of 27,000 and 2 disulfide linkages. Beef growth hormone has some 400 amino acid residues in two polypeptide chains, a molecular weight of 45,000 and 4 disulfide bridges. Monkey growth hormone also appears to have 5 disulfide bridges but a molecular weight of 25,000. Antisera to monkey or human growth hormone cross react, but do not react with growth hormone of sheep or cows. On the other hand, human and monkey growth hormone are biologically active in all species studied, whereas other growth hormones are effective in various other species but not the primates.

On the basis of radioimmunoassay procedures, species differ markedly in plasma growth hormone response to stressors. In man and monkey, stressors tend to elevate plasma growth hormone levels. In rat stressors tend to decrease plasma levels of this hormone, whereas analagous stressors do not alter growth hormone levels in the cat. The reasons for these differences are obscure.

In man and monkey, an acute fall in blood glucose increases plasma growth hormone even when the fall is from an artificially elevated level to normal. The magnitude of the fall seems generally of lesser importance than the rate. Insulin hypoglycemia is particularly effective in elevating growth hormone. As indicated in the table, stressors such as fasting, exposure to bacterial endotoxin, surgery and even moderate exercise elevate blood levels of this hormone. Interestingly cold exposure does not, although this stressor is effective in lower mammals. Glucose administration causes a fall in growth hormone, which slowly returns, to basal levels even with continuous glucose treatment. Glucose also inhibits the growth hormone rise in fasting and during exercise. Arginine and protein have the opposite effect of stimulating a growth hormone rise.

In contrast to man, the rat exposed to insulin-induced hypoglycemia, arginine infusion, fasting, cold, ether anesthesia, or exercise responds with an acute fall in growth hormone and cat plasma growth hormone is unresponsive to arginine, glucose, or insulin-induced hypoglycemia.

Somatotropin has many metabolic actions. As its name implies, it is generally growth promoting for both hard and soft tissues. It induces nitrogen retention, decreases blood amino acid concentration, promotes amino acid transport across cell membranes, and increases intracellular amino acid concentrations. Interestingly it rapidly induces ornithine decarboxylase and stimulates polyamine biosynthesis. This may plan an important role in growth hormone stimulation of protein synthesis. Somatotropin's effects on carbohydrate metabolism are no less profound. It has an anti-insulin action producing an insulin resistance, hypoglycemia due to a rapid release of glucose from liver, and increases muscle glycogen. Growth hormone also mobilizes fat depots and increases blood free fatty acid concentrations. Like glucocorticoids growth hormone appears to play a permissive role in being synergistic with other hormones and facilitating responsivity of target tissue to trophic hormones. Thus ACTH, together with somatotropin, is more effective in reversing adrenal atrophy in hypophysectomized animals than is ACTH alone. Somatotropin promotes growth without maturation whereas thyroxin promotes maturation without growth, and both are required to obtain a normal growth response. On the other hand, some antagonistic actions exist. For example glucocorticoids induce liver tyrosine transaminase, and this induction is inhibited by growth hormone, perhaps by way of its effects on glucose metabolism, since glucose administration also inhibits corticoid induction of this enzyme. Glucocorticoids also suppress the rise in growth hormone following insulin-induced hypoglycemia and such suppression may indeed account for the retarded growth of children on chronic steroid therapy for status asmaticus.

C. Thyroid

The thyroid system has often been somewhat tenuously linked with stress responses. Like the other hormones discussed, primary control seems to be exerted through a tripeptide releasing factor (TRF) consisting in the cow, the pig, and perhaps man as well of a tripeptide-pyroylglutamic-histamine proline. This releasing factor releases pituitary TSH and also stimulates prolactin secretion, although it does not appear to be PRF. Under the influence of TSH, tri-iodothyronine (T3) rises as does thyroxine, although the rise in the latter is somewhat smaller. Thyroid weight, basal metabolic rate, iodine uptake and release, protein-bound iodine, thyroxine (T4) and T3, and more recently TSH have all been used as measures of thyroid activity following stressors. However, basal metabolic rate, iodine uptake and release, and protein-bound iodine are all influenced by factors besides thyroidal activity. Nonhormonal factors altering excretion of thyroid hormones may influence pituitary activity by a feedback control independent of neural stimulation. The literature on the stress response of the thyroid is thus often ambiguous.

The most firmly established thyroid response to a stressor is that of increased activity in cold stress. Plasma TSH and T3 increase in cold exposed rats, although T4 shows only a mild increase. However, T4 is bound to protein globulins from which it can be displaced by the increased free fatty acids in plasma accompanying cold adaptation. Consequently free T4 increases in cold, even though the total does not. Whether peripheral utilization of T4 is increased in cold is unclear. Cold exposed monkeys and baboons show a lessor change in indices of thyroid activity than do rats. Although man is usually considered to respond to this stressor with a rise in thyroid activity, the apparent increase may be caused by augmented secretion compensating for the increased fecal loss that accompanies increased food consumption in the cold.

The response of the thyroid to stressors other than cold is less clear. Studies in both man and other animals suggest that thyroid function is changed by stressors, but the direction of change, its magnitude, and its duration are all subject to controversy. Furthermore much of the existing literature was obtained before the development of radioimmunoassay or other specific indices of thyroid function and relies heavily upon iodine uptake, protein-bound iodine, and thyroid weight, which as indicated above are not reflections of functional activity alone. Thus methodologic problems may contribute to the differences in observation as may the differences in experimental paradigms, especially with regard to time.

In general, it appears that the acute response of rodents to stressors is a depression of thyroid function. This has been reported for rabbit following restraint, hemorrhage and laporotomy, for the rat following thermal stress, and for the guinea pig exposed to noise or endotoxin. This is reflected in a drop in iodine uptake into the thyroid and a decrease in protein-bound iodine. More recent studies have confirmed a sharp fall in plasma TSH in rats following surgical trauma but no change in TSH after ether exposure. Other studies have indicated that ether also causes a fall in thyroid activity. Some evidence suggests that the acute fall in thyroid activity after some stress is followed by a subsequent increase in activity so that the full stress response is a biphasic one. Furthermore stressors superimposed during this second phase of response are reported to lead to augmented thyroid function rather than depression.

In contrast to rodents, sheep are reported to respond to fear with an elevated protein-bound iodine (PBI) level. A similar increase occurs in monkeys in response to conditional avoidance training, although individual differences and a disparity between overt disturbance and thyroid indices were noted. The general pattern of thyroid activity in man exposed to a variety of presumed psychologic stresses (movies, interviews, performance tasks, sensory deprivation, etc.) seems to be in the direction of increased thyroidal function, as reflected in measures such as PBI and iodine uptake, and also in TSH.

Assessing the possible role of the thyroid in stress responses and subsequent adaptation clearly requires a considerable extension of existing information using current methodologies. In particular there is a need to assess the relationship between different indices of thyroid function and their temporal changes as well as an evaluation of concomitant changes in other relevant factors. For example exogenous epinephrine reportedly elevates TSH and PBI. Conceivably endogenous elevations of epinephrine following some stressors might also influence these measures and it would seem important to determine whether transitory secondary effects of the adrenomedullary system are involved in some thyroid responses or whether primary changes in

TRF release occur. Fatty acid levels and pH influence the binding of thyroid hormones to blood globulins and thereby the availability of free hormone. Thyroidal influences on metabolism might well follow some stressors without direct activation of TRF-containing hypothalamic units. As in cold, fecal bulk and thereby hormone excretion may be altered with resultant secondary effects on thyroid activation with or without metabolic consequences. Until clarification of these and other factors, the role of thyroid in stress remains vague.

D. Other Hormonal Systems

Other hormonal systems (LH, FSH, estrogens, androgens, insulin, glucagon, and secretin) which are thought to be involved in the response to one or another stressor, cannot be described here although their influence must obviously be considered in attempting to understand the response pattern of a particular stressor. For some (i.e., LH and FSH) information on the generality or specificity of response is lacking. For others (i.e., insulin, glucagon and secretin) the responses are likely secondary to metabolic changes induced by other stress-responsive systems. Whether general or specific, primary or secondary responses, these systems contribute to the adaptive or maladaptive consequences of stress and must be considered in evaluating the response to each stressor.

V. STRESSORS

If a stressor is defined as an agent that disturbs homeostatic equilibrium and calls forth compensatory responses, then the number of stressors is legion. Transitory metabolic and physiologic adjustments occur continuously, and although these are of admitted importance stress research has largely been concerned with more massive displacements. Broadly stressors can be divided into those that actually compromise the organism and those that only threaten to do so. The real animal in the real world may suffer from hunger, thirst, infection, tissue damage, heat, cold, and exhaustion, and he may be frustrated, angered, terrified, pleased, stimulated, anxious, confused, or stupefied by events. Whereas the former are considered physiologic stressors and the latter psychologic ones, their separation is more conceptual than real, for a hungry animal may well also be anxious, an exhausted one stupified, and an injured one angry. Indeed the first classification of stressors is derived from names of the stimuli and the second from presumed psychologic states. Because stimuli are relatively easy to specify, responses to physiologic stressors appear somewhat clearer than responses to psychologic ones and there is a concomitant tendency to ignore psychologic contributions to the observed response. This tendency perhaps accounts for some of the apparent differences between human and infrahuman responses to stressors. For example fasting studies in man most often fail to show evidence of adrenocortical activation. Fasting studies on rats, however, show a marked and sustained activation. This could be attributed to the difference in the physiologic impact of starvation in a 70 kg animal with a relatively small surface to volume ratio and a correspondingly small heat loss as compared to a 0.3 kg animal with a relatively high heat loss. It could also be attributed to the difference in anxiety between the man who is assured he will not be experimentally starved to death as against the rat who has no such assurance. To the extent that different stressors evoke different physiologic responses, the failure, and often inability, to identify the component stressors in the stimuli compounds the problem of assessment of the results. On this basis animal studies are more contaminated than those in man, although in the latter, too, multiple stressors may be involved and the felt apathy of one subject or the suppressed anger of another may contribute to an unexplained variability in response to a scheduled stressor.

The difficulty in distinguishing components of psychologic stressors is even clearer. Laboratory stressors must be translated by the animal into terms commensurate with its biologic repetoire, rather than the investigators conceptual one. Not only is it unlikely that nature provided a specific adaptational response to a laboratory stressor such as an electrical storm to the tail, but also the subsequent psychologic response may range from resignation to rage and these may differ in their physiologic consequences. A few attempts to assess apparent psychologic responses do exist, largely in man, but better methodologies are needed both to clarify the stressor and to clarify the response.

It is of course impossible to describe in detail the known responses to all, or even a few, stressors. The brief section below merely illustrates some of the responses to select stressors. Although the subsequent sections are grouped according to stressor, it should be clear from the above that these are not pure groupings and that some of the responses tabulated may be the result of interaction between the designated stress and other unspecified stressors. An attempt will be made throughout to differentiate acute from chronic conditions since responses change with adaptation. Indeed the stress response is an attempt to restore homeostatic balance, and if it is successful the organism is no longer compromised and a response is unnecessary even though the stressors continues to appear uncomfortable to the investigator. Age too is an important variable in stress adaptation but it cannot be fully specified here beyond identifying young and old, because of the complexity of the literature. Very early postnatal life is of particular importance, however, and will be discussed in specific contexts.

A. Psychological Stressors

Some stressors directly and physically compromise the organism but most are either threats of potential danger or symbols of past dangers. These loosely constitute the psychologic stressors and they represent a diverse group of stimuli united only in their ability to generate emotional disequilibrium. As in all stimulus-response systems, discernment of the stimuli is essential to the response. In the physiological stressors, stimulus recognition is both automatic and relatively uniform. This is not true for the psychologic stimuli. A test, a quarrel, an angry policeman, or a late chapter elicit anxiety, anger, fear, or guilt only to the extent that the stimulus is seen as an emotional threat. A psychopath may delight in stimuli that are threatening to others and a schizophrenic may be under or overresponsive to a stressor, depending on his personal conception. Indeed evaluation of the stress responses of the mentally ill is often so difficult because of the problem in discerning the emotional meaning of the stimulus to the subject.

The difference between permissible or appropriate stimulus for man and animals also prevents easy comparisons between them. Man may respond to purely psychologic stimuli and verbally recount his psychologic responses for comparison with his physiologic ones. An animal's responses must be inferred from his performance and the process of elicitating performance often invokes physiologic stressors in conjunction with psychologic ones. A rat made anxious by a forced response is only interested in making the response if he is to be rewarded (with food for example) or punished (shock avoidance for example). In the first instance, he must be made hungry or thirsty to perform, and in the second he must be trained to anticipate an unpleasant stimulus. In both, physiologic parameters of hunger or thirst or pain are interwoven into the psychologic parameters of anxiety or fear or confusion.

In this section, then, human and animal studies have been separated and separate stressors discussed somewhat apart from each other.

1. Man

Stress is assumed to play a vital role in both mental and physical illness and most stress research has been directed at evaluating and elucidating this role. Paradoxically, although man is the relevant animal, he is the least suitable for biologic studies, while yet the most suitable for psychological ones. Even though the psychologist can attempt to reach the mind by the relatively direct route of observation and conversation, the biologist must take a more devious path to the brain through rivers of biologic fluid. The trip is not without its conceptual and practical hazards.

The prime biologic fluids for examination are blood and urine. The process of drawing blood constitutes a stressor to some individuals, and this is superimposed on that of the experimental stimulus. Collection of a urine sample is less stressful to the subject, but the sample itself is a solution collected, at least internally, over time and the temporal relationships between production and secretion is blurred and generally unknown.

Just as the variables examined are limited by availability and potential injury, the stimuli are limited to those with transitory and hopefully harmless effects. In effect, these stimuli are usually situational and are difficult to precisely define, to dissect into component stressors, or to quantify. When field studies are carried out on individuals subject to physical stressors, such as subjects on army maneuvers, stimuli are generally composites of one or more of the stressors of hunger, cold, exhaustion, injury, and fear, so that responses are complexes of different adaptations. Finally, because man is capable of anticipation, relating data to actuality rather than eventuality is difficult, and this problem is compounded by man's ability to move his mental presence from the reality of his actual environment to the fantasy of an imagined or anticipated one. Anticipatory responses are not limited to man of course. Rats warned of an impending shock by a tone, lose more weight than their equally shocked counterparts, but man is more rapidly conditioned than the rat and the form and extent of his anticipation more subtle. As a result of these and other factors, biologic studies on man are seldom clean with regard to stimuli, uniform with regard to individual bits of data, or clear with regard to interpretation. Studies do not fall into easy categories, and consequently the following discussion must be more general than specific.

The wide variety of situations that have been used in studying stress responses in man can be roughly divided into five categories: (a) those demanding responsible decision in the absence of overt physical activity; (b) those in which responsibility is coupled with physical action; (c) those in which the subject is an impotent observer in a dangerous situation; (d) those in which the subject is a vicarious participant; (e) those involving a personalized test of ability. An example of category (a) is that of an airline pilot called upon to make a difficult landing; of (b) a member of an athletic team; of (c) an airline passenger in a storm; of (d) a spectator at a movie; and of (e) a subject in a psychologic test. These situations differ in degree of necessary participation, degree of control, and importance of the outcome. The airline pilot must not make an error, but he has some control. The passenger has no control but the consequences are personally serious. The ball player shares control but the consequences of failure are not dangerous. The spectator is involved but not concerned. The student is threatened but not endangered.

Individual variation in such situations is great, probably dependent on each individual's estimation of the degree of personal involvement, extent of the threat, anticipated consequences, and degree of personal control. General trends, however, do exist.

Movies with different emotional contents have been used as stimuli in a number of human studies in the hope of relating psychologic response to stress activation. Serum and urinary corticoids, urinary epinephrine and norepinephrine, and urine volume all increased in emotional films regardless of whether the film content was horrifying, funny, or agitation provoking. Epinephrine excretion was greatest in the fear-provoking movie. These responses did not occur in neutral films in most instances. In one experiment, however, corticoid elevations in response to a neutral movie were reported in a population of patients awaiting hospital discharge. The corticoid effect in this instance was attributed to the emergence of anxiety at leaving the hospital during the film and not to responses to the film itself. This illustrates the problems in identifying the source of the response.

A number of other stress-related variables are altered by emotionally charged situations. Plasma cholesterol increases in subjects exposed to such varied stimuli as occupational overload or scholastic examinations. Serum lipoproteins and plasma free fatty acid rise in anxiety and fear probably because of concurrent elevations in catecholamines, although these various indices do not move always in concert. It has been suggested that levels of plasma free fatty acids correlate with anxiety but not hostility, triglyceride levels with both anxiety and hostility, and cholesterol levels with hostility alone.

Blood lymphocyte levels are lowered by situations such as race driving and college examinations; ion excretion is altered by psychologic tasks like rotary pursuit or stressful interviews, and as noted above stressors may alter urine flow. Because some compounds are excreted in a volume-dependent manner, such changes in urine production must be considered in evaluating stress induced changes in a urinary constituent. For example, epinephrine, norepinephrine, and 5-hydroxyindoleacetic acid excretions all strongly correlate with urine volume. Catecholamine excretion is altered in many stressful situations and some studies suggest that the ratio of excreted norepinephrine to epinephrine is related to the direction of aggression or to the degree of aggression relative to the anxiety provoked by the stimulus. Individuals with high drive are reported to excrete more catecholamine and to have higher epinephrine to norepinephrine ratios than their less ambitious counterparts. Athletes awaiting action have increased urinary epinephrine levels, whereas those involved in action have increased urinary norepinephrine excretion. Circulating norepinephrine concentrations appear correlated more with degree than with the kind of emotional response, but although urinary epinephrine and norepinephrine intercorrelate well, epinephrine but not norepinephrine correlates with 17-hydroxycorticoid excretion. This is compatible with the posited relationship between anxiety and both corticoid and epinephrine excretion.

Not all stimuli eliciting elevations in catecholamine excretion are necessarily unpleasant. Male subjects viewing sexually arousing films had markedly increased excretion of epinephrine, whereas females did not. Moderate increases in norepinephrine were observed with both sexes. As noted previously only a small fraction of the total excreted catecholamine is excreted as free amine. Most is excreted as metanephrine and normetanephrine, and these compounds appear to move in unison, being low during quiescence and high during agitation. Their ratio remains relatively constant.

Thyroid function may also be altered by some stressors. There is considerable individual variation, however. Elevations in PBI have been reported to follow scholastic examinations, viewing of stressful movies, and after continuous performance tasks. In one study stressful interviews lead to an initial decrease in protein-bound iodine followed by a subsequent slow increase suggestive of a biphasic stress response.

2. Animal Studies

A vast number of psychologic stressors have been used in animal studies ranging from sound to shock and isolation to shaking. Only excerpts from a few of these are discussed here.

a. Shock

As an experimental stressor, electric shock has the considerable advantage of control over duration and administered intensity of the stimuli. It has the disadvantage that the degree of control is more apparent than real and that the stressor itself is not a simple one. Although delivered voltage or amperage may be controlled, resistance is variable depending upon animal size and positioning and on unintended conductors like feces and urine. The animal who freezes and takes the full period of shock is stressed differently than the animal who jumps, rolls, and bridges to escape. The experience itself is a compounding of fear, pain, muscular exertion, sometimes transitory anoxia, and sometimes transitory anorexia.

Despite these difficulties shock has been used as a stressor per se, a tool for memory disruption, a model for electroconvulsive therapy, and a side product of neurophysiologic studies, particularly those on reward and punishment systems.

Like several other stimuli, electric shock is ineffective in eliciting adrenocortical activity during the early postnatal stress-nonresponsive period. Thereafter, electric shock results in the usual adrenocortical activation characterizing stress. Serum and adrenal corticoids are elevated, adrenal size is increased, and blood eosenophiles drop. Urinary sodium and potassium are not altered suggesting that mineralocorticoids are not involved. As might be expected from the fear component of the stressor, adrenal catecholamines are released and blood glucose is increased, probably by a direct action of epinephrine on glycogen stores since adrenalectomy abolishes the glucose rise. Blood glucose is also markedly elevated by other stressors having a strong fear component, such as restraint or fighting, and if renal threshold is exceeded glucosuria results.

In contrast to stressors such as cold or handling, little qualitative adaptation occurs upon repeated shock treatment, at least as measured by these indices.

Shock has recently been used to evaluate the dual questions of whether stressors modify central nervous system metabolism of monoamines, and whether such modifications involve monoamine-containing neurons mediating central and peripheral responses to stress. Activation of such neurons should be reflected in increased transmission and thereby either alterations in the steady state levels of the monoamines or an increase in their turnover. Such changes alone of course do not demonstrate primary mediation since they may also be the result of the action of stress-elicited hormones on monoamine-metabolizing enzymes.

In contrast to results with other stressors, results obtained using shock have been relatively consistent. Levels of norepinephrine appear unchanged by low-level foot shock (1.6 mA), although norepinephrine levels are decreased by more strenuous foot shock (2.6 mA). At both shock levels, norepinephrine turnover is enhanced, although with the higher intensity shock norepinephrine degradation appears to exceed synthesis. The fall in norepinephrine can be prevented by treatment with monoamine oxidase inhibitors but not by catechol-O-methyltransferase inhibitors. Catechol-O-methyltransferase is thought to be the enzyme responsible for degrading norepinephrine released into the synaptic cleft. Deaminated products of norepinephrine are the predominant metabolite during shock and normetanephrine appears to be actually decreased when low shock intensities are used and to slightly increase after higher shock intensities. This could be interpreted to indicate that the primary action of shock is to release norepinephrine from intraneuronal vesicles, whereby it is subject to intracellular deamination by mitochondrial monoamine oxidase. The increase in norepinephrine turnover might reflect release of tyrosine hydroxylase from feedback inhibition rather than increased noradrenergic activity. This, together with increased degradation of unbound norepinephrine, would lead both to increased turnover and to a rise in deaminated metabolites. Some degree of adaptation has been noted. Norepinephrine turnover in shock is accelerated by previous shocks or shock of higher intensity, and brain tyrosine hydroxylase activity is increased.

Alterations in dopamine levels are less clear. Decreased dopamine levels following shock have been reported in one study, although in others neither level nor turnover are changed. Foot shock administered to animals pretreated with the tyrosine hydroxylase blocker, α-methyl-p-tyrosine, leads to a greater fall in dopamine than that accounted for by the action of the inhibitor alone, suggesting that this monoamine, too, is under dynamic control and that its catabolism is also accelerated by shock.

Like dopamine, serotonin levels are essentially unaltered by foot shock, but turnover appears enhanced, as determined both by the increased rate of conversion of labeled tryptophan to serotonin and by an increased formation of brain 5-hydroxyindoleacetic acid. In contrast to norepinephrine, prior shock experience does not alter the extent of serotonin turnover. Acetylcholine levels are not altered by foot shock.

Although electroconvulsive shock could be considered a more severe form of foot shock, it does differ in the degree of transitory anoxia and muscular exertion. Electroshock may increase the permeability of the blood-brain barrier to norepinephrine and other agents. Chronic electroconvulsive treatment in rats increases brain weight, brain protein content, and total acetylcholinesterase. Subsequent behavior is markedly impaired.

Handing parameters also differ significantly between shock studies and electroconvulsive treatment, and as has been pointed out the usual control groups may not be appropriate to studies on electroconvulsive shock. Handling in electric shock studies is usually limited to transfer into and out of the shock box. Electroconvulsive shock requires that electrodes be directly placed on the head, and the extent and immediacy of handling adds another stress dimension. Finally rapid metabolic shifts occur during the convulsive episode that are not paralleled by events during foot shock. As an example glucose uptake by brain is retarded during convulsions and increased thereafter. For the period of the seizure itself, acetylcholine rapidly falls, ammonia production increases, brain glycogen, ATP, and glucose decrease, and oxygen consumption and blood flow increase. Restorative processes occur during the postictal phase.

Because of these differences, it is not too surprising that the extent and direction of monoamine changes in electroconvulsive shock differ somewhat from the changes with foot shock, or that findings are more discrepant in electroconvulsive shock studies. Brain norepinephrine levels following electroconvulsive treatment have been reported to be initially unchanged and then to fall slightly, acutely to rise and then to slowly fall, and after chronic treatment to initially rise in brainstem and after some hours to also increase in telencephalon and diencephalon. Turnover is reported to be increased and persistent. Amine changes are regionally specific, and within regions the temporal pattern appears to vary for each amine so that some of these conflicts may be more apparent than real. Dopamine levels are elevated by even a single electroconvulsive treatment, as is homovanillic acid, the primary dopamine catabolite. Serotonin levels are modestly increased in most but not all studies, but the rate of increase appears rather slow after a single electroconvulsive treatment and more rapid if the animal has received a series of prior shock treatments. Many of these changes, however, may be related to the handling stress rather than the electroconvulsive shock itself. Histamine levels also reportedly increase slowly following electroconvulsive treatment and the rate of increase is unaffected by prior exposure to electroconvulsive sessions.

Despite the intense stimulation of the central nervous system resulting from electric shock, initial turnover of proteins, and nucleic acids is only marginally increased, but glutaminase and ammonia increase while glutamine synthetase is unchanged.

Electrical self-stimulation is also a stressor, even though it is apparently pleasurable since it is self-induced and animals will work to receive it. In the monkey self-stimulation is accompanied by increased plasma and urinary corticoids, increased urinary epinephrine, and less consistently increased urinary norepinephrine as well. In the rat adrenal weights are elevated and brain norepinephrine is decreased whether animals are self-stimulating in brain regions eliciting appetative behavior or are instrumentally stimulated in regions eliciting aversive behavior. Such catecholamine changes reportedly occur only if emotionality is elicited. However, direct electrical stimulation in some brain areas alters adrenocortical activity, so the adrenocortical changes may be due to the spread of stimulation to areas involved in CRF release rather than to emotionality.

b. Restraint

Restraint is another commonly used laboratory stressor that has the apparent advantage of being relatively simple. Again this simplicity is more apparent than real. At best this stressor is compounded of fear, isometric muscular activity, and muscle cramps due to specific positioning. In acute experiments plasma and adrenal corticoids are elevated, and some degree of adaptation occurs. Experimentally this poses some problem since the magnitude of the stressor varies with experience and more subtly with differences in positioning and handling between experiments and experimentors. Chronic restraint (continuous restraint for 24 to 48 hr) leads to involution of the thymus and adrenal hypertrophy and to the production of gastric ulcers. The degree of ulceration and ulcer location varies with species. Mice and rats show a high ulcer incidence, guinea pigs have a lower incidence and hamsters a very low incidence of ulceration. Rabbits and monkeys ordinarily have little or no ulceration upon restraint. Chronic restraint of course is also complicated by concomitant voluntary or involuntary fasting, which varies both with accessibility of food and the emotional state of the animal.

Metabolically, peripheral tissues, such as liver and heart, show increased oxidation of glucose, pyruvate, α-ketoglutarate and succinate during acute restraint, and heart cardiolipin is decreased. Both of these effects disappear as the restraint episodes are repeated.

Tyrosine transaminase activity in liver is increased by chronic immobilization. This increase is dependent upon the adrenals and only occurs in animals showing the development of ulcers, although the rise in transaminase activity precedes ulcer formation. Tryptophan oxygenase activity is also increased twofold after 6 hr of restraint and somewhat more at the end of 24 hr. Adrenalectomy lessened but did not abolish this enzymic response. Both substrate and hormone induce tryptophan oxygenase, so these results implicate substrate induction as the mechanism for this enzymic response to restraint.

Short-term restraint (7 mins) reportedly increases brain norepinephrine concentrations in mice, particularly isolated mice. On the other hand, brain norepinephrine levels of mice, guinea pigs, or rats restrained for 2 or more than 2 hr decreased by 10 to 20%. Changes were most marked in cerebellum and hypothalamus and central noradrenergic neurons appeared depleted histochemically. On the whole inhibitor studies indicate a more rapid depletion of norepinephrine from noradrenergic neurons following restraint. However, prior housing conditions do appear important in this phenomenon, and mice raised in isolation reportedly show a faster fall in norepinephrine upon chronic restraint than those raised in grouped environments.

Acute restraint also appears to increase brain dopamine, whereas chronic restraint leads to a fall in dopamine levels. Serotonin changes appear more complex. Both long- and short-term exposure to restraint appear to elevate serotonin. However, it has also been reported that serotonin is decreased after 3 hr of restraint but returns to normal after 6 hr of restraint. Strangely enough combining shock and restraint eliminates any restraint-dependent alterations in serotonin levels. GABA levels may be slightly impaired by restraint.

c. Swimming

Swimming to exhaustion has been widely employed to study brain mono-amine changes in stress because of the initial finding that brain serotonin increased, whereas norepinephrine decreased following such treatment. Nor-epinephrine uptake by brain appears to be retarded in this stress. These changes in brain norepinephrine are analogous to those occurring when shock or restraint are employed as stressors. Contributions to these changes from the physiologic effects of exhaustion are difficult to assess, since exhaustion alone produces central effects. For example, brain histidine levels fall and serum DBH increases.

d. Shaking

Shaking has also been used as a stressor. Rats exposed to this continuous earthquake show marked adrenal activation, large and persistent increase in plasma and adrenal corticoids, and a decrease in adrenal ascorbic acid. Despite these increases, neither tyrosine transaminase nor tryptophan pyr-rolase levels increase, although both are elevated by injection of hydro-cortisone. Indeed this stressor blocks the effects of administered hydro-cortisone on tyrosine transaminase induction. Shaking adrenalectomized animals leads to an actual lowering of tyrosine aminotransferase, and this inhibitory action is partly abolished by hypophysectomy and completely abolished by hypophysectomy together with adrenalectomy. These results suggest that this stress activates a mechanism, probably pituitary in origin, that represses activation of tyrosine aminotransferase and prevents the inductive effects of hydrocortisone on this enzyme. Growth hormone has been implicated as this antagonist. More generally these results demonstrate that stress does not lead to an invariant enzymic response by glucocorticoid-stimulated hormones.

A second point emerging from such studies is that infant and adult enzymic responses to the same stressor are not necessarily identical. Infant rats shaken by this procedure do not show an elevation in corticoids until about 8 days of age. However, tyrosine aminotransferase activity, is elevated in infant animals 4 and 8 days of age, even though this same stress blocks elevations in adult animals who do respond with adrenocortical activation. Similar inhibition of this enzyme have been obtained in adult adrenalectomized animals using laparotomy or electric shock as a stressor.

B. Physiological Stressors

Animals subjected to purely psychologic stressors are often anorexic, may have exacerbations of otherwise subsymptomatic infections, may suffer from tissue damage, and often undergo transitory temperature changes. For this reason some information on physiologic stressors is of importance even to those primarily interested in psychologic stress. Because physiologic stressors are easier to define operationally, considerably more information is available on them, although in principle they are no less complex than psychologic ones. The brief reviews to follow are limited to those parameters of some relevance to the general subject of stress or illustrative of particular experimental problems and are not intended to be exhaustive.

1. Cold

Because rates of reaction are temperature dependent, the ability of homeothermic animals to maintain a relatively narrow range of internal temperature has given them a considerable evolutionary advantage. This is paid for by physiologic shifts required to meet the challenge of changing temperature. Generally these shifts are designed to alter heat loss and heat production. In the case of exposure to cold, this means a transitory increase in nonuseful work, such as shivering, changes in vascular supply, and alterations in metabolism. These in turn require a shift in homeostasis from one level to another, and in principal cold should be a stressor. Once appropriate adjustments are made, however, the altered metabolism is no longer a stress response, but rather an expression of a new level of homeostasis, and the animal's temperature is adapted until the next temperature shift. Distinctions then must be made between acute and chronic effects of this stress, which are different than those in a stressor like hunger where no final satisfactory adjustment can be made.

The discussion below is limited to adult homeothermic animals. Neonates of many warm-blooded animals are born poikelothermic and are able to survive temperatures intolerable to the adult. Indeed vasomotor mechanisms for heat regulation develop in concordance with the increasing need to maintain constancy of temperature. The developmental period of cold-bloodedness varies from species to species, being only hours in the case of Eider ducks to weeks for the rat. During such early poikelothermic periods, cold is not an equal stressor for the neonate and the adult. The newborn rat for example does not respond to cold with adrenocortical activation for the first 13 to 16 days of life.

Acute exposure of adult rodents to cold raises peripheral corticoids, adrenal corticoids, urinary excretion of corticoids, pituitary ACTH content, decreases adrenal ascorbic acids, adrenal cholesterol, and circulating eosinophiles, and increased adrenal weight. By the criterion of adrenal activation then, acute cold is a stressor.

This pattern is not uniform for all species, however. Exposure of the human to abrupt cold results in only a slight rise in plasma cortisol after a 1-hr exposure, and urinary 17-hydroxycorticoids are unchanged. There is no change in corticoids in man, if temperature is lowered gradually. Adrenal weight of the spider monkey increases somewhat by exposure to cold (but not heat), the rate of 17-hydroxycorticosteroid secretion by the adrenal of cold exposed dogs is only elevated if the dog is exposed to extremely low temperatures, and the quail responds with increased adrenocorticoid secretion but no change in adrenal ascorbic acid.

The effects of cold in rodents, are dependent on the time of exposure, the rapidity of onset, and age. Adrenal ascorbic acid initially drops, returns to normal in 48 hr after cold exposure and continues to increase to a steady peak level of 160% above normal by 10 days after exposure. This increase in ascorbic acid is not limited to the adrenal alone but occurs in other tissues as well, although only adrenal ascorbic acid is depleted by the stress of cold. In contrast blood corticoid levels of the rat acutely rise upon cold exposure and only slowly return to baseline. Blood corticoid levels are normal by day 18, but the relative rates of formation of corticosterone and 18-hydroxycorticosterone are altered, so that their ratio differs from that of controls. Finally adrenocortical activation in response to cold is more marked in young rats than in older ones owing in part to the difference in their metabolic reserves.

The autonomic nervous system is rapidly activated by cold. There is an immediate release of catecholamines from both the adrenal medulla and extramedullary sources. This response is rather general between species and occurs in the dog and man, as well as the rat. Epinephrine excretion increases more markedly than norepinephrine excretion during the period of initial challenge, suggesting a marked discharge from the adrenal medulla. With time, however, epinephrine excretion begins to decline, whereas tonic stimulation of the autonomic nervous system continues and norepinephrine levels remain high. Normetanephrine excretion is markedly elevated as well, attesting to the continual release and metabolism of norepinephrine during cold. High catecholamine levels in the adrenal parallel the increase in total urinary catecholamine, and indeed the nonshivering thermogenesis of the cold-adapted rat appears to be mediated by the catecholamines, and most probably by norepinephrine itself.

These changes in catecholamines are initially accompanied in the rat by an acute fall in pituitary growth hormone, which, however, returns to normal within 3 hr. This could result from a transient localized hypoglycemia in sensitive hypothalamic areas since growth hormone is released in hypoglycemia. However, changes in blood glucose levels are not synchronous with the time for growth hormone release. Depression of blood glucose during chronic cold exposure can occur, and with it an accompanying fall in insulin levels. Thyroid hormone is also released during the initial phase of cold exposure and secretion of pituitary TSH is increased. The persistence of these changes in cold is somewhat controversial.

These endocrinologic shifts are accompanied by a series of physiologic shifts although the exact relationship between the two is unclear. The onset of cold triggers rapid sympathetic vasoconstriction so as to control heat loss. Heat production is rapidly accelerated both in rats and in man, and metabolic rate increases at the expense of metabolic reserves. Norepinephrine mediation of lipase activity, which requires the presence of glucocorticoids, accelerates release of free fatty acids from adipose tissue, plasma free fatty acid levels markedly increase, triglycerides and other lipids accumulate in liver awaiting degradation, and as might be expected total body fat rapidly declines. The release of epinephrine promotes conversion of glycogen to glucose and glycogen storage quickly dwindles. Throughout this period there is an increased excretion of urinary nitrogen attesting to the contribution of protein to the catabolic fire.

This outpouring of metabolic activity often increases acetyl CoA levels faster than it can be utilized by the Krebs cycle, fatty acid biosynthesis, or other metabolic pathways. As a result, acetone, acetoacetic acid, and β-hydroxybutyrate accumulate, and ketosis develops. This increase of CoA levels in tissues other than adrenal inhibits synthesis of fatty acids while promoting their oxidation, and this process, together with the decline in reduced NADPH following the decrease in intracellular glycogen, decreases formation of lipid from acetate.

Not surprisingly levels of metabolic enzymes are altered during cold stress and adaptation. Within 6 hr, histidine decarboxylase activity increases and in 3 to 4 weeks there are increased hepatic activities of arginase, glutamic-oxalacetic aminotransferase, tyrosine aminotransferase, and tryptophan oxygenase. All but the latter two are attributable to the increased food consumption accompanying cold adaptation. The rise of tryptophan oxygenase occurs after the first 4 hr of cold exposure and is not abolished by prior adrenalectomy, so that this rise is not caused by adrenocortical induction of this enzyme.

During the process of adaptation, short-chain amino acids, such as alanine, glycine and serine, as well as urea and creatinine, are excreted in increased amounts. By the time of adaptation, glucose-6-phosphatase activity in liver and both glucose-6-phosphatase and glucokinase activity in muscle are elevated, whereas activities of glucose-6-phosphate dehydrogenase and 6-phosphogluconate dehydrogenase decrease. Thus formation of glucose from glucose-6-phosphate is facilitated and reflected in the increased utilization of glucose by the cold-adapted rat. Hexose-monophosphate-shunt activity is depressed at this time, but the depression disappears with longer cold exposure and adaptation. During the acute phase, however, NADPH accumulates and fatty acid synthesis is depressed.

Cold per se seems to have only a limited influence on the central nervous system. Acute cold does not change brain serotonin levels although urinary 5-hydroxyindoleacetic acid excretion becomes elevated within a few days and this elevation persists thereafter. Histamine excretion increases to peak values in 2 months of exposure and then slowly declines. Similarly brain dopamine and norepinephrine are initially constant, but rise slightly after a month of cold exposure. Peripheral catecholamine turnover is increased as is hypothalamic norepinephrine turnover. Increased norepinephrine turnover also occurs in heat stress. Adrenal tyrosine hydroxylase activity is increased in cold. Brain monoamine oxidase activity has been reported to be lowered by cold. Cholineterase activity is unchanged. Finally brain glutamic acid is decreased somewhat during acute cold exposure but returns to normal with time.

2. Heat

Thermal stress of course poses quite different problems to the organism than cold stress. Heat dissipation rather than conservation becomes critical, and subcutaneous vasodilation substitutes for vasoconstriction. Heat production must be decreased, the need for fuel is diminished, and food consumption drops. Heat does elicit a rise in adrenal corticoids. However, the rise is of modest proportions and is age dependent. Adrenal size increases with chronic exposure. Adrenal norepinephrine content is unchanged by heat, but adrenal epinephrine levels may increase slightly. Aldosterone secretion increases. Although aldosterone has some effects on enzymes such as succinoxidase, which increases in activity during heat exposure, these changes do not depend upon aldosterone secretion.

In general heat exposure produces more of a behavioral change than cold exposure. The apathy and lethargy and decreased reaction time during the heat of summer for example are familiar to all, and, even though these effects are obviously of value in reducing heat production, little is known about their central control. Neither whole brain nor hypothalamic norepinephrine levels are affected by heat as a stressor, although turnover in the hypothalamus is increased. Marginal decreases in brain serotonin levels have been reported, but serotonin turnover appears increased, and 5-HIAA is elevated. Brain glutamic acid declines in this stress as it does in acute cold.

Generally then exposure to temperature changes elicits transitory stress responses during the adaptation from one temperature range to another. Physiologic and metabolic activities of animals adapted to different temperature ranges differ, but once adaptation has occurred, these differences can no longer be truly regarded as stress responses, even though they may inadvertently be included in stress studies. It is only when adaptation cannot occur, because for example the temperature of exposure is not compatible with life, food is not available to supply the increase in metabolic needs, or hormonal function is inadequate, that temperature continues to be a stressor until death.

3. Hunger

The progression from the sensation of hunger through the metabolic adaptations in fasting to the final terminus of starvation is depressingly common in the world of nature and of man. The metabolic machine must be fueled. The adult organism stores a considerable reserve of metabolic fuel so that with few exceptions short bursts of fasting neither threaten the organism nor generate impossible discomfort. What is true for the adult is not true for the infant, however. Inadequate nutrition in early extrauterine or intrauterine life may lead to irreversible alterations of brain. Permanent decreases in total brain weight, brain DNA, and brain protein have been observed in animals reared under nutritional deprivation, and in humans body and head growth is decreased. The sociologic implications of these studies are obvious!

Since large metabolic shifts occur during fasting, and homeostasis is disturbed, fasting should be a potent physiologic stressor. Indeed blood and adrenal corticoid levels rise 18 to 20 hr after food is removed from rats normally maintained on an *ad lib* diet. On the other hand, normal or obese men fasted over moderate periods of time have normal excretion of 17-ketosteroids and 17-hydroxycorticoids during the first days of fasting and excretion tends to decrease thereafter. Plasma cortisol levels are unchanged throughout. Both biologic and psychologic factors may contribute to the difference in adrenocortical responses of man and the rat.

Biologically small animals, such as the rat, have a larger surface-to-volume ratio than larger animals and consequently lose heat more easily and must expend proportionately more energy to maintain body temperature. Similarly physical work is a function of distance, time and mass, and only the latter changes with animal size. As a consequence small animals expend relatively more energy in carrying out normal exploratory behavior than do larger animals. Even the relative proportion of the lifespan encompassed in a fixed period of fasting is greater for small than large animals. For example, 1 week of fasting for a rat represents $\frac{1}{100}$ of its lifespan. An equivalent period for a man would be nearly 8.5 months. Psychologically men are certain they will not be starved to death in the experiment. The rat has no such assurance. Indeed the physiologic consequences of anxiety may play a greater role in the early adrenocortical response to fasting than the alteration in metabolic demand.

Other hormonal systems, in addition to the adrenal cortex, are involved in hunger. Growth hormone is released in fasting in man. Growth hormone falls in the rat. Blood glucagon levels in man were found to be elevated in some, but not all studies in fasting, which may reflect individual variations in the ability to maintain blood sugar levels. Insulin levels of course are normally low since blood glucose either remains constant or falls. On the other hand, excretion of epinephrine, norepinephrine, and VMA increases in both normal and obese humans upon fasting. Catecholamine changes are largest in fasting obese subjects, but decreases in blood glucose are more pronounced in subjects of normal weight.

The mechanism for metabolic shifts in fasting differ between phyla, but the general pattern is similar. Glycogen and glucose stores are consumed, metabolism shifts from glycolysis to gluconeogenesis, lipid catabolism increases, synthesis of long-chain fatty acids decreases, and general protein synthesis decreases.

After 24 hr of fasting, 30% of brain glycogen of the rat is gone, as is 85% of liver glycogen. With this dwindling of carbohydrate reserves, lipids and proteins are mobilized and, after the first period of adaptation, lipid becomes the predominant energy source. Thus the metabolic machine is normally maintained by a balanced metabolism of fatty acid and carbohydrate in a caloric homeostasis, which is reflected in reciprocal blood levels of these materials. When glucose is high, blood fatty acids are low, and conversely a decrease in blood glucose is accompanied by an increase in fatty acids. Fatty acids are oxidized at rates roughly proportional to their blood levels. As carbohydrate stores, in the form of glycogen in liver and muscle, are consumed, the organism shifts to fat metabolism to provide 80% of the required fuel, and protein metabolism to supply the remaining 20%. The brain in particular is the great consumer of glucose, and gluconeogenisis is carried out primarily to meet this requirement. However, with continued fasting, the brain can adapt to utilize γ-hydroxybutyrate and acetoacetic acid in sufficient quantities to reduce the extent of protein catabolism. The precise mechanism for this adaptation is unclear, but it does at least delay burning down the cellular walls to maintain the cellular fire.

These metabolic shifts require enzymic participation. However, estimations of enzymic activities can be deceptive in the fasting animals because of concomitant changes in organ size and composition. For example liver decreases by 50% in the rat after 3 days of fasting, whereas soluble protein/gram liver increases slightly. As a result a wholly inert protein, being neither synthesized or degraded, will show an apparent twofold increase in activity when calculated per gram of liver and something a little less than that if activity is expressed per gram of protein.

With these considerations, there are marked changes in glycolytic and gluconeogenic enzymes during fasting. In the rat the gluconeogenic enzymes, glucose-6-phosphatase, phosphoenolpyruvate carboxykinase, fructose-1,6, diphosphatase, and pyruvate carboxylase are either preferentially spared or actually synthesized in the midst of general protein catabolism. On the other hand, the important glycolytic enzymes glucokinase, phosphofructokinase, and pyruvate kinase fall in activity. Furthermore pyruvate kinase is inhibited by free fatty acids, NADH, and ATP, which altogether provide a multilevel control for shutting off glycolysis. Metabolism of glucose via the hexose monophosphate shunt in liver is also diminished in fasting as a result of a fall in activity of glucose-6-phosphate dehydrogenase.

Concomitant with these changes is a fall in acetyl CoA carboxylase, which, together with fatty acid synthetase, forms long-chain fatty acids from malonlyl CoA. Malic enzyme and citrate-condensing enzyme also decrease in both adipose tissue and liver, further inhibiting lipogenesis.

Upon prolonged fasting heavier polysomes decrease with the formation of smaller polyribosomal chains and a decrease in the number of ribosomes accompanying accelerated RNA breakdown, particularly breakdown of ribosomal RNA. The degree of polysomal aggregation seems dependent upon tryptophan levels and the deaggregation in fasting may be due to an eventual reduction in cellular levels of this amino acid as a result of increased tryptophan oxygenase activity. Tryptophan also appears to play a key role in promoting formation of an inactive form of phosphoenolpyruvate carboxykinase, thereby inhibiting gluconeogenesis when tryptophan levels are high and relieving the inhibition when tryptophan levels are low. As might be expected, the decrease in heavier polysomes is reflected in a general fall in protein synthesis.

As mentioned previously, control mechanisms for these changes vary with different species. For example in the rat fasting elevates the levels of an inactive form of pyruvate carboxylase. This does not occur in ruminants, like sheep, however, who normally depend upon a high level of gluconeogenesis from propionate and bacterial protein. Instead in these animals fasting increases pyruvate carboxylase.

Even more marked than the interspecies variations in adaptations to fasting is the variation in organ responses within a species. Most of the changes discussed to this point have referred specifically to liver, adipose tissue, or muscle. In a sense the rather extensive changes occurring in these tissues are designed to spare the brain.

The behavioral and biochemical consequences of avitaminosis are well known. Deficiencies in thiamine, carotene, pyridoxine, nicotinamide, biotin, and pantothenic acid, especially, lead to a variety of neurologic, as well as peripheral, problems ranging from the dementia of pellagra, through the neuritis of beri beri, to the impaired vision in night-blindness. However, avitaminosis is generally a resultant of continuous undernutrition rather than the abrupt fasting in stress studies. If the effects of avitaminosis are set aside, the absence of caloric intake has remarkably little effect on the brain or upon behavior. Man has been particularly suitable for behavioral studies not only because of his rich behavioral repetoire but also because avitaminosis can be avoided by use of vitamin supplementation. Furthermore starvation can be carried out therapeutically for startling periods of time. For example obese subjects have been maintained literally without food beyond vitamin supplements for 4 months, with increased serum uric acid, decreased body potassium and protein, and, in some instances, slight drops in blood glucose as the only gross physiologic changes, and some increase in immature pranks as the only psychologic ones.

Transient fasting in rats also seems to have relatively little effect on central nervous system physiology or behavior. Fasted animals initially show an increase in exploratory behavior and transient hunger is often used as a motivating factor in behavioral studies. Some central nervous system changes have been reported but it is difficult to know whether these are related directly to decreased caloric intake or are secondary to some degree of avitaminosis, since vitamin supplementation is seldom employed in such studies and little is known about the rate of vitamin depletion in starved animals.

Despite decreases in muscle and blood glucose levels, in fasting, brain glucose is relatively stable. Uptake of inorganic phosphate, total brain phosphate and phospholipid levels decrease, however. Activities of glutamic acid dehydrogenase and to a lesser extent lactic acid dehydrogenase in brain also decrease with prolonged starvation. Free amino acid levels remain relatively stable with small fluctuations even during prolonged fasting. Although one brief report suggested that brain serotonin, but not norepinephrine or dopamine, increased in fasted mice maintained at 23°C, but not in mice maintained at 34°C, monoamine levels in the rat are unaffected by short-term fasting.

The importance of fasting to the stress literature then lies less with the direct effects of this stressor on brain per se, than with the possibility that peripheral effects of starvation may confuse interpretations of findings in stress situations in which fasting is inadvertently included. Mental turmoil may be accompanied by anorexia and insomnia just as animals exposed to continuous immobilization may be unable to eat, whereas those exposed to continuous shock may voluntarily decrease consumption. Furthermore results obtained with fasting again emphasize the nonequivalence of stressors and the difficulty in generalizing from one stress situation to another.

4. Other Stressors

Hunger and cold are the two most common physiologic stressors that are often unintentionally encountered in stress studies. Obviously a variety of other stressors, such as thirst, exhaustion, tissue damage, bone fractures, and even spontaneous tumors and pregnancy, have been studied both as stressors in their own right and as contributors to other stress studies. The variety of responses elicited by these stressors will not be discussed here. Some mention should be made of infection, however, because it is a frequent contaminant of stress studies in animals and because of its heuristic importance in again underlining the significant differences between stressors.

Unless special precautions are taken, laboratory rodents are frequently endogenously infected by *Mycoplasma mycoides* and viral murine pneumonia. Under the usual laboratory conditions, these infections are latent and the animals asymptomatic. However, under chronic stress situations, the infections may become manifest. Most investigators are all too familiar with the reddish nose, red-rimmed eyelids, and cheesy, pustulant lungs of animals with lung crud. The exacerbations of this disease by stress is caused in part by the direct anti-inflammatory and antiphagocytic properties of the adrenal corticoids elicited by the stressor. Not only may such infections confound interpretation of results but if overlooked may lead to wholly misleading conclusions.

Infection as such also poses a peculiar dilemma for the body. On the one hand, it represents a direct threat to life and should be a stressor. Furthermore corticoids stabilize cellular lysosomes and modify local blood flow, which afford the organism some protection from bacterial endotoxins. On the other hand, the normal immunosuppressive and anti-inflammatory effects of corticoids facilitate pathologic consequences of microbial invasions. As a result the response to infection is often an uneasy compromise which is dependent upon the rate and extent of the metabolic displacements elicited by the infection.

Thus pneumococcal septicemia is treated as a stressor. Adrenal corticoids are elevated, and the corticoid-sensitive enzymes tyrosine aminotransferase and tryptophan oxygenase increase in activity. All of these effects decline with time. On the other hand, bacterial pyelonephritis induced by *Streptococcus faecalis* is a slowly developing disease with formation of kidney lesions and a slow decline in renal function. Neither adrenal steroids, corticoid sensitive enzymes such as liver tyrosine aminotransferase and tryptophan oxygenase, or other stress indices are altered in this disease beyond the slight rise in serum corticoids during the initial septicemia.

VI. CONCLUSIONS

Stress research is not a research discipline so much as an orientation. The basic problems of how organisms receive, process, and respond to changes in internal and external environment is the stuff of biology generally and not stress research alone. If stress research does differ from general biology at all, it is only in a heightened concern for the consequences of one adaptational sequence on the next and on the temporal sum of adaptions on the organisms continued ability to adapt. Life is "one damn thing after another" and stress is an ever present condition. Schopenhauer remarked that "It is not what happens to a man that is important, it is what he thinks happened to him." Stressors must be perceived to be stressors and the kind and magnitude of the stressor determines the response. Hopefully it is clear from the forgoing that generalizations based on one stressor cannot be applied to other stressors. Commonalities do indeed exist and it is from these that the operational definition is made. Yet clearly the operational definition of stress and the common usage of that term differ. Not all things eliciting the operational responses are either noxious or deleterious. Furthermore phenomena, both noxious and dangerous, may not fit the operational definition. The differences between effects of stressors then are as important as the similarities between them, just as individual differences between men are as important as their remarkable similarities.

Each stress represents a relatively unique pattern of responses designed to facilitate adaptation to a particular stressor. Many effects of stressors are age dependent and aging itself is a slow continuous adaptation from one biologic stage to another. It is not surprising therefore that an interaction exists between this slow adaptation and the sudden ones required to meet specific challenges. The persistence of the stress is a further factor to be recognized. Some stressors permit adaptation, whereas others preclude it. Some demand a continuous response; others only an initial one. Metabolic processes of value in meeting an acute emergency situation may be deleterious or metabolically impossible on a chronic basis. Today's metabolic solution may be tomorrow's metabolic dilemma, just as the solution to today's needs may complicate fulfillment of tomorrow's desires. As men compromise to reconcile conflicting needs, so the body must also choose from its finite repetoire of responses those most suitable to the many conflicting needs of the body, and the ideal solution for one set of problems may not be ideal for all.

The effects of stressors are also species dependent. Evolution has shaped each species to its ecologic niche and adapted it to the particular stressors of that microenvironment. Heat is a lesser stressor to the gerbil than to the polar bear. The marmot is inured to the long fast of a winter hibernation, which would be impossible for the hummingbird. Information on the effects of stressors is generally limited to laboratory rodents, dogs, and primates. It is to be expected that alternate adaptations will be found in stress responses of other organisms.

The stressors discussed here have been discussed in isolation. In the real world, stressors cascade and the physiologic shifts required for adaptation to combinations of stressors may differ from the arithmetic sum of the responses to the individual stressors. At present even the basic components of responses to individual stressors are only poorly defined and understood, but an evaluation of the combinations and permutation of the numerous natural stressors is ultimately necessary.

A clear beginning has been made on defining the neural connections between receipt of information and activation of neuronal systems involved in release of releasing factors. This will doubtless continue until the highway map is revolved to the rich detail of street maps. Similarly the processes involved in feedback control are being elucidated as is the significance of central hormone receptors. The observations on behavioral effects of releasing factors has opened a new area to be extended to other behaviors and other releasing factors and to the more delicate problem of determining the mechanisms by which such compounds alter neuronal thresholds and patterning. Beyond this is the need to examine the dynamics of these systems as stimuli change in significance and to determine the mechanisms by which the assignment of significance is made. The ingenious approach by some investigators of using the complexities of the stress response as a tool for assessing central nervous system function in mental disease needs extention both to pathologic and normal populations.

There is no less a need to examine and to more clearly define conditions for the metabolic effects of corticoids. Many of our concepts regarding metabolic adaptation are derived from pharmacological effects of relevent hormones. Yet growth hormone is released by fasting and thyroid hormone by cold, and these interact with adrenalcortical hormones at target tissues to elicit different metabolic melodies from the otherwise constant tone of adrenocortical action. Growth hormone inhibits induction of tyrosine aminotransferase while adrenal corticoids stimulate it. Growth hormone markedly stimulates ornithine decarboxylase, and this action is augmented by thyroxine but unaffected by adrenocorticoids. Thyroid hormone inhibits liver monoamine oxidase and catechol-O-methyl transferase and perhaps thereby augments the effects of released epinephrine. Malic enzyme is decreased in fasting but stimulated by thyroxine so that a cold and hungry animal may be under different controls than one that is cold or hungry alone. Relatively little is yet known about the influence of prolactin for example on enzyme induction in different tissues and less about its effects at the physiologic levels that occur following stress. Not only must the interaction of hormones released by stressors be assessed but the parameters involved in determining their metabolic effects must be clarified as well. Growth hormone induces an increase in ornithine decarboxylase within minutes. Glucocorticoids elevate tryptophan pyrrolase within 4 hr and alanine transaminase after 1 day. How long must hormones be elevated to produce these changes under physiologic conditions? Which is determining; the duration of the response, its magnitude, or both? If I am frightened today of what use is an elevated alanine transaminase tomorrow?

Finally the interrelationships between central and peripheral phenomena need fuller examination. Some evidence suggests that tryptophan may play a key role in mediating between protein synthesis and gluconeogenesis and, that by affecting serotonin synthesis, may serve to direct the mood of the animal to meet its bodily needs. The first step in the major pathway of tryptophan degredation is a corticoid inducible hormone. Do changes in this enzyme during stress affect tryptophan availability and does this in turn serve a purpose in uniting behavioral response and bodily needs. Corticoids are picked up by specific brain regions. Does this serve a role beyond feedback inhibition in uniting brain and body?

Two-way intercommunication obviously exists on many levels and these interactions provide the basis for psychosomatic disease. There is no longer any reasonable doubt that biologic state is affected by stressors or that psychologic, social, and cultural factors contribute both to the etiology of specific syndromes and disease generally. Experimental induction of ulcers, changes in susceptability to infection, hypertension, etc. all provide evidence for such interactions. That disease syndromes in man may not be readily or indeed ever reversible by psychotherapeutic techniques does not gainsay the role of stressors in their etiology. As Mirsky has pointed out, "Surely no one should have anticipated that the resolution of psychic distress or social pressures which may have played a role in the precipitation of diabetes mellitus will restore the function of the degenerated β-cells of the islets of Langerhams which occurred in the interim." Nor does the individual variance in perception of and response to stressors mitigate against the interaction between brain and body. That the world is seen through the mirror of past experience is clear both from psychoanalytic observations and studies in physiologic psychology. Animals exposed to stressors in infancy, deprived of maternal care, or differentially housed in adolescence all respond to stressors differently than their normally raised relatives on both behavioral and biologic measures.

The problem then is no longer one of documenting the interaction but rather one of detailing the response to stressors with respect to individual genetic capacity and individual modifications of that capacity arising out of the organism's unique history. The beginnings of the task are at hand.

GENERAL REFERENCES

Blackwell, R. E., and Guilleman, R. (1973): Hypothalamic control of adrenohypophyseal secretion. *Ann. Rev. Physiol.,* 35:357–390.

Davidson, J. M., and Levine, S. (1972): Endocrine regulation of behavior. *Ann. Rev. Physiol.,* 34:375–408.

DeWeid, D., van Delft, A. M. L., Gispen, W. H., Weijnen, J. A. W. M., and van Wimersma Greidanus, T. B. (1972): The role of pituitary-adrenal system hormones in active avoidance conditioning. In: *Hormones and Behavior,* edited by S. Levine, pp. 136–172. Academic Press, New York.

Endroczi, E. (1972): Pavlovian conditioning and adaptive hormones. In: *Hormones and Behavior,* edited by S. Levine, pp. 173–208. Academic Press, New York.

Levi, L. (1972): Stress and distress in response to psychosocial stimuli. *Acta Med. Scand. Suppl.,* 528:1–166.

Mason, J. W. (1968): Organization of psychoendocrine mechanisms. *Psychosomat. Med.,* 30:564–791.

Mirsky, I. A. (1968): The Saul Albert Lecture. Some comments on psychosomatic medicine. Excerpta Medica, International Congress Series #187, pp. 107–123.

Mulrow, P. J. (1972): The adrenal cortex. *Ann. Rev. Physiol.,* 34:409–424.

Schapiro, S. (1971): Hormonal and environmental influences on rat brain development and behavior. In: Brain Development and Behavior, edited by J. B. Sterman, D. V. McGinty, and A. M. Adinolfi, pp. 307–334. Academic Press, New York.

Vernikos-Danellis, J. (1973): Effects of hormones on the central nervous system. In: *Hormones and Behavior,* edited by S. Levine, pp. 11–63. Academic Press, New York.

Yates, F. E., Russell, S. M., and Maran, J. W. (1971): Brain-adenohypophysial communication in mammals. *Ann. Rev. Physiol.,* 33:393–444.

Yuwiler, A. (1971): Stress. In: *Handbook of Neurochemistry, Vol. 6,* edited by A. Lajtha, pp. 103–192. Plenum Press, New York.

Biological Foundations of Psychiatry,
edited by R. G. Grenell and S. Galay.
Raven Press, New York © 1976.

Biologic Correlates of Psychosomatic Illness

James P. Henry and Daniel L. Ely

Department of Physiology, University of Southern California, School of Medicine, Los Angeles, California 90007

I. INTRODUCTION

The psychosomatic approach to disease started with an attempt in the early 1940s to correlate biological processes with the psychological concepts formulated during the preceding half century by Freud and others (Kimball, 1970). Impetus was provided by the physiologist Cannon's work (1929) demonstrating the autonomic and hormonal accompaniments of fear and rage, by Selye's observation (1936, 1950) of the disturbances of function that accompany the adaptive readjustments of the alarm response, and by a growing biochemical expertise that permitted analysis of adrenal responses (Mason, 1968a,b). The approach has been characterized by a progressive acceptance of the idea of the combined effect of multiple risk factors as opposed to that of a single agency that was dominant during the period when the mechanism of acute infection was a central concern of medicine (Kimball, 1970).

A further concept is that starting with the psychosocial stimulation that results from the interaction of an individual with his environment, a chain of events is triggered that eventually results in pathologic disturbances. For man as a social animal the interaction of members of the group during the daily conduct of self- and species-preservative actions constitutes a major source of strong stimuli. This chapter combines the available animal evidence with the results of work with humans to show that certain conditions of the chain of steps from stimulus to pathology have now been established. Harris and Singer (1968) and later Levi (1972) presented a valuable schematic of this sequence (see Fig. 1), which has been modified and forms a basis for this chapter.

When Alexander and French (1948) first contended in the late 1940s that psychoanalytic concepts can be used to explain the conflicts that lead to organic dysfunction, they pointed to a number of diseases whose etiology had resisted explanation. They presented the considerable evidence that conflict situations led to psychosocial activation of emotional response patterns. The diseases they selected were hyperthyroidism, neurodermatitis, peptic ulcer, rheumatoid arthritis, bronchial asthma, ulcerative colitis, and essential hypertension.

Recent progress in the neurologic sciences has led to new ideas about the patterning of the various major functional subdivisions of the central nervous system (MacLean, 1973). Bowlby (1970, 1973) and others (Tiger and Fox, 1971; Maclay and Knipe, 1972) have shown how the ethologists' concepts of attachment and territorial behavior can be used to reexpress older psychologic concepts in terms of experimentally verifiable phenomena. The effects of these instinctual drives upon neuroendocrine response patterns will be discussed. The coping factors that control the intensity of these responses will be considered and finally evidence from animal studies and human observations will be cited to show that sustained neuroendocrine disturbance will eventually lead to pathophysiologic changes.

II. PSYCHOSOCIAL PERCEPTIONS AND THE NEW SOCIOCULTURAL BRAIN

The perception and evaluation of the significance of a social event depends on an interaction between the factors delineated in Box 1 and Box 2 of

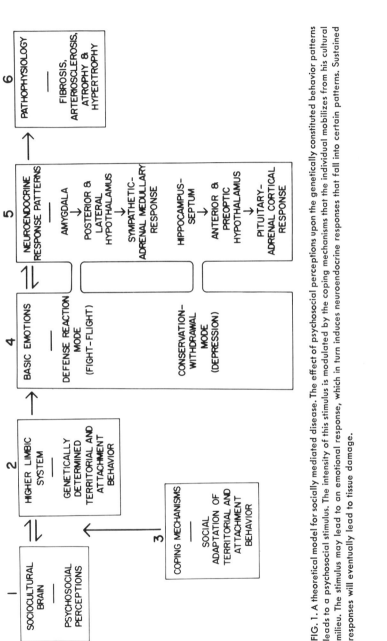

FIG. 1. A theoretical model for socially mediated disease. The effect of psychosocial perceptions upon the genetically constituted behavior patterns leads to a psychosocial stimulus. The intensity of this stimulus is modulated by the coping mechanisms that the individual mobilizes from his cultural milieu. The stimulus may lead to an emotional response, which in turn induces neuroendocrine responses that fall into certain patterns. Sustained responses will eventually lead to tissue damage.

Fig. 1. This involves consideration of the interaction of the newly evolved sociocultural brain and the limbic-striatal system that subserves emotions (MacLean, 1973). Recent research into the mechanism of aphasia and studies of the origins of language have increased understanding of the possible function of the peculiarly human large cortical association areas in the parietal region between the visual, auditory, and sensory motor primary association areas (see Harlow, McGaugh, and Thompson, 1971, pp. 397–399; Lenneberg, 1973). It is now suspected that this position between the primary cortical projection areas for the three modalities is critical for the development of the capability of abstracting from them and creating symbolic concepts, which, although they do not belong to any particular modality, can apply to all. For example, an initial step in abstraction would be to deduce from the visual appearance of an object what it would feel like and so be able to select the right object by touch. Further stages lead to symbols such as words or numbers that have no direct auditory, visual, or tactile associations. There is evidence that the human brain is programmed for language, for some primitive grammatical capacity appears to be inherited and develops spontaneously in the child (Lenneberg, 1973). A degree of programming would account for the universality and remarkably uniform level of complexity and sophistication attained in all of man's languages, even those of surviving aboriginal groups with Stone Age cultures. The limited number of approximately 40 basic phonemes used in any language, despite the enormous proliferation of words of more advanced literate cultures, might be explained by a built-in capability for basic patterns (Harlow et al., 1971).

The parietal cross-modal association area in the subordinate hemisphere appears critical for the capacity to visualize spatial relationships and for that involved in the fabrication of tools and technologic expertise (see Ganong, 1973, p. 93). The question arises whether, in addition to language, rudiments of other nonverbal patterns of complex social behavior are built into these most recently developed regions of the cortex. It is possible that patterns controlling maternal, paternal, and complex, subtle territorially determined aspects of social behavior involve a measure of programmable neocortical capacity, which must develop during maturation if the individual is to become a successfully integrated member of the group (Bowlby, 1970, 1973; Harlow et al., 1971).

Recent work by Nauta (1971) discusses the function of a further large, new association area that also attains overwhelming size in man. He suggests that the frontal lobe serves as the neocortical representative of the limbic system and works in reciprocal relationship with the new temporoparietal cross-modal association areas. It is thought to receive information from the internal milieu that has been processed in the limbic system and hypothalamus. The frontal lobe appears to determine the material to be stored in memory, facilitates planning ahead, and inhibits inappropriate activity.

TABLE 1. *Life-change events and their life-change unit weights scaled for Finland*

Event	Life-change unit weight
Health	
Recent illness (in bed for a week or hospitalization)	62
Change in heavy physical work or exercise	19
Change in sleeping habits	15
Change in eating habits	11
Work	
Recently out of work	50
Recently fired from work	50
Retirement from farming, forestry, or industry	40
Change to new type of work	36
Change in work responsibilities	29
Troubles with boss	22
Work or life going well (awards, achievements, etc.)	20
Correspondence courses (home study)	17
Change in hours of work a day	13
Home and family	
Concern over health of family member	54
Recently married	50
Separation from wife due to marital problems	48
Gaining a new family member (in the home)	39
Separation from wife due to work	34
Engaged to be married	32
New home improvements	26
Son or daughter leaving home	23
Wife began or ended work	23
Troubles with in-laws	22
Change in get-togethers with friends	21
Change to a new residence	15
Change in get-togethers with relatives	13
Vacation	11
Personal and social	
Death of wife	105
Divorce	80
Held in jail	64
Sexual difficulties	41
Change in number of arguments with wife	40
Death of a close relative	39
Financial difficulties	38
Major decisions regarding the future	38
Death of a close friend	34
Unpaid bills leading to threatened legal action	26
Recent purchases worth more than 8,000 Fmk ($2,000)	22
Change in religious or political convictions	20
Change in personal habits	12
Recent purchases worth less than 8,000 Fmk	11
Minor violations of the law	7

(From Rahe et al., 1973.)

Taken together, these two peculiarly human areas compose more than half of man's brain. Washburn and Hamburg (1968) have termed them a new social brain; for these regions are needed for mathematics, for use of language, for tool making, for complex planning, and for the long-term execution of these plans.

The first block of the schematic in Fig. 1 represents the psychosocial perceptions that the various social interactions elicit by stimulating the foregoing social brain. The life-change scale of Holmes and Rahe (1967), which has been developed and tested during the past few years, gives a quantitative feeling for the variations in intensity of such stimulation. The scale depends upon the significance to the individual of commonly occurring events, each of which is objectively verifiable, because it is a matter of personal history. Individual subjective evaluations of stimulus significance are avoided and a weighting value that has been determined for a representative group with the same culture is provided. As can be seen from the list in Table 1, many of these changes have a powerful stimulus value, for they refer to disturbing events in sensitive areas such as home and family, work, and social relations.

A recent paper by Rahe, Bennett, Romo, Siltanen, and Arthur (1973), using a Finnish population, demonstrates that the incidence of sudden death and of myocardial infarctions is significantly greater in those with higher life-change scores during the preceding 6 months. With more life changes, there is a greater incidence of arousing psychosocial interaction that initiates trains of events leading to neuroendocrine disturbances and pathophysiology.

III. TERRITORIAL AND ATTACHMENT BEHAVIOR AS INHERITED RESPONSE PATTERNS

The significance to the organism of events leading to psychosocial interactions, such as those that are the focus of the Holmes-Rahe questionnaire, depends on their stimulus value to the organism. The value is not only the result of appraisal in the sociocultural analysis, it is also strongly affected by the extent to which the culturally determined impact of the event arouses the individual's inherited basic drive mechanisms for self- and species preservation. Here the functions of the second box outlined in Fig. 1 play a role. For in addition to the new sociocultural brain, man has two others that became part of his inheritance in the course of evolution and are reproduced in each of us as ontogeny recapitulates phylogeny. MacLean (1973) presents evidence that these brains constitute three surprisingly separate biocomputers, "each with its own special kind of intelligence, sense of time, and memory." Early forebrain structures developing in the course of evolution were the reticular system, midbrain, and the corpus striatum. The striatum stands out clearly when it is differentially stained both by reagents for cholinesterase and for dopamine. MacLean suggests that in conjunction with the hypothalamus, it is responsible for the unlearned aspects of man's genetically constituted roles. These patterns include the consummatory acts like sex, eating, drinking, and maternal behavior that form the framework of the complex, stereotyped rituals of a culture. The basic patterns of territorial behavior and the associated fight-flight responses are further such material.

Interposed between the brainstem striatal complex and the new social brain is the so-called limbic system that receives olfactory and visceral information as well as inputs from the visual and auditory areas. It is composed of three subdivisions with overlapping functions (MacLean, 1973). He describes the region near the amygdala as involved in self-preservation, i.e., ingestive and fighting behavior. In addition to its role in memory, the hippocampus together with the septal region are involved in genital and the other sexually related, expressive, and feeling states involved in reproductive activity. The cingulate gyrus and the anterior thalamic nuclei constitute a third subdivision of this system. In man these are highly developed, possibly because of the primate shift of emphasis from olfaction to visual behavior, and also because in man maternal and other aspects of sociosexual behavior are prolonged and important.

IV. THE CULTURAL CANON AND COPING BEHAVIOR

A. Influence of Early Socialization of the Territorial and Attachment Responses on Later Coping Behavior

The mechanisms controlling the intensity of the psychosocial stimulus, as outlined in Box 3 of Fig. 1, are diagrammed in the schema portrayed in Fig. 2. This depicts the relationships between the above-mentioned subdivisions of the brain. The central role of the frontal lobe in transmitting information between the temporoparietal cross-modal association areas and the limbic and striatal brain is shown by depicting an arrow connecting them through this region. Then the control runs down from the hypothalamus to a neuroendocrine balance. The circles placed on the arrows represent controls to draw attention to coping processes that modulate the intensity of the brainstem neuroendocrine responses. There is evidence that these coping processes depend for their effectiveness upon the adequacy of the connections between the sociocultural brain and the limbic system and that these connections can be impaired. MacLean (1973) points to the tendency of epileptic discharges to spread in and remain confined to the limbic system. He uses it as an example of the relative independence of the limbic and striatal systems with their environmentally stable patterns of emotionally determined behavior from the new sociocultural brain with its role in linguistically, mathematically based artistic and technical performance. In his discussion of the functions of the frontal lobe, Nauta (1971) has suggested that impairment of this frontal link with the visceral system could lead to an interoceptive agnosia or disturbed ability to integrate information from the internal milieu with the

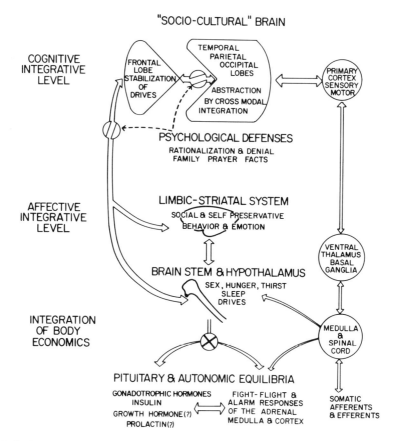

FIG. 2. Mechanisms of physiological response to psychosocial stimulation. The main current of information from the peripheral sense organs courses through the midbrain and thalamus to the primary sensory cortical projection areas. Massive neocortical cross-modal association regions provide the "semiotic" symbol-handling capacity needed for his culture and technology. The frontal pole connects this "social" brain with the amygdala, hippocampus, septum, and cingulate gyrus. These "limbic" structures together with the striatal storehouse of "ancestrally learned behavior" (MacLean, 1973) subserve emotion and are closely integrated with the hypothalamus that effects consummation of the basic drives. The circles on the arrows represent controls to draw attention to the coping mechanisms involved in the control of emotional responses (Lazarus, 1975). The hypothalamus together with the nonspecific reticular activating system modulates varied pituitary, vagal, and sympathetic reactions that eventually can lead to pathophysiologic changes.

environmental reports provided by the neocortical processing mechanisms. For, he points out, it is primarily in the frontal cortex that the pathways representing the internal and external milieus converge.

Nemiah and Sifneos (1970) have recently drawn attention to an operational mentality, which they find characteristic of patients suffering from diseases, such as coronary ischemia and rheumatoid arthritis. This type of thinking is associated with a deficiency in the expression of affect. They support Marty and de M'Uzan's (1963) characterization of the incapacity to use language to express feelings and an absence oι directed and drive-directed fantasy. They suggest that persons with psycɪ somatic illness who exhibit this syndrome may have an actual neuroanatomic deficiency in the pathways, hence in the communication, between the limbic system as the substratum of emotion and the neocortex as the region responsible for critical evaluation and the creation of complex associational systems. Such a clinical state would be reminiscent of Nauta's concept of interoceptive agnosia.

Bowlby's (1970, 1973) treatise on attachment and loss elaborates on the remoter consequences of success and failure in the development of bonds between mother and infant. Without the cementing of this dyadic relationship, later adaptation to social demands is threatened. He details massive evidence both in man and in animals of the importance of the attachment instinct. He shows the disastrous effects in the form of loss of confidence and of social expertise with consequent sociopathy that follows early injury to that bond by inadequacy of parental care. Although Bowlby starts from a psychoanalytic premise, he has successfully demonstrated how effectively the ethologic concept of maternal attachment and behavior will explain the same phenomena for which the various psychoanalytic schools developed their theoretical concepts. In related work the analytical psychologist Harding (1965) proceeds from the same base of maternal behavior and affective attachment to the infant. She describes the effects of childhood injury to the parental image upon behavior in later life, including disturbance of patterns critical for social adaptation.

Recently, direct experimental data supporting these concepts has been derived. Klaus, Jerauld, Kreger, McAlpine, Steffa, and Kennell (1972) and Salk (1970) have demonstrated that the intensity of later attachment of the human mother to her infant is determined by the extent and intensity of her exposure to the newborn during the first hours after birth. Klopfer (1971) has studied the endocrine aspects of the failure of the mother goat to respond to a kid that has been only briefly removed during the immediate postpartum period. It is likely that a related mechanism is at work in the human. The detailed studies of Harlow et al. (1971) and also Hinde (1971) demonstrate the consistent failure of maternal behavior in rhesus monkeys that were socially deprived as infants and show how critical it is for both members of the primate dyad to have had an adequate stimulus during this sensitive early period.

Ainsworth and Wittig's (1969) work in Uganda and Baltimore has shown that for the human infant this period is most intense from 6 months to approximately 2 years. With maturation the attachment broadens to include other members of the immediate group besides the mother figure. Finally, during childhood and adolescence, attachment extends to include the social group to which the child's parental figures are attached. Bowlby (1970) has described the results of a number of studies that show the importance of the childhood-parental milieu for later adult adaptation. Depending on an appropriate environment, these early attachments and acquired values will continue to develop in later life. Neumann (1954) has discussed their increasing subtlety and complexity as they extend to country and to social institutions, such as craft and professional groups, church, army, or business enterprise. Tiger and Fox (1971) have outlined the significance of male and female groupings in a recent book that draws attention to the determining significance of early programmed or preprogrammed biologic givens for the later behavior of the adult human.

The neuroanatomical (Nauta, 1971) and neurophysiologic (MacLean, 1973; Isaacson, 1974) evidence are compatible with the hypothesis that ritualized attachment behavior involves the preprogrammed systems of the limbic brain and extends then to the neocortical brain. Perhaps the experientially determined, recently acquired neocortical identifications that go for example by the names of "mother church" or "alma mater" are tied into the environmentally stable patterns of these more primitive regions. It may be that these patterns are responsible for giving them their emotional cast and strong motivating influence.

Limbic-neocortical connections may also exist between the loci for ritualized, territorially determined dominant and subordinate behavior patterns and the neocortically determined variations of the various roles that are played in a social group. All mammals show such role specialized behavior, and Maclay and Knipe (1972), using the ethologic approach, homologize between the human dominance order and the behavior of a socialized primate group, such as the baboons described by Kummer (1971). van Lawick-Goodall (1973) points to the similarity of the basic gestures of humans and chimpanzees and Eibl-Eibesfeldt (1972) has detailed the universality, regardless of culture, of certain patterns of human behavior. He regards behavior such as threat displays, subordinate-to-dominant respect rituals, greetings, flirtatious gestures, and mother-infant and adult-consort embraces as inherited patterns. Social practices and language differ from culture to culture and are critical for the extraordinary upbuilding of subtle distinctions between role and rank in the complex society of man. However, despite the intervention of the learned variations, the basic role gestures persist in man all over the world.

Ekman (1973) in quite independent studies has recently convincingly demonstrated the transcultural uniformity of facial expressions. He suggests a common inherited aspect for these important modes of nonverbal communication.

The work of Harlow's group (Harlow et al., 1971) and of Hinde (1971) and his associates with social deprivation in the monkey and the studies recounted by Bowlby (1970, 1973) demonstrating the trend to social pathology in those who had been deprived as infants show the importance of the opportunity for early normal interaction. The normal adults' sophisticated territorial and dominance-subordination relationships that hold destructive aggression sharply in check and successfully inhibit basic drives owe their development to an adequate early socialization experience. The socially deprived monkey will suicidally attack adults twice his size and act with destructive aggression to small infants that get in his way—actions that would never be seen in a normal animal (Harlow et al., 1971). Even in rodents these principles hold. In our laboratory we have shown that socially deprived mice that have been raised in isolation until they are mature at age 4 months are hyperactive and hyperaggressive, failing to develop normal hierarchies. Their constant fighting results in hypertension and adrenal hypertrophy; their dominant-subordinate relationships are disturbed by frequent fights; and the females become pregnant less often and their litters fail to survive (Ely and Henry, 1974; Watson, Henry, and Haltmeyer, 1974).

B. The Cultural Canon as an Affiliative Network Facilitating Coping Behavior

Social animals have mechanisms by which the instinct for territorial control can be patterned and the acceptance of complex role differentiation within a social hierarchy enforced. This is especially true of man, whose society must regulate the persistent and powerful mating and parental attachment instincts. The emotionally significant activities involving the formation of symbol systems connecting limbic with neocortically determined patterns may be termed the cultural canon, where the word canon refers to norms or standards representing general principles or rules commonly accepted by the group as true, valid, and fundamental. It includes the religious and secular ceremonies with which a stable, normal community surrounds personally significant events, such as birth, betrothal, marriage, pregnancy, aging, and death, as well as the critical stages of public enterprises. It involves the rites of passage into manhood and womanhood and is made the focus of the sacraments of churches. The state of anomie that the sociologist Durkheim (1951) linked with increased suicide rates is characterized by a loss of this normative ritual and emotionally supportive behavior. It has been the object of much quantitative sociologic study (McClosky and Schaar, 1965). Social breakdown involving anomie is often associated with conditions of warfare and civil violence. Migration is another source, for with it contact with the valued places in the homeland is lost and the culture group's religious, professional, and politically significant figures may fail to accompany the emigrants. Other states involving anomie include the breakup of the family with the loss of the older figures, especially the grandparents, who normally transmit the culture to the young, and finally, culture changes imposed from the outside are devastating, as when the Euro-American technology took over in Polynesia. The change can come from within, and world society has recently experienced and is currently disturbed by the industrial and electronic revolutions (Toffler, 1970).

With the loss of the detailed observance of the normative patterns of culture, there is a failure of the various preconditions for a healthy social life. Thus anomie involves a disturbance of the protective affiliative network and of the patterns, such as denial, rationalization, or sublimation by which an established stable culture protects the members of the group, satisfies their needs for attachment, and disciplines their territorial instincts. (To the ethologist, territory implies only spatial considerations. Lacking a better generic term, this powerfully evocative word is used loosely to refer not only to the spatial boundaries of the family and the national state but also to hierarchy and the status considerations associated with money, ideas, skills, and other forms of power and prestige.) Anomie or alienation may involve a degree of interoceptive agnosia or operational thinking, a condition in which there is a loss of capacity to remember and attach significance to dreams and an impoverishment of fantasy life (Nemiah and Sifneos, 1970).

Scotch and Geiger (1963) have studied the systolic and diastolic pressures of the surviving members of a disintegrating American Indian culture. They have also compared the blood pressure of South African Zulus living on reservations with those in an apartheid city. Cruz-Coke, Etcheverry, and Nagel (1964) have studied the rise in diastolic pressure of migrating Easter Islanders, and Tyroler and Cassel (1964) have demonstrated the effects of culture change when moving from a farming to an industrial community. All have shown that there is a raised incidence of cardiovascular disorders, such as high blood pressure or coronary disease, in situations in which the cultural canon is disturbed.

Henry and Cassel (1969) have summarized these data in a review of the possible role of psychosocial factors as a determinant of higher rates of rise of blood pressure with aging in some communities. They present evidence supporting this thesis, concluding that those social groups in which there is no change of blood pressure with age more commonly show a stable, traditional culture with social solidarity, adequate family support, and unchallenged established beliefs.

Psychological testing supports this concept of the consequences in terms of the disease process of the individual's loss of such social mechanisms. Harris and Singer (1968) have made an important 11-year prospective study of the role of the interaction of personality and life crisis in the pathogenesis of essential hypertension. They found that the prehypertensive college women with whom they worked had fewer personality assets than a control group with lower pressure. They were less attractive, accepted the feminine role less readily, and had more unsatisfactory marriages. Showing less social poise and ease, they were described as having a provocative chip on the shoulder attitude and yet tried to hide their emotions, which when aroused, lasted unduly long. They were found to be more likely to experience abrasive, tense, and hostile interactions with other people than a control group with lower pressure.

The recent paper by Nuckolls, Cassel, and Kaplan (1972) also shows the importance of the psychosocial assets that contribute to stability within a cultural milieu. In this case the dependent variable was the incidence of complications of pregnancy. They scored women for ego strength, adaptability, marital stability, religious affiliation, extent of family support both economically and emotionally, social resources in terms of friendship patterns, and finally the extent to which the pregnancy was desired and confidently anticipated. They showed that those who scored low for these factors and high for social stress in terms of the Holmes-Rahe life-change measures had three times the complications of those, who, while having a high life-change score, also scored high for psychosocial assets.

The Holmes-Rahe life-change scale (Table 1), mentioned earlier as a measure of the amount of psychosocial stimulation to which the individual has been exposed, assesses at the personal level what estimates of states of anomie evaluate for the social group. Both techniques arrive at similar conclusions, in part because states of anomie involve an increased incidence of life changes. They have consequences in terms of loss of the group's behavioral patterns and of the beliefs that Nuckolls and her associates have counted as social assets. An increased score for anomie or life change, together with a decreased score for social assets, can be associated with a higher incidence of emotionally arousing episodes and in consequence with increased levels of neuroendocrine disturbance.

On the other hand, the cultural canon provides a variety of mechanisms for diminishing the impact of psychosocial stimulation. In a recent comprehensive discussion, Lazarus has commented on how these coping processes control the intensity of emotional responses (Lazarus, 1966; 1975, *in press*). Currently, Cohen and Lazarus (1973) discuss the relative importance of different strategies of coping with the threat of a surgical operation. They conclude that when the issue is unpredictable, a vigilant approach involving a strategy of trying to achieve mastery by seeking information may be less successful than denial of the possibility of problems and complications. Similar findings have been reported by those working with coronary disease and renal dialysis (Sviland, 1973). In both of these more or less acute situations, moderate denial appeared to be the most successful strategy (Cohen and Lazarus, 1973).

Katz, Weiner, Gallagher, and Hellman (1970) have recently completed an excellent study of the mechanisms by which persons defend themselves from or cope with threatening situations. They studied women awaiting biopsy of a threatening lump in the breast and determined that a number of differing types of ego defenses could be effectively used to buffer the individual. They divided these into displacement, projection, and denial with rationalization. Defenses were also described involving internalized social norms using religious or philosophical practices, such as prayer and an active faith or stoicism-fatalism, which are associated with certain cultural canons. They point out that although these socially determined internalized norms have not been traditionally listed as ego defenses, nevertheless careful review convinced them that they are distinct and effective maneuvers. Finally, they comment that many persons handle their particular defense with great efficiency; nor does it necessarily have to be healthy and reality oriented in order to be effective.

Their methodology was based on the techniques developed during a series of classical studies of the long-term 17-hydroxycorticosteroid (17-OHCS) excretion rates of parents of fatally ill children (Wolff, Friedman, Hofer, and Mason, 1964a; Wolff, Hofer, and Mason, 1964). A follow-up 6-months and 2-year evaluation were made of the psychologic processes accompanying mourning. This second phase of the work was recently reported by Hofer, Wolff, Friedman, and Mason (1972a,b). The whole complex study demonstrated that the parents used any or all of a variety of maneuvers to control the grief, including hysterical defenses and projection. Some even established stable depressive equilibrium states as a method of avoiding more direct techniques of dealing with the emotional responses to the impending loss.

The authors note that when grief broke through during the months of mourning following the actual bereavement, the levels of 17-OHCS would increase in persons who might have defended successfully and had low values during the progress of the child's illness. On the other hand, one woman who used a technique of intellectualization and isolation of feeling from thought content actually lowered her 17-OHCS excretion during times of stress (M. Hofer, *personal communication,* 1974). This observation is reminiscent of Bourne (1971), who studied helicopter ambulance men and seasoned troops awaiting attack in Vietnam. So efficient were their defenses that there too, there was a depression of the 17-OHCS values despite intensely threatening situations. Bourne attributed the unexpected effect to the military culture that utilized patterns of sophisticated denial or rationalization and favored response to stimuli by externally directed action with avoidance of affect. A modification of the perception of reality may also account for the equally unexpected depression of 17-OHCS urinary excretion values in astronauts during the period while they were orbiting the earth (Lutwak, Whedon, Lachance, Reid, and Lipscomb, 1969).

The forms taken by the perceptions of reality as molded by any particular cultural canon vary enormously but, in all cases, the successful adherent gains a degree of protection against arousal of the basic emotions of anger and depression with their accompanying neuroendocrine disturbances. In one form of defense often associated with religious beliefs, the broadening of attachment and increasingly subtle and abstract concepts of territory permit the individual to feel a part of a larger and more long-lived system than the nuclear family or even a local group. Such involvement with extensive symbol systems will decrease the reticular formation arousal and depression accompanying personal setbacks and frustration. But the support of a social group is necessary for the maintenance of this complex cultural canon and for the effective employment of these coping processes. If the well-knit pattern of dogmas, beliefs, ceremonies, sacred rituals, and value systems that constitute the culture canon of a stable society are not available to the individual, an important protection against excessive neuroendocrine arousal is lost.

V. THE HYPOTHALAMUS AND THE DEFENSE AND ALARM RESPONSES

A. Limbic-Hypothalamic Pathways

The factors outlined in Box 1 and Box 2 of Fig. 1 combine in the course of psychosocial stimulation, the intensity of the ensuing response being subject to control by the coping mechanisms of Box 3. The resulting patterns in turn affect those areas responsible for initiating the neuroendocrine responses as outlined in Box 4 plus Box 5. The question arises whether the behavioral concomitants of the various basic emotions have any reliably established association with differing neuroendocrine states.

Nauta and Haymaker (1969) have detailed the extent to which the limbic system is in intimate connection with the brainstem structures controlling the body economy, and, in particular, with the hypothalamus and midbrain regions that directly control the neuroendocrine system. Scanning a large and varied body of behavioral and neurophysiological evidence, Isaacson (1974) in his recent review of *The Limbic System* suggests that this region, in conjunction with the neocortex, controls the stored memories and thus makes possible the suppression of traditional ways of responding; based on newly acquired information, it makes possible behavioral modification of the fixed patterns of the brainstem. He suggests that the hippocampus is a mechanism suppressing these activities when the unexpected happens, as for example, when there is a failure to fulfill expectations. It is relevant, as Seligman (1975) points out, that the emotion accompanying the behavioral inhibition of such failed expectancies is depression or learned helplessness. On the other hand, Isaacson suggests a contrasting role for certain portions of the amygdalar complex of the limbic system. It accentuates conditions of arousal and activation of the defense response of the hypothalamic system when external conditions are appropriate. Thus it appears that a predominantly amygdalar activation will lead to a dominant exploratory territorial strategy; whereas, hippocampal-septal activation is related to the conservation-withdrawal depressive response of the just subordinated animal.

B. The Hypophyseal-Adrenocortical System and the Alarm Response

The role of the septum and hippocampus in the activation of the hypothalamic structures controlling adrenal-cortical function is currently under debate. But there is evidence that both structures can be involved, and it may be best to speak of a septal-hippocampal complex. Thomas and Balter (1975) in their studies of the amelioration of learned helplessness, i.e., depression, in cats by cholinergic blockade of the septum cite other evidence which points to a role for this structure, while the work of Kawakami, Seto, Terasawa, Yoshida, Miyamoto, Sekiguchi, and Hattori (1968) and of Endröczi and Lissák (1963) suggests that the hippocampus is also involved in the control of ACTH release.

Once impulses have arrived at the median eminence of the hypothalamus, the pathways and mechanisms are clearer, for it is from this region that the corticotropic-releasing factor passes down the portal system to the anterior pituitary where the adrenocorticotropic hormone (ACTH) enters the bloodstream to affect the production of the corticosteroid hormones from the adrenal.

In a critical synthesis of recent psychoendocrine research into pituitary adrenal mechanisms, Mason (1968a) points to the massive evidence that psychologic influences are among the most potent natural stimuli to affect the pituitary-adrenocortical system, inducing the alarm response that was first described by Selye (1936). Bronson and Eleftheriou (1965) have shown that mice previously exposed to a fighter will later develop an increased concentration of corticosterone merely when in its presence. An extensive combination of ecologically based and laboratory work by Christian's group has led them to conclude that, in general, the higher the social rank of an individual, the less will be the effect of population density upon the adrenal output of corticosterone (Christian, Lloyd, and Davis, 1965). The role of psychosocial stimulation in controlling reproductive activity is the subject of a recent review by Christian (1971), which suggests that there are separate feedbacks regulating the gonadotropins and maintaining them in an inverse relationship with the adrenocortical hormones. Related results have been obtained for monkeys (Rose, Holaday, and Bernstein, 1971; Rose, Gordon, and Bernstein, 1972, 1975), and the clinical data obtained with humans in a large number of naturally occurring situations leave no doubt as to the responsiveness of the two systems (Cohen, 1954; Sachar, 1970).

Mason (1968a) concluded that the state of anticipation of having to cope with novel, unpredictable situations is potent in eliciting an increased output of 17-OHCS. The work of Sassenrath (1970) with subordinate rhesus monkeys takes the analysis one step further. She showed a strong covariance between ACTH-responsive levels, aggressive stimulation received, and fear-anxiety behavior, i.e., the dominant animals had far less adrenocorticosteroid response to an ACTH injection than the subordinates. She concludes that the fear-evoking component of chronic social stress is the predominant stimulus for endogenous ACTH release. Her observations would support the psychiatrist Price's (1969) interesting ethologically based argument that yielding behavior and loss of status in the social hierarchy is associated with depression. Price argues the evolutionary advantages of this depression in terms of suppression of lethal conflict, which might otherwise occur if the defeated animals kept on attempting to regain status. He maintains that the human depressive response is an expression of this built-in mechanism. His view is supported by Seligman's recent presentation of the evidence that learned helplessness and reactive depression both have their roots in the belief that valued outcomes are uncontrollable. The raised corticosteroid levels of depressed patients, which Sachar (1970) and others have demonstrated, would fit with these observations. It would suggest that a sustained hypophyseal adrenocortical response to psychosocial stimulation indicates not only a perception of the need to cope with an unpredictable situation, but also a depressive subordinate response to the challenge. This giving up and conservation-withdrawal response develops because control is perceived as unattainable.

C. The Sympathetic Adrenal-Medullary System and the Defense Reaction

The downward flow of impulses from the dorsomedial amygdalar complex to the posterior and lateral hypothalamus controls a second major neuroendocrine response pattern, the defense reaction—this one being under control of the sympathetic adrenal-medullary system (Roldán, Alvarez-Pelaez, and de Molina, 1974). Psychosocial studies of this system started with the observations of Cannon and de La Paz (1911). They showed an increased output of adrenaline in the venous blood coming from the gland when a cat was exposed to a barking dog. Cannon formulated an emergency function theory of adrenal-medullary activity, suggesting that the fear and rage responses helped the animal to cope with threatening situations. He thus laid the foundation for an understanding of the way in which physiologic responses are integrated with mental processes (Cannon, 1929).

The pioneering neurophysiologic studies of Hess and Brügger (1943) supported this theory by demonstrating that stimulation in the forward extension of the brainstem reticular formation elicits response patterns that are behaviorally and physiologically characteristic of the defense reaction. This, as Folkow and Neil (1971) point out, is a state highly suited either for attack or flight. They describe it as activated by situations inducing tenseness and alertness in anticipation of dramatic events. The somatomotor behavior characteristic of this arousal in the cat includes hissing, spitting, arching the back, and raising the hair on the back and tail. At the same time, sympathetic cholinergic vasodilator fibers to the arterioles of the skeletal muscles are activated. There is also violent excitation of the adrenergic fibers to all other parts of the vascular bed and to the heart, while the release of catecholamines from the adrenal medulla is much enhanced.

Using human subjects, Brod, Fencl, Hejl, and Jirka (1959) have elicited this response in the course of elegant experiments in which the emotional stimulus was a harassing insistence by the investigators that the heavily instrumented subjects perform accurate mental arithmetic in time with the beat of a metronome. Hemodynamically the ensuing sympathetic-adrenal-medullary arousal results in an increase in arterial pressure, cardiac output, and heart rate. The increase in cardiac output is taken up in skeletal muscle blood flow, whereas the flow through the kidneys is radically reduced. Folkow and Rubinstein (1966) have shown that the changes noted by Brod and his co-workers can be induced in rodents by direct stimulation of the anterior hypothalamus. Using an implanted electrode, they caused a moderate chronic elevation of systolic pressure in otherwise normal unanesthetized rats by exposing them to several months of mildly alerting daily stimulation of the hypothalamic defense area. The fact that the typical blood flow changes in the kidney and muscle circuits of anesthetized animals could be induced by stimulation in the same location suggests that the electrodes were eliciting the same cardiovascular response as mental stimuli (Folkow and Rubinstein, 1966). This response is a central anticipatory adjustment of the cardiovascular system, cocking the trigger, as it were. It becomes fully established before the simultaneous altering of the somatomotor system explodes into an all-out fight-or-flight response (Folkow and Neil, 1971).

The biochemical accompaniments of these complex neurophysiologic and cardiovascular changes were demonstrated by von Euler (1956) and others. They showed that the response involved two hormones and that norepinephrine, the nonmethylated homologue of epinephrine, was the adrenergic transmitter. This clarification together with the development of sensitive assays, including isotope-binding techniques, have led to many productive behaviorally oriented studies.

The mass of the current work has been reviewed by Frankenhaeuser (1975) who has done much to clarify the field. She concludes that any event perceived by the individual as emotionally arousing will be accompanied by an increased epinephrine output. The extensive observations of Levi (1972) with persons in various simulated work situations support this generalization.

The psychosocial perceptions associated with norepinephrine excretion are not so clear. However, there is some evidence that it differs from epinephrine in being associated with circumstances in which an effort is being directed at a specific goal. Thus, although failing to confirm Ax's (1953) earlier categoric subdivision of the consequences of this type of psychosocial stimulation into fear and rage responses, contemporary work does arrive at somewhat related concepts, i.e., that of overall arousal instead of fear and a directed response instead of anger. An important recent finding by Frankenhaeuser is that women respond to a challenging task with equal efficiency, but with less catecholamine excretion than men. She speculates that this sex difference, which may represent a lesser degree of emotional arousal, may contribute to their longer lifespan. She concludes her review by pointing out that the majority of observations of the sympathetic adrenal system have been made over brief periods of a few hours. It is now necessary, she says, to determine the long-term metabolic adjustments to various psychosocial stimuli that repeatedly arouse the sympathetic adrenal-medullary system.

D. Differentiation Between the Alarm Response and the Defense Reaction

Mason (1968b) has accorded the adrenal-medullary response equal status with that of the adrenal cortex, viewing it as an independent neuroendocrine system. Indeed there is gathering neurophysiologic evidence that the two response systems have different central controls. Thus the arousal that accompanies injections of epinephrine is not associated with an increase in the secretion of ACTH (Ganong, 1970), and Goldfien and Ganong (1962) have shown that when the hypothalamus is electrically stimulated, points triggering catecholamine release can be differentiated from others leading to the release of ACTH. They found it possible by stimulating the right areas to increase the output of 17-OHCS without changing that of the catecholamines and vice versa.

The idea of a dichotomy of function between the adrenal-medullary and the adrenal-cortical systems has not been generally accepted, possibly because the majority of the work has been with brief exposures to stimulation. In the event of an acute and powerful stimulus that lasts for only an hour or so, both systems are activated (Mason, 1968a,b). However, Ganong's (1970) observation that adrenergic systems in the hypothalamus may actually participate in the inhibition of ACTH secretion suggests that some suppression of the adrenal-cortical response might occur when the animal was aroused to fight. The recent work of Conner, Vernikos-Danellis, and Levine (1971) points in this direction. They have shown that solitary rats exposed to repeated shocks have higher plasma ACTH levels than paired animals receiving the same intensity. Since paired animals fight at the onset of shock, it might have been expected that the combination of shock with fighting would have elicited a greater pituitary-adrenal response than either stimulus alone. In fact the reverse was the case, and ACTH levels were lower in the fighting pairs. Since the overall level of physical activity of the animal was the same in both cases, the authors conclude that the difference in ACTH response was related to a change in the pattern of behavior. They noted the paired animals directed attacks at each other, instead of attempting to escape as the solitary animals did. Although no measurements are available, it is possible that these attacks were associated with increased levels of catecholamines.

An elegant study by Weiss shows how the intensity of adrenocortical responses is determined by the animal's perception of events. He demonstrates the sharp influence of psychologic variables on stress-induced pathology in the form of gastric ulcers. He worked with yoked rats, one of which could avoid electric shock by touching its nose to a panel, while its partner received the same shocks, but has no control over them. The measure was total length of gastric lesions after 21 hr of responding at a rate of one trial per minute. The passive animal had a highly significant excess of lesions over the active partner. Weiss (1972) concludes that ulceration is a function of two variables: It increases with the number of coping attempts that the animal makes, and it decreases in proportion to the informational feedback it receives from making the coping attempts. He implicated the adrenocortical system, noting that the more severe the ulceration, the higher the level of plasma corticosteroids.

In a related study of the effects of expectancy on the pituitary-adrenal system, Levine, Goldman, and Coover (1972) showed that rats trained to press a lever for water on a continuous reinforcement schedule showed a sharp elevation of plasma corticosterone if they were frustrated by absence of reinforcement. On the other hand, when the reward exceeded expectation, it decreased. They comment that even in the rat the respective accompanying emotions might be termed elation and frustration. Levine and co-workers also noted a progressive decrease in the intensity of the corticosterone responses as the challenge was repeated time after time. Their interpretation was that the animal perceived the situation as becoming progressively more predictable. Their results fit with those of Weiss, as they found a rise of adrenocortical response when there was a deficiency in informational feedback. Seligman (1975) in his text on *Helplessness* concludes that depression ensues when the animal learns that responding and reinforcement are independent: in subjective terms, when the subject comes to believe that responding is useless.

These results throw light on the observations that the repeated administration over a number of days of stressful stimuli, such as trauma in the Noble-Collip drum (Mikulaj and Kvetňanský, 1966), subcutaneous injections of 2% formalin (Vecsei, 1962), or repeated immobilization for 0.5 to 2 hr (Mikulaj and Mitro, 1973) uniformly lead to a decreased response of the adrenocortical mechanism. Eventually there may be only a modest elevation of plasma corticosterone in spite of the fact that the overall potential of the hypophyseal-adrenal system to respond to fresh stimuli has not been lost.

This falling off in response can be contrasted with observations of increased catecholamines (Kvetňanský and Mikulaj, 1970) and of adrenal catecholamine-synthesizing enzymes (Kvetňanský, Weise, and Kopin, 1970) during the identical series of immobilizations. With repetition of stress, there was a progressively enhanced ability to replace catecholamines. It would seem probable that with repetition the animal changes his response to the experience; at first, it might be seen as a threat that endangered him, which he could not control. Later he might perceive it as unpleasant, but as having a predictable outcome and therefore presenting possibilities for control. It is possible that a change in emotional state, i.e., from a purely depressive conservation-withdrawal response pattern to one with a larger component of the defense fight-flight reflex, might follow this changed perception.

In our own laboratory, we have worked with long-term studies of colonies of animals that stimulate each other as they move about in a population cage in search of food, water, nesting areas, and mates. We have looked for a biochemical differentiation between the dominant and subordinate members of established murine colonies whose population uniformly consisted of five males of identical age, weight, and social experience and 16 females. Bronson and Eleftheriou (1965) as well as Christian and his group (Christian et al., 1965) have shown that the corticosterone levels of the subordinate members of a rodent group are higher than those of a dominant. We confirm this for the first week or so of colony life (Fig. 3). After a month or so when a stable hierarchy starts to develop, the emerging dominant is no longer challenged and the expectations of all colony members are reliably met. At this

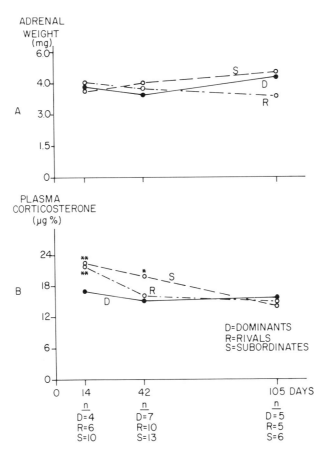

FIG. 3. Adrenocortical responses of dominant, rival, and subordinate males after different periods of normal socialization in a population cage. A: Absolute adrenal weight measured at autopsy. B: Plasma corticosterone fluorometrically measured. The n's are not identical for each social rank at 14, 42, and 105 days because different colonies were terminated at each period (* = $p < 0.05$; ** = $p < 0.01$).

stage the corticosterone levels of those accepting subordination return to normal.

In collaborative work with Dr. R. D. Ciaranello of the Department of Clinical Science, National Institute of Mental Health, we have assayed the adrenal-medullary content of tyrosine hydroxylase (TH) and phenylethanolamine N-methyltransferase (PNMT). After an initial rise in both groups, i.e., in the dominant and subordinate, this enzyme, which is controlled by sympathetic nervous impulses, continues to rise to very much higher levels in the dominant. The PNMT, which is responsible for synthesis of epinephrine from norepinephrine, is under adrenocortical as well as nervous control. It not only increases more in the dominant, but continues to rise, while the level of this enzyme is falling in the players of the other two roles (Fig. 4).

We attribute the differences in neuroendocrine response to the differing perception that the various animals have of their environment. Eventually the

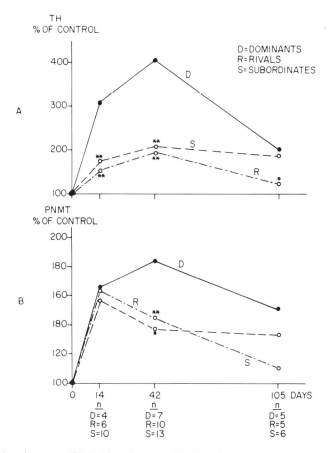

FIG. 4. A: Adrenal content of TH. B: Adrenal content of PNMT in dominants, rivals, and subordinates after 14, 42, and 105 days of normal socialization in a population cage. (See Fig. 3 for comment on n.)

colony stabilizes expectations, role behavior becomes fixed, and corresponding with this the neuroendocrine responses subside to control levels, despite
the sharp, continuing behavioral gulf between the originally evenly matched
dominant and subordinate males. However, in closed colonies in which the
subordinates cannot be driven out, after a couple of weeks, the blood pressure
of the dominant male gradually becomes significantly elevated, i.e., 150 mm
Hg versus 130 mm Hg for the subordinate, despite the near normal level of
the more direct measures of neuroendocrine function (Fig. 5). The adrenal
weight remains within normal limits throughout the experiment, pointing to
the relatively peaceable conditions involved in the socialization of normal
rodent colonies in these closed population cages.

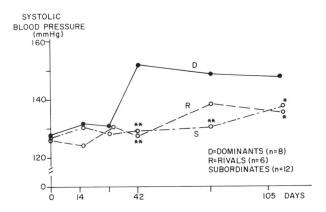

FIG. 5. Systolic blood pressure of dominants, rivals, and subordinates from eight different colonies during
normal socialization. Measurements were followed on the same animals at specific intervals throughout
the 105-day period (* = $p < 0.05$; ** = $p < 0.01$).

There is some human work that points in the direction of the foregoing
results. Jones, Bridges, and Leak (1970) have studied the response of the
pituitary adrenal-cortical and sympathetic adrenal-medullary systems during
the very considerable emotional stimulation associated with the taking of a
critical oral anatomy examination by medical students. Body build was evaluated by phenotype scoring for the characteristics: fatness, muscularity, and
linearity. Adrenal-cortical activity was assessed by measurement of plasma
11-hydroxycorticosteroids, and the systolic and diastolic blood pressures together with urinary epinephrine and norepinephrine served as measures of
the sympathetic adrenal-medullary response. There was a 50% increase of
plasma corticosteroids, a 22 mm Hg increase in systolic pressure, and a near
doubling of catecholamines following the stimulus. A striking finding was that
men with a muscular physique responded with a greater norepinephrine excretion and a smaller 11-hydroxycorticosteroid rise than the other two groups.
Lacking information on the point, the authors could only cite Ax (1953) and

tentatively suggest that the muscular subjects may have tended to respond to the situation with anger rather than with anxiety. Certainly these observations are compatible with the results of our studies of the biochemical changes accompanying dominance and subordination in mice.

E. The Inverse Relation Between the Gonadotropic Hormones and the Defense and Alarm Reactions

The classic studies of Christian (1971) and his group demonstrated the various endocrine responses that develop in crowded societies of animals and result in a decreased natality; they point to increased ACTH levels and a decrease of gonadotropin. Christian has presented an interesting control systems analysis of the various behavioral-endocrine-feedback systems that may be involved in the increased mortality and decreased natality. Recently Bronson (1973) has successfully demonstrated that the gonadotropic hormones decrease during antagonistic social interaction in male mice, whereas the adrenocortical hormones simultaneously increase. Concurrent effects on androgens were indicated by a decrease in the size of the androgen-linked sexual accessory gland of the subordinates. Dominant animals show the reverse trend with a conspicuous enlargement of the preputial gland.

Important related work by Rose et al. (1971, 1975) shows that rhesus monkeys whose social status is depressed have depressed plasma testosterone levels and vice versa. Further work showed that, if low-status depressed animals are placed in a colony composed largely of receptive females where the males can assume a dominant role, they show a sharp increase in dominant social behavior, and with it there is an accompanying rise in testosterone levels (Rose, Gordon, and Bernstein, 1972).

The work of Sachar, Fishman, and Mason (1965) with human subjects hypnotized under relaxing circumstances, that of Bourne (1971) in Vietnam with combat personnel exposed to danger (but in the line of duty), and that of Katz et al. (1970) with women awaiting biopsy reports shows that a feeling of social acceptance and high personal value is accompanied by lower plasma 17-OHCS values (Sachar, 1970). On the other hand, a variety of observations, including the dramatically increased incidence of complications of pregnancy observed by Nuckolls et al. (1972) in those who were evaluated as having weak defenses accompanied by high levels of social change, suggest that the human reproductive system is adversely affected by socially adverse perceptions.

In summary it appears that the hierarchic level occupied by an organism in the dominance-subordination scale strongly affects the activity of various neuroendocrine systems. A perception of downward social movement combined with a threat to psychosocial status and a loss of expectations is associated with a conservation-withdrawal reaction, depression, and increased ACTH and plasma corticosterone levels. The reverse pattern of success and increased status has been shown to be associated in the male with more dominant behavior, an increase in plasma testosterone level, and subnormal 17-OHCS levels. When social status is challenged, a sympathetic adrenal-medullary defense reaction ensues with a fight-flight response which involves increased catecholamines in the blood and increased catecholamine bio-synthetic-enzyme capacity. This response can be demonstrated in challenged animals when they are at the top of the social hierarchy. It is associated with attack and fighting or flight behavior as opposed to the conservation-withdrawal patterns of the subordinate. Biochemically the defense reaction is distinguished by a less marked TH response and increased PNMT and ACTH, and plasma corticosterone levels.

VI. CHRONIC PATHOPHYSIOLOGIC CONSEQUENCES OF SUSTAINED ALARM AND DEFENSE RESPONSES

A. Animal Studies

We now come to Box 6 of Fig. 1 and discuss the evidence for actual patho-physiologic changes following sustained arousal of the defense and/or alarm responses. There are a number of controlled experiments that point to tissue damage and disease as a consequence of sustained psychosocial stimulation. Von Holst has measured the extent of arousal of the sympathetic nervous system in a tree shrew that has been defeated by a dominant and yet is unable to withdraw from his territory. The peculiarity of which he took advantage was that with strong sympathetic stimulation, the hairs on the shrew's long tail will stand erect, giving it a bushy appearance. By observing the percent of the 12 hr of observation time that the tail was in this condition, he made important conclusions about the pathophysiologic consequences of the emo-tional state of the defeated animal. The subordinate when placed in a cage that is separated only by wire mesh from the victor shows a clear-cut be-havioral pattern. The subjugated animal hardly moves, spending 90% of the daily activity period lying motionless in a corner, just following the move-ments of the other with its head. Approach of the victor to the partition will often elicit fear squeaking. The rest of the time the animal is apathetic, but the hairs on the tail and body are raised continuously. The fur becomes un-tidy, for he spends less than a tenth of the time normally allotted to grooming. Although the defeated animal does consume its quota of food, it eats in a stealthy manner, and the normal activity of marking territory with the sternal glands and urine ceases (Von Holst, 1969).

If the dominant is allowed to attack this defeated animal, he lies passive while being bitten on the rump, thighs, and root of the tail. The attack is not lethal and no bleeding will be elicited, yet the animal may die within a few minutes after such an attack, presumably with a cardiac arrest of the type described by Richter (1957) in Norway rats forced to swim for their lives.

Von Holst has observed that after a couple of days to 2 weeks, the defeated shrew will sink into a coma and die in uremia due to renal insufficiency. The histologic evidence points to an acute decrease of renal blood flow with tubular necrosis and glomerular ischemia. Here then is evidence of an intense and persisting emotional state that has resulted from the confrontation between two members of the same species. Not only does the behavior of the animal betray the disturbed motivational state, but the appearance of the tail and the final death in renal failure indicate that the subjective and behavioral aspects of the emotion are accompanied by physiologic and biochemical changes.

These observations are unique in the detailed control of the circumstances (Von Holst, 1972). However, Barnett (1964) has described the submissive behavior of Norway rats introduced as intruders into a caged social group dominated by an established vigorous resident male. Although their behavior is not as dramatic as that of the tree shrew, submissive gestures suggest emotional arousal in a situation in which escape is impossible. Here too the death that ensues within a few days is not caused by wounds, but may be attributed to the accompanying neuroendocrine disturbance.

Lapin and Cherkovich (1971) have recently reported on the well-known observations of the emotional disturbance that Miminoshvili generated in a Hamadryas baboon by violating his normal social relationships. The male was separated from the females with whom he had long been associated and to which this particular species of baboon are known to become intensely attached. When another male was put in with the females, the former consort showed intense agitation. After several months, hypertension developed and Lapin and Cherkovich conclude that psychosocial stimuli that involve the species' preservative program can be highly effective in inducing a sustained emotional response.

This observation by the Sukhumi workers that chronic cardiovascular disease can be induced by chronic emotional disturbance is not unique (Lapin and Cherkovich, 1971). Ratcliffe (1968), working at the Philadelphia Zoological Gardens, has shown that the yearly death rate of mammals and birds from ischemic necrosis of the myocardium caused by arteriosclerotic stenosis of the intramural coronary vessels increased from less than 1% to more than 10% during the period from 1948 to 1968. Mean age at death and diet were not relevant. He noted that 1948 was the start of attempts to increase the interest of the exhibits by assembling family groups. This resulted in conflicts, breeding failures, and abnormal behavior, and he eventually concluded that the coronary heart disease increase was associated with behavioral responses to social situations (Ratcliffe, 1968).

In an experimental follow-up of this work, he studied the psychologic response of swine to separation and pairing after the primary social bonds of grouped animals had been formed. Grouped and paired swine responded to visitors with friendly grunts and squeals for a handout. There was give and take among the males and competition was limited to pushing and shoving. By contrast, separated swine, especially the normally sociable females, failed to respond to visitors, lying unresponsive and refusing offers of added corn. After a year of isolation, the separated females showed a significantly greater development of arteriosclerosis than those that were grouped. Thus the data from this quantitative study suggest that a sustained emotional disturbance was associated with chronic pathophysiologic changes (Ratcliffe, Luginbühl, Schnarr, and Chacko, 1969).

In a related study, Weber and Van der Walt (1973) have demonstrated cardiomyopathy in crowded New Zealand white rabbits. Four were placed in a cage, 60 × 45 × 30 cm, for 1 week. They were then housed singly for 1 week, then crowded again, then housed singly, and so on. In the course of 10 months, 35 of 48 animals had succumbed, 10 dying during the 1st week, 10 more during the 1st month, and the rest at intervals during the succeeding months. Since the animals fought intermittently, biting one another, the authors concluded that the chronic cardiomyopathy that developed and that terminated in cardiac failure was the expression of a stress reaction and that the cause of death was not wounding or starvation. In those that died within a few days, they observed severe myocardial necrosis and interstitial edema with patchy accumulations of acid mucopolysaccharides in the subendo-cardium and myocardium. Those that survived longer developed fusiform foci of myocardial fibrosis with collagen fibers and endocardial fibroelastosis. There was compensatory myocardial hypertrophy in the fibers adjacent to these fibrotic areas.

In our own laboratories we have contrasted the social behavior of mice that have been raised in isolation from weaning until adult at 4 months with that of socialized animals. Role behavior was determined by using a magnetic detection system to follow the movements of tagged mice through an inter-communicating box system in which they were permanently housed. As noted above, the normally socialized animals eventually form a stable hierarchy with dominant male, rival males, and subordinate males and a differentiation of territory into nesting boxes, feeding, latrine, and subordinate areas. The so-cially deprived animals consistently show more aggression toward each other and are less successful in maintaining a stable hierarchy. This results in early death, elevated blood pressure, and failure to raise young (Ely and Henry, 1974; Watson, Henry, and Haltmeyer, 1974).

In separate studies colonies of former isolates lacking social coping re-sources developed violent and repeated fights in which biting occurred. They showed the expected sustained blood pressure increase (Henry, Meehan, and Stephens, 1967) and with it a gross elevation of the catecholamine biosyn-thetic enzymes TH and PNMT. The same animals kept in isolation showed a lowering of the enzymes compared with normal boxed controls, in spite of their increased responsiveness to social interaction (Henry, Stephens, Axel-rod, and Mueller, 1971b) (Fig. 6). It is presumably the repeated stimulation

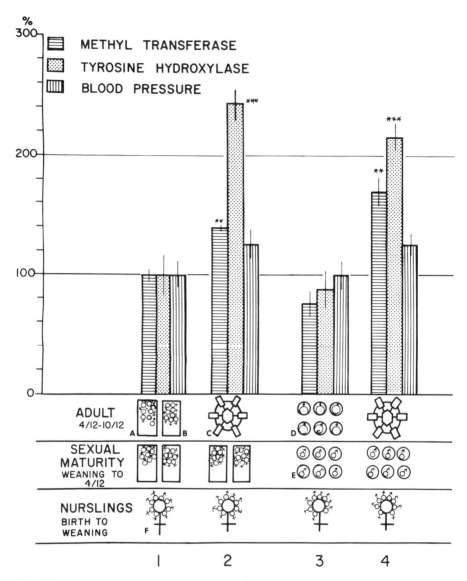

FIG. 6. Effects of various psychosocial procedures on adrenal content of PNMT and TH. Figures in bottom three rows symbolize different procedures as indicated by the above descriptions. A, males kept in standard $11 \times 5 \times 5$ inch boxes; B, females in standard boxes; C, standard boxes interconnected by 1.25 inch I.D. tubing; D, mature isolated male; E, immature isolated male; F, nursing mother with litter of mixed sexes. Controls in Group 1 are normally raised, normally boxed siblings. In both Groups 2 and 4, the enzymes differ significantly from the control value, i.e., PNMT $= p < 0.01$ and TH $= p < 0.001$. (From Henry et al., 1971b).

of the neuroendocrine system that leads to an increase in TH, which is dependent upon integrity of the sympathetic nerve supply to the medulla. The increase in PNMT may be due in part to nervous induction, but as noted there is evidence that in this case there is also induction from corticoids of the adrenal cortex. Hence arousal of the defense sympathetic adrenal-medullary and the alarm or hypophyseal adrenal-cortical response may both be involved. The isolated animals experienced less stimulation, hence their enzyme levels were lower. A further point is that it requires many hours and therefore repeated stimulation for the increase in enzyme level to attain its fullest extent. When combined with Folkow's structural vascular adaptation in response to stimulation (Folkow and Neil, 1971), the existence of such a slowly moving induction mechanism will bridge the gap between the immediate fight-flight and alarm responses, i.e., brief episodes of fighting and con-

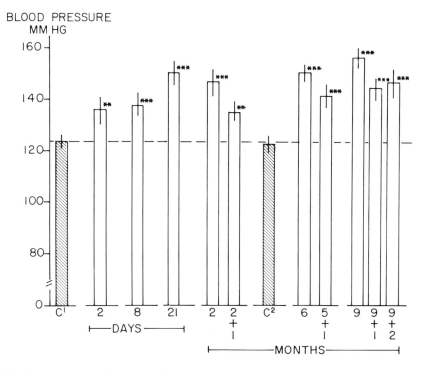

FIG. 7. *Abscissa* represents the number of days or months that a series of colonies consisting of 16 male and 16 female CBA mice were exposed to social interaction in standard population cages. The +1 and +2 represent colonies which were disbanded and the members returned to isolation and no longer socially stimulated for 1 and 2 months, respectively. *Ordinate* represents the final systolic blood pressure of the 16 males in the 10 colonies under study. The vertical lines represent standard errors of the mean. The horizontal shaded bar represents the mean and standard error for control males isolated for 6 months. The significance of the differences between the control pressures and those of the various groups was determined by paired Student's *t*-tests. The asterisks denote significant differences from these control values in various groups: * = $p < 0.05$; ** = $p < 0.01$; and *** = $p < 0.001$.

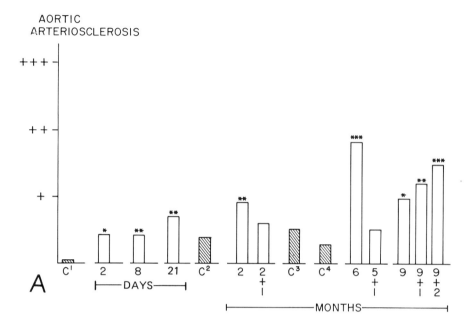

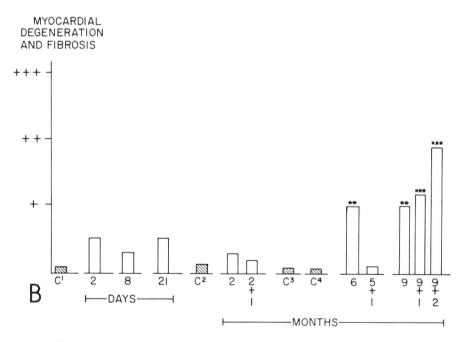

FIG. 8. A: The incidence of aortic arteriosclerosis in the 16 males of each colony of the series presented in Fig. 7. (For scoring see *Atherosclerosis,* 14:203, 1971.) Control groups were composed as follows: C_1 boxed siblings 4 months old, $n = 20$; C_2 siblings 6 to 8 months, $n = 17$; C_3 siblings 10 to 15 months, $n = 28$; C_4 isolated animals 10 months old, $n = 8$. B: The incidence of myocardial fibrosis in the 16 males of each colony of the series presented in Fig. 7. Control groups as for A.

frontation and sustained changes of blood pressure. Taken together sustained changes in metabolic balance, cardiovascular set points, and structural vascular arrangements would explain the arteriosclerotic deterioration that is observed in animals exposed to repeated episodes of psychosocial stimulation for months.

In the CBA strain that we use, the increase of blood pressure following social interaction is from a normal control of 125 ± 12 mm Hg to a mean of approximately 160 ± 20 mm Hg. It might be questioned whether the pressure elevation that is observed when these psychosocially stimulated mice are tested will also be found after they have been returned to isolation. In a recent study, 10 colonies of formerly isolated animals were observed for periods ranging up to 9 months. Systolic pressure was measured in the conscious animals by the tail cuff oscillometric method (Henry et al., 1967) once every 4 weeks. It returned to near-normal levels in a colony stimulated for only 2 months, but this return was less marked at 5 months; at 9 months the pressure at the time of measurement was significantly elevated despite 8 weeks of isolation (Fig. 7). The heart and adrenal weights and the adrenal PNMT levels of the two 9-month colonies also remained elevated. Thus there is evidence of sustained and irreversible cardiovascular and endocrine changes after psychosocial stimulation has persisted for a long time (Henry, Stephens, and Santisteban, 1975).

The incidence of histologic changes in the heart muscle and the aortas of nearly 300 males and females socially stimulated for 6 months was contrasted with nearly 200 controls. In confirmation of previous work (Henry, Ely, Stephens, Ratcliffe, Santisteban, and Shapiro, 1971a), there was a significant increase of myocardial fibrosis and aortic arteriosclerosis in the socially stressed mice (Fig. 8A,B) (Henry et al., 1975).

B. Human Observations

These animal observations suggesting that psychosocially induced neuroendocrine changes will lead to pathophysiologic disturbances are supported by blood pressure studies of human populations. Graham (1945) found hypertension (180 mm Hg or more) in over 30% of an English armored battalion resting on the beaches after years of arduous tank warfare in the Libyan desert. Within 2 months, most of these elevated pressures were returning to normal. On the other hand, Foster (1927) and Tung (1927) both observed a reduction in blood pressure of American doctors and nurses after they had been working for some time in Chinese mission hospitals. Both the rise in soldiers and the fall in medical groups could be attributed to the changed psychosocial circumstances they encountered.

Henry and Cassel (1969) have shown that observations of a number of social groups coming from different races can be chosen from the many blood pressure surveys that recently have been made in various parts of the world.

They observed that despite the nonrepresentative nature of many of the groups studied, the differences in rates of blood pressure rise could often be meaningfully linked to the social history of the group (Fig. 9). They support the hypothesis of Scotch and Geiger (1963), Lowenstein (1961), and others (Cruz-Coke et al., 1964) who have related the rise in blood pressure with age to psychosocial stress. That is, on the one hand, to the stimulus (i.e., to the life changes) and, on the other hand, to the effectiveness with which the cultural canon protects from neuroendocrine overresponse. Figure 9 presents a series of pressures from different social groups that illustrate this point. Thus in colored females in the Virgin Islands in 1942, the mean systolic blood pressure of the 50 to 55 year olds was 168 mm Hg as opposed to 150 mm Hg for the males of the same age group (Saunders and Bancroft, 1942). On looking into possible sources of psychosocial stimulation, it was noted that most women at age 50 had raised their families alone (U.S. Women's Bureau, 1935). Forced into the role of matriarchs in a severely impoverished subsistence economy, they had received little help from their mates. The male Virgin Islanders of the 1940s had little motivation to work and traditionally had little to do with the children. It is possible that this

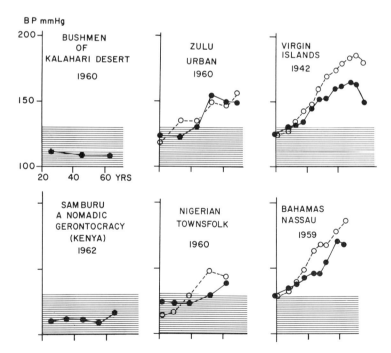

FIG. 9. Rates of change of systolic blood pressure with age in different populations contrast generally lower pressures in traditional, stable cultures (left) with cultures undergoing intermediate sociocultural change (middle) and those subject to social disorganization and loss of cultural norms (right).

group of Negro women had suppressed anger at the lack of support from their social system (Henry and Cassel, 1969).

The figure includes five other cases that show the varying relationship between blood pressure and age in different social groups of Negroes. Conditions in the Bahamas in the late 1950s would appear to have been similar to those in the Virgin Islands (Moser, Morgan, Hale, Hoobler, Remington, Dodge, and Macaulay, 1959). By contrast the less severe changes shown in middle set of pressure tables derives from a group of Zulu living in an apartheid community in the suburbs of Durban (Scotch, 1960). The old people found their tribal traditions distorted and engulfed in the new demands of the urban environment. There is a significant rise in the pressure of both men and women. The same holds for those living in a town near the city of Ibadan in Nigeria (Abrahams, Able, and Barnard, 1960). These are rural people who, while adapting to cultural change, still have strong traditions from the past. In both cases there is a significant elevation of pressure in the older groups, although not as severe as in the case of the two Caribbean islands. The left set of graphs show a still different picture. One diagram presents the results of the first of two independent studies that have been made of the !Kung Bushmen of Southwest Africa. Both came to the same conclusion (Kaminer and Lutz, 1960; Truswell, Kennelly, Hansen, and Lee, 1972). Despite crowding in their exceedingly primitive camping grounds and the harsh and difficult conditions for survival of these Stone Age food gatherers (Draper, 1973), the average casual systolic blood pressure of the older males remains an amazing 110 mm Hg. Van der Post (1961) has presented aspects of the culture of these people. The intense myth-making and ritual ceremonial activity points to an effective culture canon in this relatively undisturbed and isolated group.

The final diagram refers to the Samburu who are related to the Masai and when measured still lived in their original state on some 10,000 square miles of arid hill country south of Lake Rudolf in Northern Kenya (Spencer, 1965). They are nomads subsisting on cattle, sheep, and goats. They do not practice agriculture. Their essentially warrior society is rigidly structured, highly differentiated, and places great emphasis on conformity and respect. Ceremony is a vital part of their culture, with complex rituals and elaborate rites of passage from boyhood to manhood and thence to the "elder" state with political power and the right to marry. Still occupying their ancestral lands, the people are remarkably untouched by modern technology and competitive commercialism.

The striking incidence of hypertension and peptic ulcers in air traffic controllers as compared with second class airmen that has recently been reported by Cobb and Rose (1973) may be an expression of a trend in another group in the opposite direction. Air traffic controllers, especially in busy airports, are exposed to repeated daily arousal and to moments of crisis and difficult decision making. The matched group of airmen were qualified to co-pilot big commercial airliners. Their moments of arousal and difficult decision making may be less frequent. The relative socioeconomic stability of the two groups and the extent to which they were satisfied with and adapted to their jobs and lifestyles remain to be determined. It is however interesting that in 1964 the systolic blood pressure of United States naval aviators who had entered flying training in World War II was still normal (Oberman, Lane, Harlan, Graybiel, and Mitchell, 1967) despite an average age in the 50s.

Recently, Kunin and McCormack (1968) have contrasted the incidence of bacteriuria and blood pressure elevation among nuns with those of an equivalent group of women not in holy orders. They sampled over 2,000 working women divided into age periods of 15 to 34, 34 to 54, and 54 years or more. Bacteriuria was 13, 3.0, and 1.4 times higher for the successive age periods in the control groups than in the nuns. The differences were even greater in Negro women as contrasted with Negro nuns. Pregnancies in white women did not significantly affect the incidence of bacteriuria. Both systolic and diastolic blood pressure was lower for all ages among the nuns. However, in both groups there was a progressive elevation in the older women. Smith's recent work with the baboon shows the powerful potential control of the hypothalamus over the renal circulation (Smith, Stephenson, and Randall, 1974) and Shapiro (1963) has shown an enhanced susceptibility to bacterial infection in animals with vasoconstricted kidneys. He has also shown that a hypertensive human population is clearly at risk for the development of bacteriuria (Shapiro, Sapira, and Scheib, 1971). Thus there is a mechanism by which the incidence of bacteriuria can be related to episodes of arousal of the fight-flight response.

This evidence of greater renal involvement during the early years of women living in the general society is reminiscent of our observations of a higher incidence of interstitial nephritis and renal failure in highly competitive as opposed to socially structured colonies of mice. The cultural canon to which the nuns subscribe gives the perception of a secure place in a stable hierarchic society and supports them with valuable social coping assetts. Incidentally these were not cloistered women; all were exposed to interaction with the general society since their communities were devoted to teaching, nursing, social, and missionary work.

The psychometrist Caffrey (1966) has discussed the significance of the fact that the incidence of coronary heart disease is very much lower in cloistered Benedictine brothers than it is in Benedictine priests eating the same diet, but involved in parish work and teaching. In the 1930s, the blood pressure of Bavarian Trappist monks was shown to remain at normal levels despite old age (Seile, 1930), but contemporary studies have shown a sharp increase in the pressure of aging American Trappists (C. B. Quinlan, 1967, *personal communication*). Recent changes in the stability of Catholic institutional patterns may be involved in the pressure rise of the older community members. They may have felt threatened by changes in the outside culture that intrude on their traditional rule, which they have followed for so long.

VII. CONCLUSIONS

These observations on religious groups in our society point to the significance of the cultural canon as an affiliative network supporting coping behavior. Although sacrificing the direct expression of their reproductive instincts, young nuns and monks escape many of the confrontations to which lovers, married people, and parents are exposed. In addition they belong to a group that offers hope of a rewarding, confrontation-free future life. They follow a highly evolved, noncompetitive, emotionally satisfying, and until recently, stable canon. As long as the faith is intact, it is probable that the coping mechanism that they have been provided by the church society successfully blunts the intensity of their neuroendocrine responses to psychosocial stimulation. This buffering against intense and sustained neuroendocrine arousal may have played a part in the observed decrease in the incidence of bacteriuria, coronary artery disease, and high blood pressure. On the other hand, this protection appears to be absent in those high-risk Benedictine parish priests and teachers who are described by Caffrey (1968) as "Type A persons in a Type A atmosphere." Type A refers to the Rosenmann-Friedman scale in which aggression, impatience, time urgency, and competitiveness rate high and are associated with an increased incidence of coronary disease (Jenkins, 1971). Such behavioral traits tend to be fostered by certain institutions of highly organized competitive civilizations (Toffler, 1970).

In a recent summary of his work on the growth and decline of human societies, the historian Toynbee (1972) suggests that the higher religions originated as a means of "partial disengagement from the social matrix of the times." The objective, he says, was to escape from civilization's obsession with the collective attempt to control "nonhuman nature." The operational thinking mentioned earlier is characteristically involved in just such a Type A drive for control. For it focuses on critical evaluation and is primarily cognitive, being concerned with facts and figures. But man, Toynbee says, is "a social species whose sociability is not yet automatically enforced by built-in instinct as it is in the social species of insects." Lacking this compulsion and obsessed by the cognitive operational thinking mode (Fig. 2), the civilization neglects the development of what Toynbee terms "self-mastery." This, he says, is the goal of the religious disengagement from the social matrix. The cloister and mysticism involve a behavior that is complementary to operational thinking; for fasting, prayer, and meditation are concerned with the controlled cultivation of drive-directed fantasy. Thus the active religious movement reverses the tables by encouraging an affective mode (Fig. 2).

The civilization that is being effectively compensated by such a higher religion will show a controlled ritualization of the territorial and attachment instincts by a stable cultural canon. It thereby avoids the danger of over-dependence on the purely cognitive mode. In the search for self-mastery, those subscribing to the canon seek to avoid even covert "rage, fear, and despair"; on the other hand, the cultivation of attachment relationships is encouraged. Thus its coping influence helps the individual to avoid excessive arousal of the defense and alarm responses. This may be one of the reasons why essential hypertension is rarely found in stable cultures that are free from external perturbation and honor traditional forms (Henry and Cassel, 1969).

VIII. SUMMARY

The confrontations that occur between the various members of a social grouping of mammals, including man, as they seek food, nesting areas, and mates are accompanied by psychosocial stimulation with behavioral evidence of emotional arousal.

Coping mechanisms provided by the cultural milieu are important in blocking or decreasing the intensity of arousal by psychosocial stimuli. Conversely sociocultural deficiencies can be responsible for impaired control and disturbed response patterns.

The physiologic concomitants of psychosocial stimulation include the arousal of at least two separate neuroendocrine response patterns: the hippocampal-septal triggered pituitary adrenal-cortical alarm reaction and the amygdala-driven sympathetic adrenal-medullary defense response.

Social interactions that lead to a downward displacement in the hierarchy are associated with subordinate behavior indicative of depression, with decreased gonadotropin levels, and stimulation of the hypophyseal adrenal-cortical system. The struggle to maintain a threatened status is associated with agonistic behavior and enhanced sympathetic adrenal-medullary responses. A rise in status leads to increased dominant display, a decrease in the foregoing responses, and stimulates the gonadotropic system leading to increased plasma testosterone in the male.

ACKNOWLEDGMENT

The work in our laboratories reported in this chapter was made possible by the support of U.S. Public Health Service Grant No. MH 19441 from the National Institutes of Health.

REFERENCES

Abrahams, D. C., Able, C. A., and Barnard, B. G. (1960): Systemic blood pressure in a rural West Africa community. *W. Afr. Med. J.,* 9:45–58.

Ainsworth, M. D. S., and Wittig, B. A. (1969): Attachment and exploratory behavior of one-year-olds in a strange situation. In: *Determinants of Infant Behaviour, Vol. 4,* edited by B. M. Foss, pp. 111–136. Methuen, London.

Alexander, F. G., and French, T. M. (1948): *Studies in Psychosomatic Medicine; An Approach to the Cause and Treatment of Vegetative Disturbances.* Ronald Press, New York.

Ax, A. F. (1953): The physiological differentiation between fear and anger in humans. *Psychosom. Med.,* 15:433–442.

Barnett, S. A. (1964): Social stress: The concept of stress. In: *Viewpoints in Biology, Vol. 3,* edited by J. D. Carthy and C. L. Duddington, pp. 170–218. Butterworths, London.

Bourne, P. G. (1971): Altered adrenal function in two combat situations in Viet Nam. In: *The Physiology of Aggression and Defeat,* edited by B. E. Eleftheriou and J. P. Scott, pp. 265–290. Plenum Press, New York.

Bowlby, J. (1970): *Attachment and Loss, Vol. 1, Attachment.* Hogarth Press, London.

Bowlby, J. (1973): *Attachment and Loss, Vol. 2, Separation, Anxiety and Anger.* Hogarth Press, London.

Brod, J., Fencl, V., Hejl, A., and Jirka, J. (1959): Circulatory changes underlying blood pressure elevation during acute emotional stress (mental arithmetic) in normotensive and hypertensive subjects. *Clin. Sci.,* 18:269–279.

Bronson, F. H. (1973): Establishment of social rank among grouped male mice: Relative effects on circulating FSH, LH, and corticosterone. *Physiol. Behav.,* 10:947–951.

Bronson, F. H., and Eleftheriou, B. E. (1965): Behavioral, pituitary, and adrenal correlates of controlled fighting (defeat) in mice. *Physiol. Zool.,* 38:406–411.

Caffrey, C. B. (1966): *Behavior patterns and personality characteristics as related to prevalence rates of coronary heart diseases in Trappist and Benedictine monks.* Ph.D. Dissertation, Clinical Psychology, The Catholic University of America, Washington, D.C. (University Microfilms, Inc., Ann Arbor, Mich., No. 67–1830, pp. 45–48 coronary heart disease rates).

Caffrey, B. (1968): Reliability and validity of personality and behavioral measures in a study of coronary heart disease. *J. Chron. Dis.,* 21:191–204.

Cannon, W. B. (1929): *Bodily Changes in Pain, Hunger, Fear and Rage; An Account of Recent Researches Into the Function of Emotional Excitement.* Appleton, New York.

Cannon, W. B., and de La Paz, D. (1911): Emotional stimulation of adrenal secretion. *Am. J. Physiol.,* 27:64–70.

Christian, J. J. (1971): Population density and reproductive efficiency. *Biol. Reprod.,* 4:248–294.

Christian, J. J., Lloyd, J. A., and Davis, D. E. (1965): The role of endocrines in the self-regulation of mammalian populations. *Rec. Prog. Horm. Res.,* 21:501–578.

Cobb, S., and Rose, R. M. (1973): Hypertension, peptic ulcer, and diabetes in air traffic controllers. *JAMA,* 224:489–492.

Cohen, E. A. (1954): *Human Behavior in the Concentration Camp.* Jonathan Cape, London.

Cohen, F., and Lazarus, R. S. (1973): Active coping processes, coping dispositions, and recovery from surgery. *Psychosom. Med.,* 35:375–389.

Conner, R. L., Vernikos-Danellis, J., and Levine, S. (1971): Stress, fighting and neuroendocrine function. *Nature,* 234:564–566.

Cruz-Coke, R., Etcheverry, R., and Nagel, R. (1964): Influence of migration on blood-pressure of Easter Islanders. *Lancet,* 1:697–699.

Draper, P. (1973): Crowding among hunter-gatherers: The !Kung Bushmen. *Science,* 182:301–303.

Durkheim, E. (1951): *Suicide: A Study in Sociology,* translated by J. A. Spaulding and G. Simpson. Free Press, Glencoe, Ill.

Eibl-Eibesfeldt, I. (1972): *Love and Hate: The Natural History of Behavior Patterns,* translated by G. Strachan. Holt, Rinehart and Winston, New York.

Ekman, Paul (1973): Darwin and cross cultural studies of facial expression. In: *Darwin and Facial Expression: A Century of Research in Review,* edited by Paul Ekman. Academic Press, New York.

Ely, D. L., and Henry, J. P. (1974): Effects of prolonged social deprivation on murine behavior patterns, blood pressure and adrenal weight. *J. Comp. Physiol. Psychol.*, 87:733–740.

Endröczi, E. and Lissák, K. (1963): Effect of hypothalamic and brain stem structure stimulation on pituitary-adrenocortical function. *Acta Physiol. Acad. Sci. Hung.*, 24:67–77.

Folkow, B., and Neil, E. (1971): *Circulation*, pp. 344–349. Oxford University Press, London.

Folkow, B., and Rubinstein, E. H. (1966): Cardiovascular effects of acute and chronic stimulations of the hypothalamic defence area in the rat. *Acta Physiol. Scand.*, 68:48–57.

Foster, J. H. (1927): High blood pressure of foreigners in China. *Arch. Intern. Med.*, 40:38–45.

Frankenhaeuser, M. (1975): Experimental approaches to the study of catecholamines and emotion. In: *Emotions: Their Parameters and Measurement*, edited by L. Levi, pp. 209–234. Raven Press, New York.

Ganong, W. F. (1970): Control of adrenocorticotrophin and melanocyte-stimulating hormone secretion. In: *The Hypothalamus*, edited by L. Martini, M. Motta, and F. Fraschini, pp. 313–331. Academic Press, New York.

Ganong, W. F. (1973): Higher functions of the nervous system: Conditioned reflexes, learning, & related phenomena. In: *Review of Medical Physiology*, p. 193. Lange Medical Publications, Los Altos, Calif.

Goldfien, A., and Ganong, W. F. (1962): Adrenal medullary and adrenal cortical response to stimulation of diencephalon. *Am. J. Physiol.*, 202:205–211.

Graham, J. D. P. (1945): High blood pressure after battle. *Lancet*, 1:239–249.

Harding, M. E. (1965): *The Parental Image: Its Injury and Reconstruction. A Study in Analytical Psychology*, Putnam, New York.

Harlow, H. F., McGaugh, J. L., and Thompson, R. F. (1971): *Psychology*. Albion Publishing Co., San Francisco.

Harris, R. E., and Singer, M. T. (1968): Interaction of personality and stress in the pathogenesis of essential hypertension. In: *Hypertension: Neural Control of Arterial Pressure, Vol. 16. Proceedings of the Council for High Blood Pressure Research*, pp. 104–114. American Heart Association, New York.

Henry, J. P., and Cassel, J. C. (1969): Psychosocial factors in essential hypertension: Recent epidemiologic and animal experimental evidence. *Am. J. Epidemiol.*, 90:171–200.

Henry, J. P., Ely, D. L., Stephens, P. M., Ratcliffe, H. L., Santisteban, G. A., and Shapiro, A. P. (1971a): The role of psychosocial factors in the development of arteriosclerosis in CBA mice: Observations on the heart, kidney, and aorta. *Atherosclerosis*, 14:203–218.

Henry, J. P., Meehan, J. P., and Stephens, P. M. (1967): The use of psychosocial stimuli to induce prolonged systolic hypertension in mice. *Psychosom. Med.*, 29:408–432.

Henry, J. P., Stephens, P. M., Axelrod, J., and Mueller, R. A. (1971b): Effect of psychosocial stimulation on the enzymes involved in the biosynthesis and metabolism of noradrenaline and adrenaline. *Psychosom. Med.*, 33:227–237.

Henry, J. P., Stephens, P. M., and Santisteban, G. A. (1975): A model of psychosocial hypertension showing reversibility and progression of cardiovascular complications. *Circ. Res.*, 36:156–164.

Hess, W. R., and Brügger, M. (1943): Das subkortikale Zentrum der affektiven Abwehrreaktion. *Helv. Physiol. Acta*, 1:33–52.

Hinde, R. A. (1971): Development of social behavior. In: *Behavior of Nonhuman Primates: Modern Research Trends, Vol. 3*, edited by A. M. Schrier and F. Stollnitz, pp. 1–60. Academic Press, New York.

Hofer, M. A., Wolff, C. T., Friedman, S. B., and Mason, J. W. (1972a): A psychoendocrine study of bereavement. Part I. 17-hydroxycorticosteroid excretion rates of parents following death of their children from leukemia. *Psychosom. Med.*, 34:481–491.

Hofer, M. A., Wolff, C. T., Friedman, S. B., and Mason, J. W. (1972b): A psychoendocrine study of bereavement. Part II. Observations on the process of mourning in relation to adrenocortical function. *Psychosom. Med.*, 34:492–504.

Holmes, T. H., and Rahe, R. H. (1967): The social readjustment rating scale. *J. Psychosom. Res.,* 11:213–218.

Isaacson, R. L. (1974): *The Limbic System.* Plenum Press, New York.

Jenkins, C. D. (1971): Psychologic and social precursors of coronary disease (in two parts). *N. Engl. J. Med.,* 284:244–255; 307–317.

Jones, M. T., Bridges, P. K., and Leak, D. (1970): Correlation between psychic and endocrinological responses to emotional stress. In: *Progress in Brain Research, Vol. 32, Pituitary, Adrenal and the Brain,* edited by D. de Wied and J. A. W. M. Weijnen, pp. 325–335. Elsevier, Amsterdam.

Kaminer, B., and Lutz, W. P. (1960): Blood pressure in Bushmen of the Kalahari Desert. *Circulation,* 22:289–295.

Katz, J. L., Weiner, H., Gallagher, T. F., and Hellman, L. (1970): Stress, distress, and ego defenses: Psychoendocrine response to impending breast tumor biopsy. *Arch. Gen. Psychiatry,* 23:131–142.

Kawakami, M., Seto, K., Terasawa, E., Yoshida, K., Miyamoto, T., Sekiguchi, M., and Hattori, Y. (1968): Influence of electrical stimulation and lesion in limbic structure upon biosynthesis of adrenocorticoid in the rabbit. *Neuroendocrinology,* 3:337–348.

Kimball, C. P. (1970): Conceptual developments in psychosomatic medicine: 1939–1969. *Ann. Intern. Med.,* 73:307–316.

Klaus, M. H., Jerauld, R., Kreger, N. C., McAlpine, W., Steffa, M., and Kennell, J. H. (1972): Maternal attachment: Importance of the first post-partum days. *N. Engl. J. Med.,* 286:460–463.

Klopfer, P. H. (1971): Mother love: What turns it on? Studies of maternal arousal and attachment in ungulates may have implications for man. *Am. Sci.,* 59:404–407.

Kummer, H. (1971): *Primate Societies: Group Techniques of Ecological Adaptation.* Aldine-Atherton, Chicago.

Kunin, C. M., and McCormack, R. C. (1968): An epidemiologic study of bacteriuria and blood pressure among nuns and working women. *N. Engl. J. Med.,* 278:635–642.

Kvetňanský, R., and Mikulaj, L. (1970): Adrenal and urinary catecholamines in rats during adaptation to repeated immobilization stress. *Endocrinology,* 87:738–743.

Kvetňanský, R., Weise, V. K., and Kopin, I. J. (1970): Elevation of adrenal tyrosine hydroxylase and phenylethanolamine-*N*-methyl transferase by repeated immobilization of rats. *Endocrinology,* 87:744–749.

Lapin, B. A., and Cherkovich, G. M. (1971): Environmental change causing the development of neuroses and corticovisceral pathology in monkeys. In: *Society, Stress and Disease, Vol. 1, The Psychosocial Environment and Psychosomatic Diseases,* edited by L. Levi, pp. 266–280. Oxford University Press, London.

Lazarus, R. S. (1966): *Psychological Stress and the Coping Process.* McGraw-Hill, New York.

Lazarus, R. S. (1975): The self-regulation of emotion. In: *Emotions: Their Parameters and Measurement,* edited by L. Levi, pp. 47–67. Raven Press, New York.

Lenneberg, E. H. (1973): What is meant by knowing a language? In: *Communication and Affect: Language and Thought,* edited by P. Pliner, L. Krames, and T. Alloway, pp. 1–7. Academic Press, New York.

Levi, L., editor (1972): Stress and distress in response to psychosocial stimuli: Laboratory and real life studies on sympathoadrenomedullary and related reactions. Supplement No. 528 to Acta Medica Scandinavica, Vol. 191.

Levine, S., Goldman, L., and Coover, G. D. (1972): Expectancy and the pituitary-adrenal system. In: *Physiology, Emotion and Psychosomatic Illness,* Ciba Foundation Symposium 8 (new series), pp. 281–296. Associated Scientific Publishers, Amsterdam.

Lowenstein, F. W. (1961): Blood-pressure in relation to age and sex in the tropics and subtropics: A review of the literature and an investigation in two tribes of Brazil Indians. *Lancet,* 1:389–392.

Lutwak, L., Whedon, G. D., Lachance, P. A., Reid, J. M., and Lipscomb, H. S. (1969): Mineral, electrolyte and nitrogen balance studies of the Gemini-VII fourteen-day orbital space flight. *J. Clin. Endocrinol. Metab.,* 29:1140–1156.

Maclay, G., and Knipe, H. (1972): *The Dominant Man: The Pecking Order in Human Society.* Delacorte Press, New York.

MacLean, P. D. (1973): The brain's generation gap: Some human implications. *ZYGON/ J. Relig. Sci.*, 8:113–127.

Marty, P., and de M'Uzan, M. (1963): La "pensée opératoire." *Rev. Franc. Psychanal.*, 27:345–356.

Mason, J. W. (1968a): A review of psychoendocrine research on the pituitary-adrenal cortical system. *Psychosom. Med.* 30:576–607.

Mason, J. W. (1968b): A review of psychoendocrine research on the sympathetic-adrenal medullary system. *Psychosom. Med.*, 30:631–653.

McClosky, H., and Schaar, J. H. (1965): Psychological dimensions of anomy. *Am. Sociol. Rev.*, 30:14–40.

Mikulaj, L., and Kvetňanský, R. (1966): Changes in adrenocortical activity prior to and following adaptation to trauma in the Noble-Collip drum. *Physiol. Bohemoslov.*, 15:439–446.

Mikulaj, L., and Mitro, A. (1973): Endocrine functions during adaptation to stress. In: *Advances in Experimental Medicine and Biology, Vol. 33, Neurohumoral and Metabolic Aspects of Injury, Proceedings of the IUPS Satellite Symposium, August 3–7, 1971, Budapest, Hungary,* edited by A. G. B. Kovach, H. B. Stoner, and J. J. Spitzer, pp. 631–638. Plenum Press, New York.

Moser, M., Morgan, R., Hale, M., Hoobler, S., Remington, R., Dodge, H., and Macaulay, A. (1959): Epidemiology of hypertension with particular reference to the Bahamas. *Am. J. Cardiol.*, 4:727–733.

Nauta, W. J. H. (1971): The problem of the frontal lobe: A reinterpretation. *J. Psychiatr. Res.*, 8:167–187.

Nauta, W. J. H., and Haymaker, W. (1969): Hypothalamic nuclei and fiber connections. In: *The Hypothalamus,* edited by W. Haymaker, E. Anderson, and W. J. H. Nauta, pp. 136–209. Charles C. Thomas, Springfield, Ill.

Nemiah, J. C., and Sifneos, P. E. (1970): Affect and fantasy in patients with psychosomatic disorders. In: *Modern Trends in Psychosomatic Medicine, Vol. 2,* edited by O. W. Hill, pp. 26–34. Appleton-Century-Crofts, New York.

Neumann, E. (1954): *The Origins and History of Consciousness,* translated by R. F. C. Hull. Routledge & Kegan Paul, London.

Nuckolls, K. B., Cassel, J., and Kaplan, B. H. (1972): Psychosocial assets, life crisis and the prognosis of pregnancy. *Am. J. Epidemiol.*, 95:431–441.

Oberman, A., Lane, N. E., Harlan, W. R., Graybiel, A., and Mitchell, R. E. (1967): Trends in systolic blood pressure in the thousand aviator cohort over a twenty-four year period. *Circulation,* 36:812–822.

Price, J. S. (1969): The ritualization of agonistic behavior as a determinant of variation along the neuroticism/stability dimension of personality. *Proc. R. Soc. Med.*, 62:37–40.

Rahe, R. H., Bennett, L., Romo, M., Siltanen, P., and Arthur, R. J. (1973): Subjects' recent life changes and coronary heart disease in Finland. *Am. J. Psychiatry,* 130:1222–1226.

Ratcliffe, H. L. (1968): Environment, behavior and disease. In: *Progress in Physiological Psychology, Vol. 1,* edited by E. Stellar and J. M. Sprague, pp. 161–229. Academic Press, New York.

Ratcliffe, H. L., Luginbühl, H., Schnarr, W. R., and Chacko, K. (1969): Coronary arteriosclerosis in swine: Evidence of a relation to behavior. *J. Comp. Physiol. Psychol.*, 68:385–392.

Richter, C. P. (1957): On the phenomenon of sudden death in animals and man. *Psychosom. Med.*, 19:191–198.

Roldán, E., Alvarez-Pelaez, R., and de Molina, F. (1974): Electrographic study of the amygdaloid defense response. *Physiol. Behav.*, 13:779–787.

Rose, R. M., Bernstein, I. S., and Gordon, T. P. (1975): Consequences of social conflict on plasma testosterone levels in rhesus monkeys. *Psychosom. Med.*, 37:50–61.

Rose, R. M., Gordon, T. P., and Bernstein, I. S. (1972): Plasma testosterone levels in the male rhesus: Influences of sexual and social stimuli. *Science,* 178:643–645.

Rose, R. M., Holaday, J. W., and Bernstein, I. S. (1971): Plasma testosterone, dominance rank and aggressive behaviour in male rhesus monkeys. *Nature,* 231:366–368.

Sachar, E. J. (1970): Psychological factors relating to activation and inhibition of the adrenocortical stress response in man: A Review. In: *Progress in Brain Research, Vol. 32, Pituitary, Adrenal and the Brain,* edited by D. de Wied and J. A. W. M. Weijnen, pp. 316–324. Elsevier, Amsterdam.

Sachar, E. J., Fishman, J. R., and Mason, J. W. (1965): Influence of the hypnotic trance on plasma 17-hydroxycorticosteroid concentration. *Psychosom. Med.,* 27:330–341.

Salk, L. (1970): The critical nature of the post-partum period in the human for the establishment of the mother-infant bond: A controlled study. *Dis. Nerv. Syst.,* 31(Suppl.):110–116.

Sassenrath, E. N. (1970): Increased adrenal responsiveness related to social stress in rhesus monkeys. *Horm. Behav.,* 1:283–298.

Saunders, G. M., and Bancroft, H. (1942): Blood pressure studies on Negro and white men and women living in the Virgin Islands of the United States. *Am. Heart J.,* 23:410–423.

Scotch, N. A. (1960): Preliminary report on the relation of sociocultural factors of hypertension among the Zulu. *Ann. N. Y. Acad. Sci.,* 84:1000–1009.

Scotch, N. A., and Geiger, H. J. (1963): The epidemiology of essential hypertension: A review with special attention to psychologic and sociocultural factors. II. Psychologic and sociocultural factors in etiology. *J. Chron. Dis.,* 16:1183–1213.

Seile, F. (1930): Uber den Einfluss der vegetarischen Ernahrung auf den Blutdruck. *Med. Klin.,* 26:929–931.

Seligman, M. E. P. (1975): *Helplessness. On Depression, Development, and Death.* W. H. Freeman and Company, San Francisco.

Selye, H. (1936): A syndrome produced by diverse nocuos agents. *Nature,* 138:32.

Selye, H. (1950): *The Physiology and Pathology of Exposure to Stress.* Acta Inc., Montreal.

Shapiro, A. P. (1963): Experimental pyelonephritis and hypertension: Implications for the clinical problem. *Ann. Intern. Med.,* 59:37–52.

Shapiro, A. P., Sapira, J. D., and Scheib, E. T. (1971): Development of bacteriuria in a hypertensive population: A 7-year follow-up study. *Ann. Internal Med.,* 74:861–868.

Smith, O. A., Stephenson, R. B., and Randall, D. C. (1974): Range of control of cardiovascular variables by the hypothalamus. In: *Recent Studies of Hypothalamic Function,* edited by K. Lederis and K. E. Cooper. (Proceedings of a Symposium in Calgary, Alberta, May 1973) Albert J. Phiebig, White Plains, N.Y.

Spencer, P. (1965): *The Samburu.* University of California Press, Berkeley.

Sviland, M. A. P. (1973): Quantative denial and home hemodialysis success: Implication for psychotherapeutic intervention. *Psychosom. Med.,* 35:451.

Thomas, E. and Balter, A. (1975): Learned helplessness in cats: amelioration of symptoms by cholinergic blockage of the septum. *J. Comp. Physiol. Psychol.,* in press.

Tiger, L., and Fox, R. (1971): *The Imperial Animal.* Secker & Warburg, London.

Toffler, A. (1970): *Future Shock.* Random House, New York.

Toynbee, A. (1972): *A Study of History.* Oxford University Press, London.

Truswell, A. S., Kennelly, B. M., Hansen, J. D. L., and Lee, R. B. (1972): Blood pressures of !Kung Bushmen in Northern Botswana. *Am. Heart J.,* 84:5–12.

Tung, C. L. (1927): Relative hypotension of foreigners in China. *Arch. Intern. Med.,* 40:154–158.

Tyroler, H. A., and Cassel, J. (1964): Health consequences of culture change. II. The effect of urbanization on coronary heart mortality in rural residents. *J. Chron. Dis.,* 17:167–177.

U. S. Women's Bureau (1935): *The Economic Problems of the Women of the Virgin Islands.* Bulletin 142 of the United States Women's Bureau.

van der Post, L. (1961): *The Heart of the Hunter.* Hogarth Press, London.

Van Lawick-Goodall, J. (1973): The behavior of chimpanzees in their natural habitat. *Am. J. Psychiatry,* 130:1–12.

Von Euler, U. S. (1956): *Noradrenaline: Chemistry, Physiology, Pharmacology and Clinical Aspects.* Charles C. Thomas, Springfield, Ill.

Biological Foundations of Psychiatry,
edited by R. G. Grenell and S. Gabay.
Raven Press, New York © 1976.

An Information-Processing Model of Mind

R. G. Grenell and D. McCulloch

Section of Neurobiology, Institute of Psychiatry and Human Behavior, University of Maryland
Hospital, Baltimore, Maryland 20014

This chapter deals with brain, mind, and behavior. We attempt to show how integration of interdisciplinary observations can allow formulation of an information model, which itself can represent the mind. Although not a neural model, the information-processing model is directly related to structure. It is indeed almost impossible to talk about brain function without talking about structure. Most of the system is comprised of functional as well as structural nonhomogeneous units.

Perhaps this can be looked on as one of the first differences between the brain and the computer. In the latter, structure and function can be separated and discussed in an abstract way. The computer hardware maker and builder and the computer programmer need not know anything about each other's work. In the brain, however, knowledge of principles is insufficient. Detailed analysis of elements and elementary processes is essential. In fact, such considerations (in addition to making clear the superiority and complexity of the brain over the computer, as will be seen) lead to the realization that we are severely limited by our present ignorance in any attempt to model adequately the behavior of an animal, or even to deal with interrelationships of informational, computational, functional, and structural levels.

Consequently the proposed model suffers from what ultimately may be unwarranted assumptions, oversimplifications, etc.; nonetheless it will be useful. Its greatest utility may lie in the questions it can help us to formulate in dealing with the basic issue, i.e., how neural activity processes information to yield the kind of data necessary to study adaptive behavior. As stated by Arbib (1): "We try to analyze how, for an animal with a given metabolic machinery and a given gross structure, changes in its receptor organization and its ability to combine present information with past experience can best contribute to its improved handling of its environment. An animal can survive better in an environment if it has receptors which can detect an enemy far away; but these receptors are only useful if the animal can compute on that information to find appropriate avoiding action before the enemy is upon it." Interesting associated questions are involved as well, concerning errors, distortions, blocks, or other interferences with adaptive processing resulting in abnormal overt behavior patterns.

What we are concerned with, then, is processing, the processing machinery, and the interference with these that gives rise to what the clinician sees in his patients. Too often this sort of an endeavor is looked on by the clinician as a rather futile exercise. Perhaps his view stems in part from the consideration that perceptual signs of sensory processing may be difficult to observe. The machinery might be evidenced only when it is over- or underloaded with specific inputs to which it is sensitive. As Mackay pointed out, under such circumstances if the subsystem concerned is "plastic" or "self-adjusting," its operation may change so that a normally balanced input may be processed anomalously for some time afterward.

The postulated model is not intended to be either a rigorous treatment of the informational aspects of a self-adjusting communication system or a rigorous discussion of the "fine structure" of neural events. Rather it is meant to stress an overview of considerations regarding brain and mind as a totality, with neither brain nor mind regarded as a separate or unrelated entity for which no encompassing rationale may be developed. The information point of view, however, is not purely mechanistic. Information systems become "discrete" and lead to specific decisions only when the cumulative probabilities for their bounded operations reach a level of certainty which is highly predictable. Although processing associated with the system may be modeled by one or more mathematical treatments, no single such mode of analysis would encompass an information system so elaborate as that of man. Indeed, one finds that the literature is replete with a considerable variety of models, each addressing a particular function as suggested by neurobiological observations. Thus in the ensuing discussion the system is discussed heuristically rather than being rigidly modeled. A hierarchy of functional entities is displayed without delineating in detail the processing within a particular unit.

Our assumption is that this approach is sufficiently broad to encompass all forms of human behavior, normal and abnormal. Although a specific behavioral pattern might be difficult to structure in the admittedly imperfect and incomplete scheme proposed, the potential for the information approach must form the basis for such behavioral considerations.

Only within an empirical and scientifically testable information framework can the clinician hope to classify, refine, and develop further his understanding of what he observes and his therapeutic interaction with the patient.

I. THE MODEL

The model represents a hierarchy of *information states*. The term "information state" means the lowest order of discrete event, which, taken in aggregate form, sums to a particular system or subsystem. Stated in another way, an information state could be looked on as the sum of the simplest message signals interacting with preprogrammed memory. In a sense, the interaction defines the information state. Analogous to such an event would be the information encoded in the simplest form of rudimentary signal in a communications system. In the behavioral sense the event is salient, with high information content and importance for the subject. Such signals constitute important and inherent properties of any neurally based information system but cannot represent all forms of informational activity for that system. The analogy is useful in underscoring another point; i.e., that the information event—whether it be electrical signal, neurochemical, field-related, or mechanostructural—is in itself the end result of a large number of more microscopic events acting cooperatively.

A microscopic information system could treat these processes. However, such a system would be concerned with the endproduct of these microscopic events—the signal itself, and finally with the information included in that signal. The "granular species" for the model proposed here is such an information event. A neuroelectric signal, for example, results when a series of membrane-related events (permeability changes, ionic fluxes, etc.) trigger a traveling wave of depolarization which ultimately reaches the presynaptic terminal. Intracellular physical and chemical processes are involved, as are a series of events at the synaptic junction, as well as field phenomena, etc. Although the model presented here is not directly concerned with these "micro" processes, it must be recognized that they play a major role in the basic operation of the system. Figure 1 shows the complex events involved at this level. As the figure suggests, it is possible that, during training, conformational changes in synaptic proteins occur rapidly to temporarily change neuronal connectivity associated with the formation of short-term memory, but that the events following conformational changes in the nuclear proteins are necessary for the permanent connectivity changes that underlie the formation of long-term memory.

The transition from signal to information is an encoding process. It might be useful here to discuss briefly this encoding process which relates signals to information. Bioelectric (or neuroelectric) signals represent one of the most extensively studied classes of signals in terms of their encoded information and consequent functional properties. It should be noted, however, that other signals and substrates for information exist in great variety and wide proliferation in the brain. A signal may be discussed purely in terms of its properties as a signal *per se* or in terms of its message content. Whatever information messages are carried are encoded within the signal parameters. The variety of possible codes is enormous and may fall into discrete digital ("yes" and "no") and analogue ("graded") categories or into more probabilistic forms. Candidate codes have been isolated within these major categories. These are patterns of information coding associated with neural function at

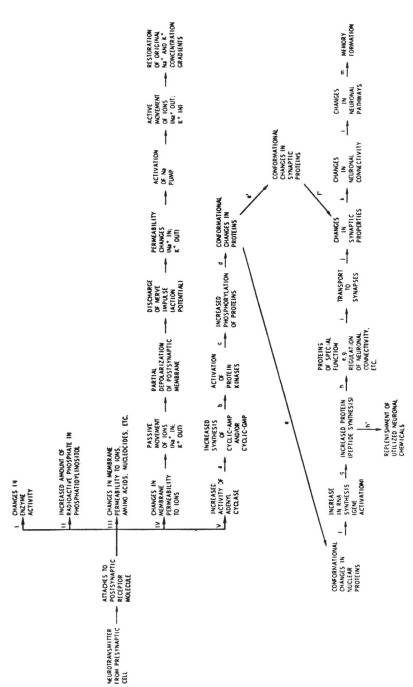

FIG. 1. Some chemical events that follow the attachment of a neurotransmitter to a neuron. (From ref. 2.)

TABLE 1. *Candidate neural codes, or forms of representation of information in the nervous system*

Neuronal events other than impulses
Intracellular events
   Receptor potential: amplitude
   Synaptic potential: amplitude
   Synaptic conductance change: amplitude
   Synaptic conductance change: spatial distribution
   Membrane potential: spatial and temporal distribution
   Graded potential in axonal terminals
Intercellular events
   Transmitter released
   Potassium ion released
   Neurosecretion released
   Electrotonic coupling between specific cells
   Electrotonic interaction via extracellular space

Impulses in unit neurons
Representation by identity of active fiber
   Labeled lines
Codes based on temporal properties of impulses
   Time of occurrence
     Instant of firing
     Phase locking to stimulus
   Interval statistics codes
     Frequency: weighted average
     Frequency: instantaneous
     Frequency: increment above background
     Frequency: rate of change
     Frequency of firing/missing at fixed intervals
     Coefficient of variation
     Higher moments; interval histogram shape
   Temporal pattern of impulses
   Number of impulses or duration of burst
   Velocity change in axon
Codes based on other properties
   Amplitude change in axon
   Spatial sequencing

Ensemble activity
Representation by spatial array
   Topographic distribution of active fibers
Codes based on temporal relations among active channels
   Latency distribution
   Phase distribution
   Probability of firing after stimulus: PST histogram shape
Representation by form of composite of multiunit activity
   Evoked potential shape
   Slow waves in ongoing EEG

From Perkel and Bullock, with permission.

the "microscopic" level and with higher function at the "macroscopic" level. Although investigators in this area generally refer particularly to neuroelectric signals as shown in Table 1 (3), the model under discussion is "intended" to include all possible encoding mechanisms. It is necessary *not* to restrict these considerations to any single type of signal for two reasons. First, the model is to be a comprehensive one, encompassing the most abstract and general forms of human behavior. Furthermore, the system itself exhibits a characteristic and vital *plasticity* without which adaptation would be impossible.

Plasticity exists at several levels. At any level, in general terms, plasticity connotes the ability of the system either to change from one set pattern or modus operandi to another, or to undergo modification of a given operational framework. Such ability to adjust occurs at all levels, from the finest submicroscopic structural level to the most complex macroscopic informational and behavioral levels. Self-adjustive modifications in the system may occur as graded phenomena (e.g., at synapses) or as ungraded, selective, or stepwise processes (digital, yes-no, all-or-nothing, on-off, etc.). Other than the complete adaptive behavior of the organism, certain specific examples of plasticity at the neurophysiological level may serve to clarify the concept:

1. Changes in synaptic membrane events and molecular conformation associated with particular electrical inputs, drug actions, hormone actions, learning events, etc.

2. Subtle alterations in the relationship between neuronal firing and muscular contraction may be produced by conditioning techniques (Fetz and Finocchio, 1971). Thus the linkage between cortical neuronal function and movement may be a plastic one, capable of change during learning or recovery from local neuronal damage.

3. Prolonged but subtle changes in firing of precentral neurons have been shown to follow periods of cortical stimulation at intensities too weak to influence movements. These prolonged aftereffects of the period of stimulation may be of the same nature as the long-term modifications of function of cortical cells demonstrated by Rusinov, Morrell, and others. Cortical cells which discharged in relation to spontaneous movements in conscious monkeys could be influenced by local stimulation of adjacent motor cortex. Repetitive stimulation for 5 min produced statistically significant changes in the neuronal discharge patterns associated with movement, and these changes were still evident 30 min after the end of cortical stimulation. The demonstration of this capacity for change is important in considering the mechanisms by which recombinations of cortical efferent patterns may be learned during training to a skilled task.

4. At a more macroscopic level in a sensory system, it should be noted that auditory thresholds undergo temporary and reversible or permanent and irreversible self-limiting shifts as the result of acute exposure to noise, etc.

A second important characteristic of the information system found in higher animals and man is its redundancy, particularly in relation to less complex forms of information processing as they occur at lower levels of the hierarchy. Implicit to redundancy is the fact that there need not be a one-to-one correspondence between some particular external input and the code used for its representation. In other words, one code serves a variety of inputs, thus effecting parsimony and efficiency in the system. This is not to imply the absence of information systems dedicated to particular inputs in the same manner as "core" is dedicated in a computer.

The latter notion, however, necessitates immediate clarification of the fact that the brain is neither merely a simple digital computer nor an analogue signal processor. The system is an active system with information sources which are entirely internal and self-generating. Second, the system exhibits not only adaptation but growth and decay cycles as well. Further, although a computer might be made probabilistic in some function, it is not characteristically so; the information system, however, is probabilistic in many of its processes.

With this brief background, let us now consider a model of mind, a model of "function," directly related to structure. Let us consider the brain as a three-dimensional system sliced through at one plane (Fig. 2). The slice is then opened outward from the highest centers of the brain so that inputs lie along one side of the slice and outputs along the other side. Such an opened slice (Fig. 3) contains a series of progressively larger information centers, or diagrammatic boxes. The largest lie along the center of the diagram; the smallest are the ellipses, which are at the extreme input and output ends of the model. The system is hierarchical; i.e., the information organization is mediated by and controlled from the highest centers, shown as N^{th} order logical centers. The upward flow of information to these centers proceeds from the 0th (zeroth) order point processors at the input end upward toward the highest level. Information may terminate at or be processed through one or more of the intermediate centers shown in the diagram. A Kth level is shown at which a parallel afferent control system exists. The latter mirrors the hierarchical dominance of the input system. Information flow is upward from input on the (right-hand) afferent side of the model, and proceeds downward to output on the efferent side. Note that an entire half of the model is devoted to control of this signal flow. It becomes control feedback in the (top) efferent half, and descending control of the feed-forward type in the (lower) afferent half.

The information boxes or way stations are not arbitrarily chosen but represent a particular form of logical function, be it a simple transducer at the 0th order stage or a language processor at the Nth order level. The legend which shows the general features of these logic function units is magnified in Fig. 4A. The figure shows one of several possible logical functionings that would be appropriate for certain higher brain centers. In Fig. 4 B, the box labeled LAD is a language-acquisition device in the process of decoding language and of enriching its own repertoire of interpretive strategies. We considered more normal logic levels (such as are found in a computer) for dis-

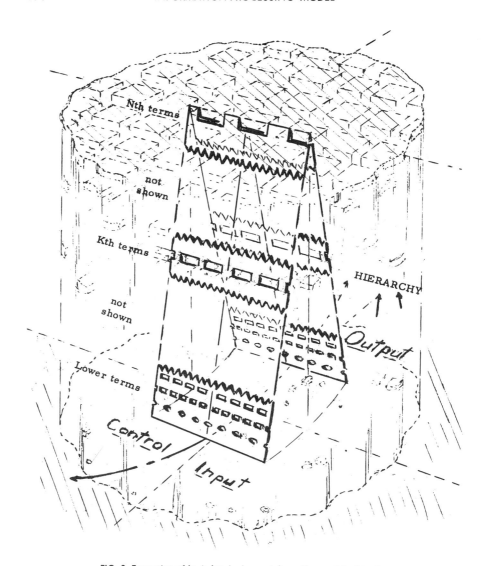

FIG. 2. Formation of logic level schema, information model of brain.

cussion, but the plasticity common to the vertebrate brain clearly invalidates such a simplistic approach. Thus logic functioning in the sense used here would include such complex tasks as perception.

The triangle labeled L is a limiter—an internal control device which interacts with the acquisition system in mediating the information flow within the logic address. A set of features common to all such entities is demonstrated. There is a dual boundary surrounding the particular function to which the entity is committed. The outer boundary represents a feature one would find in any communications transducer, i.e., a filter. We hesitate to speak of such

OUTPUT

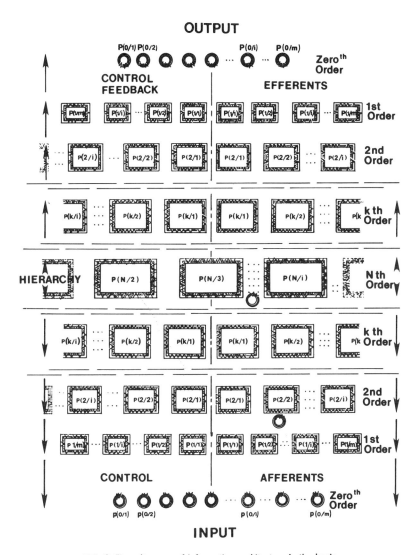

FIG. 3. Flow diagram of information architecture in the brain.

filters in merely trivial terms (i.e., band-pass, low-pass, etc.) since they indeed combine not only the intrinsic membranous properties of particular neural nets but their functional information state as well. The inner shell is hatched for all such logic locations. It contains both known read-in and postulated mechanisms for information storage and recall (memory). The small triangular points shown as decoder and recoder represent, on one hand, the conversion of digitized information signals from other discrete logical processors to analogue form, and on the other hand the digitization of the functional analogue process, which is ongoing for this logic station. We noted the importance of a three-way interactive process between a particular function, the memory of the system, and its filtering capability in performing its requisite signal processing.

The information system we are discussing is probabilistic in terms of the analyses commonly applied to its signals. Even continuous firings for particular neurons would appear to occur within the limitations of some serial probability recognized in the labels or "addresses" which define the information system, e.g., P_{k2}, P_{o1}. The prefix P gives the probability weighting to a particular logic address. Such weightings are unique to a given state and a given entity; i.e., they are nonstationary in mathematical terms. The numbers within brackets define: (1) the hierarchic level, and (2) the term, or par-

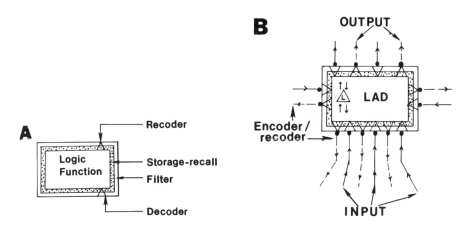

FIG. 4. Detail of logic function address. Language processing. LAD, language-acquisition device. See text for details.

ticular information processor at this level. The model also makes provision not for a discrete number of levels or terms but for N ascending or descending levels and M terms per level—N and M in this sense being the result of redundancy, uncertainty, and on-going plasticity for individual events.

However, the system, although probabilistic in its microscopic nature, becomes a far more discrete and predictable ("certain"?) system macroscopically in its logical functioning. This is so for two reasons. First, information is characteristically assigned to a large number of parallel neural fibers, and so the uncertainty decreases inversely with the square root of this number when the fibers are assigned a like task. Second, the hierarchy of the system itself imposes control and order.

Let us attempt now to demonstrate how such a system might work in terms of "mind"—not brain. Our first axiom is that information is completely embodied in the electrochemical activity of the system as related to its structure at any particular time in the life of the organism. The point is that such

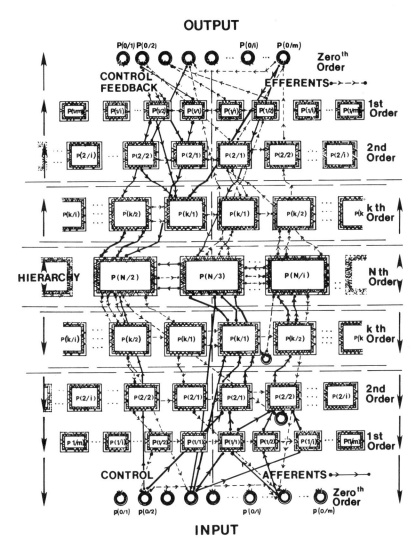

FIG. 5. "Normal" information processing.

electrochemical events completely characterize the system, and that any relevant model for its information architecture must be grounded solidly in what is known of the organization of such electrochemical events. A mechanistic analysis of the electrochemical events alone does not characterize the information state of the system.

Figure 5 shows a "normal" system of information processing. The solid interconnecting lines represent input information flow in the system at any instant in time; the broken lines show the interconnected control systems and output. Note that although addresses for particular logical functions may show several interconnecting lines in both input-output and control, none is "saturated" by such connections. Note also that the richest proliferation of exchanges occurs at the uppermost hierarchical level. The point must be made now that functional information addresses from the Kth order upward are not merely oscillatory but *are capable of generating information without external input*. They are not only processors in the informational sense but miniature systems as well, with active sources enclosed within each logical boundary. Our hierarchical selection for the Kth order is defined by the existence of internal information sources.

The Nth order logic addresses are capable not only of bidirectional information routine but of bidirectional information generation and control either singly or cooperatively. It is well known that the nervous system is a feedback system and includes not only overall feedback from output to input and feedforward from input to output, but also a variety of interstage loops and, indeed, inhibitory, rudimentary control even at the 0th order, point-processing level. There are many such interstage information loops for the "normal" situation in this model, all under hierarchical dominance of ascending addresses. Note that the proliferation of control interconnections in general parallels that for the input-output information, and informational symmetry of sorts exists, although it need not be geometric. We now can discuss some situation of primary interest with regard to abnormal behavior patterns.

Consider what happens if peripheral control is lacking in the system (Fig. 6). 0th order input processors generate a massive amount of information, which tends to saturate the capacity of interstage logical processors at the first-, second-, and higher-order levels. So saturated, these systems may produce fewer than normal signals at the Kth hierarchical level (Fig. 6). On the other hand, if such lower-order interstage processors are critically excited (Fig. 7), they may then produce massive amounts of *ascending* information in the absence of control. If the Nth order—the highest-level systems—are in turn critically excited, they may foster a massive, descending avalanche of information to the output side. "Critical excitation" refers to that level of incoming signals which produces maximal output for a given logic entity. Not shown in the model are direct input-output exchanges, not under hierarchical control, which might also be fostered if control were minimal or inactivated. A second critical excitation point exists with its own triggering mechanisms for signal exchange within a given hierarchical level (Fig. 8). In this case, exchange with lower- or upper-level logic systems is minimal. Fully encoded and structured information signals exchanged in such a parallel hierarchical fashion can occur only from the Kth level upward. Although the normal information system may sometimes be unstably activated—such that it exhibits (1) saturation or critical excitation, or (2) some form of signal blocking (from input to output or control, or from level to level)—its characteristic state for the normal processor will be as in Fig. 5.

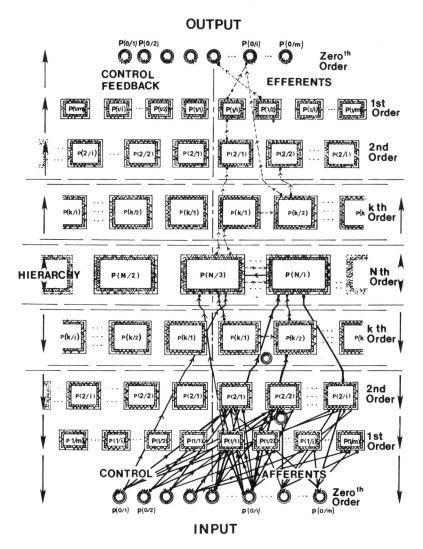

FIG. 6. Peripheral control lacking. Saturated input.

One might question where emotion, motivation, mood, etc. are in this model. Interconnections similar to those previously shown for "normal" processing, but with heightened activity for logic addresses at the Nth order, are seen in Fig. 9. In this case emotional infusion has been triggered by the information content (meaning?) of the system and is generated through interconnected recognition and memory systems across boundaries ("distributed") and within each boundary ("local"). The information corresponding to what is meant by an emotional weighting in all probability would pre-exist as

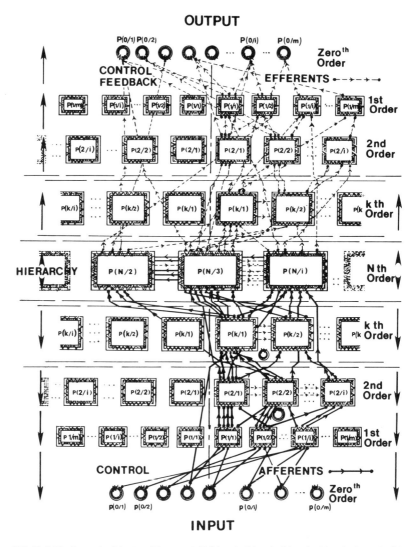

FIG. 7. Critically excited logic addresses. P (1/1), P (1/2), P (2/1), P (2/2), P (K/1), P (N/3).

triggerable information events resident in memory of Kth order logic levels and above. Needless to say, since we are considering a total information system, the usual interconnections will be established to a variety of visceral and other peripheral locations. However, in this case the system is not in a grossly unstable state, since control exists in much the same manner as for the system without the additional emotional weightings. Signal weightings corresponding to emotional states would exist for the system describing "normal" behavioral criteria but would be heightened either episodically or

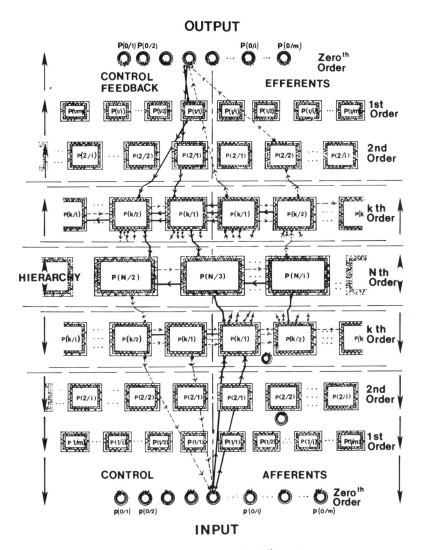

FIG. 8. Critical exchange within K^{th} level.

continuously under conditions which describe abnormal behavioral patterns.

Again this point serves to illustrate that a most characteristic set of information signals describes a behavioral state rather than the full gamut of signals which could exist within that state. Considerations such as emotion and what it means in an information system might illustrate one of two things: Either the information system may not be easily amenable to a conventional notion of what is meant by emotion, or our definition of the term emotion is by no means clear as applied to an information system.

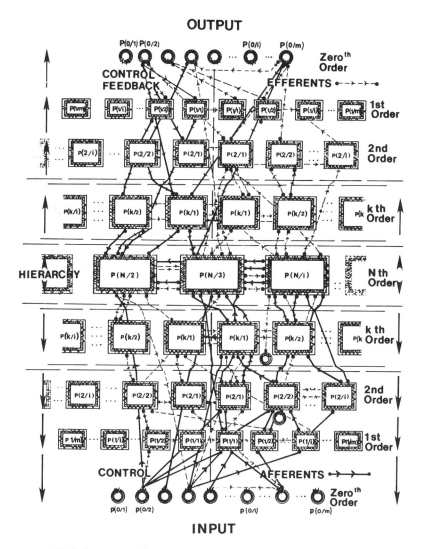

FIG. 9. Heightened N^{th}-order activity in normal functioning, as in emotion.

Hallucinations are frequent overt manifestations of the psychotic state. In Fig. 10 we show interconnections which would allow hallucinatory phenomena to exist. Note that below the Kth order signals from the control centers have blocked out most input and precluded most output. There is an exceedingly rich exchange of parallel information signals at the highest hierarchical level, accompanied by little if any control. This exchange descends to the Kth order on both sides of the hierarchy. Although control is minimal at these highest centers, it is dominant at the lowest. The information exchanged

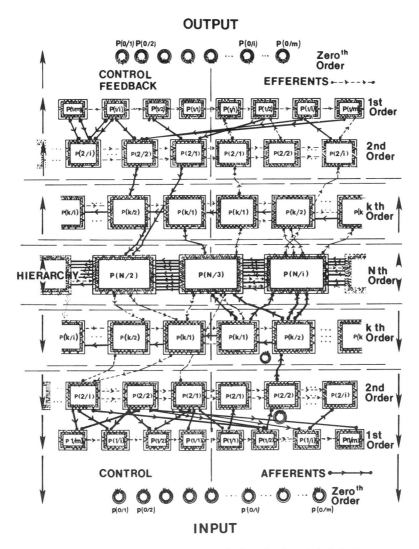

FIG. 10. Isolated, uncontrolled higher-order logic levels, as in hallucination.

between these centers, then, is internal information, released from storage (*generated*) in the absence of normally anticipated or recognizable input. In addition, control internal to the specific logic address may be shunted or abolished, resulting in the massive parallel interchange shown. It can be seen in the model, however, that such generation of "abnormal" information can proceed in the presence of at least a minimal amount of "normal" afferent or efferent processing, or both. Probabilistic considerations alone make such minimal peripheral involvement necessary.

It is of more than passing interest to examine the model from the developmental point of view. Let us attempt to describe early pre- and postnatal processes.

With the origin of neural activity, a core information system exists. This system exhibits neither the hierarchical elaboration nor the proliferation and refinement at any particular level, which the system acquires as development proceeds.

The system explodes outward, upward, and downward. Its logical boundaries become more distinct. As it develops the system becomes, almost simultaneously, both increasingly hierarchically plastic and in some functions more discretely and specifically dedicated to particular information-processing routines. A reverse process may occur with aging, as the associated structural underlay deteriorates.

II. SUMMARY

Simply stated, we have suggested that clinical psychiatry could be significantly advanced by a new way of considering the mental processes with which it is concerned. We proposed a way of looking at the bases of behavior —a scheme which has its foundation solidly rooted in the basic facts of anatomy, biochemistry, and physiology. We stressed the fact that the brain is far more beautiful, subtle, and remarkable than any computer, and that there is a good deal to be gained from thinking in terms not of a "neural system" but of an information system. Thus we conclude that the information state of mind is superimposed on the signal state of the brain, but that the former is hierarchical to the latter. Signals are a necessary precursor to information but are not in themselves sufficient to elicit the information state. It follows therefore that a sufficient condition for the neurophysiological analysis of brain can occur only if the information state of the mind is also considered. These two domains are inextricably interwoven.

REFERENCES

1. Arbib, M. A. (1969): Automata theory as an abstract boundary condition for the study of information processing in the nervous system. In: *Information Processing in the Nervous System,* edited by K. N. Leibovic. Springer-Verlag, New York.
2. Fetz, E., and Finocchio, D. V. (1971): Operant conditioning of specific patterns of neural and muscular activity. *Science,* 174:4007.
3. Glassman, E. (1974): Macromolecules and behavior: A commentary. In: *The Neurosciences, Third Study Program,* edited by F. O. Schmitt and F. G. Worden. M.I.T. Press, Cambridge, Mass.
4. Morrell, F. (1967): Electrical signs of sensory coding. In: *The Neurosciences, A Study Program,* edited by G. C. Quarton, T. Melnechuk, and F. O. Schmitt. The Rockefeller Press, New York.
5. Perkel, D. H., and Bullock, H. (1968): Neural coding. *Neurosci. Res. Prog. Bull.,* 6:3.

Biological Foundations of Psychiatry,
edited by R. G. Grenell and S. Gabay.
Raven Press, New York © 1976.

Neuropsychiatry and Neuropsychology

Karl H. Pribram

Department of Psychology, Stanford University, Stanford, California 94305

I. INTRODUCTION

A century ago, psychiatry and neurology shared a common scientific base. Thus the term neuropsychiatry accurately described a field of endeavor dedicated to the diagnosis and treatment of psychological illnesses that were assumed to reflect disorders of the nervous system. Two developments, more than any others, served to separate psychiatry from these early assumptions. The first of these has been the recognition that the study of behavior, verbal and nonverbal, provides powerful insights into the processes that psychiatrists encounter independent of any knowledge of neural function. In addition, behavioral techniques for modifying these processes were developed, again with no reference to the functions of the nervous system.

Second, the rapid and fruitful development of the social sciences, the study of interbehavioral processes, turned psychiatry away from its early involvement with neurology. A large number of psychopathologies could be understood in terms of the relationships with parents and peers, with family and culture, which engaged the disturbed individual. Knowledge of neurology became as irrelevant as knowledge of computer hardware is for the average programmer versed in high-level languages.

What then remains of neuropsychiatry? Is there a domain where an intimate knowledge of brain function is still relevant to the concerns of the practitioner in psychological and behavioral disorders? I believe there is, and, reverting to the analogy with computer sciences used above, the role of the neuropsychiatrist becomes obvious. Someone must be able to work with machine language, to construct the compilers, assemblers and systems programs that fit the higher level language programs for use with particular computers. I am not speaking here of the hardware specialist who constructs the computers per se. Nor do I identify the neuropsychiatrist with the neurophysiologist, neuropharmacologist, or even the psychopharmacologist. I believe there is a place in today's practice for a group of physicians, diagnosticians, and therapists equally at home in these fields and the behavioral sciences who can help match the patient's behavioral and interbehavioral activities to his particular constitution.

Surprisingly, such a group of practitioners does not exist today. Psychiatry and its younger sibling, clinical psychology, have become fragmented into disciplines, technique-bound enclaves that have all but eschewed any effort at differential diagnosis and thus an attempt at making the therapy fit the individual's disturbances. Today's patient must make such a diagnostic himself by shopping among available technicians until he finds one suitable to his constitutional needs. When the professionals are confronted with this state of affairs, their retort is almost always: there is not enough known at the other levels to be integrated with ours.

I want to propose that over the past quarter of the century, this argument, although tenable, has become obsolete. The fantastic growth of knowledge at every level since World War II begs to be integrated in the service of the patient. Neuropsychology, which to date has restricted its interest to clinical neurology, can provide such integration and neuropsychiatry the service. The time is ripe for the establishment of groups of clinically oriented scientists and practitioners versed in the machine language that can tie the many substantial advances in the behavioral sciences to the constitutional needs of the individual patient.

II. FREUD'S PROJECT FOR A SCIENTIFIC PSYCHOLOGY

In order to implement this proposal, Merton Gill and I undertook a reexamination of the roots of psychoanalytic theory that has provided one of the richest sources of organized knowledge upon which current psychiatric therapy of whatever persuasion is in part based. With others (e.g., George Klein and Robert Holt) we discerned many contemporary conceptual difficulties that became amenable to analysis once we distinguished between two types of theoretical statements: those based on the observation of the verbal and nonverbal behavior of patients in clinical settings and those that refer to mechanism. Furthermore, we became convinced that a good deal of the contemporary confusion could be traced to the statements about mechanism. When we traced these to their roots in Freud's "Project for a Scientific Psychology," we discovered operational definitions of these terms and that the defining operations were neuropsychological. In short, we found that those portions of psychoanalytic theory that were concerned with mechanism actually constituted a detailed neuropsychological theory that could be tested against current neurobiological and experimental psychological knowledge. Since much of the psychological part of the theory concerned cognitive and control processes, contemporary cognitive and control theory proved to be relevant.

The results of our inquiry will presently appear in book form (Pribram and Gill, 1976) and it may be useful to summarize the contents briefly for the audience of the present volume, if for no other reason than to pique interest. But, of course, the issue is the larger one I have been discussing: the foundation of a disciplined neuropsychiatry and the enlarging of the scope of neuropsychology to encompass the neurobiological aspects of disturbed control and cognitive processes.

III. THE REGULATORY PRINCIPLES

Our discussion begins with an analysis of what are called the regulatory principles in psychoanalysis. These principles presumably determine the control of behavior, and we therefore examine them in the light of contemporary control theory. Central to the operation of the control of behavior are such concepts as energy, work, effort, and the signals that serve the mechanism by which controls become operative. We found that Freud's Project unequivocally defines energy as biochemical and neurochemical and the controlling signals as neuroelectric. Thus, when given neurological definitions, energy concepts, such as cathexis, that pervade psychoanalytic theory, become divested of their mystery.

We found further that many specific neural and behavioral servomechanisms (negative feedback) and positive feedback processes are described. These regulate the reinforcement of behavior and the effort that must be expended in order to maintain the organisms's control and equilibrium in the face of life's exigencies. Neuroelectric energy comes in two forms: (1) action currents, translated as currents-in-flow (as measured by rapid deflections of a galvanometer), i.e., nerve impulses, and (2) occupying potentials, translated as *cathexes* (as measured by slow drifts of the galvanometer needle), which today we attribute to local, nontransmitted, graded potential changes. That such a sophisticated view of neural function could be attained in 1895 when the Project was written, initially surprised us, but on tracing its history we found it commonplace in Viennese neurology of that time (e.g., Exner, 1894).

IV. ENERGY CONCEPTS, PRIMARY AND SECONDARY PROCESSES

In the light of these statements in the Project, we suggest that it is premature to abandon energy concepts in the behavioral sciences—provided these concepts are used as they are in physics, to describe differences in the state of systems under observation. In the case of behaving biological systems, these states are biochemical and neurochemical, so any reference to the control of energy in the behavioral sciences must be anchored in the biology of the organisms comprising the systems.

Specific examples concern the operation of physiological drives. Freud's Project defines a set of chemical processes that involve neural sensitivities and "key" secretory neurons. When these processes become organized into a positive feedback loop, the resultant is called "the generation of unpleasure." In later writings, this term is used as shorthand—would it not be better in the light of present knowledge to begin to unpack the "unpleasure" circuit into its serotonergic and catecholaminergic components among others, in order to provide better comprehension of feelings of depression and elation, of lassitude and great motivation?

A distinction that arises early in the Project is the difference between primary and secondary processes of control. Freud bases the distinction on the difference between total neural discharge and more complexly organized functions of the nervous system engendered by the fact that when one neuron in a matrix discharges onto another, that neuron in turn discharges, and so on. In any network of neurons, therefore, some sort of organization develops that delays or even prevents complete discharge of the entire system.

We wondered whether the contemporary view of the nervous system as an information processing mechanism might be relevant to the description in the Project of secondary processes and found that in fact the concepts in the Project in many instances are decidedly richer than contemporary ideas. Thus the Project distinguishes sharply between primary processes characterized by discharge (such as the biochemical generation of unpleasure already mentioned, the occurrence of impulsive behavior, and the relatively unstructured association among neuroelectric events) and cognitive processes that are well organized by a variety of mechanisms that are spelled out in amazing detail.

These considerations led to a reexamination of information measurement theory itself with the consequence that information processing and error processing were distinguished. Error processing results when the familiar closed-loop feedback, servomechanism is operative. By contrast information processing occurs largely by way of feedforward, open-loop mechanisms as when computer programs run themselves off to completion. Most biological (and computer) systems combine feedbacks and feedforwards but the distinction can be most useful (see, e.g., McFarland, 1971; Pribram, 1971).

V. SOME DEFINITIONS OF PRIMARY PROCESSES

As already noted, much of the Project is concerned with neurobiological mechanisms. The following glossary gives a taste of the rich definitional matrix that makes these psychoanalytic concepts understandable—and therefore approachable and testable—to the biologist.

We have already met the definition of *unpleasure* as a biochemical circuit involving neural sensitivities and key secretory neurons. The triggering of this circuit is *defended* against by an inherent high threshold that routes nerve impulses in other directions within a multiply interconnected part of the brain—the primary brain—called ψ. This part of the brain is distinguished from cortex and from the sensorimotor systems. Therefore ψ refers to the basal, core regions of the brain and includes a nuclear portion, most likely the mesencephalic and diencephalic areas, which contain the neural elements sensitive to and secretory of biochemical substances.

Defenses are initially primary, in that the routing of nerve impulses, called current-in-flow, through ψ leads to muscular discharge and behavior. Thus the baby cries, flails about when stimulation from inside his body or from outside exceeds a certain amount. However, in the presence of a caretaking person, more specific interactions occur. The caretaking person knows how to relieve the excessive stimulation (e.g., by feeding the baby). Thus certain interactions between internal and external stimulation take place, mediated by the infant's own behavior and terminated satisfactorily by the offices of a caretaking person. (The passages in the Project that describe this process could as well have been written by Sullivan as by Freud.)

Repetition of this sequence of events (that constitute defense) lays down a memory trace in ψ .This occurs because synaptic resistances are *facilitated* by use. An important insight is now attained. Facilitated pathways in the nervous system guide behavior. Therefore, each memory trace also serves as part of the motive structure that directs behavior. The Project proposes a neural memory based theory of motivation that gives internal stimulation (drive—usually translated as instinctual drive) an important but limited role. External stimulation can trigger the memory-motive structure (e.g., as when pain produces unpleasure). Perhaps more important, the composition of this memory-motive structure is seen to have three sources: drives, feedback from the organism's own muscular efforts, and the crucial presence of the caretaking person.

Thus the psychoanalytic concepts of a drive based *id* and a societal based *superego* are seen as equally primitive in the make-up of the defensive memory-motive structure which comes to be defined as a *wish*. For the most part, wishes become aroused by drive stimuli that accrue gradually. When an external event triggers the memory-motive structure, the sequence of events is usually more abrupt, leading to sudden neural discharge which is called *affect*. Affect is neither pleasant nor unpleasant but may have pleasurable consequences (lasting discharge) or lead to unpleasure (the biochemical positive feedback).

VI. COGNITIVE SECONDARY PROCESSES

So far we have encountered only primary processes. Note, however, that these primary processes already have considerable structure. For the most part, however, the structure is closed-loop feedback or else leads rather quickly to indiscriminant discharge. To prevent this, Freud invokes an executive neural process that inhibits and delays discharge. In the Project this mechanism depends on developing neural pathways lateral to the main paths of facilitated conduction. Neural inhibition had not as yet been discovered, nor had the inhibitory functions of the frontal and limbic forebrains been detailed (see Skinner and Lindsley, 1973; Sauerland and Clemente, 1973; and Pribram, 1973).

In the Project these executive processes that manage the memory-motive mechanism are called *ego* functions. The formation of the ego depends on another mechanism that involves *attention, judgment,* and *reality testing.* Whereas memory-motive and ego process describe neural mechanisms that ordinarily operate without awareness, attention and reality testing involve the cerebral cortex which is assumed to be the locus of perception and consciousness.

The Project distinguishes between quantitative energy concepts and the qualitative concepts of perception such as color, melody, and harmony. This distinction rests on a difference in the neural mechanisms involved as does every definition in the Project. In this case the configuration and connectivity of the ψ system that organizes the quantitative concepts as we have thus far described them is contrasted with the organization of the sensorimotor projection systems called ϕ. The ψ systems, as we noted, are composed of networks of short fine-fibered neurons with many branches. By contrast the ϕ systems are made up of long parallel fiber tracts containing few synapses. Furthermore these ϕ systems are directly connected with the sensory receptors and thus subject from birth to much excitation. This operates to lower the synaptic resistance in the few synapses that are present until, very shortly, there is practically no resistance in the ϕ paths of conduction. The ϕ system is then able to transmit the patterns, the periodicities, the frequency patterns of excitation originating in the receptors. Thus sensory quality is a funcion of the undistorted transmission of frequency patterns that occur in the cortex at the terminals of the ϕ system. To appreciate the contemporary ring of this proposal, compare it with those of Lashley (1942), Hebb (1949), and Pribram (1971). When one realizes that only a century earlier, perceptual and intellectual functions were localized in the spirits of the brain's ventricular system, the advance in neuropsychological conceptions portrayed in the Project is doubly striking.

But this is not all. Perception is not simply achieved. The Project details a match-mismatch mechanism organized in the cerebral cortex that must be activated in order for perception to occur. The activation, called primary attention, originates in the ψ system from the memory-motive structure, the wish, and produces a pattern of lowered threshold in the cortex. When an input from the ϕ system matches this threshold, a report of the match is fed back to the ψ system, which then in turn produces by way of secondary attention perceptual images or images of action in the cortex. Thus a double feedback, the mechanism of attention, is necessary for the activation of perception and/or action. When a mismatch results, one of two other possible mechanisms becomes activated. Either the organism moves so as to change the input to ϕ—this is called *reality testing*—or he alters his wishes to conform with the ϕ input, a process called *judgment*. Repetition of the judgmental and reality testing processes until match is produced is called the cognitive or secondary process and requires the delay mechanism, the inhibition produced by ego processes. When the cognitive process leads to action that produces prolonged satisfaction, i.e., appropriate discharge, the action is called specific or *willed*. Thus *will* or *intention* is a secondary process to be distinguished from wish, the primary memory-motive process that operates in the absence of inhibition by ego mechanisms.

Cognitive processes make up thoughts that can be actualized not only by activities of the larger muscle of the body, but by speech. This thought and speech can, under the appropriate circumstances, provide implicit acts, tests of reality which have lesser consequences in the expenditure of effort (work, energy) than would the action itself. This conservation of effort is made the basis of psychoanalytic therapy where the consequences of acting out and working through occur in a controlled situation and can therefore be attempted with safety, that is without the total disruption of his cognitive processes, the expenditure of his defenses that would leave the patient at the mercy of his biochemical positive feedback, the accruing spiral of unpleasure.

VII. RELEVANCE TO NEUROPSYCHIATRY

Such total expenditure of defenses occurs only in psychosis. But more organized primary processes become manifest in other situations. Thus during sleep, the cognitive process based on a functioning ego is temporarily out of commission so that primary associations among memory-motive structures occur. Dreams represent therefore the operations of wishes in the absence of attention, perception, and reality testing. Reports of dreams can therefore be used to investigate a person's wishes.

Wishes, i.e., memory-motive mechanisms, can also become manifest when the organism has developed inappropriate cognitive processes. The impropriety leads to perceptions and actions that do not match the wish, yet the wishes fail to become modified perhaps because they have become overly entrenched through previous experience. Cognitive controls, ego functions, must therefore become excessive in order to prevent their breakdown—the total expenditure of defenses. The resulting conflict between cognitive controls and frustrated unmodified wishes leads to repression, the failure of the memory-motive structure to contribute its share to the patterns of lowered threshold in the cortex. This type of conflicting primary-secondary process functioning is called *compromise formation* and is seen in *neurosis*. It is to such problems that psychoanalytic therapy with its thought and talk in controlled situations is addressed.

To conclude, this brief summary of the Project does not of course do it justice. The reader cannot for himself gauge the accuracy of my interpretation without reference to quotations from the Project. Those interested can find such quotations (Pribram and Gill, 1976; Strachey, 1966).

Why should anyone today be so concerned with a document published in 1895, three quarters of a century and more ago? I believe as stated in the introductory remarks of this chapter that the time is ripe for a neuropsychologically based neuropsychiatry. This proposal does not envision a primary process eclecticism but a cognitive effort that leads to specific actions after adequate reality testing has taken place. Neuropsychiatry thus conceived should be able to furnish a diagnostic based on psychoanalytic cognitive and control theory as set forth in the Project and continuously brought up to date in minute detail. This diagnostic should determine whether pharmacologic, analytic, or social group therapy, or some combination is indicated.

Neuropsychology and neuropsychiatry so conceived ought to heal the schisms, the disciplinary encapsulations within psychiatry and clinical psychology that now make it mandatory for the patient himself to choose his own therapeutics. The Project, by furnishing a Rosetta stone that allows operational neuropsychological definitions of so many of the concepts that have guided the psychosocial psychiatry, can help bridge the gap between organicists and behaviorists, between biological psychiatrists and analysts, between neurologists and cognitive experimental psychologists, between psychopharmacologists and social therapists. The Project has been in the public domain for a quarter of a century and as yet has found little perusal even in psychoanalytic institutes. Obviously its time had not yet come, probably because neuropsychological and neurobiological data had not yet matched its early insights. This is no longer true. The time appears now to be ripe for renewed study of data that integrate brain function, experience, and behavior with a practical therapeutic purpose. The suggestion of this chapter is that such study will be enriched by reference to the Project which constitutes a useful "Preface to Contemporary Cognitive Theory and Neuropsychology."

REFERENCES

Exner, S. (1894): *Entwurf zu einer physiologischen Erklärung der psychischen Erscheinungen.* Deuticke, Vienna.

Hebb, D. O. (1949): *The Organization of Behavior: A Neuropsychological Theory.* Wiley, New York.

Lashley, K. S., (1942): The problem of cerebral organization in vision. In: *Biological Symposia, Vol. VII Visual Mechanisms.* Jacques Cattell, Lancaster.

McFarland, D. J. (1971): *Feedback Mechanisms in Animal Behavior.* Academic, London.

Pribram, K. H. (1971): *Languages of the Brain: Experimental Paradoxes and Principles in Neuropsychology.* Prentice-Hall, Englewood Cliffs, N.J.

Pribram, K. K. The primate frontal cortex—Executive of the brain. In: *Psychophysiology of the Frontal Lobes,* edited by K. H. Primbram and A. R. Luria, pp. 293–314. Academic, New York.

Pribram, K. H., and Gill, M. M. (1976): *Freud's "Project for a Scientific Psy-*

chology": Preface to Contemporary Cognitive Theory and Neuropsychology. Hutchinson Publishing, London; Basic Books, New York.

Sauerland, E. K., and Clemente, C. D. (1973): The role of the brain stem in orbital cortex induced inhibition of somatic reflexes. In: *Psychophysiology of the Frontal Lobes,* edited by K. H. Pribram and A. R. Luria, pp. 167–184. Academic, New York.

Skinner, J. E., and Lindsely, D. B. (1973): The nonspecific mediothalamic-frontocortical system: Its influence on electrocortical activity and behavior. In: *Psychophysiology of the Frontal Lobes,* edited by K. H. Pribram and A. R. Luria, pp. 185–234. Academic, New York.

Strachey, J. (1966): *The Standard Edition of the Complete Psychological Works of Sigmund Freud, Vol. 1.* Hogarth, London.

Subject Index

Benzomorphan, 865, 867-868
Benzphetamine (Didrex), 829
Benztropine (Cogentin), 811-812
Betaine, and transmethylation,
    related to schizophrenia,
    658, 671
Bilirubin, blood-brain barrier to, 599
Biofeedback training, sleep distur-
    bances and, 481, 486
Biperiden (Akineton), 811-812
Birth anomalies, related to chromo-
    some aberrations, 19
Bleeding, effect on thirst, 298
Blood-brain barrier
    action on amines, 374-375
        in sleep studies, 461
        ventricular injection of
            catecholamines, 389-392
    brain development relating to,
        597-599
Brain
    damage
        attention deficits in, 544-546
        effect on memory, 513
        jaundice in newborn infant
            and, 598, 599
    development of
        anatomical, 593-597
        biochemical maturation in,
            599-610
        blood-brain barrier accom-
            panying, 597-599
        congenital metabolic defects
            related to, 615-622
        electrophysiologic, 610-615
        theories of, 591-593
    evolution of, 180-181, 946-951
    focal lesions, and reasoning
        deficits, 546, 562, 564,
        see also Lesions
    mechanisms, emotion and per-
        ception related to,
        255-271
    metabolism, glucocorticoids
        affecting, 910
    neomammalian, 181-183
    paleomammalian, 181
    -reward behaviors, 321-447, *see*
        also Hypothalamus
        amine system and, 371-401,
            419-422
        centers of, 337
        drive factor in, 339-348,
            422-425
        drug addiction and, 337-339
        electrical stimulation of
            hypothalamus and,
            324-356, 410-417
            drug action on, 376-382
        feeding behavior and, 335
        hormones and, 396,
            404-408, 425-429

    lesion effect on, 350, 356-371,
        383-386, 417-419
    neurons related to, 327-331, 349
    pain tolerance and, 334-335, 349
    priming and, 340, 347-349
    satiation of, 339
    unit activity of brain altered by, 507
sociocultural
    evolution of, 946-951
    relation to psychosomatic illness,
        946-986
    structure; information-processing model
        of, 987-1004
    triune, 177-198
Brainstem
    evolution of, 181
    sleep related to, 461
    ventral cephalic, behavior related to, 66
Brainwashing, to induce psychosis, 757-758
Bufotenine
    related to psychoses, 748
    structure and function of, 731, 734, 739
Bulbocapnine, effect on histamine
    action, 772
Butaperazine
    antipsychotic use of, 837
    kinetics of, 843
Butyrophenones
    action on amines, 371
    antipsychotic use of, 813-814

Caffeine
    effect on perception, 536
    in sleep studies, 482
    tolerance to and dependency on,
        882, 883
Calcium ions
    barbiturate intoxication involving, 878
    chelator factor, 394
Cannabinols, structure and function of,
    732, 733
Cannabis sativa (hemp), 757, 762,
    774-775, 778-780
Cantron, *see* Pheniprazine
Caramiphen, 777
Carbachol-induced thirst, 301, 304
Carbamates, 821
Carbamylcholine, 392, 395
Carbohydrate metabolism
    congenital defects of, 621-622
    hormonal effects on, 901
Carbon dioxide inhalation therapy, 814
Cardiac physiology, sleep and, 465
Cardiovascular disease, induced by
    emotional disturbance, 970, 978
    infarction, episodic memory disorders
        in, 549
Carnosine, brain development and, 619
Carphenazine (Proketazine), 812
Castration, brain-reward behavioral studies
    and, 341
Catalepsy, 184, 769, 772, 777, 779, 783

Evoked potentials (event-related potentials, ERP) *(contd.)*
sensory evoked responses (SER) *(contd.)*
characteristics of, 211-213
in delirium, 224-225
drug effect on, 239-243
methodology of, 206-207
in perception, 182
personality factor in, 231-233
in psychiatric disorders, 235-237
in sleep, 222-224
slow potential [CNV; expectancy (E) wave]
attention phenomena effect on, 228-229
characteristics of, 220-222
during coma, 225
memory studies and, 504
in psychiatric disorders, 238-239
stimulators and stimulus problems, 205-207
subject factors in, 210-211
variability of wave shapes, measurements, 209
vestibular, 120
visual evoked responses (VER)
attention phenomena effect on, 225-228
characteristics of, 216-219
drug effect on, 239-243
during coma, 225
during delirium, 224-225
ERP stimulus problems in, 205-206
intelligence factor in, 229-231
personality factor in, 232-233
in psychiatric patients, 233, 237
Evolution
of brain, 1, 8-10
cerebral dominance and, 564-574
cultural and social, 62-64
in development of cognitive skills, 56-64
of forebrain, emotional processes related to, 178, 180
gene function, a product of, 24, 25
perception in relation to, 50-56
Expectancy (E) wave, *see* Evoked potentials, slow potentials
Experiences, memory of, neural basis for, 499-525
Exploratory behavior, neurotransmitter action on, 397
Exteroceptors, role in activating sensation, 179, 186, 191
Extrapyramidal motor system, brain-reward behavior and, 396-397, 419

Fabry's disease, congenital metabolic defect in, 620-621
Fastigial nuclei, proprioception and, 266, 268
threat and attack behavior in animals and, 279

Fatty acids, in developing brain, 610
Fear behavior
endocrine functioning in, 925
hormonal action on, 409, 425
leading to psychosomatic illness, 960
psychomotor epilepsy and, 189
Feeding behavior, *see* Consummatory behavior
Fenfluramine, tolerance to and dependency on, 861
Field dependence, and lateralization of brain function, 167-168
Fight-flight responses
defense reactions and, 962, 968, 969
territorial behavior associated with, 951
6-Fluoro-DET
psychotomimetic effects of, 769
Fluphenazine (Prolixin; Permitil), 812
effect on evoked potentials, 240-241
Flurazepam (Dalmane), 820-821
Focal cerebral damage, and memory deficits, 546
lesions and reasoning deficits, 562, 564
Folic acid, and schizophrenia, 670, 672
Follicle-stimulating hormone (FSH), 915-916
Forebrain
amine depletion in, and brain-reward-drive studies, 386
behavioral activation induced by neurotransmitters in, 393, 395, 400
brain reward and, 410-414, 421
emotion related to, 184-185, 260-261
evolution of, 178-181, 950-951
hunger related to, 304
norepinephrine fibers in, 419
Forgetting, *see also* Memory, 502-503
Fornix
amnesia related to damage to circuit involving, 550
lesions of, and memory deficits, 554
sectioning of, and hippocampal stimulation, 192
threat and attack behavior in animals and, 282-283
Fourier analysis, applied to evoked potential wave forms, 208, 230
Freud's Project for a Scientific Psychology, 1006-1013
Frontal lobes
planning of behavior and, 67
role in attention, 536-538
role in sociocultural brain functioning, 948-951
Fucosidosis, congenital metabolic defect in, 620-621

GABA, *see* γ-Aminobutyric acid
Galactisol, related to cataract formation, 622

Parachlorophenylalanine (PCPA), see
  p-Chlorophenylalanine
Parahippocampal cortex, see Cortex,
  parahippocampal
Paraldehyde, 815, 821-822
Paranoia
  dopamine role in, 748
  drug-induced, 768-772
  limbic system's role in, 186
  sensory deprivation-induced, 759
Parasympathetic system, relation to sleep,
  466
Paraventricular nucleus of hypothalamus
  oxytocin release from electrical stimula-
    tion of, 342, 406, 426-427
Pargyline
  action on amines, related to brain-
    reward studies, 380
  effect on brain-reward-drive systems,
    388-389
Parica, 731
Parietal lobes
  attention related to, 536, 538-540, 542
  cross-modal association related to,
    948, 951, 953
  disease of, and memory deficits, 560
  in denial of illness, 163
Parkinsonism, 184, 660, 705, 773, 808
Parnate, see Tranylcypromine
PCPA, see p-Chlorophenylalanine
Pedal pressing
  brain-reward behaviors and, 331-335,
    340, 399, 411, 415
  chemical injections and, 394-395
Peduncle, superior cerebellar, and threat
    and attack behavior in animals,
    279
Penfluridol, 814
Penile tumescence, during sleep, 465-466
Pentamethylenetetrazol (Metrazol), effect
    on evoked potentials, 240
Pentazocine, 865, 872, 874
Pentylenetetrazol (Metrazol), 822
  effect on memory, 512, 517
Peptide hormones, cAMP action on, 374
    420, 425, 428-429
Perception
  brain sites for, 258-271
  contents of, 65-66
  coping behavior and, 958
  deficits of, 529-535, 563
  definition of, 178-180
  deprivation of, 530
  emotion relation to, physical sub-
    strate for, 255-271
  evolution of behavior related to, 50-56
  of form, in neocortical sensory areas,
    182
  Freud's concepts of, 1010
  hallucinogens effect on, 742-745
  limbic system's role in, 186-193

localization of, 68-71
mechanisms of, 183
psychosocial, 945-950
  parietal cross-modal association area
    and, 948
  related to disease, 945-986
  sensory processing and behavior related
    to, 47-143
  spatial schemata and cognitive theory
    of, 759
Percodan, to treat sleep disorders, 485
Performance
  cognitive deficits involving, 551-561
  skilled p., memory deficits involving,
    557-561
Periamygdaloid cortex, and brain-reward-
    drive behaviors, 397
Perifornical region, and anger, 192
Permitil, see Fluphenazine
Perphenazine (Trilafon; Triavil), 810, 812,
    824, 844
Perseveration, cognitive deficits and,
    551-552
Personality
  disorders, genetics of, 28, 36-37
  as factor in evoked response recordings,
    231-233
Personal unity, 156
Pertofrane, see Desipramine
Peyote, 757, 771
  as psychotherapy, 831-832
  structure and function of, 730-731
PGO spike activity, in sleep studies, 460,
    462, 464, 474, 480
Pharmacogenetics, 21
Phenaglycodal (Ultran), 820-821
Phenazocine, 865, 872
Phencyclidine (Sernyl; PCP)
  psychotomimetic effects of, 762-763,
    775-777, 779-780
  sensory deprivation to mimic effects
    of, 759, 760
  structure and function of, 732-733
Phenelzine (Nardil), 823, 828-829
Phenethylamine, effect on brain-reward
    behavior, 380, 381
Pheniprazine (Cantron), 823
Phenmetrazine (Preludin), 829
P3 phenomenon, see Evoked potentials
Phenothiazines
  action on amines, 371
  antipsychotic use of, 801, 810-813,
    822, 824, 833, 844
  augmenting-reducing effect of, 241
  depression induced by, 783
  inhibitors of ACTH, 892
  response to, in genetic defects, 21
  schizophrenia treated with, 668-669
Phenotype, defined, 22
Phentolamine, effect on alcoholic with-
    drawal, 877